Measuring Up®

to the

Texas Essential Knowledge and Skills

and Success Strategies for the TAKS

Mathematics

This book is customized for Texas and the lessons cover ALL TEKS.
The Measuring Up® program includes instructional worktexts, Diagnostic Practice Tests (DPTs), and PAKS, a preliminary diagnostic test, which are available separately.

Exit Level

800-822-1080
www.TXStandardsHelp.com

PEOPLES PUBLISHING GROUP
299 Market Street, Saddle Brook, NJ 07663

Publisher: Diane Miller

Editorial Development: MATHQueue, Inc.

Editorial Director: Marie Spano

Director of Mathematics: April Barth

Executive Mathematics Editor: Martha Torn

Editors: Rosemary McLaughlin, Rachel E. Kay

Director of Marketing: Victoria Ameer Kiely

Pre-Press & Production Manager: Doreen Smith

Project Manager: Jennifer J. Tully

Senior Book Coordinator: Matt Hjembo

Production Assistants: Gregg Hussey, Sharon MacGregor, Anna Rose Waider

Designer: Jodi Notowitz

Copy Editor: Michael Goodman

Photo Researcher/Permissions Manager: Kristine Liebman

Illustrators: Armando Báez, Sal Esposito

Technical Art: Matt Hjembo, Sharon MacGregor,

Cover Design: Cynthia Mackowicz, Michele Sakow, Yadiro Henriquez

Developmental Editing:

Pinnacle Education Associates, Inc. Grapevine, Texas

Texas Advisory Panel, Elementary:

Shelly Caldwell, Grade 3 Teacher, Sugar Land, Texas

Barbara Cobaugh, Educator, Houston, Texas

Raul Ramirez, Grade 3 Bilingual/GT Teacher-Royalgate Elementary School, South San Antonio ISD, San Antonio, Texas

Texas Advisory Panel, High School:

Jean Goff, Math Teacher- Carrollton-Farmers Branch ISD, Carrollton, Texas

Julie Merrill, High School Math Teacher, Carrollton-Farmers Branch ISD, Carrollton, Texas

Sherry Woods, High School Math Teacher, Creekview High School, Carrollton-Farmers Branch ISD, Carrollton, Texas

ISBN 1-4138-0472-1

The Peoples Publishing Group, Inc.
299 Market Street
Saddle Brook, New Jersey 07663

Printed in the United States of America.

10 9 8 7 6 5 4 3 2

Measuring Up® Contents

TEKS in bold are assessed on the TAKS.

CHAPTER 2 Properties and Attributes of Functions

CHAPTER 3 Linear Functions

These lessons cover 13 TEKS.

CHAPTER 4 Solving Linear Equations and Inequalities

These lessons cover 9 TEKS.

TEKS in bold are assessed on the TAKS.

CHAPTER 5 Quadratic Functions

TEKS in bold are assessed on the TAKS.

TEKS in bold are assessed on the TAKS.

These lessons cover 12 TEKS.

CHAPTER 9 Percents, Proportional Relationships, Probability, and Statistics

These lessons cover 9 TEKS.

TEKS in bold are assessed on the TAKS.

Student Resources

Correlation to the Texas Essential Knowledge and Skills

This worktext is customized to the Texas Essential Knowledge and Skills and provides complete practice for the TAKS.

The correlation chart shows how Measuring Up® is vertically aligned to the TEKS because the lessons are customized for the TEKS. To see our complete vertical and horizontal alignment for the Measuring Up® program, visit www.TXStandardsHelp.com. As the lesson for each student expectation is completed, place a (✓) to indicate Mastery or an (✗) to indicate Review Needed.

PART 1: Algebra Chapter 1: Functional Relationships										
	Review Skill									
	Mastered Skill									
	Lessons	1	2	3	4	N/A	N/A	N/A	N/A	B
TEKS A(b)1	**Foundations for functions.** The student understands that a function represents a dependence of one quantity on another and can be described in a variety of ways. The student is expected to:									
(A)	**describe independent and dependent quantities in functional relationships;**	★	✓	✓	✓					★
(B)	**gather and record data, or use data sets, to determine functional (systematic) relationships between quantities;**	❍	★	✓	✓					★
(C)	**describe functional relationships for given problem situations and write equations or inequalities to answer questions arising from the situations;**	❍	❍	★	✓					★
(D)	**represent relationships among quantities using concrete models, tables, graphs, diagrams, verbal descriptions, equations, and inequalities;**	❍	❍	❍	★					★
(E)	**interpret and make inferences from functional relationships.**	❍	❍	❍	★					★
TEKS 8.14	**Underlying processes and mathematical tools.** The student applies Grade 8 mathematics to solve problems connected to everyday experiences, investigations in other disciplines, and activities in and outside of school. The student is expected to:									
(A)	**identify and apply mathematics to everyday experiences, to activities in and outside of school, with other disciplines, and with other mathematical topics;**	❍	❍	★	✓					★
(D)	**select tools such as real objects, manipulatives, paper/pencil, and technology or techniques such as mental math, estimation, and number sense to solve problems.**	❍	❍	★	✓					★
TEKS 8.15	**Underlying processes and mathematical tools.** The student communicates about Grade 8 mathematics through informal and mathematical language, representations, and models. The student is expected to:									
(B)	**evaluate the effectiveness of different representations to communicate ideas.**	❍	❍	❍	★					★
TEKS 8.16	**Underlying processes and mathematical tools.** The student uses logical reasoning to make conjectures and verify conclusions. The student is expected to:									
(B)	**validate his/her conclusions using mathematical properties and relationships.**	❍	❍	❍	★					★

Chapter 2: Properties and Attributes of Functions										
	Review Skill									
	Mastered Skill									
	Lessons	5	6	7	8	9	10	11	N/A	B
TEKS A(b)2	**Foundations for functions.** The student uses the properties and attributes of functions. The student is expected to:									
(A)	**identify and sketch the general forms of linear ($y = x$) and quadratic ($y = x^2$) parent functions;**	★	✓	✓	✓	✓	✓	✓		★
(B)	**for a variety of situations, identify the mathematical domains and ranges and determine reasonable domain and range values for given situations;**	❍	★	✓	✓	✓	✓	✓		★
(C)	**interpret situations in terms of given graphs or create situations that fit given graphs;**	❍	❍	★	✓	✓	✓	✓		★
(D)	**in solving problems, collect and organize data, make and interpret scatterplots, and model, predict, and make decisions and critical judgments.**	❍	❍	❍	★	✓	✓	✓		★
TEKS A(b)3	**Foundations for functions.** The student understands how algebra can be used to express generalizations and recognizes and uses the power of symbols to represent situations. The student is expected to:									
(A)	**use symbols to represent unknowns and variables;**	★	✓	✓	✓	✓	✓	✓		★
(B)	**given situations, look for patterns and represent generalizations algebraically.**	❍	★	✓	✓	✓	✓	✓		★
TEKS A(b)4	**Foundations for functions.** The student understands the importance of the skills required to manipulate symbols in order to solve problems and uses the necessary algebraic skills required to simplify algebraic expressions and solve equations and inequalities in problem situations. The student is expected to:									
(A)	**find specific function values, simplify polynomial expressions, transform and solve equations, and factor as necessary in problem situations;**	❍	❍	❍	❍	★	★	★		★

B Building Stamina™

★ Standards covered

❍ Standards to be covered

✓ Standards previously covered

TEKS in bold are assessed on the TAKS.

Chapter 2: Properties and Attributes of Functions (continued)

	Review Skill								
	Mastered Skill								
	Lessons	5	6	7	8	9	10	11	N/A	B
(B)	**use the commutative, associative, and distributive properties to simplify algebraic expressions.**	○	○	○	○	○	★	✓		★
TEKS A(c)1	**Linear functions.** The student understands that linear functions can be represented in different ways and translates among their various representations. The student is expected to:									
(B)	**determine the domain and range values for which linear functions make sense for given situations.**	○	★	✓	✓	✓	✓	✓		★
TEKS 8.12	**Probability and statistics.** The student uses statistical procedures to describe data. The student is expected to:									
(B)	**draw conclusions and make predictions by analyzing trends in scatterplots.**	○	○	○	★	✓	✓	✓		★
TEKS 8.14	**Underlying processes and mathematical tools.** The student applies Grade 8 mathematics to solve problems connected to everyday experiences, investigations in other disciplines, and activities in and outside of school. The student is expected to:									
(A)	**identify and apply mathematics to everyday experiences, to activities in and outside of school, with other disciplines, and with other mathematical topics;**	✓	✓	★	★	★	★	✓		★
(B)	**use a problem-solving model that incorporates understanding the problem, making a plan, carrying out the plan, and evaluating the solution for reasonableness;**	○	○	○	○	○	★	✓		★
(D)	**select tools such as real objects, manipulatives, paper/pencil, and technology or techniques such as mental math, estimation, and number sense to solve problems.**	✓	✓	✓	✓	✓	✓	★		★
TEKS 8.15	**Underlying processes and mathematical tools.** The student communicates about Grade 8 mathematics through informal and mathematical language, representations, and models. The student is expected to:									
(A)	**communicate mathematical ideas using language, efficient tools, appropriate units, and graphical, numerical, physical, or algebraic mathematical models.**	○	○	○	○	○	○	★		★
TEKS 8.16	**Underlying processes and mathematical tools.** The student uses logical reasoning to make conjectures and verify conclusions. The student is expected to:									
(A)	**make conjectures from patterns or sets of examples and nonexamples.**	○	★	★	★	✓	✓	✓		★

Chapter 3: Linear Functions

	Review Skill									
	Mastered Skill									
	Lessons	12	13	14	15	16	N/A	N/A	N/A	B
TEKS A(c)1	**Linear functions.** The student understands that linear functions can be represented in different ways and translates among their various representations. The student is expected to:									
(A)	**determine whether or not given situations can be represented by linear functions;**	★	✓	✓	✓	✓				★
(B)	**determine the domain and range values for which linear functions make sense for given situations;.**	★	✓	✓	✓	✓				★
(C)	**translate among and use algebraic, tabular, graphical, or verbal descriptions of linear functions.**	★	✓	✓	✓	✓				★
TEKS A(c)2	**Linear functions.** The student understands the meaning of slope and intercepts of linear functions and interprets and describes the effects of changes in parameters of linear functions in real-world and mathematical situations. The student is expected to:									
(A)	**develop the concept of slope as rate of change and determine the slopes from graphs, tables, and algebraic representations;**	○	★	✓	✓	✓				★
(B)	**interpret the meaning of slope and intercepts in situations using data, symbolic representations, or graphs;.**	○	★	✓	✓	✓				★
(C)	**investigate, describe, and predict the effects of changes in *m* and *b* on the graph of $y = mx + b$;**	○	○	★	✓	✓				★
(D)	**graph and write equations of lines given characteristics such as two points, a point and a slope, or a slope and *y*-intercept;**	○	○	○	★	✓				★
(E)	**determine the intercepts of linear functions from graphs, tables, and algebraic representations;**	○	★	✓	✓	✓				★
(F)	**interpret and predict the effects of changing slope and *y*-intercept in applied situations;**	○	○	★	✓	✓				★
(G)	**relate direct variation to linear functions and solve problems involving proportional change.**	○	○	○	○	★				★
TEKS 8.14	**Underlying processes and mathematical tools.** The student applies Grade 8 mathematics to solve problems connected to everyday experiences, investigations in other disciplines, and activities in and outside of school. The student is expected to:									
(A)	**identify and apply mathematics to everyday experiences, to activities inside and outside of school, with other disciplines, and with other mathematical topics.**	✓	✓	★	✓	✓				★

TEKS in bold are assessed on the TAKS.

Chapter 3: Linear Functions (continued)

	Review Skill								
	Mastered Skill								
	Lessons	**12**	**13**	**14**	**15**	**16**	**N/A**	**N/A**	**N/A**	**B**
TEKS 8.15	**Underlying processes and mathematical tools.** The student communicates about Grade 8 mathematics through informal and mathematical language, representations, and models. The student is expected to:									
(A)	**communicate mathematical ideas using language, efficient tools, appropriate units, and graphical, numerical, physical, or algebraic mathematical models.**	★	✓	✓	✓	✓				★
TEKS 8.16	**Underlying processes and mathematical tools.** The student uses logical reasoning to make conjectures and verify conclusions.The student is expected to:									
(A)	**make conjectures from patterns or sets of examples and nonexamples.**	✓	★	✓	✓	✓				★

Chapter 4: Solving Linear Equations and Inequalities

	Review Skill								
	Mastered Skill								
	Lessons	**17**	**18**	**19**	**20**	**21**	**N/A**	**N/A**	**N/A**	**B**
TEKS A(c)3	**Linear functions.** The student formulates equations and inequalities based on linear functions, uses a variety of methods to solve them, and analyzes the solutions in terms of the situation. The student is expected to:									
(A)	**analyze situations involving linear functions and formulate linear equations or inequalities to solve problems;**	★	★	✓	✓	✓				★
(B)	**investigate methods for solving linear equations and inequalities using concrete models, graphs, and the properties of equality, select a method, and solve the equations and inequalities;**	★	★	✓	✓	✓				★
(C)	**for given concepts, interpret and determine the reasonableness of solutions to linear equations and inequalities.**	❍	❍	❍	❍	★				★
TEKS A(c)4	**Linear functions.** The student formulates systems of linear equations from problem situations, uses a variety of methods to solve them, and analyzes the solutions in terms of the situation. The student is expected to:									
(A)	**analyze situations and formulate systems of linear equations to solve problems;**	❍	❍	★	✓	✓				★
(B)	**solve systems of linear equations using concrete models, graphs, tables and algebraic methods;**	❍	❍	❍	★	✓				★
(C)	**for given contexts, interpret and determine the reasonableness of solutions of linear equations.**	❍	❍	❍	❍	★				★
TEKS 8.14	**Underlying processes and mathematical tools.** The student applies Grade 8 mathematics to solve problems connected to everyday experiences, investigations in other disciplines, and activities in and outside of school. The student is expected to:									
(A)	**identify and apply mathematics to everyday experiences, to activities inside and outside of school, with other disciplines, and with other mathematical topics;**	★	★	★	★	✓				★
(B)	**use a problem-solving model that incorporates understanding the problem, making a plan, carrying out the plan, and evaluating the solution for reasonableness;**	★	★	✓	★	★				★
(C)	**select or develop an appropriate problem-solving strategy from a variety of different types, including drawing a picture, looking for a pattern, systematic guessing and checking, acting it out, making a table, working a simpler problem, or working backwards to solve a problem.**	★	★	✓	★	★				★

Chapter 5: Quadratic Functions

	Review Skill								
	Mastered Skill								
	Lessons	**22**	**23**	**24**	**25**	**26**	**27**	**N/A**	**N/A**	**B**
TEKS A(b)2	**Foundations for functions.** The student uses the properties and attributes of functions. The student is expected to:									
(A)	**identify and sketch the general forms of linear ($y = x$) and quadratic ($y = x^2$) parent functions.**	★	✓	✓	✓	✓	✓			★
TEKS A(d)1	**Quadratic and other nonlinear functions.** The student understands that the graphs of quadratic equations are affected by the parameters of the function and can interpret and describe the effects of changes in the parameters of quadratic functions. The student is expected to:									
(A)	**determine the domain and range values for which quadratic functions make sense for given situations;**	★	✓	✓	✓	✓	✓			★
(B)	**investigate, describe, and predict the effects of changes in a on the graph of $y = ax^2$;**	★	✓	✓	✓	✓	✓			★
(C)	**investigate, describe, and predict the effects of changes in c on the graph of $y = x^2 + c$;**	★	✓	✓	✓	✓	✓			★
(D)	**for problem situations, analyze graphs of quadratic functions and draw conclusions.**	❍	★	✓	✓	✓	✓			★

B **Building Stamina**™

★ Standards covered

❍ Standards to be covered

✓ Standards previously covered

TEKS in bold are assessed on the TAKS.

Chapter 5: Quadratic Functions (continued)

		22	23	24	25	26	27	N/A	N/A	B
	Review Skill									
	Mastered Skill									
TEKS A(d)2	**Quadratic and other nonlinear functions.** The student understands there is more than one way to solve a quadratic equation and solves them using appropriate methods. The student is expected to:									
(A)	**solve quadratic equations using concrete models, tables, graphs, and algebraic methods;**	❍	❍	★	✓	✓	✓			★
(B)	**relate the solutions of quadratic equations to the roots of their functions.**	❍	❍	★	✓	✓	✓			★
TEKS A(d)3	**Quadratic and other nonlinear functions.** The student understands there are situations modeled by functions that are neither linear nor quadratic and models the situations. The student is expected to:									
(A)	**use patterns to generate the laws of exponents and apply them in problem-solving situations;**	❍	❍	❍	★	✓	✓			★
(B)	**analyze data and represent situations involving inverse variation using concrete models, tables, graphs, or algebraic methods;**	❍	❍	❍	❍	★	✓			★
(C)	**analyze data and represent situations involving exponential growth and decay using concrete models, tables, graphs, or algebraic methods.**	❍	❍	❍	❍	❍	★			★
TEKS 8.14	**Underlying processes and mathematical tools.** The student applies Grade 8 mathematics to solve problems connected to everyday experiences, investigations in other disciplines, and activities in and outside of school. The student is expected to:									
(A)	**identify and apply mathematics to everyday experiences, to activities in and outside of school, with other disciplines, and with other mathematical topics.**	✓	✓	✓	✓	★	★			★
TEKS 8.15	**Underlying processes and mathematical tools.** The student communicates about Grade 8 mathematics through informal and mathematical language, representations, and models. The student is expected to:									
(A)	**communicate mathematical ideas using language, efficient tools, appropriate units, and graphical, numerical, physical, or algebraic mathematical models.**	✓	✓	★	✓	✓	✓			★
TEKS 8.16	**Underlying processes and mathematical tools.** The student uses logical reasoning to make conjectures and verify conclusions. The student is expected to:									
(B)	**validate his/her conclusions using mathematical properties and relationships.**	✓	★	✓	✓	✓	✓			★

PART 2: Geometry, Percents, Proportional Relationships, Probability, and Statistics

Chapter 6: Geometric Relationships and Reasoning

		28	29	30	31	32	33	34	35	36	37	B
	Review Skill											
	Mastered Skill											
TEKS G(b)1	**Geometric structure.** The student understands the structure of, and relationships within, an axiomatic system. The student is expected to:											
(A)	**develop an awareness of the structure of a mathematical system, connecting definitions, postulates, logical reasoning, and theorems;**	❍	★	✓	✓	✓	✓	✓	✓	✓	✓	★
(B)	**recognize that mathematics is developed for a variety of purposes;**	★	✓	✓	✓	✓	✓	✓	✓	✓	✓	★
(C)	**compare and contrast the structures and implications of Euclidean and non-Euclidean geometries.**	★	✓	✓	✓	✓	✓	✓	✓	✓	✓	★
TEKS G(b)2	**Geometric structure.** The student analyzes geometric relationships in order to make and verify conjectures. The student is expected to:											
(A)	**use constructions to explore attributes of geometric figures and to make conjectures about geometric relationships;**	❍	★	✓	✓	✓	✓	✓	✓	✓	✓	★
(B)	**make and verify conjectures about angles, lines, polygons, circles, and three-dimensional figures, choosing from a variety of approaches such as coordinate, transformational, or axiomatic.**	❍	★	✓	✓	✓	✓	✓	✓	✓	✓	★
TEKS G(b)3	**Geometric structure.** The student understands the importance of logical reasoning, justification, and proof in mathematics. The student is expected to:											
(A)	**determine if the converse of a conditional statement is true or false;**	❍	❍	❍	❍	❍	❍	❍	★	✓	✓	★
(B)	**construct and justify statements about geometric figures and their properties;**	❍	❍	❍	❍	❍	❍	❍	★	✓	✓	★
(C)	**demonstrate what it means to prove mathematically that statements are true;**	❍	❍	❍	❍	❍	❍	❍	❍	★	✓	★
(D)	**use inductive reasoning to formulate a conjecture;**	❍	❍	❍	❍	❍	❍	❍	❍	❍	★	★
(E)	**use deductive reasoning to prove a statement.**	❍	❍	❍	❍	❍	❍	❍	❍	★	✓	★
TEKS G(b)4	**Geometric structure.** The student uses a variety of representations to describe geometric relationships and solve problems. The student is expected to:											

TEKS in bold are assessed on the TAKS.

Chapter 6: Geometric Relationships and Reasoning

	Review Skill											
	Mastered Skill											
	Lessons	28	29	30	31	32	33	34	35	36	37	B
(A)	**select an appropriate representation (concrete,) pictorial, graphical, verbal, or symbolic) in order to solve problems.**	❍	❍	❍	❍	❍	❍	❍	★	✓	✓	★
TEKS G(c)1	**Geometric patterns.** The student identifies, analyzes, and describes patterns that emerge from two- and three-dimensional geometric figures. The student is expected to:											
(A)	**use numeric and geometric patterns to make generalizations about geometric properties, including properties of polygons, ratios in similar figures and solids, and angle relationships in polygons and circles;**	❍	❍	★	✓	✓	✓	✓	✓	✓	✓	★
(B)	**use the properties of transformations and their compositions such as tessellations or fractals;**	❍	❍	❍	★	★	✓	✓	✓	✓	✓	★
(C)	**identify and apply patterns from right triangles to solve problems, including special right triangles (45-45-90 and 30-60-90) and triangles whose sides are Pythagorean triples.**	❍	❍	❍	❍	❍	★	★	✓	✓	✓	★
TEKS G(d)2	**Dimensionality and the geometry of location.** The student understands that coordinate systems provide convenient and efficient ways of representing geometric figures and uses them accordingly. The student is expected to:											
(B)	**use slopes and equations of lines to investigate geometric relationships, including parallel lines, perpendicular lines, and special segments of triangles and other polygons.**	❍	★	✓	✓	✓	✓	✓	✓	✓	✓	★
TEKS G(e)1	**Congruence and the geometry of size.** The student extends measurement concepts to find area, perimeter, and volume in problem situations. The student is expected to:											
(C)	**develop, extend, and use the Pythagorean Theorem.**	❍	❍	❍	❍	❍	★	✓	✓	✓	✓	★
TEKS G(e)2	**Congruence and the geometry of size.** The student analyzes properties and describes relationships in geometric figures. The student is expected to:											
(A)	**based on explanations and using concrete models, formulate and test conjectures about the properties of parallel and perpendicular lines.**	❍	★	✓	✓	✓	✓	✓	✓	✓	✓	★
TEKS G(e)3	**Congruence and the geometry of size.** The student applies the concept of congruence to justify properties of figures and solve problems. The student is expected to:											
(A)	**use congruence transformations to make conjectures and justify properties of geometric figures.**	❍	❍	★	✓	✓	✓	✓	✓	✓	✓	★
TEKS G(f)1	**Similarity and the geometry of shape.** The student applies the concepts of similarity to justify properties of figures and solve problems. The student is expected to:											
(A)	**use similarity properties and transformations to explore and justify conjectures about geometric figures.**	❍	❍	❍	★	✓	✓	✓	✓	✓	✓	★
TEKS 8.14	**Underlying processes and mathematical tools.** The student applies Grade 8 mathematics to solve problems connected to everyday experiences, investigations in other disciplines, and activities in and outside of school. The student is expected to:											
(A)	**identify and apply mathematics to everyday experiences, to activities in and outside of school, with other disciplines, and with other mathematical topics;**	✓	✓	✓	✓	✓	✓	★	✓	✓	✓	★
(B)	**use a problem-solving model that incorporates understanding the problem, making a plan, carrying out the plan, and evaluating the solution for reasonableness.**	✓	✓	✓	✓	✓	✓	★	✓	✓	✓	★

Chapter 7: Two- and Three-Dimensional Representations

	Review Skill											
	Mastered Skill											
	Lessons	38	39	40	41	42	43	N/A	N/A	N/A	N/A	B
TEKS G(d)1	**Dimensionality and the geometry of location.** The student analyzes the relationship between three-dimensional objects and related two-dimensional representations and uses these representations to solve problems. The student is expected to:											
(A)	**describe, and draw cross sections and other slices of three-dimensional objects;**	❍	★	✓	✓	✓	✓					★
(B)	**use nets to represent and construct three-dimensional objects;**	❍	❍	★	✓	✓	✓					★
(C)	**use top, front, side, and corner views of three-dimensional objects to create accurate and complete representations and solve problems.**	❍	❍	❍	★	✓	✓					★
TEKS G(d)2	**Dimensionality and the geometry of location.** The student understands that coordinate systems provide convenient and efficient ways of representing geometric figures and uses them accordingly. The student is expected to:											
(A)	**use one- and two-dimensional coordinate systems to represent points, lines, line segments, and figures;**	❍	❍	❍	❍	★	✓					★
(B)	**use slopes and equations of lines to investigate geometric relationships, including parallel lines, perpendicular lines, and special segments of triangles and other polygons;**	✓	✓	✓	✓	★	✓					★
(C)	**develop and use formulas including distance and midpoint.**	❍	❍	❍	❍	❍	★					★
TEKS G(e)2	**Congruence and the geometry of size.** The student analyzes properties and describes relationships in geometric figures. The student is expected to:											

TEKS in bold are assessed on the TAKS.

Chapter 7: Two- and Three Dimensional Representations (continued)											
Review Skill											
Mastered Skill											
Lessons	38	39	40	41	42	43	N/A	N/A	N/A	N/A	B
(A) **based on explanations and using concrete models, formulate and test conjectures about the properties of parallel and perpendicular lines;**	✓	✓	✓	✓	★	✓					★
(D) **analyze the characteristics of three-dimensional figures and their component parts.**	★	✓	✓	✓	✓	✓					★
TEKS 8.14 **Underlying processes and mathematical tools.** The student applies Grade 8 mathematics to solve problems connected to everyday experiences, investigations in other disciplines, and activities in and outside of school. The student is expected to:											
(A) **identify and apply mathematics to everyday experiences, to activities in and outside of school, with other disciplines, and with other mathematical topics.**	✓	★	✓	✓	✓	✓					★
TEKS 8.15 **Underlying processes and mathematical tools.** The student communicates about Grade 8 mathematics through informal and mathematical language, representations, and models. The student is expected to:											
(A) **communicate mathematical ideas using language, efficient tools, appropriate units, and graphical, numerical, physical, or algebraic mathematical models.**	✓	★	✓	✓	✓	✓					★

Chapter 8: Geometry of Size and Shape											
Review Skill											
Mastered Skill											
Lessons	44	45	46	47	48	49	50	51	52	N/A	B
TEKS G(b)2 **Geometric structure.** The student analyzes geometric relationships in order to make and verify conjectures. The student is expected to:											
(B) **make and verify conjectures about angles, lines, polygons, circles, and three-dimensional figures, choosing from a variety of approaches such as coordinate, transformational, or axiomatic.**	✓	★	★	✓	✓	✓	✓	✓	✓		★
TEKS G(c)1 **Geometric patterns.** The student identifies, analyzes, and describes patterns that emerge from two- and three-dimensional geometric figures. The student is expected to:											
(A) **use numeric and geometric patterns to make generalizations about geometric properties, including properties of polygons, ratios in similar figures and solids, and angle relationships in polygons and circles.**	★	✓	★	✓	✓	✓	✓	★	✓		★
TEKS G(e)1 **Congruence and the geometry of size.** The student extends measurement concepts to find area, perimeter, and volume in problem situations. The student is expected to:											
(A) **find areas of regular polygons and composite figures;**	★	✓	✓	✓	✓	✓	✓	✓	✓		★
(B) **find areas of sectors and arc lengths of circles using proportional reasoning;**	❍	★	✓	✓	✓	✓	✓	✓	✓		★
(D) **find surface areas and volumes of prisms, pyramids, spheres, cones, and cylinders in problem situations.**	❍	❍	❍	★	★	✓	✓	✓	✓		★
TEKS G(e)2 **Congruence and the geometry of size.** The student analyzes properties and describes relationships in geometric figures. The student is expected to:											
(B) **formulate and test conjectures about the properties and attributes of polygons and their component parts;**	★	✓	✓	✓	✓	✓	✓	✓	✓		★
(C) **formulate and test conjectures about the properties and attributes of circles and the lines that intersect them.**	❍	❍	★	✓	✓	✓	✓	✓	✓		★
TEKS G(e)3 **Congruence and the geometry of size.** The student applies the concept of congruence to justify properties of figures and solve problems. The student is expected to:											
(B) **justify and apply triangle congruence relationships.**	❍	❍	❍	❍	❍	❍	★	✓	✓		★
TEKS G(f)1 **Similarity and the geometry of shape.** The student applies the concepts of similarity to justify property of figures and solve problems. The student is expected to:											
(A) **use similarity properties and transformations to explore and justify conjectures about geometric figures;**	✓	✓	✓	✓	✓	✓	✓	★	✓		★
(B) **use ratios to solve problems involving similar figures;**	❍	❍	❍	❍	❍	❍	❍	★	✓		★
(C) **develop, apply, and justify triangle similarity relationships, such as right triangle ratios, trigonometric ratios, and Pythagorean triples;**	❍	❍	❍	❍	❍	❍	❍	❍	★		★
(D) **describe the effect on perimeter, area, and volume when length, width, or height of a three-dimensional solid is changed and apply this idea in solving problems.**	★	✓	✓	✓	✓	★	✓	✓	✓		★

B **Building Stamina**™

★ Standards covered

❍ Standards to be covered

✓ Standards previously covered

TEKS in bold are assessed on the TAKS.

Chapter 9 : Percents, Proportional Relationships, Probability, and Statistics

	Review Skill											
	Mastered Skill											
	Lessons	53	54	55	56	57	58	59	N/A	N/A	N/A	B
TEKS 8.3	**Patterns, relationships, and algebraic thinking.** The student identifies proportional relationships in problem situations and solves problems. The student is expected to:											
(A)	**compare and contrast proportional and non-proportional relationships;**	★	✓	✓	✓	✓	✓	✓				★
(B)	**estimate and find solutions to application problems involving percents and proportional relationships such as similarity and rates.**	★	★	✓	✓	✓	✓	✓				★
TEKS 8.11	**Probability and statistics.** The student applies concepts of theoretical and experimental probability to make predictions. The student is expected to:											
(A)	**find the probabilities of compound events (dependent and independent);**	❍	❍	❍	★	✓	✓	✓				★
(B)	**use theoretical probabilities and experimental results to make predictions and decisions;**	❍	❍	★	✓	✓	✓	✓				★
(C)	**select and use different models to simulate an event.**	❍	❍	★	✓	✓	✓	✓				★
TEKS 8.12	**Probability and statistics.** The student uses statistical procedures to describe data. The student is expected to:											
(A)	**select the appropriate measure of central tendency to describe a set of data for a particular purpose;**	❍	❍	❍	❍	★	✓	✓				★
(C)	**construct circle graphs, bar graphs, and histograms, with and without technology.**	❍	❍	❍	❍	❍	★	✓				★
TEKS 8.13	**Probability and statistics.** The student evaluates predictions and conclusions based on statistical data. The student is expected to:											
(A)	**evaluate methods of sampling to determine validity of an inference made from a set of data;**	❍	❍	❍	❍	❍	❍	★				★
(B)	**recognize misuses of graphical or numerical information and evaluate predictions and conclusion based on data analysis.**	❍	❍	❍	❍	❍	❍	★				★

B **Building Stamina**™

★ Standards covered

❍ Standards to be covered

✓ Standards previously covered

TEKS in bold are assessed on the TAKS.

To the Student:

When you play a sport or perform on stage, the key to success is practice, practice, practice. The same is true when you are learning mathematics skills. The lessons in the Measuring Up® book are geared to help you review and practice the Texas state standards, or TEKS. "TEKS" stands for Texas Essential Knowledge and Skills, and they describe the mathematics skills you should have acquired after completing your grade level.

Measuring Up® has two parts. Part 1 focuses on algebra. Part 2 focuses on geometry and also includes percents, proportional relationships, probability, and statistics. Each lesson consists of four main sections:

- **Focus on TEKS** introduces the TEKS skills which will be covered in the lesson.
- **Guided Instruction** uses worked-out examples to explain the skills you will need for successful learning.
- **Apply the TEKS** gives you the opportunity to practice important TEKS concepts and skills with short response and open-ended questions.
- **TAKS Practice** gives you experience in responding to questions in the test format.

In addition to the lessons, other sections in the book are called **Building Stamina**™. These sections contain both multiple-choice and open-ended, gridded-response questions that help build your intellectual brain power. Each question involves multiple TEKS and may require higher-level thinking.

In the spring, you will take the Texas Assessment of Knowledge and Skills (TAKS) exam. It will be an important step forward. The TAKS will show how well you measure up to the Texas state standards. It is just one of the many important tests you will take throughout your academic career. Success on the TAKS will prepare you for the next level of challenges in mathematics. Have a great and successful year!

to the
Texas Essential Knowledge and Skills
and Success Strategies for the TAKS

To Parents and Families:

All students need mathematics skills to succeed. Texas educators have created the Texas Essential Knowledge and Skills, or TEKS, for Mathematics. It sets the standards that all Texas students should meet at each grade level. Students need to meet these standards to graduate, and these skills will be assessed by the Texas Assessment of Knowledge and Skills (TAKS) exam in the spring.

The TAKS is directly related to the TEKS. The TAKS emphasizes higher-level thinking skills. Students must learn to think on a higher level—to consider, analyze, interpret, and evaluate—instead of just recalling simple facts.

Measuring Up® will help your child to review the TEKS and prepare for mathematics exams. It contains:

- **Lessons**, which focus on practicing the TEKS;
- **Guided Instruction**, in which students are shown the steps and skills necessary to solve a variety of mathematics problems;
- **TAKS Practice**, which clarifies how individual TEKS can be understood through multiple-choice and griddable questions;
- **Building Stamina**™, which gives practice in solving problems and answering multiple-choice and griddable questions that require higher-level thinking.

For success in school and the real world, your child needs good mathematics skills. Your involvement is crucial to your child's success. Here are some suggestions:

- Make sure your home shows that mathematics is important. Involve everyone in activities that require mathematics, such as mixing recipes, balancing checkbooks, and shopping.
- Help to find appropriate Internet sites for mathematics. Note how mathematics is used when you are out with your family. Discuss how mathematics is used in financial and banking matters, in careers such as engineering, architecture, and medicine, in space exploration, and in other real-life applications.
- Invite your child to write and talk about what he or she has learned in math class.
- Encourage your child to take time to review and check his or her homework. Just solving a problem is not enough. Ask your child whether or not his or her answers are reasonable and then to justify the answers.

Get involved! Work this year to ensure your child's success. Mathematics skills are essential for success throughout your child's life.

What's Ahead in Measuring Up®

This book was created for Texas students. Each lesson, question, and selection is aimed at helping you master the TEKS and prepare for the TAKS or any other mathematics exam you take during the school year.

About the TAKS Test

Texas educators have developed the Texas Essential Knowledge and Skills, or TEKS, for mathematics. These standards spell out what is expected of all students at each grade level. The Texas Assessment of Knowledge and Skills, or TAKS, measures how well students have mastered the TEKS. TAKS questions go along with the TEKS and meet the following mathematics TAKS objectives:

Algebra

1. The student will describe functional relationships in a variety of ways.
2. The student will demonstrate an understanding of the properties and attributes of functions.
3. The student will demonstrate an understanding of linear functions.
4. The student will formulate and use linear equations and inequalities.
5. The student will demonstrate an understanding of quadratic and other nonlinear functions.

Geometry and Measurement

6. The student will demonstrate an understanding of geometric relationships and spatial reasoning.
7. The student will demonstrate an understanding of two- and three-dimensional representations of geometric relationships and shapes.
8. The student will demonstrate an understanding of the concepts and uses of measurement and similarity.

Percents, Proportional Relationships, Probability, Statistics, and Mathematical Processes

9. The student will demonstrate an understanding of percents, proportional relationships, probability, and statistics in application problems.
10. The student will demonstrate and understanding of the mathematical processes and tools used in problem solving.

Format of the TAKS

- The Texas Assessment of Knowledge and Skills for Mathematics has two types of questions: multiple-choice questions and open-ended griddable questions.
- Students are allowed to use a calculator during the test and a Mathematics Chart that contains measurement conversions, formulas, and metric customary rulers.

Test-Taking Tips

General test-preparation tips:

- Start preparing now. Spend a few minutes a day practicing answers to test questions. Right now, the test may seem far away, but time has a way of marching on quickly.
- Get a good night's sleep the night before the test. Do not expect to cram everything into your head the night before. You can't remember much that way, and you will be too tired to do well.
- Eat a good breakfast. If you are hungry during the test, you will be distracted and unable to think clearly.
- Think positively. Do not focus on the things you do not know. Nobody is perfect. If you are unsure of an answer, mark that question and move on to the next. After you have worked through the test, return to those questions you have marked.

Measuring Up® on Multiple-Choice Questions

In multiple-choice items there is a question followed by four answer choices. Your task is to pick the one correct choice. On the TAKS, you will answer many multiple-choice questions. Here are some tips:

- Always try to work the problem without looking at the choices. Once you arrive at an answer, compare your response with the choices.
- If your answer is not one of the choices, check your work. Sometimes "Not Here" is a choice. Rework the problem carefully because the answer may be one of the choices and an error may lead you astray.
- Some multiple-choice questions refer to a graphic such as an illustration, a graph, a table, or a picture. You will be asked to read or interpret the graphic. Read the question carefully, and use the graphic to answer the specific question.
- Do not forget that you can use your calculator to work the problems. It is still a good idea to write down the steps to ensure that you do not miss one or mistype when keying into the calculator.
- Many questions test higher-level thinking skills. You will not find the exact answers staring at you. You must connect the ideas and information to come up with the right answers.
- Even if you do not know the answer to a multiple-choice question, you can guess and get the question right. So, rule out obviously wrong answers immediately. By narrowing the possibilities to two choices, you can guess and have a 50% chance of choosing the correct answer.
- Check and double-check your answers before you turn in the test. Be sure of your answers.

Measuring Up® on Open-Ended Griddable Items

Open-ended griddable items require you to find a numeric answer, record your response, and then fill in a bubble for each digit in your answer. Here are some tips for answering open-ended griddable items:

- Carefully work the problem. Because you do not have answer choices as a way to check yourself, it is important to take your time and follow all the steps carefully.
- Once you have an answer, carefully write it into the chart using place values. Then fill in the bubble for the correct digit in each column.
- If an answer is a whole number, the zeros to the right of a decimal place do not have to be filled in. If you do include them in your answer, it will not be counted as incorrect.
- After completing the test, look back at all the open-ended griddable items and verify that the bubbles are filled in correctly in each column.

Measuring Up® with Building Stamina™

A unique feature of Measuring Up® is the **Building Stamina**™ sections, designed to give you practice and build your confidence and endurance for completing higher-level thinking activities. These activities include answering questions that cover multiple TEKS. Each chapter ends with a **Building Stamina**™ section. A **Building Stamina**™ section is also at the end of each of the two parts of the book. At the end of the book is a longer, more comprehensive **Building Stamina**™ section, which is a complete review of all the TEKS covered in the lessons.

Higher-Level Thinking Skills ☆

The TAKS is designed to tap your higher-level thinking skills. More than just a test of simple recall, it stimulates you to analyze, interpret, and evaluate. For instance, instead of being asked to recall how to add two numbers, you might be asked to solve a word problem using addition and other operations. Instead of being asked to graph a function, you might need to describe how changing the value of a constant would affect the graph. Instead of being asked to determine the length of a segment, you might have to solve a problem using the Pythagorean Theorem and similar triangles. In Measuring Up®, all higher-level thinking skills questions are starred for easy identification.

- **Building Stamina**™ *in PART 1*
  The **Building Stamina**™ sections in Part 1 are designed to give you practice on harder questions. They provide the type of questions involving algebraic skills you will be expected to solve. These questions vary in length to help you build endurance.

Higher-Level Thinking Skills (continued)

- **Building Stamina**™ *in PART 2*
  The **Building Stamina**™ sections in Part 2 contain problems covering a wide variety of topics including geometry, similarity, percents, probability, and statistics.

- *End-of-Book* **Building Stamina**™
  All of the skills covered in this book are mixed and combined in this section. After completing the lessons and reviewing all the TEKS, you will have enough stamina to successfully complete this comprehensive **Building Stamina**™ section.

By the time you have come to the end of Measuring Up®, you will have reviewed and practiced the TEKS, completed TAKS Practice, and built up your stamina to answer tough questions. You will more than measure up. You will be a smashing success!

PART 1 Algebra

Chapter 1 Functional Relationships

In this chapter, you will study and practice:

- how to identify independent and dependent variables
- how to determine if a relation is a function
- how to represent and interpret functional relationships
- ★ **Building Stamina**™ This section gives you a chance to sharpen your understanding of mathematical relationships and to strengthen your test-taking abilities.

Chapter 2 Properties and Attributes of Functions

In this chapter, you will study and practice:

- how to identify the parent forms of linear and quadratic functions
- how to find patterns in functions
- how to show pattern situations in graphs
- how to create scatterplots
- how to find the values of a function
- how to simplify expressions
- how to solve equations
- ★ **Building Stamina**™ This section gives you a chance to sharpen your ability to simplify and solve functions and to strengthen your test-taking abilities.

Chapter 3 Linear Functions

In this chapter, you will study and practice:

- how to represent linear functions
- how to identify the slope and intercept of a linear function
- how to recognize the effects of changing slope and intercepts
- how to graph equations of lines
- how to write equations of lines
- how to calculate direct variation
- ★ **Building Stamina**™ This section gives you a chance to sharpen your interpreting and graphing skills and to strengthen your test-taking abilities.

Chapter 4 Solving Linear Equations and Inequalities

In this chapter, you will study and practice:

- how to solve linear equations and linear inequalities
- how to solve systems of linear equations
- how to interpret the solution to a system of linear equations
- how to determine if a solution is reasonable
- ★ **Building Stamina**™ This section gives you a chance to sharpen your skills in manipulating symbols and solving equations and to strengthen your test-taking abilities.

Chapter 5 Quadratic Functions

In this chapter, you will study and practice:

- how to describe and predict the effects of changes on a parent function
- how to analyze graphs of quadratic functions
- how to solve quadratic equations
- how to apply the laws of exponents
- how to identify inverse variations
- how to calculate exponential growth and decay
- ★ **Building Stamina**™ This section gives you a chance to sharpen your skills at computations using exponents and to strengthen your test-taking abilities.

Focus on TEKS — Lesson 1 Independent and Dependent Quantities

TEKS A(b)1A Describe independent and dependent quantities in functional relationships.

Everything you learn in mathematics is about relationships.

In an **ordered pair**, two people, things, or numbers are related to each other in some way. In a set of ordered pairs, all ordered pairs are related to each other in the same way.

Mathematically, a **relationship** is a set of ordered pairs. A relationship in which one number depends on another number is a **dependent relationship.**

In a dependent relationship between numbers, the number that relies on and is determined by the other number is called the **dependent quantity**.

The number that *determines* the dependent quantity is called the **independent quantity**. The independent quantity is listed first in the ordered pair.

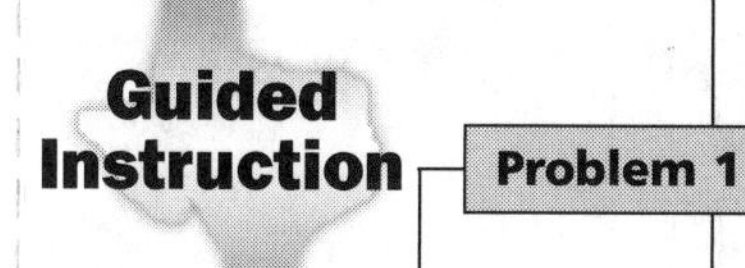

Problem 1

The history of the stock market has proven that a young person has a great opportunity to watch an investment of a relatively small amount of money grow successfully over time to become a significantly larger amount. Which is the independent quantity, and which is the dependent quantity?

$10,000 Investment with 8% Average Rate of Return	
Time (yrs)	Value of Investment
0	$10,000
1	$10,800
5	$14,693
10	$21,589
15	$31,722
20	$46,609
25	$68,484
30	$100,627

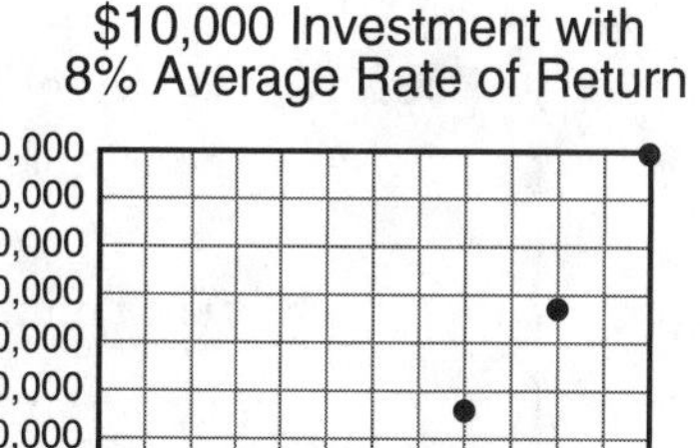

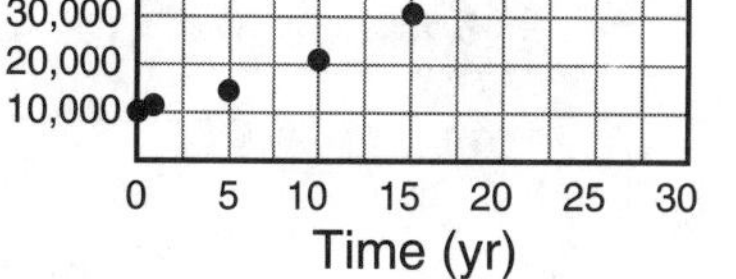

Use the table, graph, and description of the situation to determine the independent quantity and the dependent quantity.

Step 1 What two quantities are being related to each other?

The value of the investment is being related to time.

Step 2 Which quantity determines the other quantity? Which quantity relies on the other quantity?

The amount of time the investment is allowed to grow determines the value of the investment. The value of the investment depends on the amount of time.

Solution Time is the independent quantity, and value of the investment is the dependent quantity.

Guided Instruction

More Problems

Problem 2

Will is moving to a new apartment. He has 24 boxes of books. It takes two people to lift and carry each box from the moving truck, up three flights of stairs, and into the new apartment. The more friends who help him move, the fewer trips up the stairs each person will have to make. This relationship can be expressed by the function $f(h) = \frac{48}{h+1}$, where h is an odd number of friends that help Will move. Identify both the independent and dependent quantities.

Step 1 What two quantities are being related to each other?

The number of helpers is being related to the number of trips that each will have to make up the stairs.

Step 2 Make a table of ordered pairs to help you see the relationship between the two quantities. Solve $f(h)$ for h = 1, 3, 5, 7, 9, 11.

Helpers	h	1	3	5	7	9	11
Trips Up the Stairs	$f(h)$	24	12	8	6	4.8	4

Step 3 Which quantity determines the other quantity? Which quantity depends on the other quantity?

The number of helpers determines how many trips each will have to make up the stairs.

Solution The number of friends who help is the independent quantity, and the number of trips that each person will have to make up the stairs is the dependent quantity.

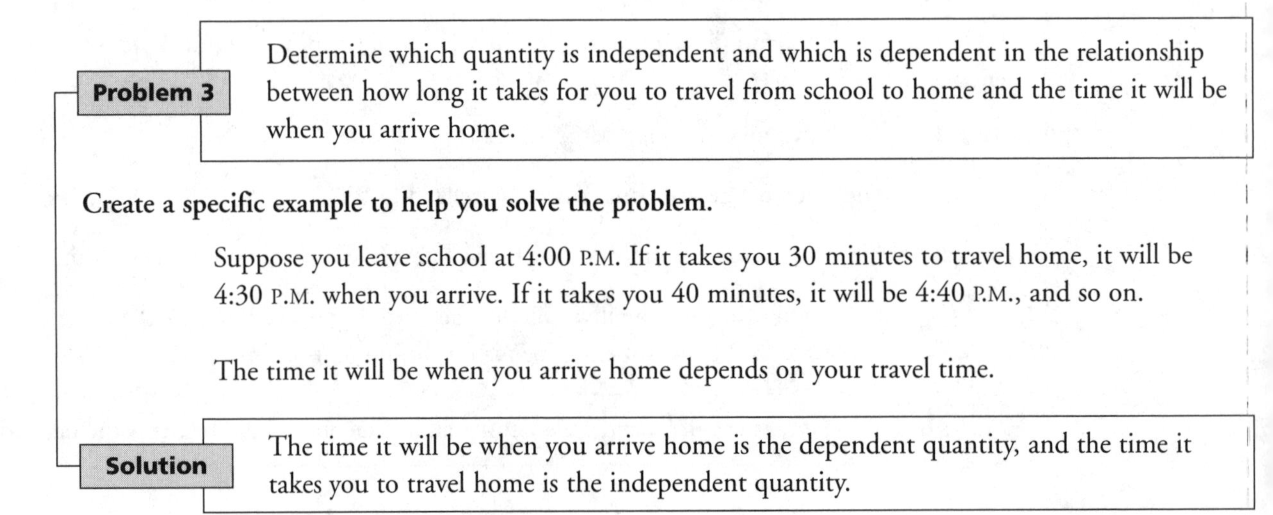

Problem 3

Determine which quantity is independent and which is dependent in the relationship between how long it takes for you to travel from school to home and the time it will be when you arrive home.

Create a specific example to help you solve the problem.

Suppose you leave school at 4:00 P.M. If it takes you 30 minutes to travel home, it will be 4:30 P.M. when you arrive. If it takes you 40 minutes, it will be 4:40 P.M., and so on.

The time it will be when you arrive home depends on your travel time.

Solution The time it will be when you arrive home is the dependent quantity, and the time it takes you to travel home is the independent quantity.

Apply the TEKS **Determine which quantity is independent and which is dependent.**

1. Ellie works for a window-washing company. She is paid $5.50 an hour plus $2.50 for every window she washes. To find her pay for a one-hour job she uses the function $f(w) = 5.50 + 2.50w$, where w is the number of windows washed.

   independent: ______________________ dependent: ______________________

2. Sound travels at about 760 miles per hour, which is about 0.2 miles per second. From her window, Kathi is watching a storm move toward her house. As it gets closer, the claps of thunder are getting closer and closer to their respective flashes of lightning. The distance between Kathi and the lightning can be approximated by the function $f(s) = 0.2s$, where s is the number of seconds that Kathi counts between each lightning and thunder.

   independent: ______________________ dependent: ______________________

3.

Phone Bill	$21.29	$23.95	$29.13	$44.18
Long Distance Time (min)	0	38	112	327

   independent: ______________________

   dependent: ______________________

4.

Length of Side (ft)	1	5	3	2	4
Area of Square (ft^2)	1	25	9	4	16

   independent: ______________________

   dependent: ______________________

5.

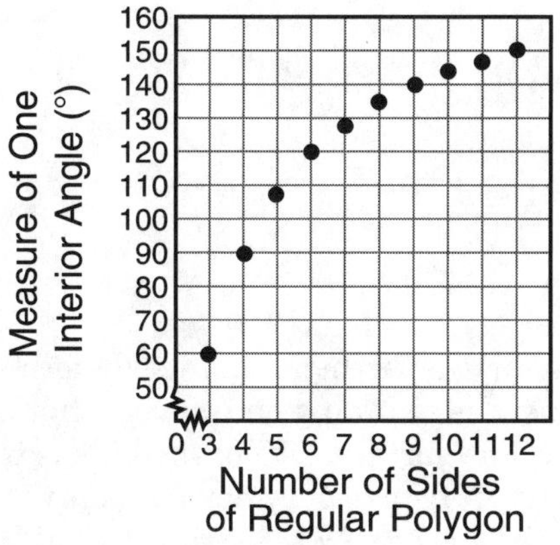

Measure of One Interior Angle (°)
160, 150, 140, 130, 120, 110, 100, 90, 80, 70, 60, 50
0 3 4 5 6 7 8 9 10 11 12
Number of Sides of Regular Polygon

   independent: ______________________

   dependent: ______________________

6.

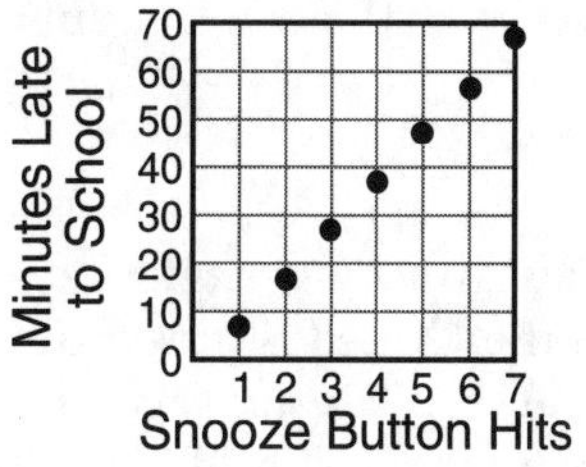

Minutes Late to School
70, 60, 50, 40, 30, 20, 10, 0
1 2 3 4 5 6 7
Snooze Button Hits

   independent: ______________________

   dependent: ______________________

7. Outside temperature and hours of AC use

   independent: ______________________

   dependent: ______________________

8. The weight of an object and how far you can throw it

   independent: ______________________

   dependent: ______________________

Solve the problem.

9. Write a sentence that describes a dependent relationship. Identify the independent and dependent quantities.

____

TAKS Objective 1 The student will describe functional relationships in a variety of ways.
TEKS A(b)1A

DIRECTIONS Read each question. Then circle the letter for the correct answer. If a correct answer is not here, circle the letter for "Not Here."

1 The cost for an advertisement during a television show has doubled since the show's rating has improved. The show's rating is—

A the ordered pair
B the independent quantity
C the dependent quantity
D two times what it was before

2 Which of these ordered pairs does NOT model (independent quantity, dependent quantity)?

F (Typing speed, time it takes to type a paper)
G (Cookies eaten, calories consumed)
H (Hours practicing guitar, guitar skills)
J (Length of hair, weeks without a haircut)

3 Earth is tilted on its axis at a 23.4° angle. During the summer in the United States, Earth's axis is tilting toward the sun. During the winter, the axis is tilting away from the sun. Which statement is true?

A The seasons depend on whether Earth's axis is tilting toward or away from the sun.
B The angle at which Earth tilts depends on the season.
C The seasons depend on the angle at which Earth tilts.
D The angle at which Earth tilts depends on which direction the Earth's axis is pointing.

4 Which is the dependent quantity in the table below?

Miles Before Empty	25	50	75	100	125
Gas in Tank (gals)	1	2	3	4	5

F Miles driven before the tank is empty
G Gallons of gas in tank
H Miles per gallon of gas
J Not Here

5 If $y = f(x)$ and $f(x) = 4x - 2$, then what is the dependent quantity?

A y
B x
C $4x$
D Not Here

6 The treasury department of a newly formed government is planning on issuing a national currency. The surface area of the bills is more important to the treasury department than the length. They know they want the width of the bills to be 2.5 inches, so they will work with the equation $\ell = \frac{A}{2.5}$. Identify the independent variable.

F Area of the paper currency
G Length of the paper currency
H Width of the paper currency
J 2.5 in.

Focus on TEKS

Lesson 2 Determining Functional Relationships

TEKS A(b)1B Use data sets to determine functional relationships between quantities.

You can use what you have learned about dependent relationships to determine if a relationship is a function.

A **function** is a set of ordered pairs, where each first value is paired with exactly one second value. The first value is the independent value and the second value is the dependent value.

Guided Instruction

Problem 1

Is the data on the first 13 states to enter the Union and the years they were admitted a functional relationship? If so, which is the independent quantity?

First 13 States to Enter the Union				
CT 1788	DE 1787	GA 1788	MA 1788	MD 1788
NC 1789	NH 1788	NJ 1787	NY 1788	PA 1787
RI 1790	SC 1788	VA 1788		

Answer the following questions to help you solve the problem.

1. If the given value is 1788, what is the state? You cannot know for sure which state. Eight states entered the Union in 1788.

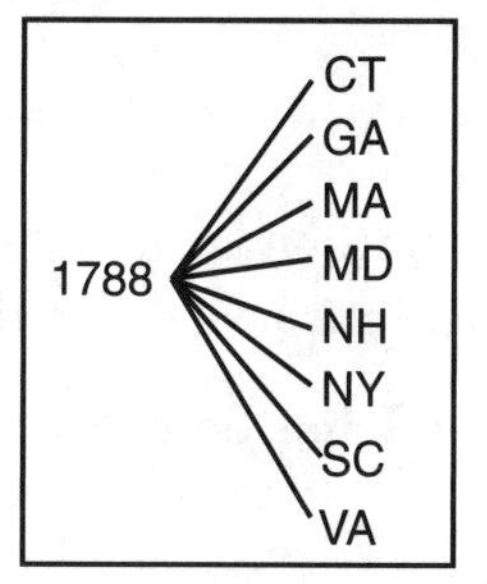

One-to-Many Relationship:
One value associates with many second values.
This is not a functional relationship.

2. If the given value is PA, what is the year? You can know for sure that the year is 1787.

DE, NJ, PA → 1787

Many-to-One Relationship:
Many values associate with one second value.
This is a functional relationship.

3. If the given value is 1789, what is the second value?
You can know for sure that the state is NC.

One-to-One Relationship:
One value associates with one and only one second value.
This is a functional relationship.

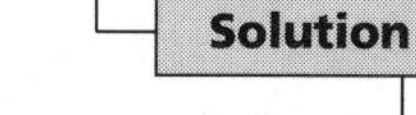

The data is a functional relationship when states are the independent values.

DE, NJ, PA → 1787
CT, GA, MA, MD, NH, NY, SC, VA → 1788
NC — 1789
RI — 1790

If you are given any one of the 13 states, you can know exactly what the year is. The mapping represents this functional relationship.

But if you are given any one year, you might not know exactly which one state is being associated with that year.

More Problems

Guided Instruction

Problem 2 Determine if the set of ordered pairs is a function.
(2, 2), (5, 4), (1, 2), (5, 6), (8, 8), (10, 9), (3, 3), (7, 8), (5, 8)

Create a mapping to organize the data visually.

If you are given the number 5 as the independent value, you cannot determine whether the second value is 4, 6, or 8.

Solution The number 5 has a one-to-many relationship with the numbers 4, 6, and 8. So the set of ordered pairs is not a function.

Problem 3 Is $y = \frac{1}{2}x + 1$ a function?

Another method for determining if a relationship is a function is the vertical line test. If any vertical line intersects the graph of the relationship at more than one point, then the relationship is not a function.

Use the vertical line test to determine if $y = \frac{1}{2}x + 1$ is a function.

Step 1 Graph the equation.

Draw or imagine vertical lines at all points on the graph.

The vertical line test shows that if you are given any x value you can know for sure the y value.

Solution No vertical line intersects the graph at more than one point. So $y = \frac{1}{2}x + 1$ is a function.

Apply the TEKS Make a mapping of each ordered pair. Determine if the relationship is a function. Describe each relationship with all of these that apply: *one-to-many, many-to-one, one-to-one.*

1. (2, 5), (1, 4), (2, 2), (3, 5)

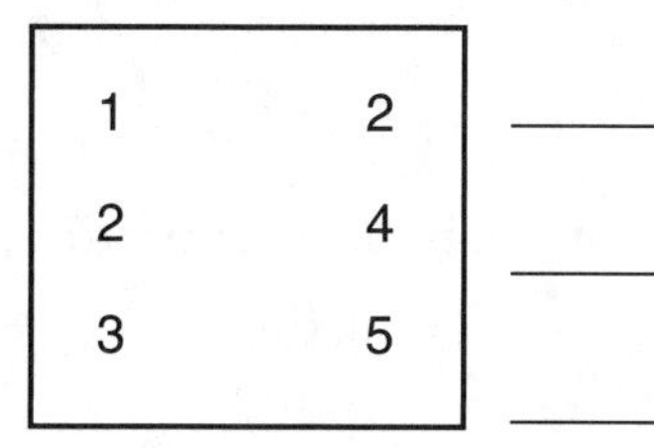

____

____

____

2. (shirt, black), (pants, khaki), (socks, gray), (shoes, black)

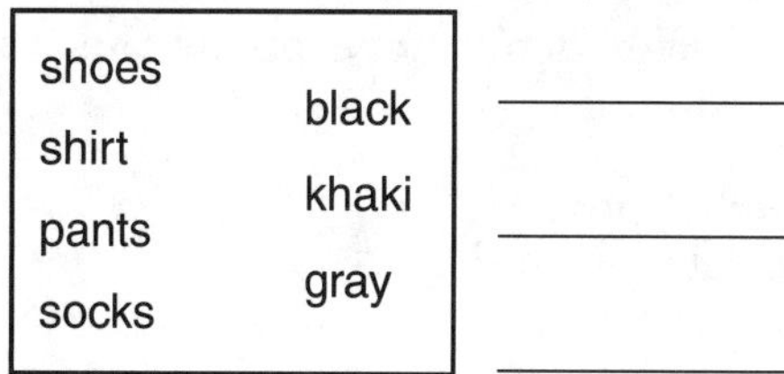

____

____

____

Determine if each relationship is a function.

3.

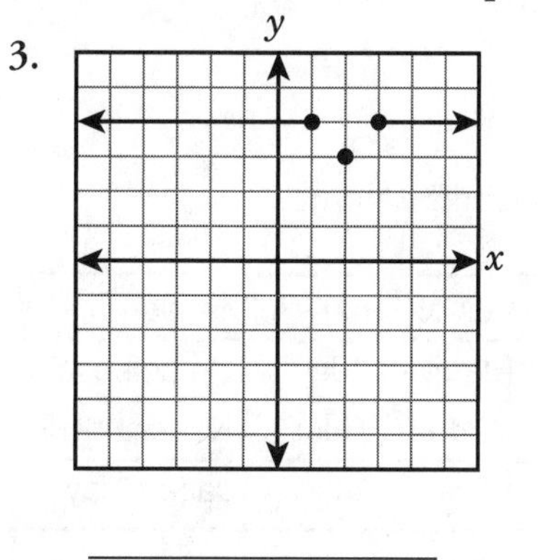

____

4.

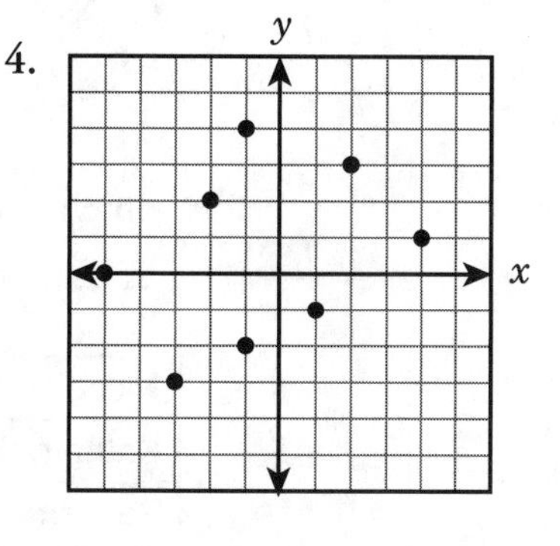

____

5.

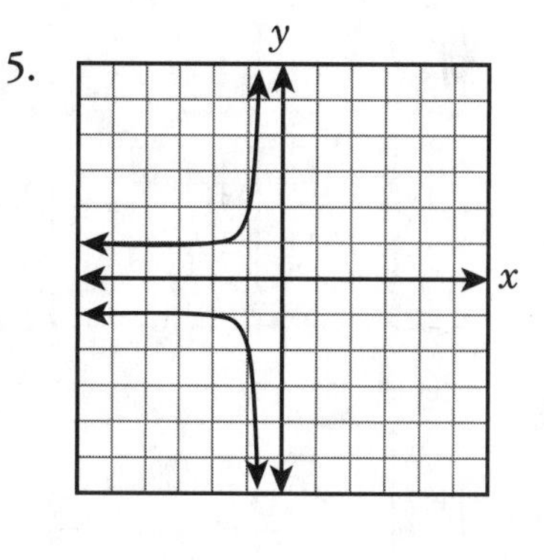

____

Graph and use the vertical line test to determine if the relationship is a function.

6. $x = 4$

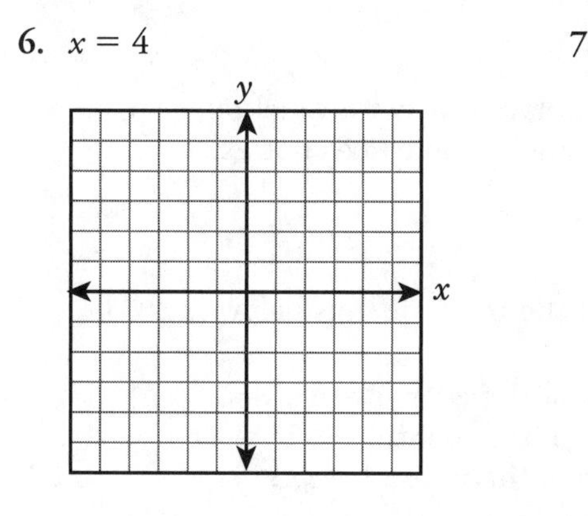

____

7. $x + y = 2 + x$

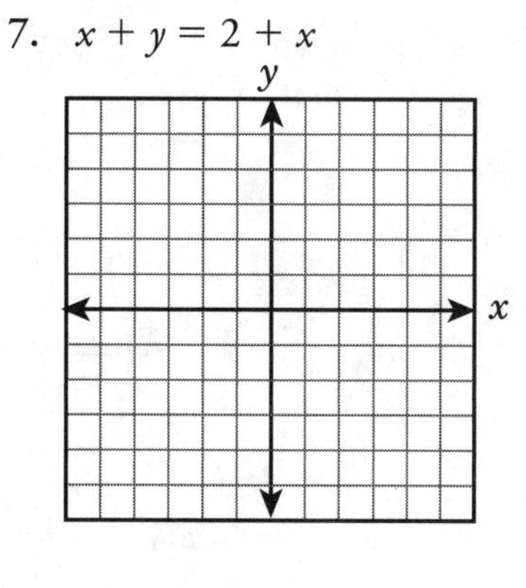

____

8. $y = x^2 - 2$

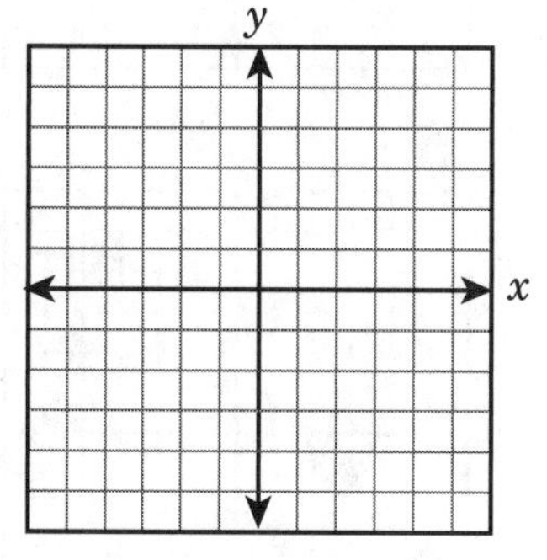

____

Determine if the data is a functional relationship. If so, which is the independent value?

9.

Week's Daily Rainfall and High Temperatures						
0.5 in.	0 in.	2.0 in.	0.75 in.	0 in.	1.25 in.	0 in.
72°F	88°F	39°F	48°F	52°F	72°F	65°F

____

10.

Number of Play Periods in Major Sports					
Baseball	9	Hockey	3	Basketball	4
Soccer	2	Football	4	Golf	18

____

TAKS Objective 1 The student will describe functional relationships in a variety of ways.
TEKS A(b)1B

DIRECTIONS Read each question. Then circle the letter for the correct answer. If a correct answer is <u>not here</u>, circle the letter for "Not Here."

1 Which graph represents a functional relationship?

A

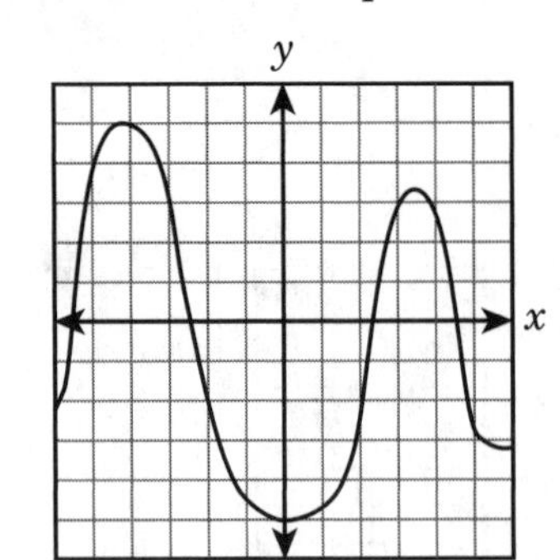

B

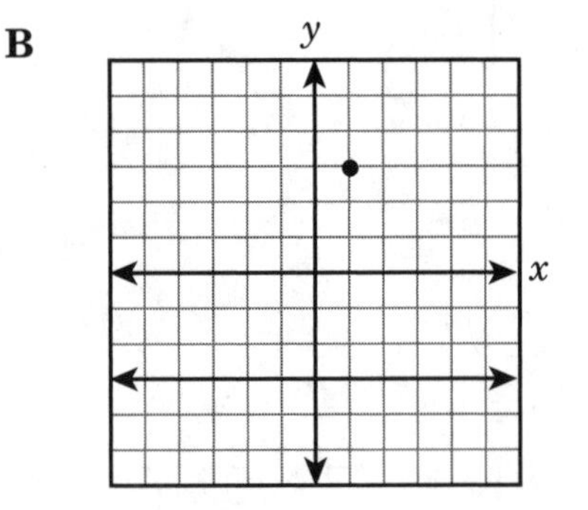

C

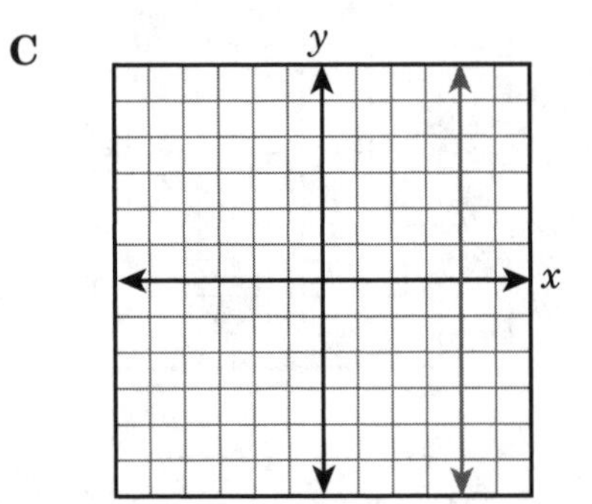

D

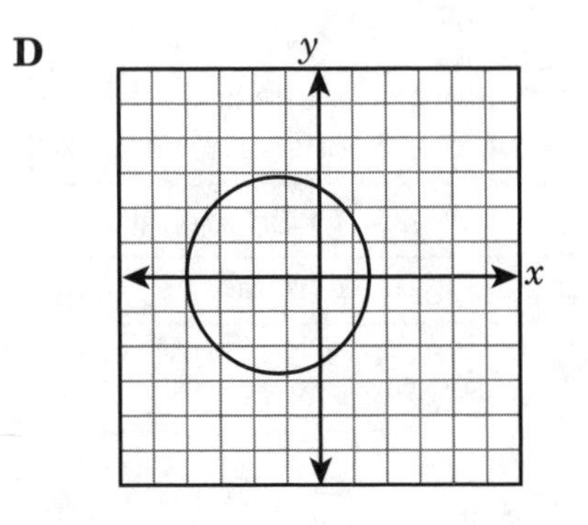

2 Which set of ordered pairs is a function?

F $(-1, 8), (0, 8), (3, 8), (-6, 0)$

G $(4, -3), (2, 7), (4, 1), (-5, 12)$

H $(86, 1), (94, 2), (94, 2), (83, 4)$

J Not Here

3 Which is the dependent value?

Nicknames of Tommy's Friends		
Nicholas "Nic"	Jamison "Jay"	Suzanne "Suz"
Kathryn "Kat"	Eldrick "Tiger"	Karissa "Kris"
Rakeem "Rocky"	Kristin "Kris"	Jacob "Jay"

A Name

B Nickname

C Both A and B

D The relation is not a function, so a dependent value does not exist.

4 Which of the relationships below is NOT a function?

day of the year: $1 \leq r \leq 365$
day of the month: $1 \leq m \leq 31$
day of the week: $1 \leq w \leq 7$

F (day of the year, month)

G (day of the year, day of the month)

H (day of the week, day of the month)

J (day of the month, day of the week)

Focus on TEKS

Lesson 3 Describing Functional Relationships

TEKS A(b)1C Describe functional relationships for given problem situations and write equations or inequalities to answer questions arising from the situations.

TEKS 8.14A Identify and apply mathematics to everyday experiences, to activities in and outside of school, with other disciplines, and with other mathematical topics.

TEKS 8.14D Select tools such as real objects, manipulatives, paper/pencil, and technology or techniques such as mental math, estimation, and number sense to solve problems.

If a relationship is a function, then you can use an equation to help you answer questions about the relationship.

A **variable** is a symbol used to represent a quantity.

A **coefficient** is a number multiplied by the variable.

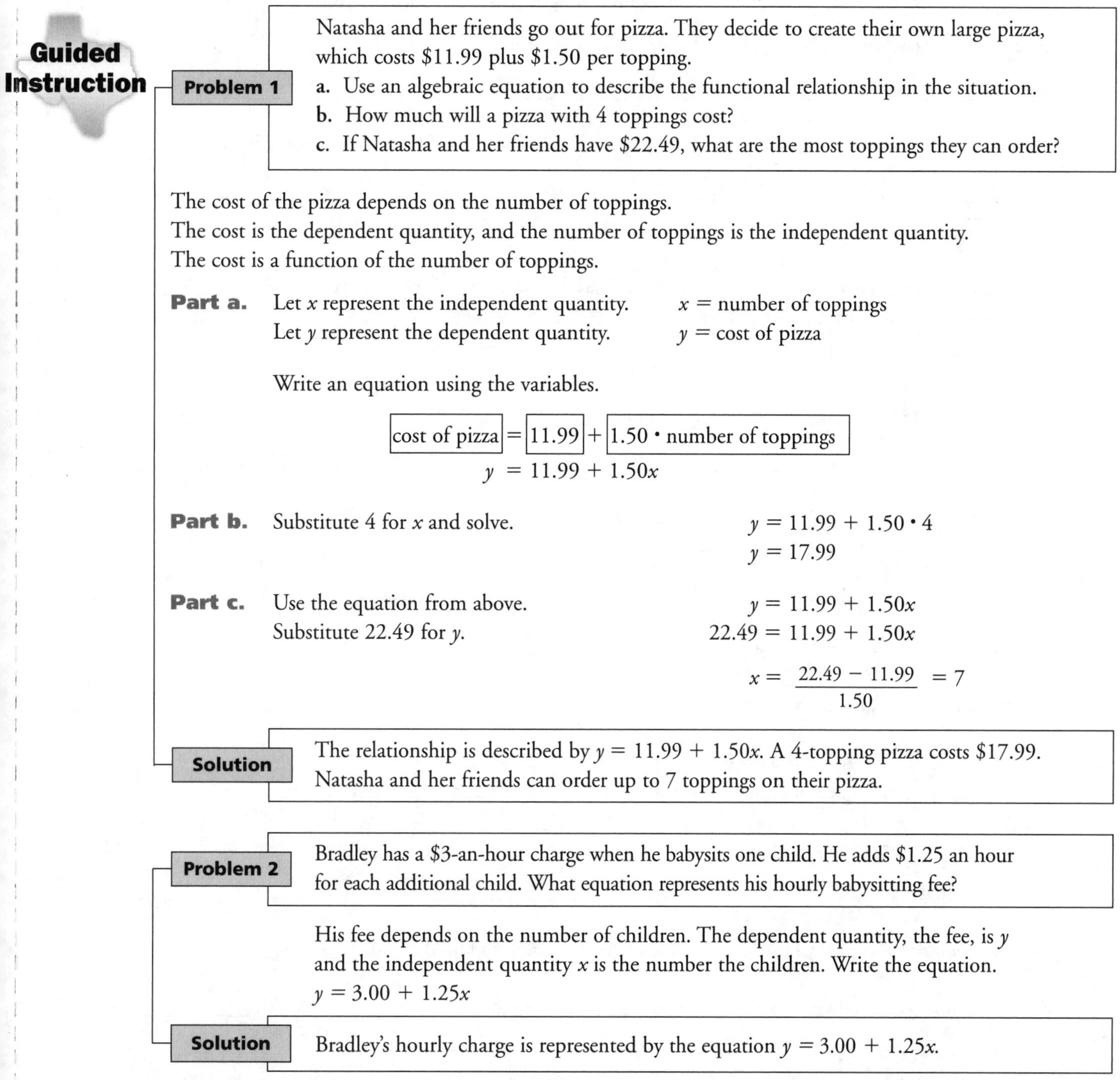

Guided Instruction

Problem 1

Natasha and her friends go out for pizza. They decide to create their own large pizza, which costs $11.99 plus $1.50 per topping.

a. Use an algebraic equation to describe the functional relationship in the situation.

b. How much will a pizza with 4 toppings cost?

c. If Natasha and her friends have $22.49, what are the most toppings they can order?

The cost of the pizza depends on the number of toppings.
The cost is the dependent quantity, and the number of toppings is the independent quantity.
The cost is a function of the number of toppings.

Part a. Let x represent the independent quantity. x = number of toppings
Let y represent the dependent quantity. y = cost of pizza

Write an equation using the variables.

$$\boxed{\text{cost of pizza}} = \boxed{11.99} + \boxed{1.50 \cdot \text{number of toppings}}$$

$$y = 11.99 + 1.50x$$

Part b. Substitute 4 for x and solve.

$$y = 11.99 + 1.50 \cdot 4$$
$$y = 17.99$$

Part c. Use the equation from above.
Substitute 22.49 for y.

$$y = 11.99 + 1.50x$$
$$22.49 = 11.99 + 1.50x$$
$$x = \frac{22.49 - 11.99}{1.50} = 7$$

Solution

The relationship is described by $y = 11.99 + 1.50x$. A 4-topping pizza costs $17.99. Natasha and her friends can order up to 7 toppings on their pizza.

Problem 2

Bradley has a $3-an-hour charge when he babysits one child. He adds $1.25 an hour for each additional child. What equation represents his hourly babysitting fee?

His fee depends on the number of children. The dependent quantity, the fee, is y and the independent quantity x is the number the children. Write the equation.
$y = 3.00 + 1.25x$

Solution

Bradley's hourly charge is represented by the equation $y = 3.00 + 1.25x$.

Apply the TEKS **Write a sentence to describe each functional relationship. Name the independent quantity and the dependent quantity.**

1. Sam forgot that she had borrowed a book from the library. The library charges 10 cents for each day a book is overdue.

____

2. Steve is having car trouble and therefore takes his car to a mechanic. The mechanic charges $58.63 per hour of labor. The parts needed to repair Steve's car cost $349.21.

____

Write an equation that models each functional relationship. Tell what each variable you use represents.

3. Lance's soccer team won each of its first four games by one goal.

____

4. Alicia's hair is 18.6 centimeters long. Her hair grows at an average rate of 0.25 centimeters per week.

____

Solve each problem.

5. Since Kenyon is an active person he requires 20 calories for every pound that his body weighs.
   a. Write an equation for the functional relationship. Define the variables you use.

   ____

   b. If he weighs 160 pounds, what is his daily requirement of calories?

   ____

6. A taxi company charges $1.60 for the first $\frac{1}{8}$ mile and $0.20 for each additional $\frac{1}{8}$ mile.
   a. Write an equation for the functional relationship. Define the variables you use.

   ____

   b. How much will the fare be for a 2.5 mile ride? _______________

   c. If the total fare comes to $3.60, how far did the rider travel in the taxi? _______________

7. Hye-sun is on page 36 of a book she is reading. She reads $\frac{1}{4}$ page every minute.
   a. Write an equation to describe the functional relationship. Define the variables you use.

   ____

   b. On what page will she be on after 48 minutes? _______________

   c. If the book has 156 pages, how long will it take her to finish reading the book? _______________

   d. Explain how you used the equation to answer Exercises b and c. _______________

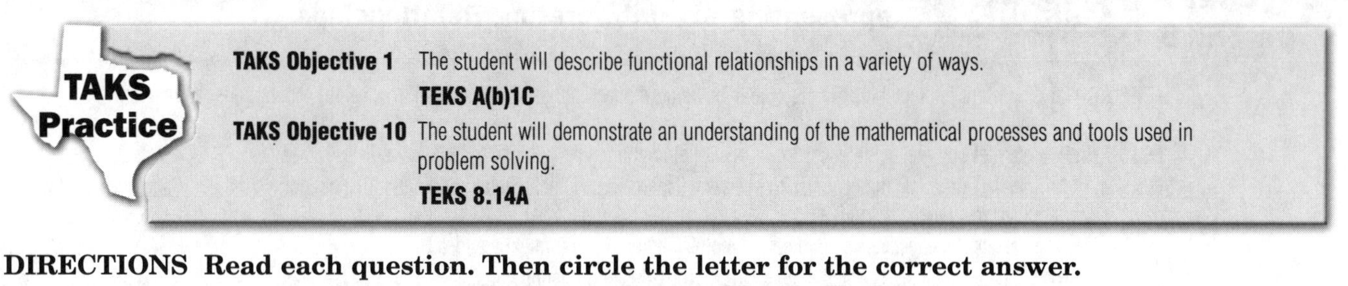

DIRECTIONS Read each question. Then circle the letter for the correct answer. If a correct answer is not here, circle the letter for "Not Here."

1 Josh wants to invest an amount of money in an account that earns 5% annual interest. Which of these is a description of a functional relationship for the amount of interest earned in one year?

A The amount of interest he will earn depends on the size of the bank.

B The amount of interest he will earn depends on the invested amount.

C The invested amount depends on the interest rate.

D The amount invested depends on the amount of interest he will earn.

2 To join a health club, Jennifer must pay a $99 startup fee and a $45 fee for each month she is a member. Which equation describes y, the total cost of the club membership?

F $y = 99 + 45$

G $y = 45 + 99x$

H $x = 99 + 45y$

J $y = 99 + 45x$

3 In basketball, points can be scored by making a 1-point, 2-point, or 3-point basket. Which equation describes y, the total points made by Bryce's team?

A $y = 1 + 2 + 3$

B $y = 6x$

C $y = 1a + 2b + 3c$

D Not Here

4 A Chinese chef starts with one large noodle. He stretches and folds the noodle to get two noodles. He stretches and folds those two noodles to get four noodles. He stretches and folds those four noodles to get eight noodles. How many noodles has the chef created after five folds?

Record your answer and fill in the bubbles on the grid below. Be sure to use the correct place value.

				.			
0	0	0	0		0	0	0
1	1	1	1		1	1	1
2	2	2	2		2	2	2
3	3	3	3		3	3	3
4	4	4	4		4	4	4
5	5	5	5		5	5	5
6	6	6	6		6	6	6
7	7	7	7		7	7	7
8	8	8	8		8	8	8
9	9	9	9		9	9	9

5 Together, Luke and James have never eaten more than 16 pieces of pizza at one time. Which equation describes y, the total number of pieces that Luke has eaten at one time given x, the number of pieces that James has eaten?

A $y \leq 16 - x$

B $y \geq 16 - x$

C $y = 16 - x$

D Not Here

Focus on TEKS

Lesson 4 Representing and Interpreting Relationships

TEKS A(b)1D Represent relationships among quantities using models, tables, graphs, diagrams, verbal descriptions, equations, and inequalities.
TEKS A(b)1E Interpret and make inferences from functional relationships.
TEKS 8.14A Identify and apply mathematics to everyday experiences, to activities in and outside of school, with other disciplines, and with other mathematical topics.
TEKS 8.15B Evaluate the effectiveness of different representations to communicate ideas.
TEKS 8.16B Validate conclusions using mathematical properties and relationships.

You can use models, tables, graphs, and diagrams as well as equations, inequalities, and verbal descriptions to help you represent and interpret relationships.

Guided Instruction

Problem 1

An apple grower is planting a new orchard. He wants the orchard to have a square shape. The trees must be planted 8 feet apart and in rows 8 feet apart. Represent the relationship using a table and a graph.

8 ft

Solution

8-ft lengths per side	Trees
1	4
2	9
3	16

Number of Apple Trees in Orchard

Trees
16
14
12
10
8
6
4
2
0 2 4 6 8 10 12 14 16
8-ft Lengths Per Side

More Problems

Problem 2

How many apple trees will be in the orchard if the grower has enough land to make each side of the orchard 136 feet from corner tree to corner tree?

You could continue making models by drawing more dot patterns, or you could extend the table or the graph. However, in this case, each of these tasks would take considerable time and paper.

Determine a rule that describes the relationship between the number of 8-ft lengths in a side of the orchard and the number of apple trees in the orchard.

Step 1 Divide 136 by 8 to find number of 8-ft spaces. $136 \div 8 = 17$

Step 2 Analyze the data to determine a rule. $\text{trees} = (\text{8-ft lengths} + 1)^2$

Step 3 Assign variables to represent the unknowns. $y = (x + 1)^2$

Step 4 Substitute 17 for x. $y = (17 + 1)^2 = 18^2 = 324$

Solution If the orchard has sides that are 136 feet, then it will have 324 apple trees.

Guided Instruction

When representing functions as graphs, it is important to know the difference between discontinuous (also called discrete) and continuous functions. The plotted points of the graphs of **discontinuous functions** are not connected. If the points were connected, then the graph of the relationship would not make sense. The points of the graph of the apple orchards problem on page 14 were not connected by a line because it is only possible to have whole trees.

The plotted points of the graphs of **continuous functions** are connected. The graph of the problem below is connected by a line because as the water gets higher, it crosses every point of depth.

Problem 3

Cheryl's 6-foot swimming pool already has $\frac{1}{2}$ foot of water in it. Cheryl begins filling the rest of the pool to reach a level of 5.75 feet. When the water reaches 2 feet, Cheryl stops for one hour to run a few errands. She continues to fill the pool when she returns home. Represent filling the pool using a table and a graph.

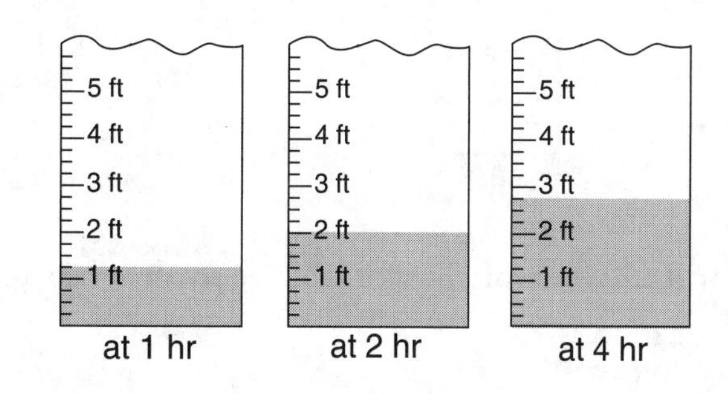

Solution

Hours	Depth(ft)	Hours	Depth(ft)
0	0.5	5	3.5
1	1.25	6	4.25
2	2.0	7	5.0
3	2.0	8	5.75
4	2.75		

Pool Water Depth

Water Depth (ft)

0 1 2 3 4 5 6 7 8

Hours

Apply the TEKS Translate each table to a graph and each graph to a table.

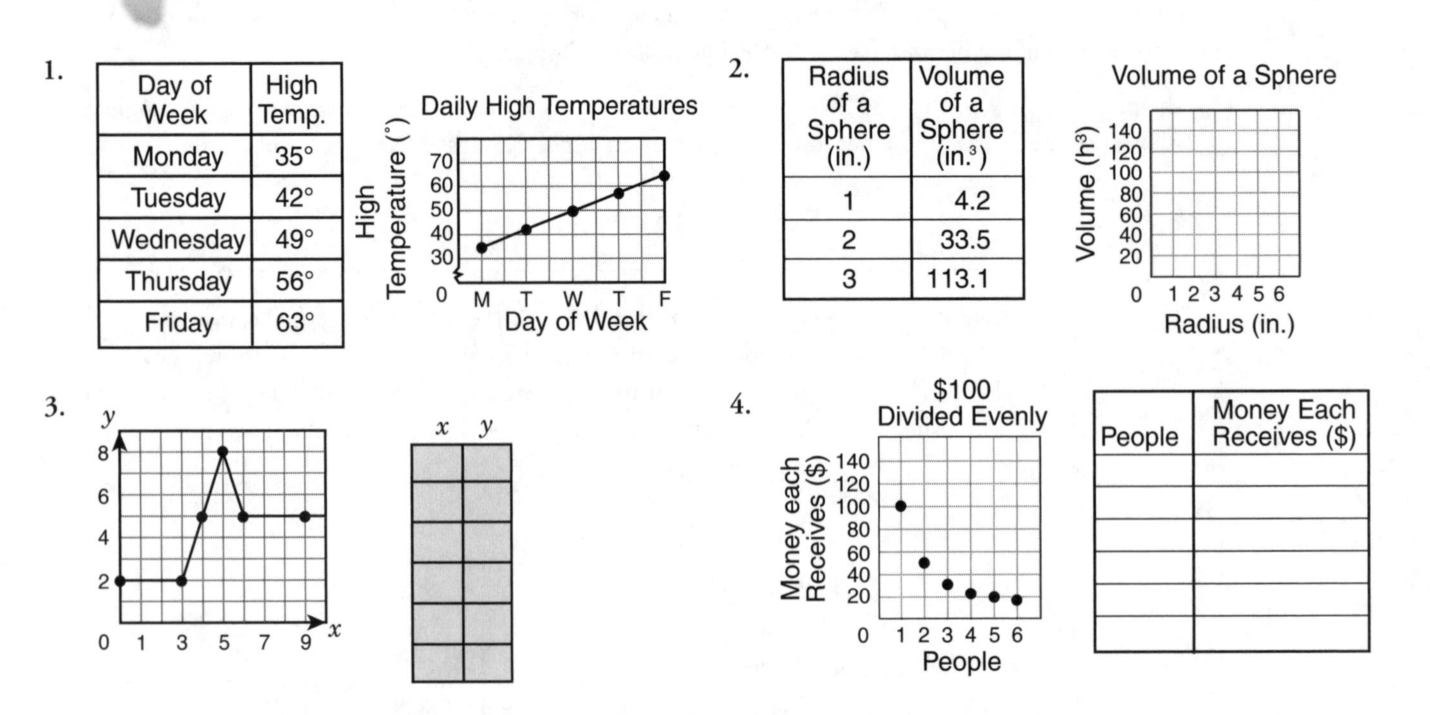

1.

Day of Week	High Temp.
Monday	35°
Tuesday	42°
Wednesday	49°
Thursday	56°
Friday	63°

2.

Radius of a Sphere (in.)	Volume of a Sphere (in.³)
1	4.2
2	33.5
3	113.1

3.

x	y

4.

People	Money Each Receives ($)

Determine the rule for the relationship in each table or graph. Then answer the question.

5.

Pace (min per mi)	Time to Run 5 mi (min)
6	30
7	35
8	40
10	50

a. ______________

b. How many minutes will it take to run 5 miles at a pace of 15 minutes per mile? ______________

6.

Flood Level of River After Crest

a. ______________

b. How many feet above flood stage will the river be after 12 hours? ______________

7.

T-Shirts Ordered	Total Cost ($) (Including Shipping Costs)
1	13
2	21
3	29
4	37

a. ______________

b. What is the total bill if 24 T-shirts are purchased?

____

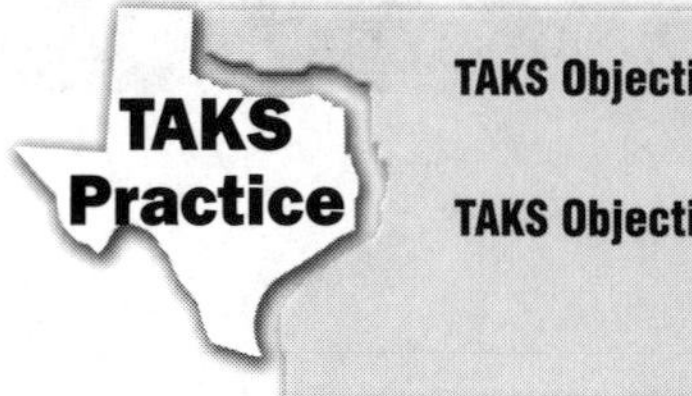

TAKS Objective 1 The student will describe functional relationships in a variety of ways.
TEKS A(b)1D, A(b)1E

TAKS Objective 10 The student will demonstrate an understanding of the mathematical processes and tools used in problem solving.
TEKS 8.14A, 8.15B, **8.16B**

DIRECTIONS Read each question. Then circle the letter for the correct answer. If a correct answer is not here, circle the letter for "Not Here."

1 Which of the following does NOT represent the functional relationship in the table?

Hours Traveled	Distance from Home (mi)
0	250
1	195
2	140
3	85

A $y = 250 - 55x$

B

C

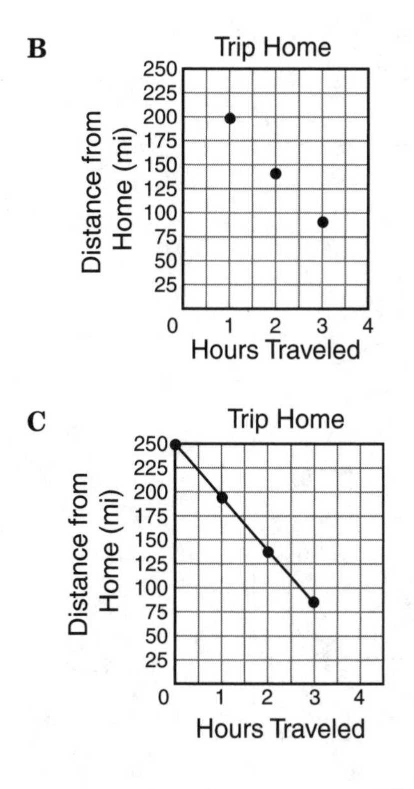

D The travelers begin 250 miles away from home, and they travel toward home at 55 miles per hour.

2 How much is the postage for a 13-ounce letter sent first-class in 2004?

Maximum Weight (oz)	Rate
1	$0.37
2	$0.60
3	$0.83
4	$1.06

Record your answer and fill in the bubbles on the grid below. Be sure to use the correct place value.

Which of the situations could NOT possibly be represented by the graph?

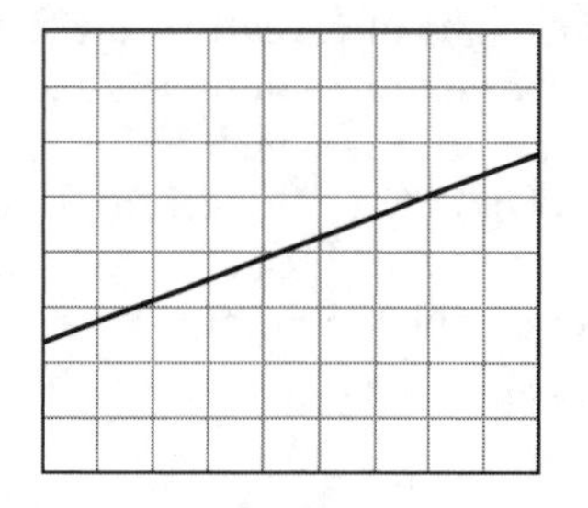

A A plane approaching its destination

B Combined weight of x number of people

C Summer morning temperature

D Price of pizza with extra toppings

DIRECTIONS Read each question. Then circle the letter for the correct answer. If a correct answer is not here, circle the letter for "Not Here."

1 Which of these represents the relationship between the number of sides of a regular polygon and the number of diagonals it has?

A (3, 1), (4, 2), (5, 3), (6, 4), . . . , $(n, n - 2)$

B

Sides	Diagonals
3	0
4	2
5	5
6	9
n	$\frac{n(n-3)}{2}$

C (triangle, 3), (square, 4), (pentagon, 5), (hexagon, 6), . . . , (n-gon, n)

D

Sides	Diagonals
3	0
4	4
5	10
6	18
n	$n(n-3)$

2 Two friends eat out at a restaurant. They have a coupon for x amount of dollars. After the coupon is taken off, the check is for $23.95. They want to tip 20% of the original amount before the coupon was deducted. Which of these represents the tip amount?

F $y = 0.20(23.95 + x)$

G $y = 23.95 + 0.20x$

H $x = 0.20(23.95 + y)$

J Not Here

3 Which of these does NOT represent a function?

A

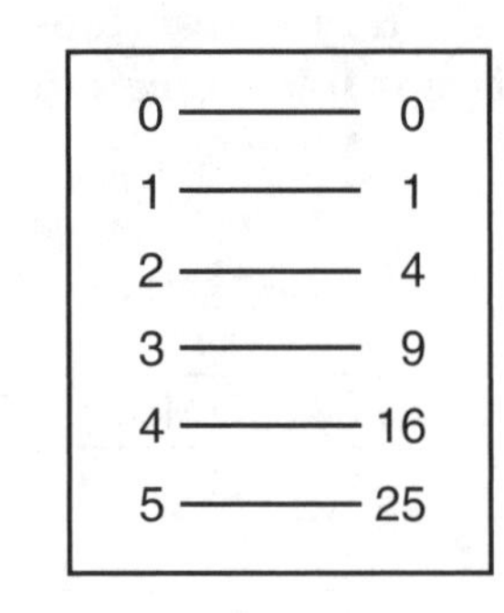

B

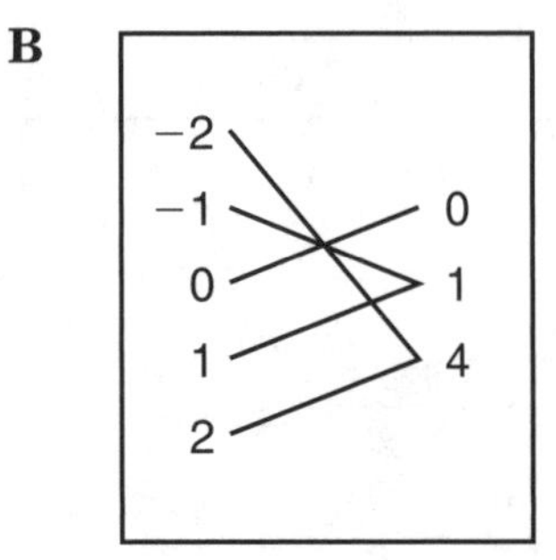

C

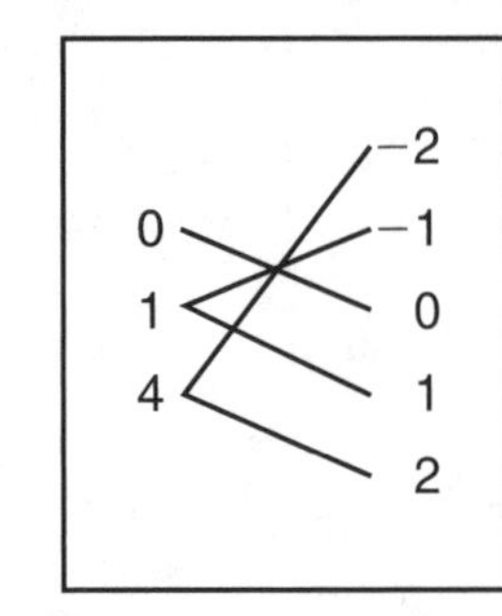

D

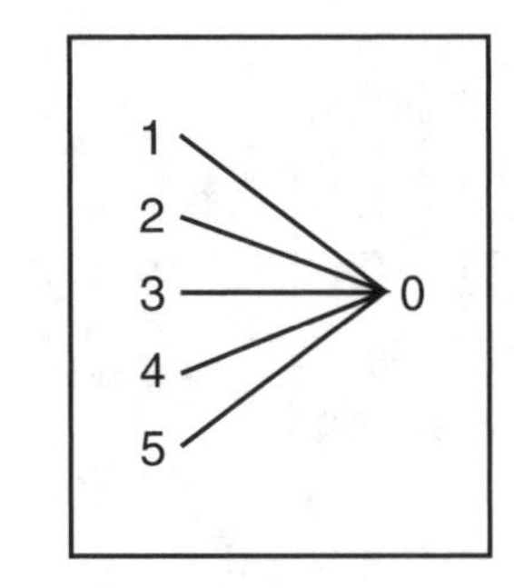

4 On the game show *The Price Is Right*, some contestants get to spin a giant wheel. The idea is to spin a number as close to 100 as possible without going over. The wheel must make at least one revolution.

Number of Complete Revolutions the Wheel Makes on the First Spin	Number the Spinner Lands on
1	80
3	25
2	100
4	25
1	10
2	65

Given the table below, which is the dependent variable?

F The number of complete revolutions

G The number the spinner lands on

H The distance the person stands from the wheel

J Not Here

5 Jeremy rides his bike directly to school x miles and then directly back home from school x miles every weekday. He rides his bike 8 miles every weekend. Which equation represents how many miles Jeremy rides his bike per week?

A $y = 10x + 8$

B $y = 5x + 8$

C $y = 13x$

D Not Here

6 Which of these graphs represents a functional relationship?

F

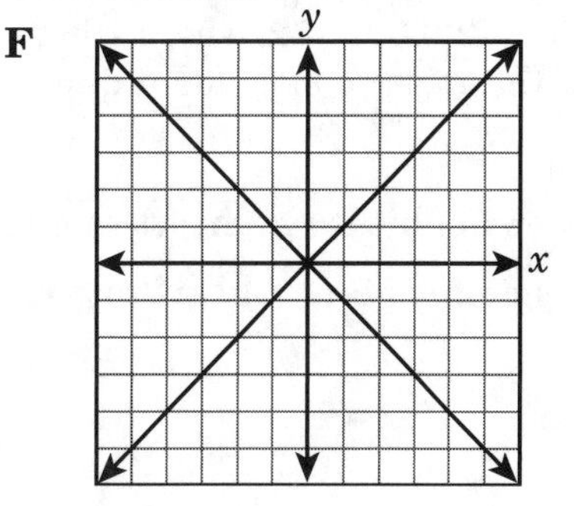

G

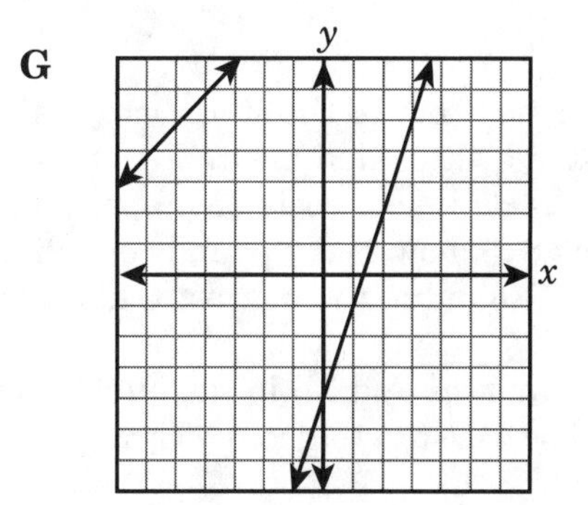

H

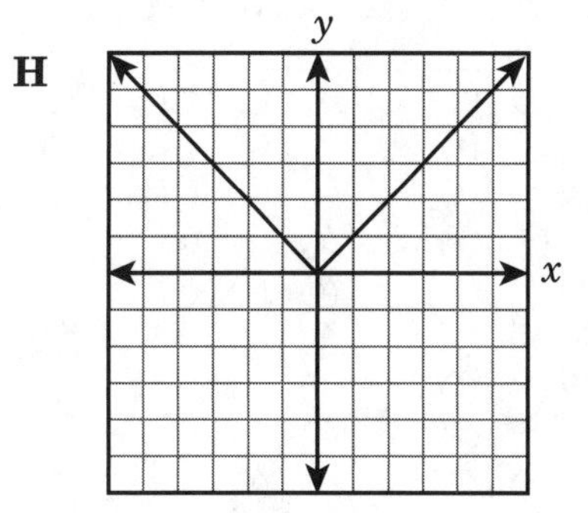

J

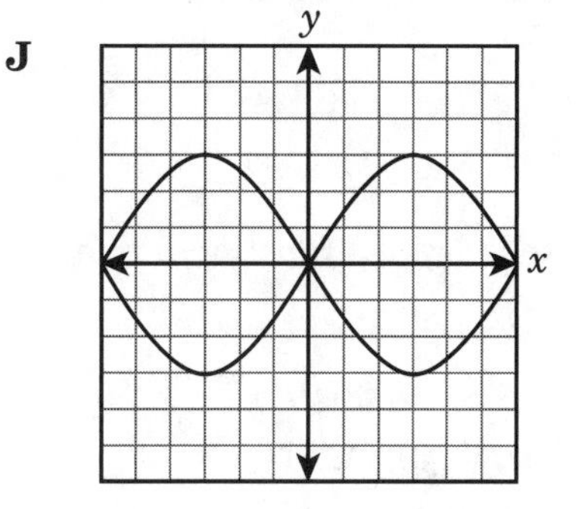

7 Joe is calculating the low end of his target heart rate range. He is using the formula $y = [(220 - x) - 72]0.60 + 72$, where x is his age. Which of these is the dependent quantity?

A His age

B The high end of his target heart rate range

C The low end of his target heart rate range

D Not Here

8 Sarah's mom sent her to the store for a loaf of bread and some sliced deli meat. The bread costs $2.69, and the deli meat costs $3.49 per pound. If Sarah has $15, how many pounds of deli meat can she buy? Round to the nearest tenth.

Record your answer and fill in the bubbles on the grid below. Be sure to use the correct place value.

				.			
0	0	0	0		0	0	0
1	1	1	1		1	1	1
2	2	2	2		2	2	2
3	3	3	3		3	3	3
4	4	4	4		4	4	4
5	5	5	5		5	5	5
6	6	6	6		6	6	6
7	7	7	7		7	7	7
8	8	8	8		8	8	8
9	9	9	9		9	9	9

9 Which of these is NOT a functional relationship?

A (1, 0), (0, 1), (1, 0), (0, 1)

B (1, 0), (2, 0), (3, 0), (4, 0)

C (1, 1), (2, 2), (3, 3), (4, 4)

D (1, 0), (1, 1), (1, 2), (1, 3)

10 What percent grade did Tonya get on her test if she missed 14 questions?

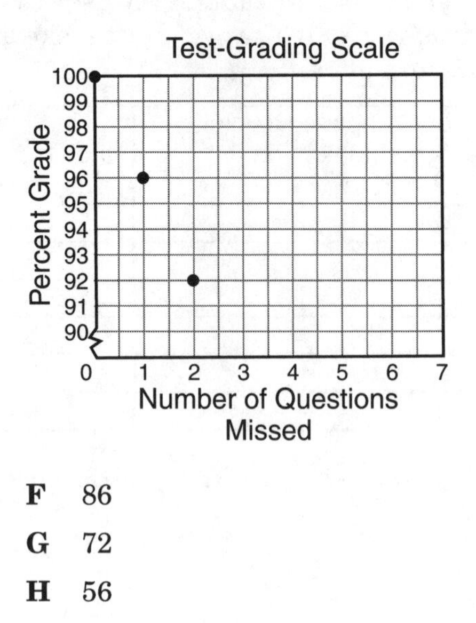

F 86

G 72

H 56

J 44

11 Charlie lives in Dallas, Texas. He receives a phone call from an old friend. His friend mentions that his time is one hour different from Charlie's because he is in another time zone. Why does Charlie still not know exactly what time zone his friend is in?

A The time zone depends on which direction, east or west, his friend is from Dallas.

B The time zone depends on Dallas being west of the international time zone.

C Dallas is in the central time zone.

D Not Here

12 Shonte's grandfather put $2,000 in a savings account for her college education fund. Starting this month, Shonte wants to put x amount of dollars into the account each month. Shonte's goal is to have the total contributions from herself and her grandfather grow to $3,920 in 4 years. How much does Shonte's monthly contribution need to be?

Record your answer and fill in the bubbles on the grid below. Be sure to use the correct place value.

				.			
0	0	0	0		0	0	0
1	1	1	1		1	1	1
2	2	2	2		2	2	2
3	3	3	3		3	3	3
4	4	4	4		4	4	4
5	5	5	5		5	5	5
6	6	6	6		6	6	6
7	7	7	7		7	7	7
8	8	8	8		8	8	8
9	9	9	9		9	9	9

13 Denise pays $29.99 per month for her cell phone plan. The plan includes 250 minutes of peak-hour usage and unlimited nonpeak-hour usage. She is charged $0.35 for each minute she goes over her limits. Let x represent the total number of peak-hour minutes used during a month in which Denise has used more than 250 peak-hour minutes. Which equation describes how much Denise's cell phone bill will be for that month?

A $y = 29.99 + 0.35x$

B $y = 29.99 + 0.35(x - 250)$

C $y = 29.99 + 0.35(250 - x)$

D $y = 29.99 + 0.35(250 + x)$

14 Use the data about Denise's cell phone plan given in Question 13. Last month Denise used the phone 321 peak-hour minutes. How much was her cell phone bill?

F $200.14

G $142.34

H $112.35

J $54.84

15 Compare each vowel to its sounds in the words given.

Letter Symbols	Letter Sounds (in italics)
a	m*a*th, s*a*fe
e	w*e*, j*e*t
i	h*i*, f*i*sh
o	*o*dd, h*o*pe
u	s*u*n, d*u*de

The set of letter sounds is represented by the italicized letters {a, e, i, o, u} in each word. Which ordered pair represents a functional relationship?

A (Sound of the letter, letter symbol)

B (Letter symbol, sound of the letter)

C Both ordered pairs are a many-to-one relationship.

D Not Here

Focus on TEKS Lesson 5 Using Symbols in the General Form and Parent Functions

TEKS A(b)2A Identify and sketch the general forms of linear ($y = x$) and quadratic ($y = x^2$) parent functions.
TEKS A(b)3A Use symbols to represent unknowns and variables.

Functions that share common characteristics are often grouped into families of functions having a parent function.

A **linear function** is a function whose graph is a straight line.
A **quadratic function** is a function whose graph is U-shaped.
A **parent function** is the most basic function upon which a family of functions is based. Linear functions are based on $y = x$, while quadratic functions are based on $y = x^2$.

Guided Instruction

Problem 1 Make a table of values and sketch the parent function, $y = x$.

Step 1 Choose several values for x. Be sure to use 0 as well as positive and negative integers.

x	−3	−2	−1	0	1	2	3
y							

Step 2 Since $y = x$, copy the corresponding value of x in the appropriate column for y to complete the table.

x	−3	−2	−1	0	1	2	3
y	−3	−2	−1	0	1	2	3

Solution Plot the points on a coordinate grid. Connect the points. The graph is a straight line that passes through the origin.

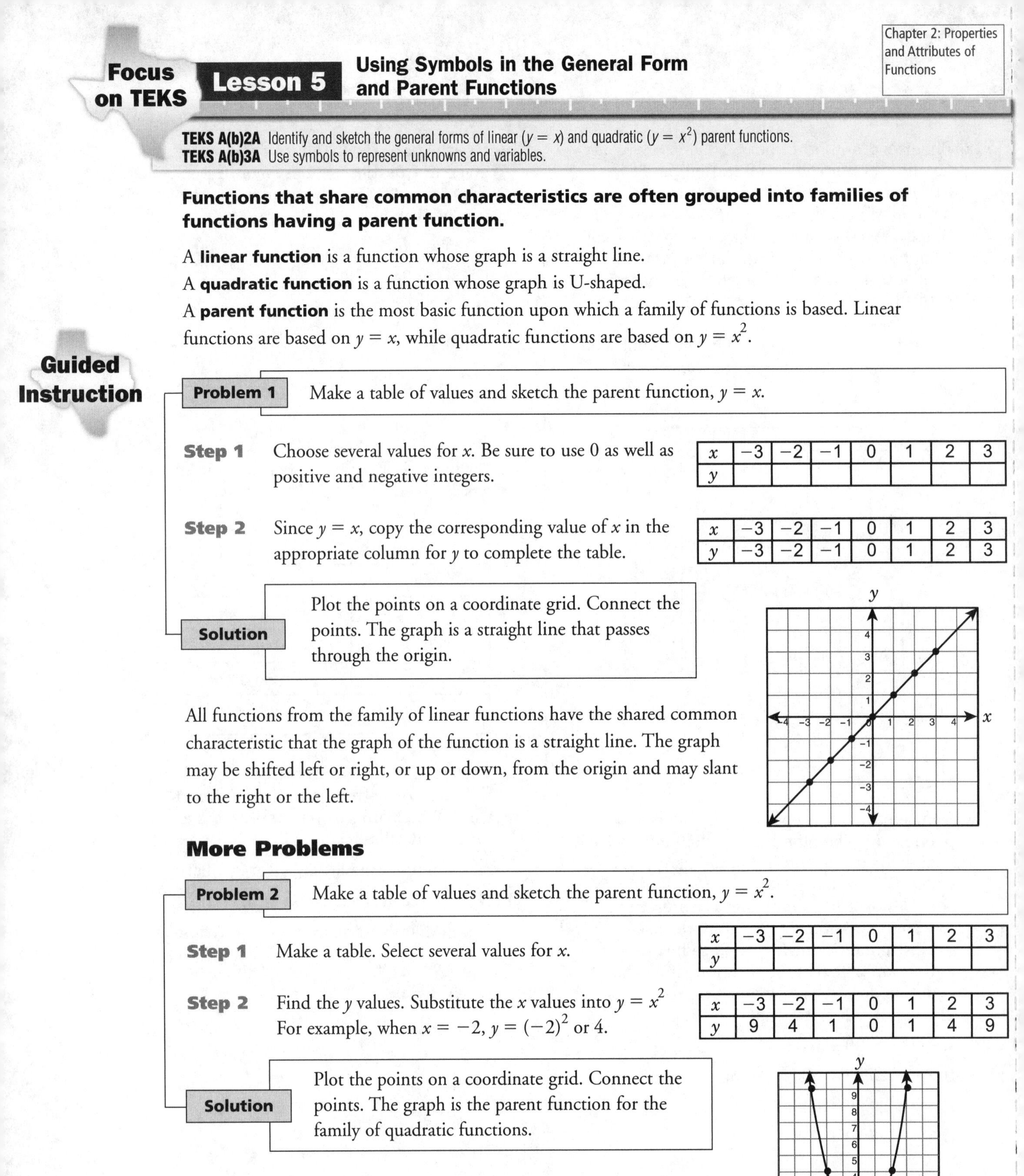

All functions from the family of linear functions have the shared common characteristic that the graph of the function is a straight line. The graph may be shifted left or right, or up or down, from the origin and may slant to the right or the left.

More Problems

Problem 2 Make a table of values and sketch the parent function, $y = x^2$.

Step 1 Make a table. Select several values for x.

x	−3	−2	−1	0	1	2	3
y							

Step 2 Find the y values. Substitute the x values into $y = x^2$ For example, when $x = -2$, $y = (-2)^2$ or 4.

x	−3	−2	−1	0	1	2	3
y	9	4	1	0	1	4	9

Solution Plot the points on a coordinate grid. Connect the points. The graph is the parent function for the family of quadratic functions.

The graph of any function from the family of quadratic functions will have a similar U shape. The graph may open upward, downward, be shifted away from the origin or stretched vertically or horizontally.

Guided Instruction

The general form of a linear function is $y = ax + b$, where a and b are real numbers. The general form of a quadratic function is $y = ax^2 + bx + c$, where a, b, and c are real numbers and $a \neq 0$.

Problem 3 Tell if the equation $2y + 4x = 10$ represents a linear or a quadratic function.

You can also tell whether or not a function belongs to either of these families by examining its equation or graph.

Step 1 Solve the equation for y. Subtract $4x$ from both sides.

$$2y + 4x = 10$$
$$2y = 10 - 4x$$

Step 2 Divide both sides by 2. Rearrange terms.

$$y = -2x + 5$$

Solution The equation $y = -2x + 5$ is in the general form of a linear function.

Problem 4 Tell if the function shown on the graphing calculator is a linear or a quadratic function.

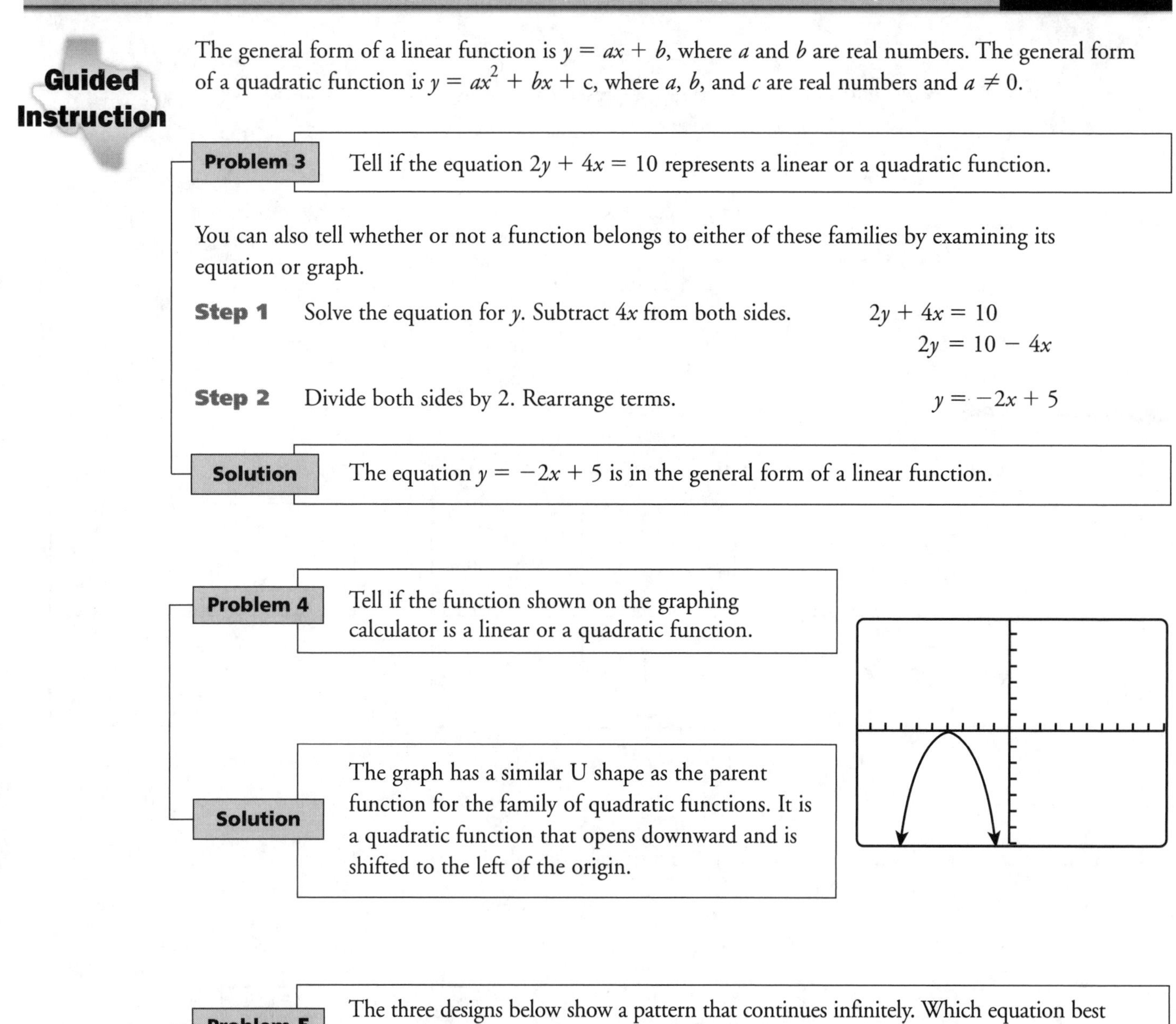

Solution The graph has a similar U shape as the parent function for the family of quadratic functions. It is a quadratic function that opens downward and is shifted to the left of the origin.

Problem 5 The three designs below show a pattern that continues infinitely. Which equation best represents the pattern illustrated and is the relationship linear or quadratic?

Notice that the dots form a square with dimensions that increase by 1 at each step.

Solution The equation that represents this pattern is $y = (x + 1)^2$. Since the equation has a term raised to the second power, it represents a quadratic function.

Apply the TEKS Determine which kind of function is represented by each equation. Write *linear*, *quadratic*, or *neither*.

1. $5x - 3y = 11$

____

2. $17x^2 = 3y + 9$

____

3. $-13x^4 + 7x^2 = 4y - 1$

____

4. $y = \frac{1}{x} + 12$

____

5. $3x + 1.4y = 2.9$

____

6. $-6(x + 3y) = -21$

____

Determine which kind of function is represented by each graph. Write *linear*, *quadratic*, or *neither*.

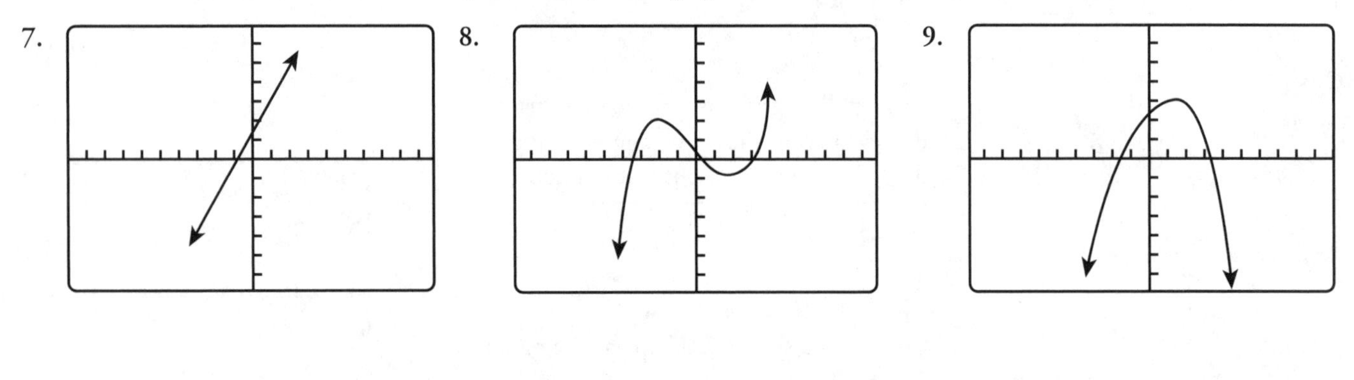

_______________ _______________ _______________

Plot both functions on the same set of axes by making a table of values.

10. $y = x, y = x + 2$

11. $y = x^2, y = x^2 + 2$

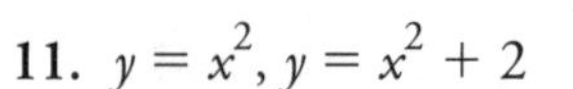

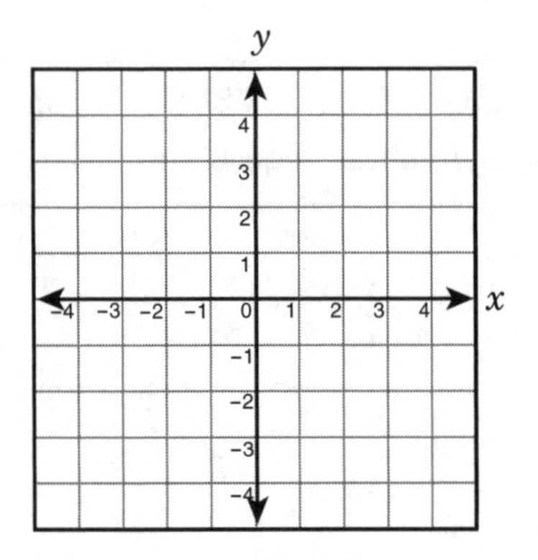

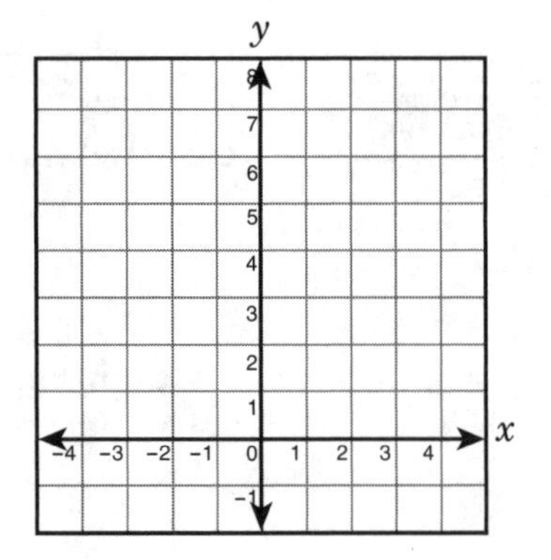

12. What do you notice about the graphs in Exercises 10 and 11? Is this what you expected would happen?

____

Rewrite each function using more meaningful variables.

13. The population of a city is given by the equation $y = 10{,}450 + 560x$, where x is in decades.

____

14. A company's profit is given by the equation $y = 4.9x - 2{,}500$, where x is the number of units sold.

____

TAKS Practice

TAKS Objective 2 The student will demonstrate an understanding of the properties and attributes of functions.
TEKS A(b)2A, A(b)3A

DIRECTIONS Read each question. Then circle the letter for the correct answer. If a correct answer is not here, circle the letter for "Not Here."

1 Which of the following equations does NOT represent a linear function?

A $x + 3y = 5$

B $y = 4x - 1$

C $-5y - \sqrt{x} = 4x$

D $21 = 3(y + x)$

2 Which kind of function is represented by the data in the table?

x	−10	−5	−2	0	2	5	10
y	100	25	4	0	4	25	100

F A linear function

G A quadratic function

H A cubic function

J Not Here

3 Use the pattern illustrated below. Determine which expression best represents the relationship between n, the position of any given group of dots within the pattern, and the number of dots in that group.

● ●● ●●● ●●●●
● ●● ●●● ●●●●

A $n + 2$

B $2(n + 2)$

C $2n + 2$

D $2n$

4 Which of the following functions would produce this table of values?

x	−6	−4	−2	0	2	4	6
y	−7	−5	−3	−1	1	3	5

F $y = x + 1$

G $y = x - 1$

H $y = x^2 - 1$

J Not Here

5 What kind of function is shown in the graph?

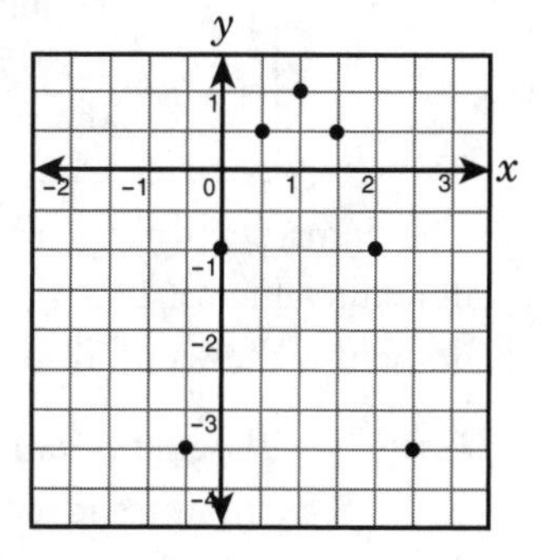

A A linear function

B A quadratic function

C An absolute value function

D A step function

Focus on TEKS

Lesson 6 Using Domain and Range to Find Patterns in Functions

TEKS A(b)2B For a variety of situations, identify the mathematical domains and ranges and determine reasonable domain and range values for given situations.
TEKS A(b)3B Given situations, look for patterns and represent generalizations algebraically.
TEKS A(c)1B Determine the domain and range values for which linear functions make sense for given situations.
TEKS 8.16A Make conjectures from patterns or sets of examples and nonexamples.

When working with functions it is important to know which values you can use to evaluate the function as well as which values the function will produce when evaluated.

The **domain** of a function is the set of all input values for which the function is defined. In ordered pairs (x, y), the domain is the set of all the first coordinates, or the x-coordinates.

The **range** of a function is the set of all output values. In ordered pairs (x, y), the range is the set of all the second coordinates, or the y-coordinates.

(x, y)
domain ↗ ↖ range

Guided Instruction

Problem 1

The table shows the cost of hiring a plumber based upon how long the job takes.

minutes, x	30	45	60	75	90
cost, y	\$18	\$27	\$36	\$45	\$54

a. Determine the domain and range for the cost function represented by the table.
b. Suppose the plumber charges for a minimum of 30 minutes on every job. Give a reasonable domain and range for the cost function if the maximum time a job takes is 3 hours.
c. If a customer hires the plumber for a 3-hour job, what will the charge be?

The domain and range of a function is often given using set notation. For example, if a function has domain values of 1, 2, 3, and 4, the domain may be written as Domain: $\{x: x = 1, 2, 3, 4\}$ and read as the domain is the set of all x values such that x equals 1, 2, 3, or 4.

Part a Use set notation to list the domain and range of the values shown in the table. The number of minutes is the domain. Since the cost depends on the time, the cost is the dependent variable or the range.

Domain: $\{x: x = 30, 45, 60, 75, 90\}$
Range: $\{y: y = 18, 27, 36, 45, 54\}$

Part b Consider x values between 30 minutes and 3 hours.

Domain: $\{x: 30 \leq x \leq 180\}$,
Range: $\{y: 18 \leq y \leq 108\}$

Part c Look for a pattern in the table. Notice that for every 15-minute increase, the cost increases by \$9. Use this pattern to write out the next several time increments.

minutes, x	105	120	135	150	165	180
cost, y	\$63	\$72	\$81	\$90	\$99	\$108

For a 3-hour job (180 minutes), the cost is \$108.

Solution Based on the domain and range values given in parts **a** and **b**, the cost of a 3-hour job is \$108.

Guided Instruction

More Problems

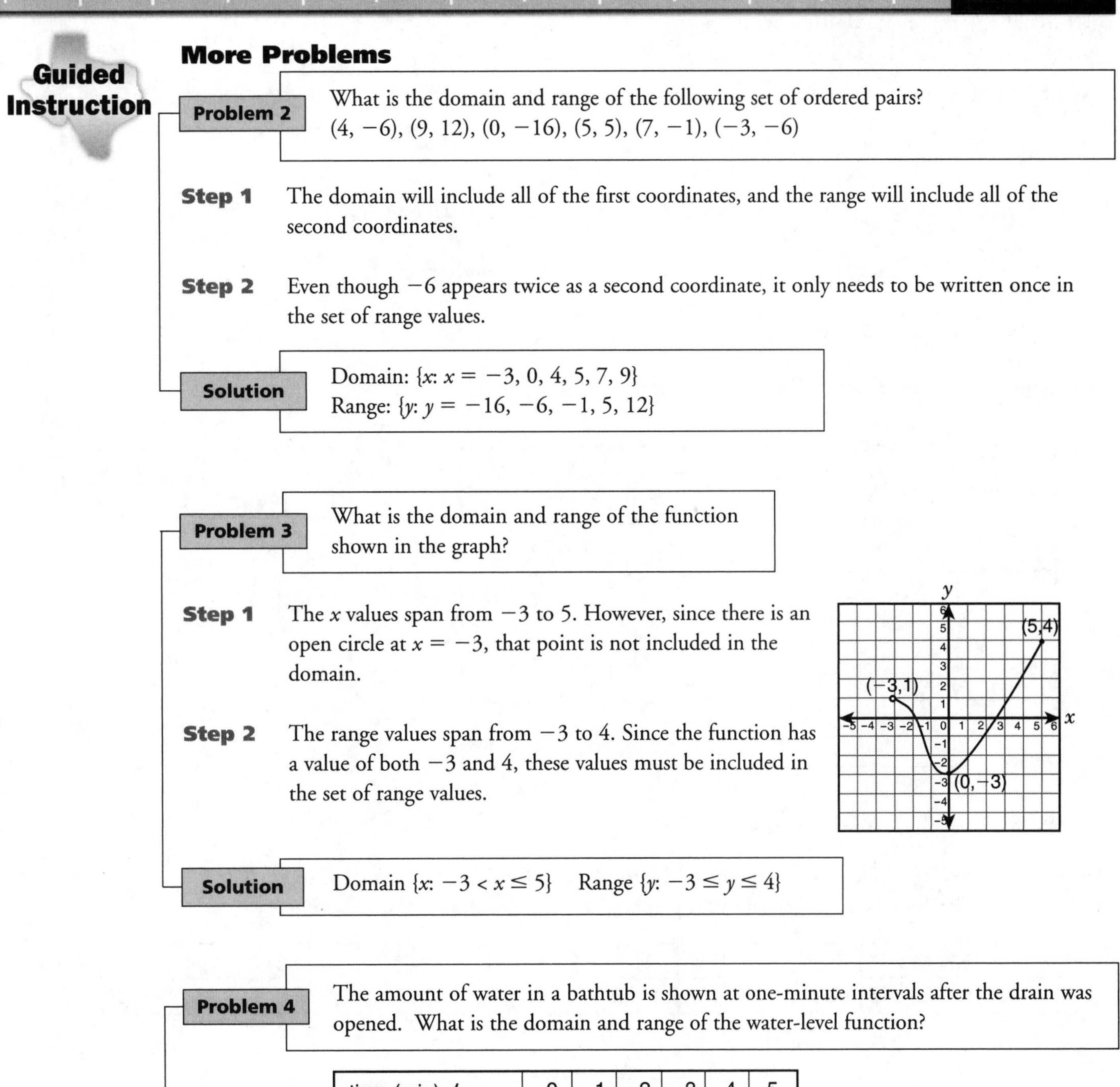

Problem 2

What is the domain and range of the following set of ordered pairs?
(4, −6), (9, 12), (0, −16), (5, 5), (7, −1), (−3, −6)

Step 1 The domain will include all of the first coordinates, and the range will include all of the second coordinates.

Step 2 Even though −6 appears twice as a second coordinate, it only needs to be written once in the set of range values.

Solution

Domain: $\{x: x = -3, 0, 4, 5, 7, 9\}$
Range: $\{y: y = -16, -6, -1, 5, 12\}$

Problem 3

What is the domain and range of the function shown in the graph?

Step 1 The x values span from −3 to 5. However, since there is an open circle at $x = -3$, that point is not included in the domain.

Step 2 The range values span from −3 to 4. Since the function has a value of both −3 and 4, these values must be included in the set of range values.

Solution

Domain $\{x: -3 < x \leq 5\}$ Range $\{y: -3 \leq y \leq 4\}$

Problem 4

The amount of water in a bathtub is shown at one-minute intervals after the drain was opened. What is the domain and range of the water-level function?

time (min), t	0	1	2	3	4	5
water (gal), w	80	64	48	32	16	0

Solution

Domain: $\{t: 0 \leq t \leq 5 \text{ minutes}\}$ Range: $\{w: 0 \leq w \leq 80 \text{ gallons}\}$

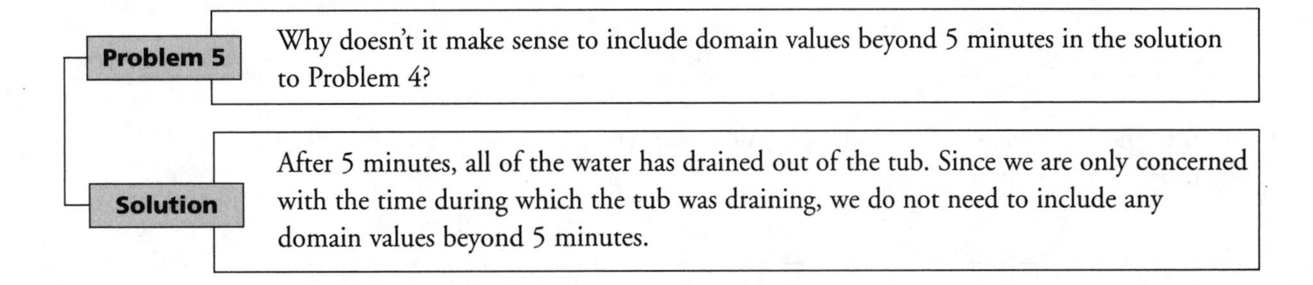

Problem 5

Why doesn't it make sense to include domain values beyond 5 minutes in the solution to Problem 4?

Solution

After 5 minutes, all of the water has drained out of the tub. Since we are only concerned with the time during which the tub was draining, we do not need to include any domain values beyond 5 minutes.

Apply the TEKS Determine the domain and range for each set of ordered pairs.

1. (1, −5), (−9, 0), (11, 2), (−4, −4), (3, 7)

Domain: ____________________

Range: ____________________

2. (6.3, 8.1), (−4.2, 2.7), (8.6, −5.5), (0.4, 2.2)

Domain: ____________________

Range: ____________________

Determine the domain and range for each function.

3. (graph: line segment from (−3, −4) to (3, 2))

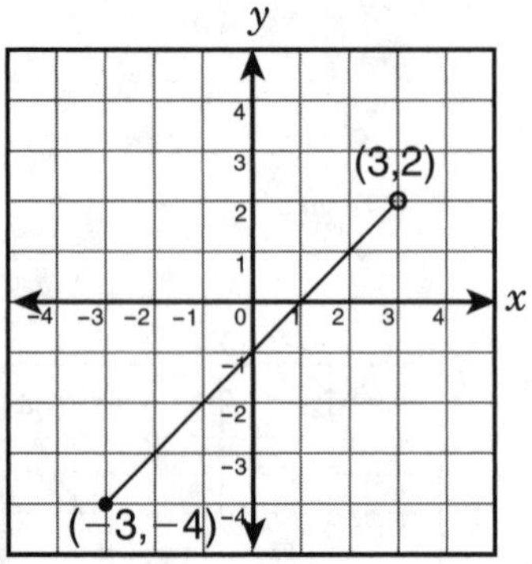

Domain: ____________________

Range: ____________________

4. (graph of points)

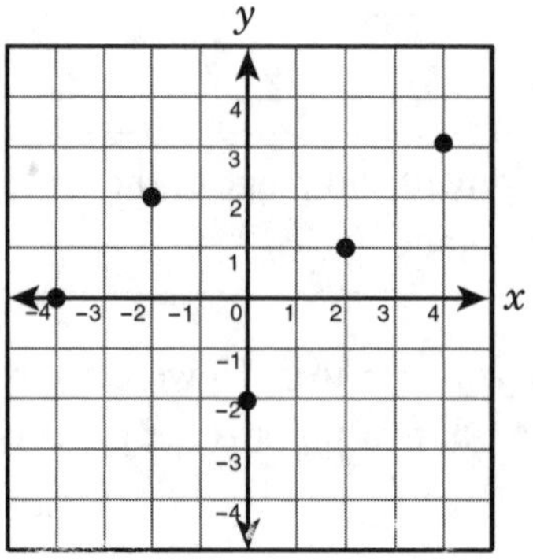

Domain: ____________________

Range: ____________________

5.

x	5	7	−8	9	0
y	10	6	3	7	0

Domain: ____________________

Range: ____________________

The standard viewing window on a graphing calculator shows x from −10 to 10 and y from −10 to 10. What would be a good window for graphing functions with the following values?

6.

x	33	50	44	39	51
y	101	54	80	75	63

____

7.

x	−4	7	5	0	−8
y	3	8	4	−4	−9

____

8.

x	58	94	−14	66	−97
y	−82	90	43	11	−25

____

Solve each problem.

9. The table shows the height of a hot-air balloon t minutes after it began to ascend. Complete the table.

time (min), t	0	5	10	15	
height (ft), h	0	75	150		300

10. Use the data to write a function for the height of the balloon after t minutes.

____

11. If the hot-air balloon in Exercise 9 continues to ascend at a constant rate, what will the balloon's height be after 1 hour?

____

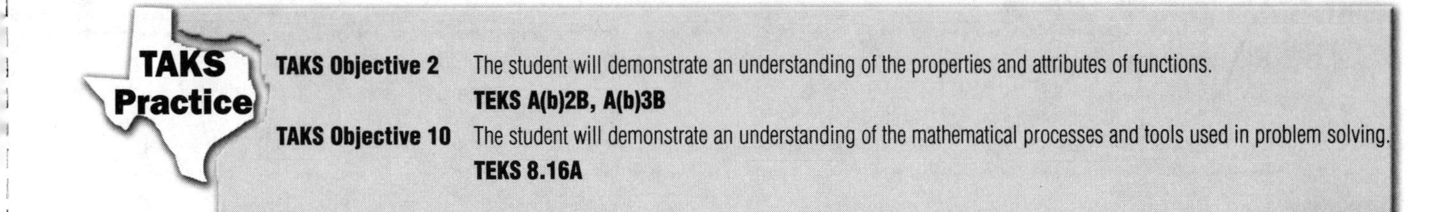

TAKS Objective 2 The student will demonstrate an understanding of the properties and attributes of functions.
TEKS A(b)2B, A(b)3B

TAKS Objective 10 The student will demonstrate an understanding of the mathematical processes and tools used in problem solving.
TEKS 8.16A

DIRECTIONS Read each question. Then circle the letter for the correct answer. If a correct answer is not here, circle the letter for "Not Here."

1 Which of the following values does NOT belong to the domain of the function shown in the graph?

$-3, -2, -1, 0, 1, 2, 3, 4$

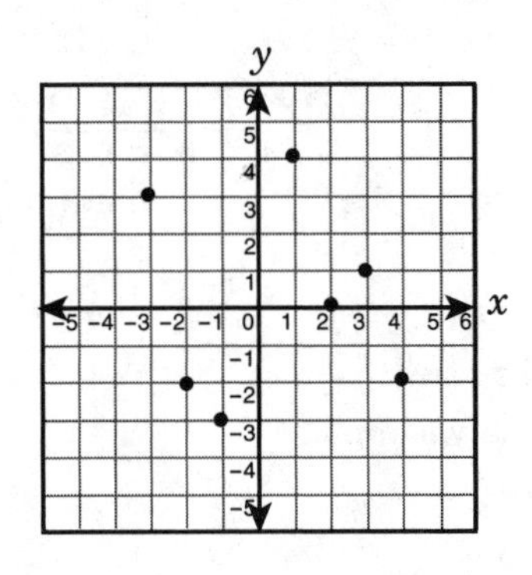

Record your answer and fill in the bubbles on the grid below. Be sure to use the correct place value.

				.			
0	0	0	0		0	0	0
1	1	1	1		1	1	1
2	2	2	2		2	2	2
3	3	3	3		3	3	3
4	4	4	4		4	4	4
5	5	5	5		5	5	5
6	6	6	6		6	6	6
7	7	7	7		7	7	7
8	8	8	8		8	8	8
9	9	9	9		9	9	9

2 A catering service charges a $120 setup fee plus $4 for each guest ($g$) in attendance. Which of the following functions illustrates the total cost (C) of using the service?

F $C = 4g + 120$

G $C = 120g + 4$

H $C = 4(g + 120)$

J Not Here

3 Which linear function would produce the domain and range values shown in the table?

x	0	1	2	3	4
y	−5	−2	1	4	7

A $y = 3x - 5$

B $y = 2x - 4$

C $y = 2x + 6$

D $y = 3(x - 1)$

4 A function produces the values (45, 188), (62, 208), (53, 144), and (57, 163). A student needs to resize the window on his calculator to graph the function. Which is the best window for the domain?

F $ymin = -10, ymax = 10$

G $xmin = 30, xmax = 60$

H $xmin = 40, xmax = 65$

J $ymin = 135, ymax = 215$

5 What is the domain of the linear parent function $y = x$?

A All negative integers

B All real numbers

C All real numbers greater than 0

D Not Here

Focus on TEKS

Lesson 7 Showing Situations in Graphs

TEKS A(b)2C Interpret situations in terms of given graphs or create situations that fit given graphs.
TEKS 8.14A Identify and apply mathematics to everyday experiences, to activities in and outside of school, with other disciplines, and with other mathematical topics.
TEKS 8.16A Make conjectures from patterns or sets of examples and nonexamples.

Graphs can be used to model many different real-world situations. The ability to interpret the information found in graphs is an important mathematical tool.

Guided Instruction

Problem 1

The graph shows the distance traveled by two runners in a 1-mile race as a function of time. Interpret the data in the graph to answer the following questions.

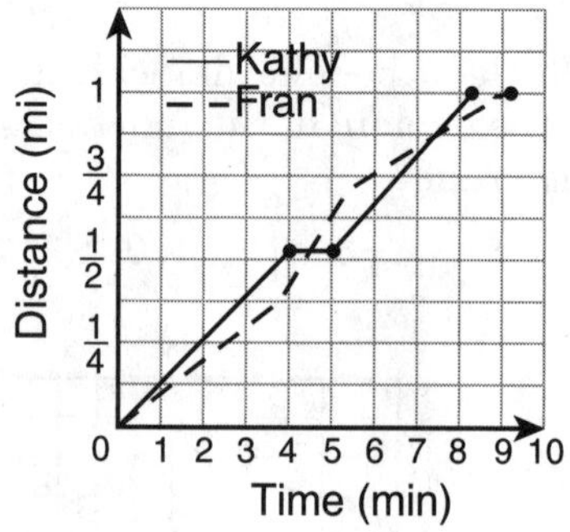

a. Who was the winner of the race?
b. Describe Kathy's progress between minutes 4 and 5 and give a possible explanation for this.
c. How much faster did the winner complete the race than the other runner?

Kathy
Fran
Distance (mi)
1
$\frac{3}{4}$
$\frac{1}{2}$
$\frac{1}{4}$
0 1 2 3 4 5 6 7 8 9 10
Time (min)

Part a **Step 1** Examine the vertical axis. Both graphs reach the 1-mile point on the vertical axis, so we know that both runners finished the race.

Step 2 Think: the winner of the race is the one who ran the mile in the shorter amount of time.

Step 3 Examine the horizontal axis. Notice that Kathy's graph reaches the 1-mile point to the left of Fran's graph on the horizontal axis. This tells us that Kathy reached the 1-mile point before Fran.

Kathy was the winner of the race.

Part b Kathy was not running between minutes 4 and 5. A possible explanation for this is that she was tired and took a break.

Part c **Step 1** Examine the horizontal time axis. Kathy's graph stops at the point (8, 1). Fran's graph stops at the point (9, 1).

Step 2 Compare the domains.

It took Kathy 8 minutes to complete the race, and it took Fran 9 minutes.

Solution Kathy was the winner of the race. She may have taken a break between minutes 4 and 5. Kathy's race time was one minute less than Fran's time.

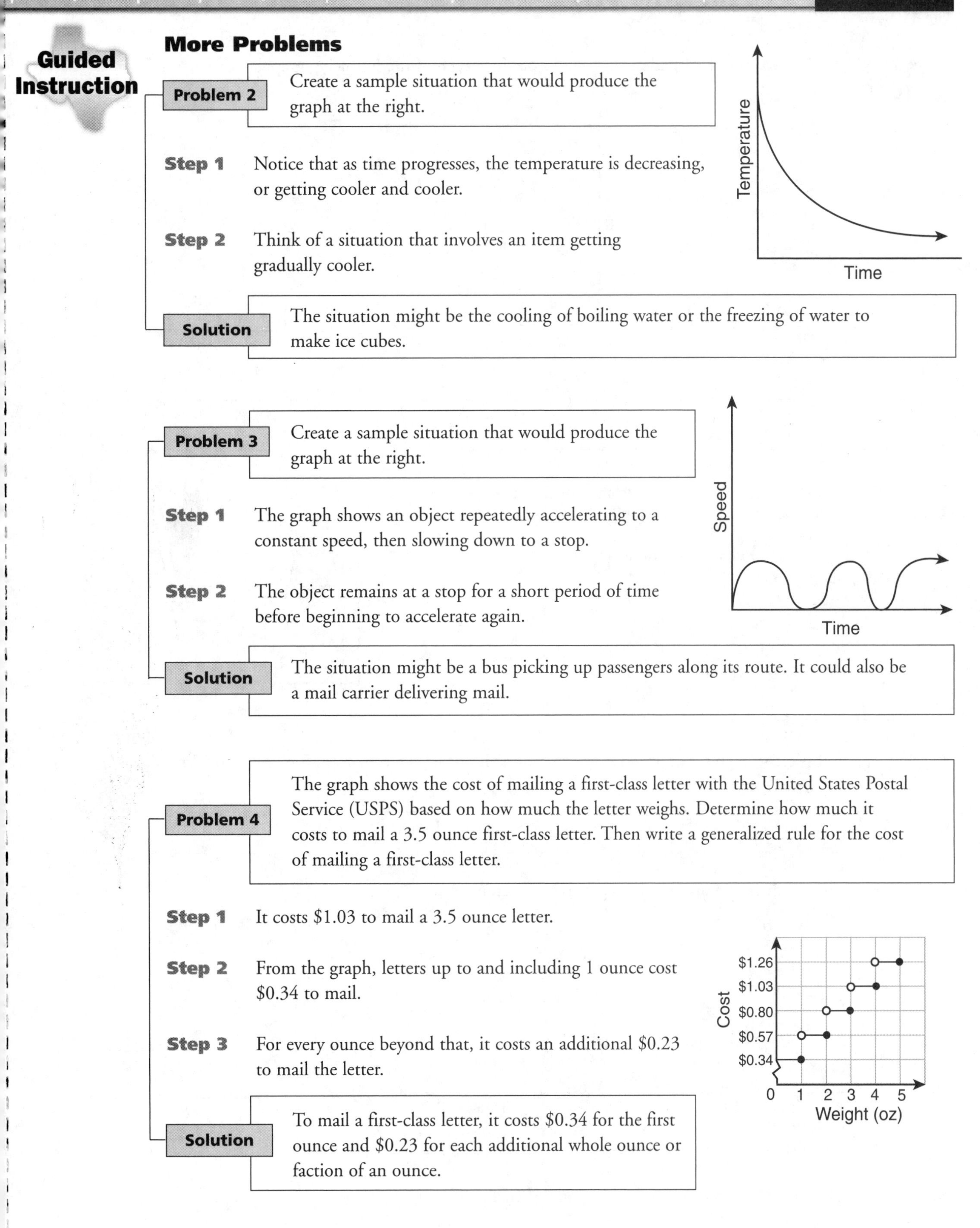

Guided Instruction

More Problems

Problem 2 Create a sample situation that would produce the graph at the right.

Step 1 Notice that as time progresses, the temperature is decreasing, or getting cooler and cooler.

Step 2 Think of a situation that involves an item getting gradually cooler.

Solution The situation might be the cooling of boiling water or the freezing of water to make ice cubes.

Problem 3 Create a sample situation that would produce the graph at the right.

Step 1 The graph shows an object repeatedly accelerating to a constant speed, then slowing down to a stop.

Step 2 The object remains at a stop for a short period of time before beginning to accelerate again.

Solution The situation might be a bus picking up passengers along its route. It could also be a mail carrier delivering mail.

Problem 4 The graph shows the cost of mailing a first-class letter with the United States Postal Service (USPS) based on how much the letter weighs. Determine how much it costs to mail a 3.5 ounce first-class letter. Then write a generalized rule for the cost of mailing a first-class letter.

Step 1 It costs $1.03 to mail a 3.5 ounce letter.

Step 2 From the graph, letters up to and including 1 ounce cost $0.34 to mail.

Step 3 For every ounce beyond that, it costs an additional $0.23 to mail the letter.

Solution To mail a first-class letter, it costs $0.34 for the first ounce and $0.23 for each additional whole ounce or faction of an ounce.

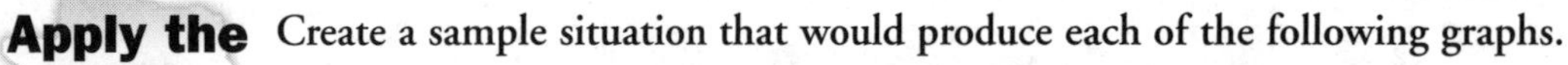

Apply the TEKS Create a sample situation that would produce each of the following graphs.

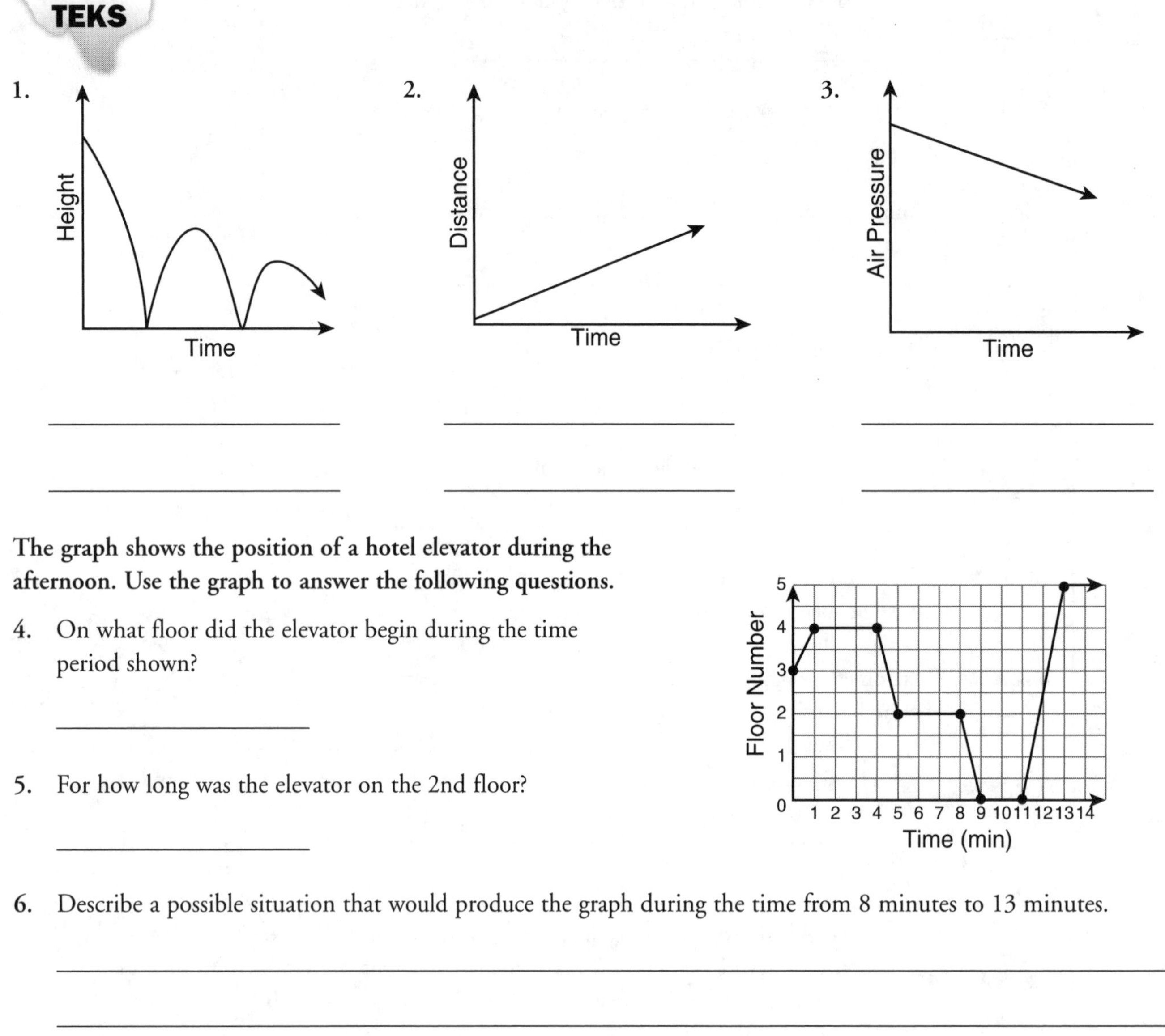

1. ____________________
____

2. ____________________
____

3. ____________________
____

The graph shows the position of a hotel elevator during the afternoon. Use the graph to answer the following questions.

4. On what floor did the elevator begin during the time period shown?

____

5. For how long was the elevator on the 2nd floor?

____

6. Describe a possible situation that would produce the graph during the time from 8 minutes to 13 minutes.

____

____

In Exercises 7–9, match each graph to the appropriate situation.

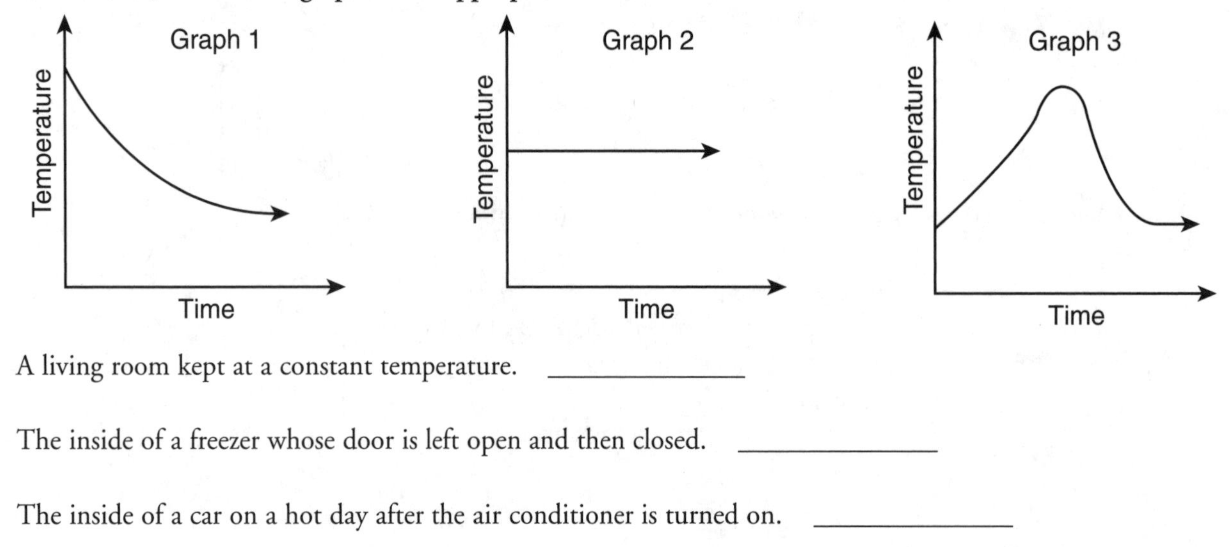

7. A living room kept at a constant temperature. ____________

8. The inside of a freezer whose door is left open and then closed. ____________

9. The inside of a car on a hot day after the air conditioner is turned on. ____________

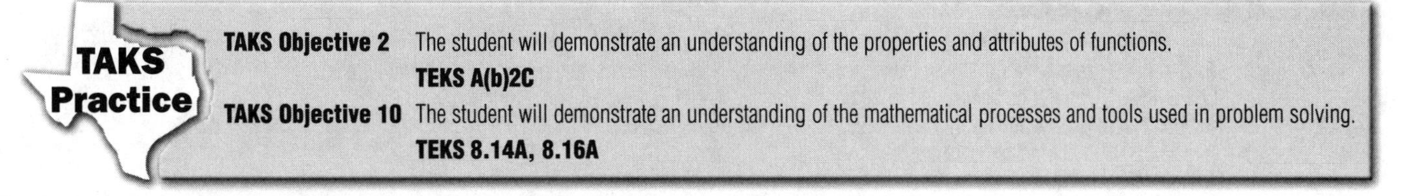

DIRECTIONS Read each question. Then circle the letter for the correct answer. If a correct answer is <u>not</u> <u>here</u>, circle the letter for "Not Here."

1 Tom was riding his bike to a friend's house when he got a flat tire. He stopped to examine the tire, then walked the rest of the way. Which of the following graphs best models this situation?

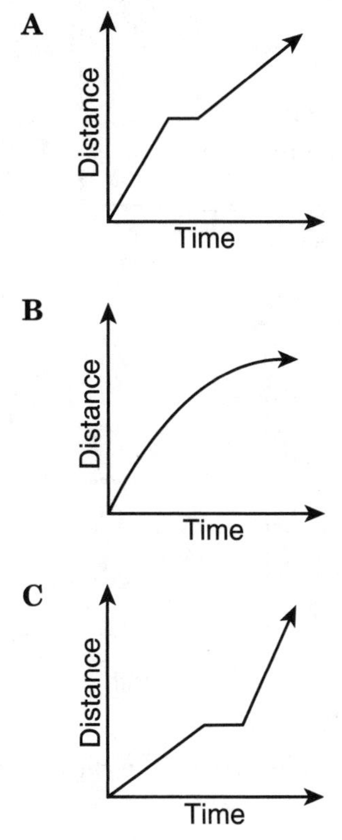

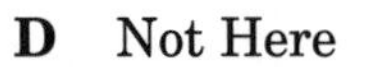

D Not Here

2 A graph shows an airplane's altitude as a function of the time since it took off. Which of the following would be the most appropriate domain for the graph?

F $\{t: t > 0 \text{ sec}\}$

G $\{t: t > 0 \text{ min}\}$

H $\{t: t = 1, 2, 3, 4 \text{ days}\}$

J $\{t: t > 15{,}000 \text{ ft}\}$

3 Which of the following situations would produce the graph shown?

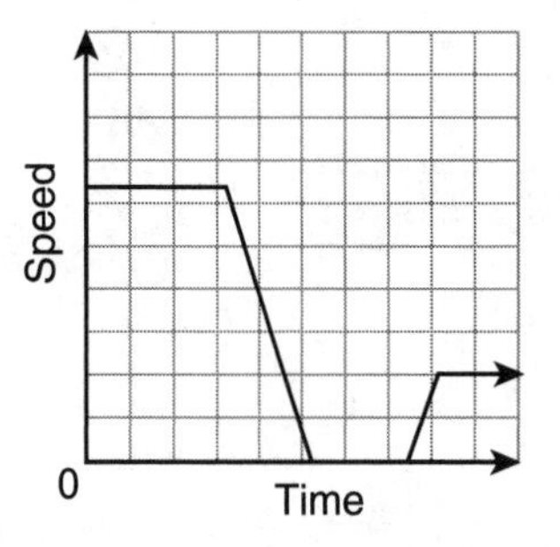

A Malcom began walking, rested for a while, then began to run.

B Malcom started at a slow jog, then gradually increased to a sprint.

C Malcom started sprinting, then gradually slowed down to a jog.

D Not Here

4 Based on the graph, what is the most likely outcome in the 3-kilometer race?

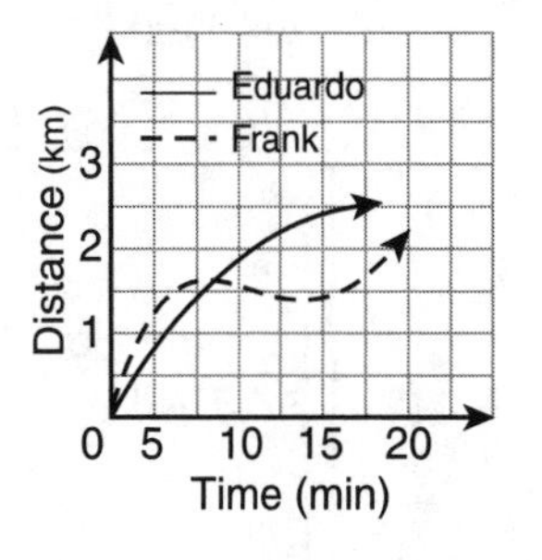

F Frank will win the race.

G Eduardo will win the race.

H The race will result in a tie.

J Frank will finish the race last.

Focus on TEKS

Lesson 8 Trends in Scatterplots

TEKS A(b)2D In solving problems, make and interpret scatterplots, and make decisions and critical judgements.
TEKS 8.12B Draw conclusions and make predictions by analyzing trends in scatterplots.
TEKS 8.14A Identify and apply mathematics to everyday experiences, to activities in and outside of school, with other disciplines, and with other mathematical topics.
TEKS 8.16A Make conjectures from patterns or sets of examples and nonexamples.

You can apply what you have learned about graphs to analyze the relationship between two different sets of data.

A **scatterplot** is a graph in which two sets of data are plotted as ordered pairs on a coordinate grid.

Guided Instruction

Problem 1

Scientists study samples of species and make generalizations about the patterns they observe. The table contains data on the length and weight of several Western Diamondback rattlesnakes studied.

Length (ft)	Weight (lb)
4.5	12.8
3.8	11.9
6.6	18.4
3.0	9.4
5.7	16.8
5.0	14.3
6.1	17.0
5.3	16.1

a. Use the data to create a scatterplot.

b. Describe the relationship between the two variables shown in the scatterplot. What kind of correlation do the data exhibit?

Part a **Step 1** Since the weight of each snake may depend on its length, label the horizontal axis *Length* and include appropriate length values.

Step 2 Label the vertical axis *Weight* and include range values up to 20 pounds to account for all of the data points.

Step 3 Plot the data points on the coordinate grid as ordered pairs to create the scatterplot.

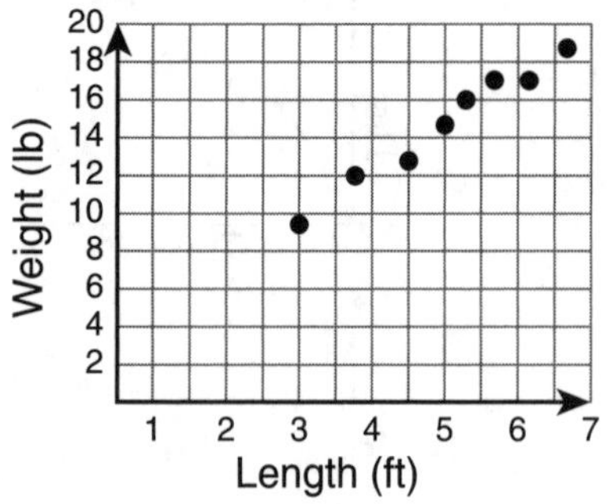

Part b When two sets of data exhibit a definite pattern, the data are said to be correlated. If y increases as x increases, the data have a *positive correlation.* If y decreases as x increases, the data have a *negative correlation.* If there is no correlation between x and y, the data are said to be *independent*.

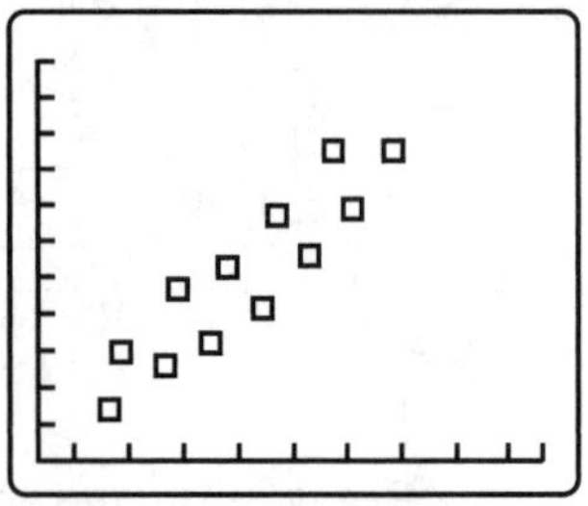

positive correlation

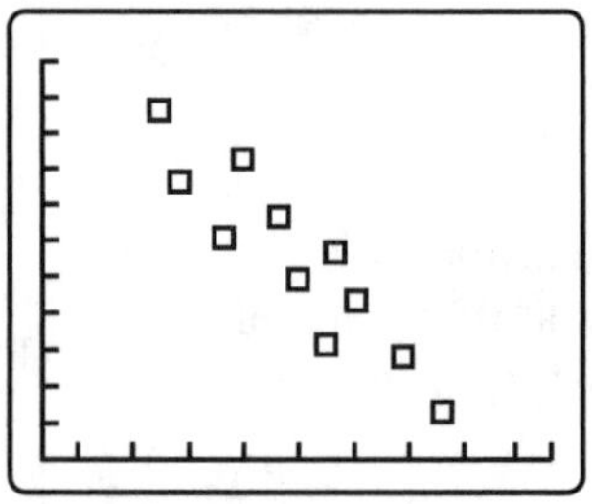

negative correlation

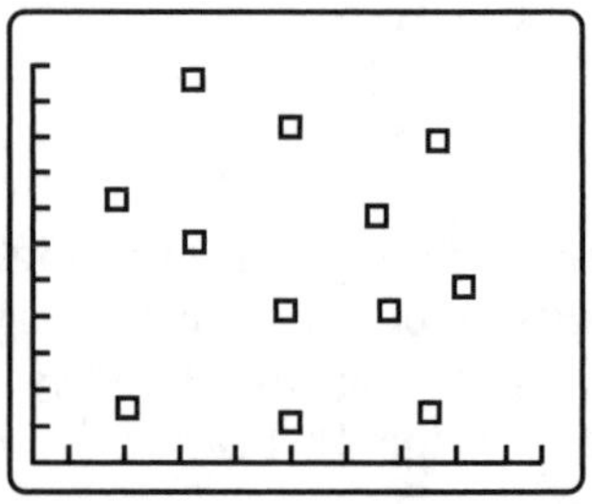

no correlation

Solution According to the scatterplot, as the length of a Western Diamondback rattlesnake increases, so does the snake's weight. The two variables have a positive correlation.

Guided Instruction

More Problems

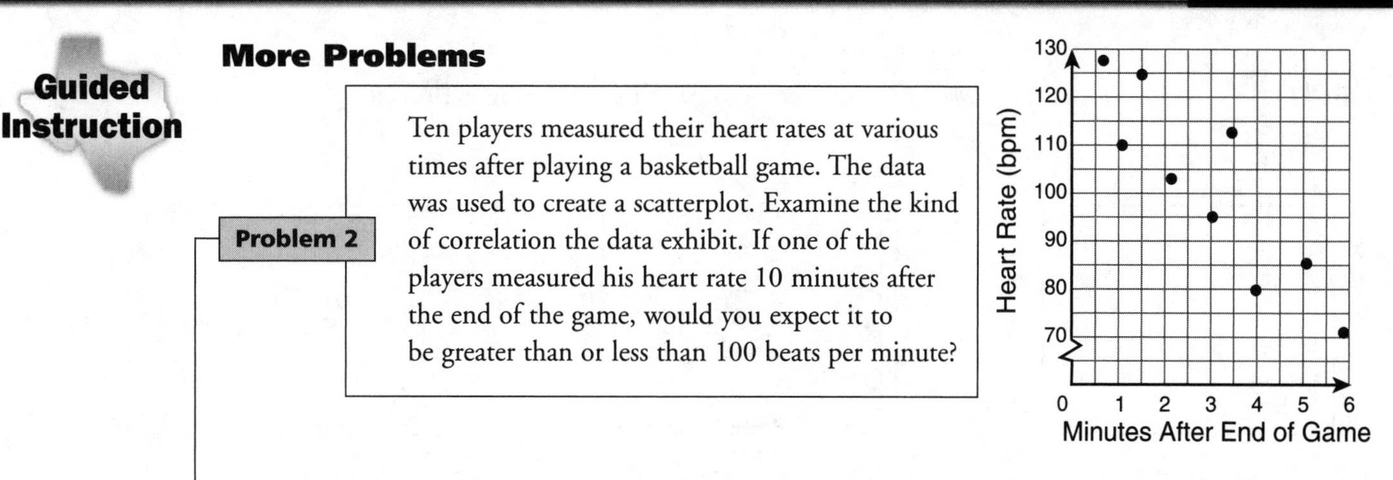

Problem 2

Ten players measured their heart rates at various times after playing a basketball game. The data was used to create a scatterplot. Examine the kind of correlation the data exhibit. If one of the players measured his heart rate 10 minutes after the end of the game, would you expect it to be greater than or less than 100 beats per minute?

As the time since the game was completed increases, the heart rates of the players decrease. The data show a negative correlation. Look for a trend in the scatterplot. After 3 or 4 minutes of rest, all of the players have heart rates less than 100 beats per minute (bpm).

Solution So after 10 minutes of rest, the player's heart rate will most likely be less than 100 bpm.

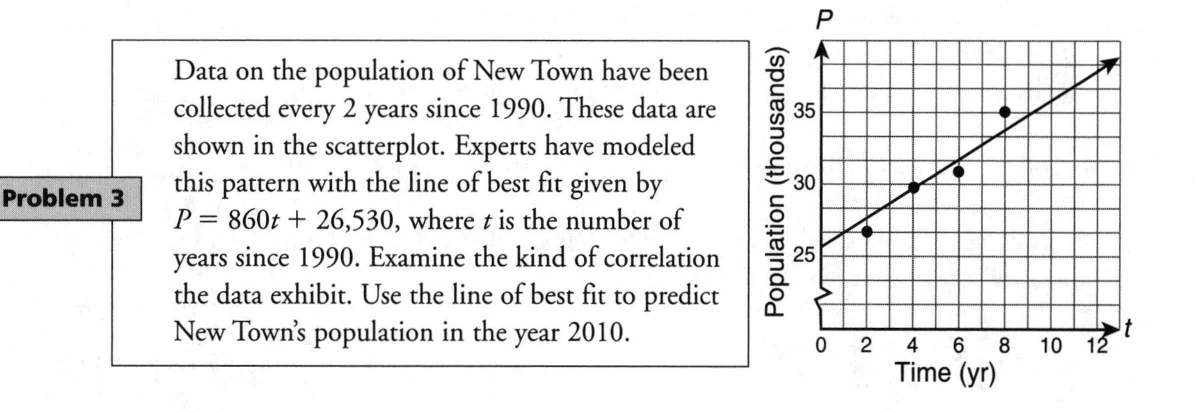

Problem 3

Data on the population of New Town have been collected every 2 years since 1990. These data are shown in the scatterplot. Experts have modeled this pattern with the line of best fit given by $P = 860t + 26{,}530$, where t is the number of years since 1990. Examine the kind of correlation the data exhibit. Use the line of best fit to predict New Town's population in the year 2010.

When data exhibit a positive or negative correlation, a *line of best fit* can be drawn to model the pattern. This line can then be used to make predictions about the two variables.

Step 1 As time increases, the population increases so the data show a positive correlation.

Step 2 Since t is the number of years since 1990, 2010 corresponds to $t = 20$.

Step 3 Solve for P when $t = 20$ using the line of best fit.

$$P = 860t + 26{,}530$$
$$P = 860 \cdot 20 + 26{,}530$$
$$P = 17{,}200 + 26{,}530$$
$$P = 43{,}730$$

Solution The population will be about 43,730 in 2010.

Apply the TEKS Write *positive*, *negative*, or *no correlation* to describe the data in each scatterplot.

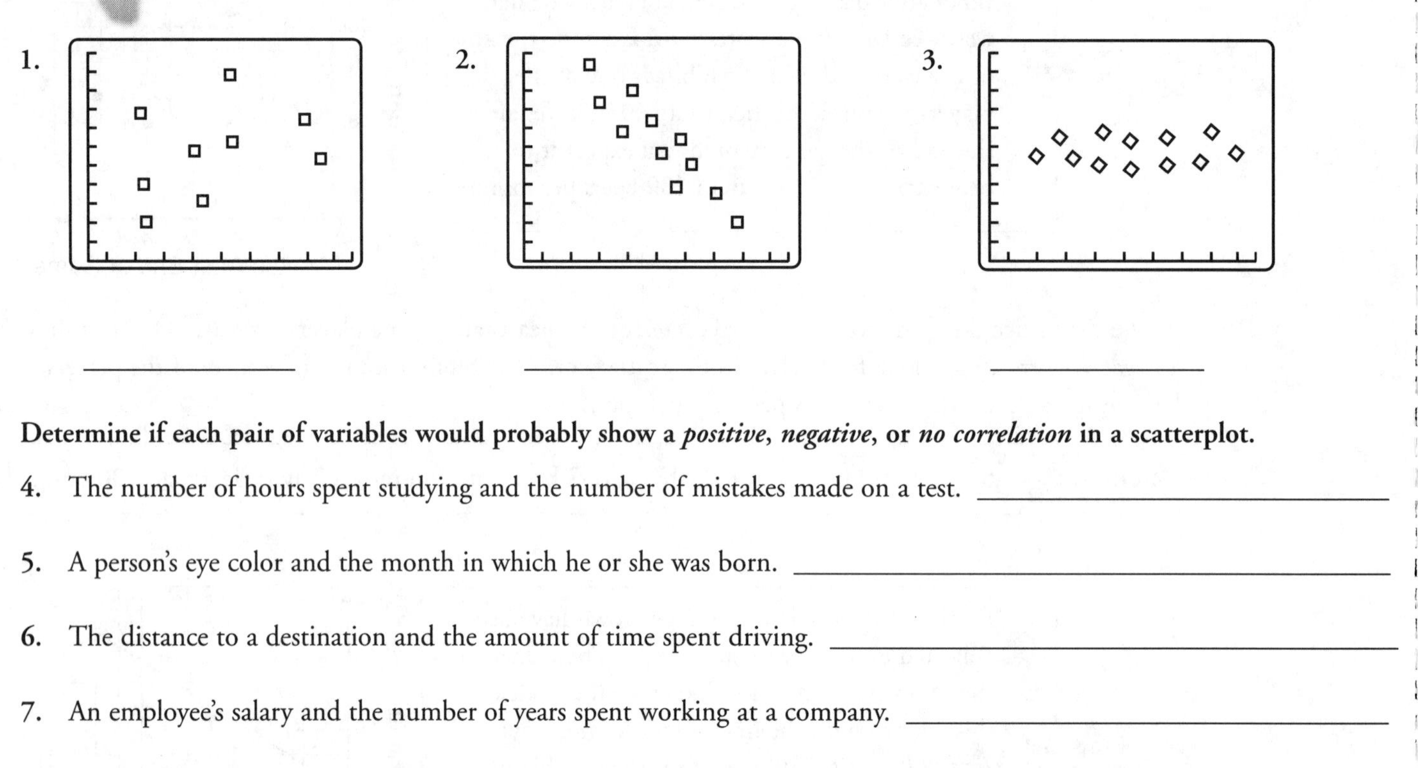

1. ____________ 2. ____________ 3. ____________

Determine if each pair of variables would probably show a *positive*, *negative*, or *no correlation* in a scatterplot.

4. The number of hours spent studying and the number of mistakes made on a test. ____________

5. A person's eye color and the month in which he or she was born. ____________

6. The distance to a destination and the amount of time spent driving. ____________

7. An employee's salary and the number of years spent working at a company. ____________

Create a scatterplot using the data in each table. Tell whether a line of best fit would have a *positive*, *negative*, or *no correlation*.

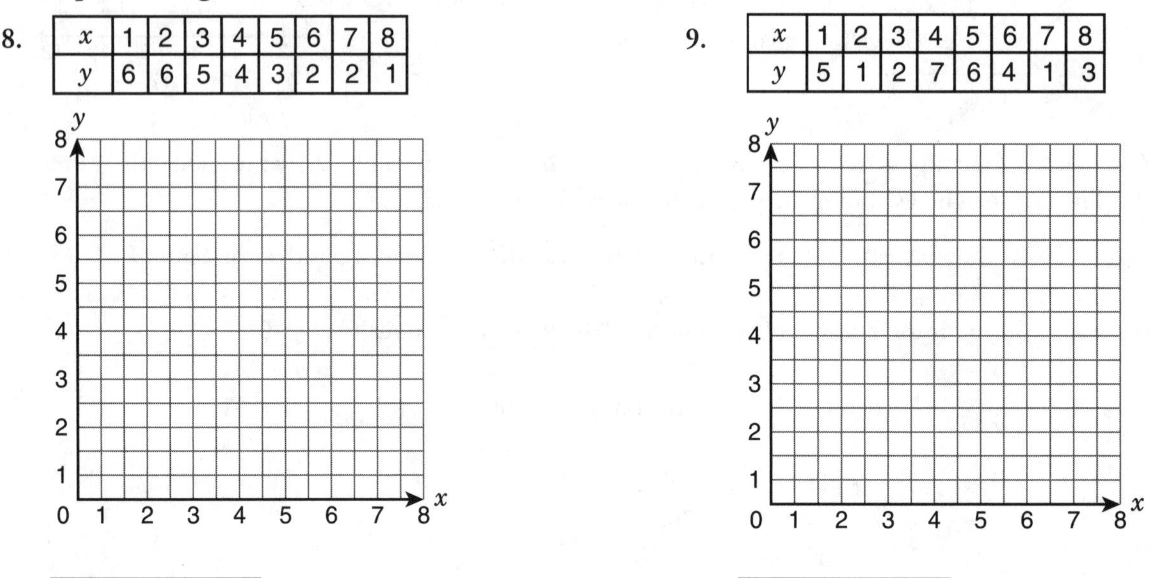

8.

x	1	2	3	4	5	6	7	8
y	6	6	5	4	3	2	2	1

____

9.

x	1	2	3	4	5	6	7	8
y	5	1	2	7	6	4	1	3

____

Solve the problem.

10. Based on preliminary sales figures, financial analysts expect the price of one share of a new tech-stock to follow the line of best fit given by $P = 0.34d + 17.55$. In the equation, d is the number of days since the start of the company. According to the model, what will be the cost of one share when the company is 3 weeks old?

____

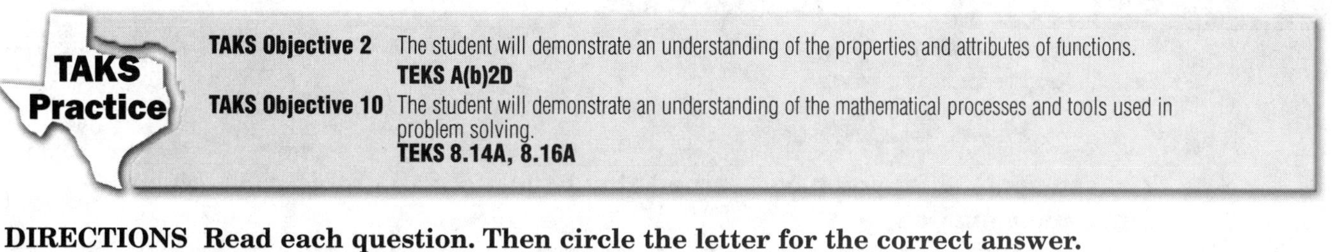

DIRECTIONS Read each question. Then circle the letter for the correct answer. If a correct answer is not here, circle the letter for "Not Here."

1 For which of the scatterplots is there NO correlation between the variables?

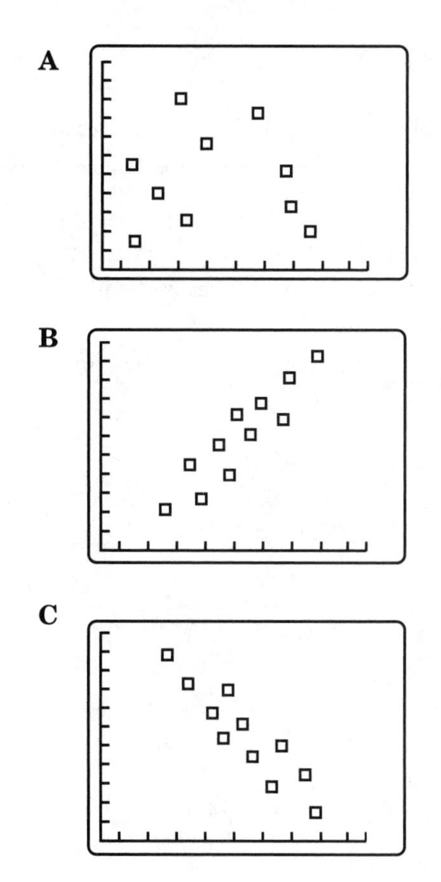

D Not Here

2 According to the line of best fit $y = -1.3x + 80$, in which set of range values is y most likely to be if $x = 22$?

F $\{y: 0 \leq y < 50\}$

G $\{y: 50 \leq y < 75\}$

H $\{y: 75 \leq y < 100\}$

J Not Here

3 What type of relationship most likely exists between the following two variables: sale price of an item and number of items sold?

A Positive correlation

B Negative correlation

C No correlation

D Low correlation

4 Which pair of variables is most likely modeled by the following scatterplot?

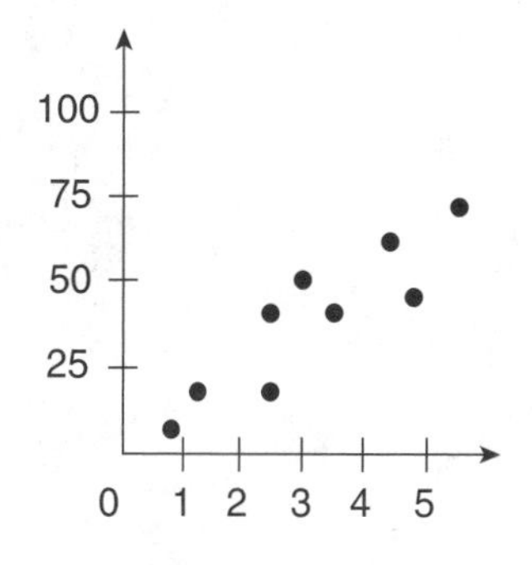

F The amount of calories burned and the person's height

G The amount of calories burned and the amount of time resting after a run

H The amount of calories burned and the amount of time spent exercising

J The amount of calories burned and the amount of time spent sleeping

Focus on TEKS

Lesson 9 Finding Function Values

TEKS A(b)4A Find specific function values.
TEKS 8.14A Identify and apply mathematics to everyday experiences, to activities in and outside of school, with other disciplines, and with other mathematical topics.

You can apply what you have learned about functions to problems involving function evaluation.

Guided Instruction

Problem 1

The height of a baseball thrown straight up with an initial velocity of 40 feet per second is given by the equation $y = -16x^2 + 40x$. In the equation, x is the number of seconds since the ball was thrown.

a. Rewrite the equation using functional notation.
b. What is the height of the ball after 1 second?
c. Evaluate the function for $t = 2.5$, and give a physical interpretation of the result.

Part a Functions in the form of an equation can be written using *functional notation.* For example, the function $y = 4x - 1$ written in functional notation is $f(x) = 4x - 1$. The expression $f(x)$ is read "f of x." Letters other than f are also used as function names, such as $g(x)$ and $h(x)$.

Step 1 Choose a more descriptive letter to represent the dependent variable. Since the function depends on time, replace x with t.

Step 2 Name the function f, and replace every x with a t.

The new function is $f(t) = -16t^2 + 40t$.

Part b **Step 1** Evaluate the function for $t = 1$. Substitute 1 for t in the equation.

$$f(t) = -16t^2 + 40t$$
$$f(1) = -16(1)^2 + 40 \cdot 1$$

Step 2 Simplify the equation.

$$f(1) = -16(1) + 40$$
$$f(1) = -16 + 40$$
$$f(1) = 24$$

After 1 second, the ball's height is 24 feet.

Part c **Step 1** Substitute 2.5 for t in the equation.

$$f(t) = -16t^2 + 40t$$
$$f(2.5) = -16(2.5)^2 + 40 \cdot 2.5$$

Step 2 Simplify.

$$f(2.5) = -16(2.5)^2 + 40 \cdot 2.5$$
$$f(2.5) = -16(6.25) + 100$$
$$f(2.5) = -100 + 100$$
$$f(2.5) = 0$$

At $t = 2.5$ seconds, the function value is 0. The ball has landed on the ground.

Solution Using the new function, the height of the ball after 1 second is 24 feet, and after 2.5 seconds the ball has landed on the ground.

Guided Instruction

More Problems

Problem 2 If $h(x) = 3(x - 2) + 1$, find each function value.

a. $h(5)$ **b.** $h(-2)$

Step 1 Substitute the given values of the dependent variable into the function for x.

Part a

$h(x) = 3(x - 2) + 1$
$h(5) = 3(5 - 2) + 1$

Part b

$h(x) = 3(x - 2) + 1$
$h(-2) = 3(-2 - 2) + 1$

Step 2 Simplify.

Part a:
$h(5) = 3(3) + 1$
$h(5) = 9 + 1$
$h(5) = 10$

Part b:
$h(-2) = 3(-4) + 1$
$h(-2) = -12 + 1$
$h(-2) = -11$

Solution The function values are $h(5) = 10$ and $h(-2) = -11$.

Problem 3 If $f(x) = x^2 + 3x$ and $g(x) = 5x - 7$, find $f(g(2))$

When given two functions $f(x)$ and $g(x)$, the new function $f(g(x))$ is called a *composite function*. You can evaluate the composite function $f(g(x))$ by first finding the value of $g(x)$. The range value of $g(x)$ then becomes the domain value of $f(x)$.

Step 1 Find the value of the innermost function, $g(x)$, when $x = 2$.

$g(x) = 5x - 7$
$g(2) = 5 \cdot 2 - 7$

Step 2 Simplify the equation.

$g(2) = 10 - 7$
$g(2) = 3$

Step 3 Evaluate $f(x)$ for the value of $g(x)$.

$f(x) = x^2 + 3x$
$f(3) = 3^2 + 3 \cdot 3$

Step 4 Simplify the equation.

$f(3) = 9 + 9$
$f(3) = 18$

Solution The composite function value is $f(g(2)) = 18$.

Problem 4 If $g(x) = 3x^2 - 7x + 5$, find $g(a)$.

When a function is evaluated as an expression that is not a number, follow the same procedure as before. In this case, simply substitute a into the equation for $g(x)$ where you see an x.

Solution The function value is $g(a) = 3a^2 - 7a + 5$.

Apply the TEKS If $f(x) = 3x^2 + x - 2$ and $h(x) = 7x + 3$, find each value.

1. $f(5)$ ________

2. $h(-4)$ ________

3. $2[f(-1)]$ ________

4. $f(3) - h(2)$ ________

5. $4[h(\frac{1}{2})]$ ________

6. $f(a) + h(a)$ ________

Use the data given to answer the following questions.

7. Hi-Tech Inc. is a consulting company that charges $750 up front plus $475 for each day of computer training.
   a. Write an equation in functional notation that describes the cost of hiring the consulting company for *d* days of employee training.

   ____

   b. What would the cost be if you hired the consulting company for 3 days of training?

   ____

   c. Another training company, Software Specialists Group, provides computer training for a flat rate of $600 per day. Which company offers the better deal if you need 7 days of employee computer training? How much would the training cost?

   ____

If $f(x) = 6(x - 3)$ and $h(x) = x^2 + 4$, write the letter for the correct composite function values.

8. $f(h(1))$ ________

9. $f(h(-3))$ ________

10. $h(f(2))$ ________

11. $h(f(1))$ ________

A. 40
B. 60
C. 12
D. 148

Solve the problem.

12. The cost of a long-distance call to Europe is given by the function $C(t) = 0.95 + 0.6t$, where t is the length of the call in minutes. How much would a 15-minute phone call cost?

____

TAKS Practice

TAKS Objective 2	The student will demonstrate an understanding of the properties and attributes of functions. **TEKS A(b)4A**
TAKS Objective 10	The student will demonstrate an understanding of the mathematical processes and tools used in problem solving. **TEKS 8.14A**

DIRECTIONS Read each question. Then circle the letter for the correct answer. If a correct answer is not here, circle the letter for "Not Here."

1 What is the value of the function $f(x) = -4x^2 + 3x + 2$ when it is evaluated at the point where $x = -3$?

A 31

B -20

C -25

D Not Here

2 What is the range of $f(x) = -2(x + 1)$ when the domain is $\{-3, 0, 4\}$?

F $\{5, 1, -6\}$

G $\{-4, 3, 7\}$

H $\{4, -2, -10\}$

J Not Here

3 Alexander is paid $12.30 per hour plus one and a half times that amount for every hour worked over 40 hours. What would his gross pay be if he worked 46 hours in a week?

Record your answer and fill in the bubbles on the grid below. Be sure to use the correct place value.

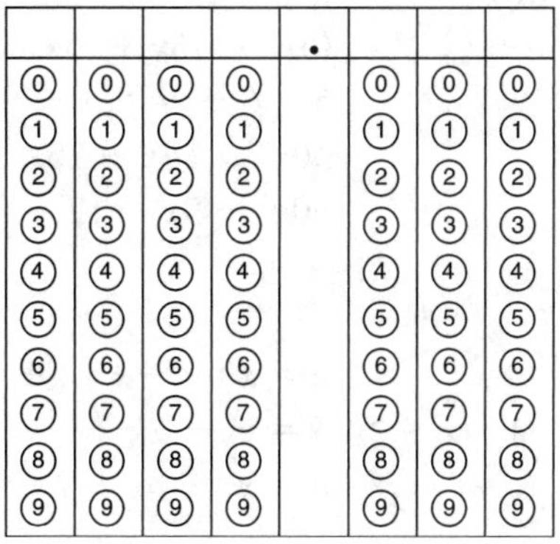

				.			
0	0	0	0		0	0	0
1	1	1	1		1	1	1
2	2	2	2		2	2	2
3	3	3	3		3	3	3
4	4	4	4		4	4	4
5	5	5	5		5	5	5
6	6	6	6		6	6	6
7	7	7	7		7	7	7
8	8	8	8		8	8	8
9	9	9	9		9	9	9

4 If $f(x) = 2x^2 + 3$ and $g(x) = -x^2 + 5$, what is the value of the composite function $f(g(x))$ at the point where $x = 2$?

F -116

G 5

H 14

J 112

5 Which graph shows the range values of the function $f(x) = 2(x - 1)^2 - 4$ when the domain is $\{-1, 0, 2, 3\}$?

A

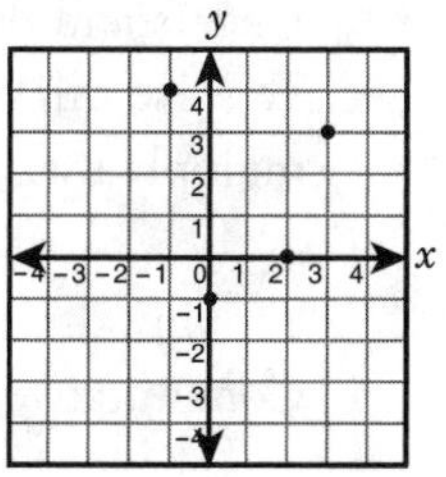

B

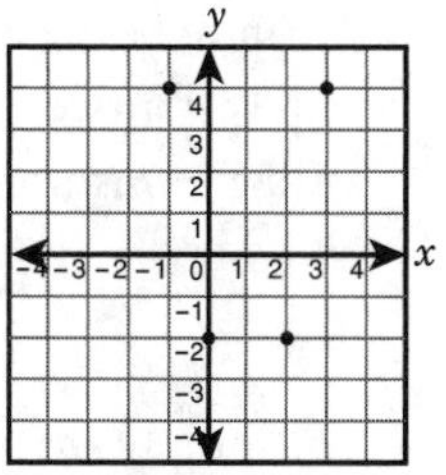

C

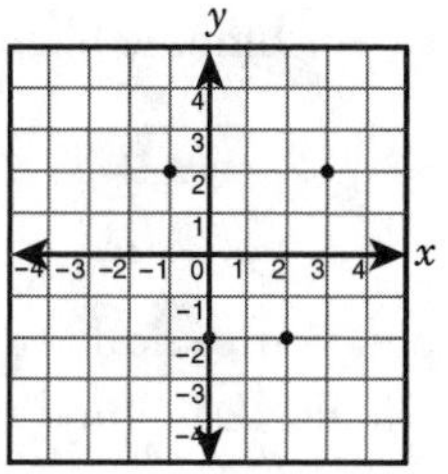

D Not Here

Focus on TEKS

Lesson 10 Simplifying Expressions

TEKS A(b)4A Simplify polynomial expressions.
TEKS A(b)4B Use the commutative, associative, and distributive properties to simplify algebraic expressions.
TEKS 8.14A Identify and apply mathematics to everyday experiences, to activities in and outside of school, with other disciplines, and with other mathematical topics.
TEKS 8.14B Use a problem-solving model that incorporates understanding the problem, making a plan, carrying out the plan, and evaluating the solution for reasonableness.

The Commutative, Associative, and Distributive properties can be applied to problems involving simplifying polynomial expressions.

The **Commutative Property** states that for any real numbers a and b, $a + b = b + a$ and $a \cdot b = b \cdot a$.
The **Associative Property** states that for any real numbers a, b, and c, $(a + b) + c = a + (b + c)$ and $(ab)c = a(bc)$.
The **Distributive Property** states that for any real numbers a, b, and c, $a(b + c) = ab + ac$, $(b + c)a = ba + ca$, $a(b - c) = ab - ac$, and $(b - c)a = ba - ca$.

Guided Instruction

Problem 1

Find a simplified expression for the area of the large rectangle with the given dimensions.

4x − 3
2(x + 3)
3x + 1
2x − 5

Step 1 Understand the problem. The area of a rectangle is found by multiplying its length by its width. To solve this problem, you must find a simplified expression for the length and width. Then multiply them.

Step 2 Simplify the expression for the length. Apply the Commutative Property to group like terms and simplify.

$3x + 1 + 2x - 5$
$3x + 2x + 1 - 5$
$5x - 4$

Step 3 Simplify the expression for the width. First use the Distributive Property to simplify $2(x + 3)$. Then group like terms using the Commutative Property and simplify.

$4x - 3 + 2(x + 3)$
$4x - 3 + 2 \cdot x + 2 \cdot 3$
$4x - 3 + 2x + 6$
$4x + 2x - 3 + 6$
$6x + 3$

Step 4 Multiply the length by the width using the Distributive Property. Then apply the Distributive Property again, combine like terms, and simplify.

$(5x - 4)(6x + 3)$
$(5x - 4)6x + (5x - 4)3$
$5x \cdot 6x - 4 \cdot 6x + 5x \cdot 3 - 4 \cdot 3$
$30x^2 - 24x + 15x - 12$
$30x^2 - 9x - 12$

In Step 4, you could have also used what is commonly called the FOIL method to multiply the length and the width. The FOIL method finds the product of the two First terms, the two Outer terms, the two Inner terms, and the two Last terms. These terms are then added together. Either method will produce the same answer.

F L I O
$(x + 1)\ (x + 2)$

$n = x \cdot x + x \cdot 2 + 1 \cdot x + 1 \cdot 2$
$n = x^2 + 2x + x + 2$
$n = x^2 + 3x + 2$

Solution The simplified expression for the area of the rectangle is $30x^2 - 9x - 12$.

Guided Instruction

More Problems

Problem 2 Simplify the expression $(x^2 + 3x) - 2(x + 1) + (2x^2 + 4x)$.

Step 1 Apply the Distributive Property.

$x^2 + 3x - 2 \cdot x - 2 \cdot 1 + 2x^2 + 4x$
$x^2 + 3x - 2x - 2 + 2x^2 + 4x$

Step 2 Apply the Commutative Property to rearrange terms.

$x^2 + 2x^2 + 3x - 2x + 4x - 2$

Step 3 Apply the Associative Property to group like terms. Simplify.

$(x^2 + 2x^2) + (3x - 2x + 4x) - 2$
$3x^2 + 5x - 2$

Solution The simplified expression is $3x^2 + 5x - 2$.

Problem 3 Simplify the expression $3(2a - 4b)(\frac{2a}{3} + \frac{b}{3})$.

Before beginning to simplify the expression, notice that both of the terms in the second binomial have a 3 in the denominator. Multiply the second binomial by the 3 because it will clear the fractions and make the problem much simpler.

Step 1 Apply the Commutative Property.

$3(2a - 4b)\left(\frac{2a}{3} + \frac{b}{3}\right)$

$3\left(\frac{2a}{3} + \frac{b}{3}\right)(2a - 4b)$

Step 2 Distribute the 3 over the first binomial.

$\left(3 \cdot \frac{2a}{3} + 3 \cdot \frac{b}{3}\right)(2a - 4b)$

Simplify by clearing the fractions.

$(2a + b)(2a - 4b)$

Step 3 Find the product of the two binomials, using the FOIL method.

$(2a + b)(2a - 4b)$
$2a \cdot 2a + 2a \cdot (-4b) + b \cdot 2a + b \cdot (-4b)$

Step 4 Apply the Commutative and Associative Properties and simplify.

$(2)(2)(a)(a) + (2)(-4)ab + 2ab + (-4)(b)(b)$
$4a^2 - 8ab + 2ab - 4b^2$
$4a^2 - 6ab - 4b^2$

Solution The simplified expression is $4a^2 - 6ab - 4b^2$.

Apply the TEKS Simplify each expression.

1. $6a + 3b - 2a + b$

2. $5 + 2(x - 1) + 8x$

3. $7b^2 - 2 + 6b^2$

4. $4.1(m - 2) + 3.6m + 6$

5. $\frac{1}{2}(6mn + 10m) - 2mn$

6. $\frac{1}{3}a + 4 - \frac{5}{6}a$

The area of a triangle is given by the formula $A = \frac{1}{2}bh$, where b is the base and h is the height. Find the area of each triangle with the given dimensions.

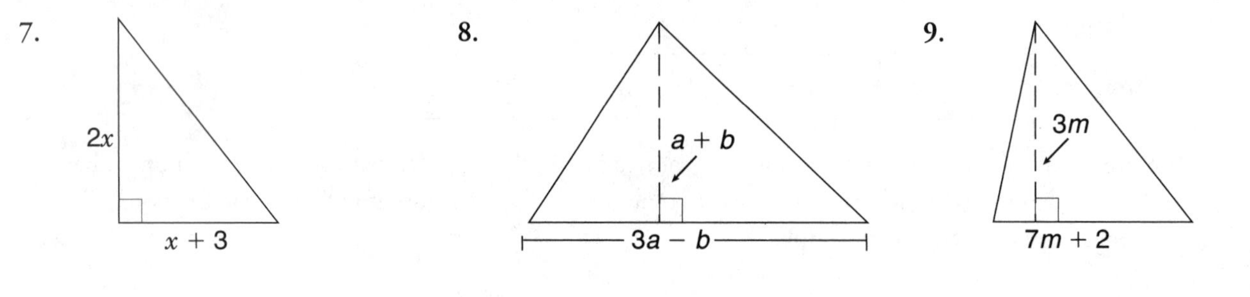

10. Find a simplified expression for the area of the rectangle with the given dimensions.

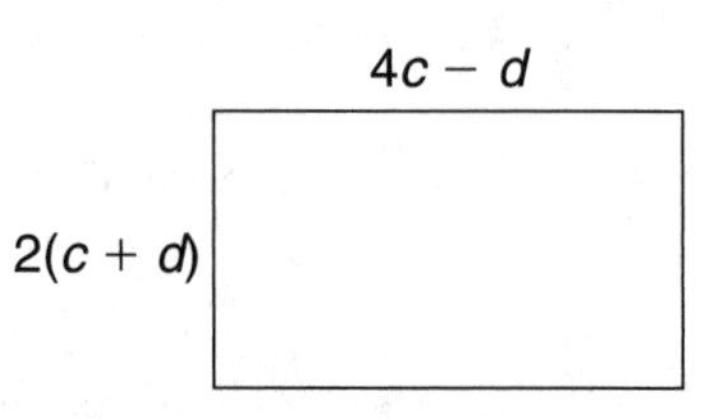

Simplify each expression.

11. $(3a + b)(4a - 2b)$

12. $5(x - y)(x + y)$

13. $\left(\frac{m}{8} + \frac{3n}{4}\right)(3m - 2n)(8)$

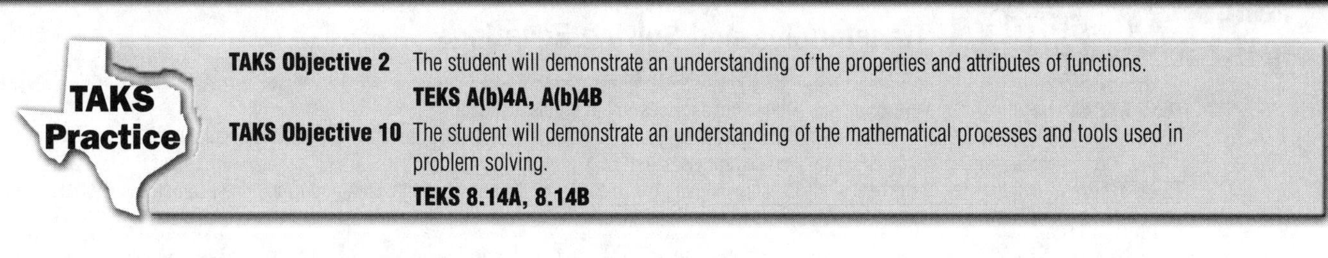

DIRECTIONS Read each question. Then circle the letter for the correct answer. If a correct answer is not here, circle the letter for "Not Here."

1 Which expression is equal to $(4x^2 + 5) + (3x - 2) + (x^2 + 8x)$?

A $5x^2 + 11x + 3$

B $4x^2 + 10x - 4$

C $7x^2 - 8x + 6$

D Not Here

2 What is the result if the polynomial functions $f(x) = 3x^2 - x + 1$ and $g(x) = 4(x + 1)$ are added to form $h(x)$?

F $h(x) = 7x^2 + 3x - 2$

G $h(x) = 3x^2 + 3x + 5$

H $h(x) = 6x^2 + 5x - 4$

J $h(x) = 3x^2 - 3x - 5$

3 What is the area of the rectangle in simplified form?

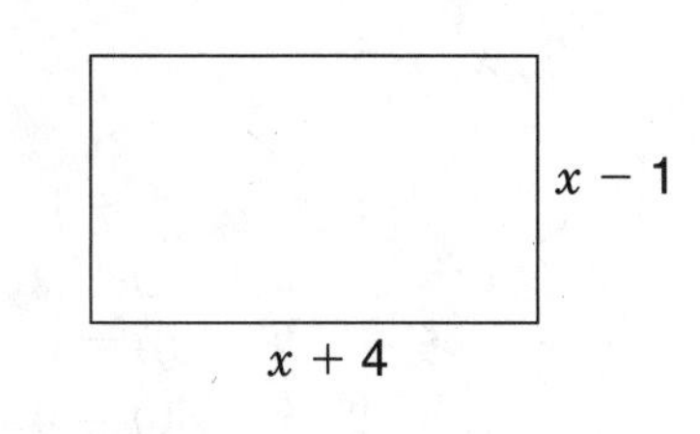

A $x^2 + 4x - 1$

B $2x^2 + 3x - 1$

C $4x^2 + 5x + 3$

D $x^2 + 3x - 4$

4 Which expression gives the area of the shaded region of the rectangle?

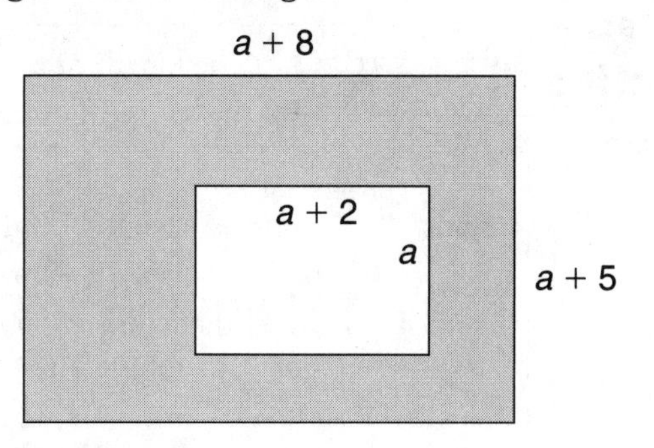

F $11a + 40$

G $a^2 + 13a + 40$

H $15a + 10$

J Not Here

5 What is the result when $(a + b)$ is multiplied by $(2a - 2b)$?

A $2a^2 + 4ab - 2b^2$

B $4a^2 - 2b^2$

C $4a^2 - 2ab - 4b^2$

D $2a^2 - 2b^2$

Focus on TEKS **Lesson 11**

Transforming and Solving Equations

TEKS A(b)4A Transform and solve equations and factors as necessary in problem situations.
TEKS 8.14D Select tools such as real objects, manipulatives, paper/pencil, and technology or techniques such as mental math, estimation, and number sense to solve problems.
TEKS 8.15A Communicate mathematical ideas using language, efficient tools, appropriate units, and graphical, numerical, physical, or algebraic mathematical models.

You can use your knowledge of simplifying expressions to factor and solve equations.

The Zero Product Rule states that for all numbers a and b, if $ab = 0$, then either $a = 0$ or $b = 0$, or both a and b equal 0.

Guided Instruction

Problem 1 The length of a rectangular parking lot is 10 feet longer than twice its width. The area of the lot is 3,600 feet^2. Write and solve an equation for the length and the width of the lot.

Step 1 Sketch a rectangle and use the information from the problem to write expressions for the length and width. Label the width x. Since the length is 10 feet longer than twice the width, label it $2x + 10$.

x

$2x + 10$

Step 2 The area of a rectangle is equal to the length multiplied by the width. Multiply the expressions from Step 1 and set them equal to the area of the lot, 3,600 feet^2. Rewrite the equation so that it is equal to 0.

$$x(2x + 10) = 3{,}600$$
$$2x^2 + 10x = 3{,}600$$
$$2x^2 + 10x - 3{,}600 = 3{,}600 - 3{,}600$$
$$2x^2 + 10x - 3{,}600 = 0$$

Step 3 Since 2 is a factor of all terms in the equation, multiply both sides by $\frac{1}{2}$ to further simplify the equation.

$$\frac{1}{2}[2x^2 + 10x - 3{,}600] = \frac{1}{2}(0)$$
$$\frac{1}{2}(2x^2) + \frac{1}{2}(10x) - \frac{1}{2}(3{,}600) = 0$$
$$x^2 + 5x - 1{,}800 = 0$$

Step 4 Factor the equation.The first term of each binomial must be x. The second terms must have a product of $-1{,}800$ and sum of 5. Trial and error will find these to be 45 and -40.

$$x^2 + 5x - 1{,}800 = 0$$
$$(x + \_\_)(x + \_\_) = 0$$
$$(x + 45)(x + (-40)) = 0$$
$$(x + 45)(x - 40) = 0$$

Step 5 Use the zero product rule. Set each factor equal to 0. Solve for x.

$x + 45 = 0$ or $x - 40 = 0$
$x + 45 - 45 = -45$ or $x - 40 + 40 = 40$
$x = -45$ or $x = 40$

Step 6 The solution to the equation is $x = -45$ or $x = 40$. Since x represents the width of a parking lot, it cannot be a negative number. So $x = 40$ feet.

Solution The width of the parking lot is 40 feet and the length is $2(40) + 10$, which equals 90 feet.
Check: Area: $(40 \text{ ft})(90 \text{ ft}) = 3{,}600 \text{ ft}^2$

Guided Instruction

More Problems

Problem 2 Solve the equation $4m(2m + 6) = 0$. Check the solution.

Step 1 The equation is already in factored form.

$$4m(2m + 6) = 0$$

Since 4 is factor of both sides, multiply by $\frac{1}{4}$.

$$\frac{1}{4}[4m(2m + 6)] = \frac{1}{4}(0)$$

$$m(2m + 6) = 0$$

Step 2 Apply the zero product rule. Set both factors equal to zero and solve for m.

$$m = 0 \quad \text{or} \quad 2m + 6 = 0$$
$$2m + 6 - 6 = -6$$
$$2m = -6$$
$$\frac{2m}{2} = \frac{-6}{2}$$
$$m = -3$$

Step 3 Use the original equation to check the solutions

$$4(0)(2(0) + 6) = 0 \quad \text{or} \quad 4(-3)(2(-3) + 6) = 0$$
$$0(0 + 6) = 0 \quad \text{or} \quad -12(-6 + 6) = 0$$
$$0(6) = 0 \ \textit{true} \quad \text{or} \quad -12(0) = 0 \ \textit{true}$$

Solution The solutions are $x = 0$ and $x = -3$.

Problem 3 Solve the equation $x^2 - 2x - 24 = 0$.

Step 1 Since the coefficient of the x^2 term is 1, we know the first term of each binomial must be x.

$$x^2 - 2x - 24 = 0$$
$$(x + \_\_)(x + \_\_) = 0$$

Step 2 Find two numbers whose product is -24 and whose sum is -2. Set up a table of values to find the numbers.

Product	Sum
$8(-3) = -24$	$8 + (-3) = 5$
$3(-8) = -24$	$3 + (-8) = -5$
$6(-4) = -24$	$6 + (-4) = 2$
$4(-6) = -24$	$4 + (-6) = -2$

Step 3 In the fourth row of the table, the terms 4 and -6 give the desired product and sum.
$(x + 4)(x + (-6)) = 0$
$(x + 4)(x - 6) = 0$

Step 4 Apply the zero product rule and solve for x.

$$x + 4 = 0 \quad \text{or} \quad x - 6 = 0$$
$$x + 4 - 4 = -4 \quad \text{or} \quad x - 6 + 6 = 6$$
$$x = -4 \quad \text{or} \quad x = 6$$

Solution The solutions are $x = -4$ and $x = 6$. You should check these by substituting them into the original equation and making sure they produce a true statement.

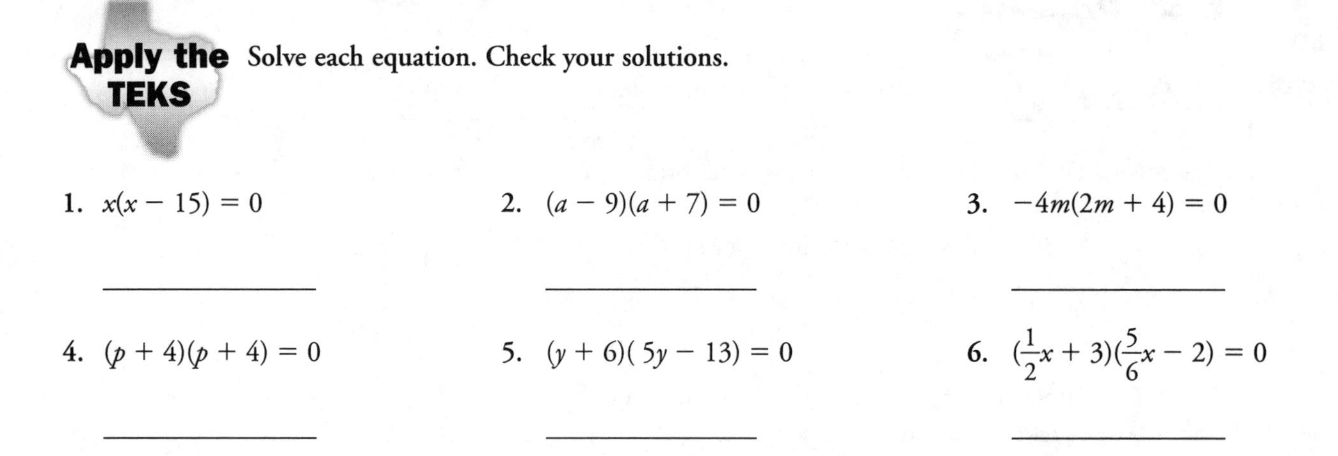

Solve each equation. Check your solutions.

1. $x(x - 15) = 0$ ____________

2. $(a - 9)(a + 7) = 0$ ____________

3. $-4m(2m + 4) = 0$ ____________

4. $(p + 4)(p + 4) = 0$ ____________

5. $(y + 6)(5y - 13) = 0$ ____________

6. $(\frac{1}{2}x + 3)(\frac{5}{6}x - 2) = 0$ ____________

Write and solve an equation to find the length and width of each rectangle with the given dimensions and specified area.

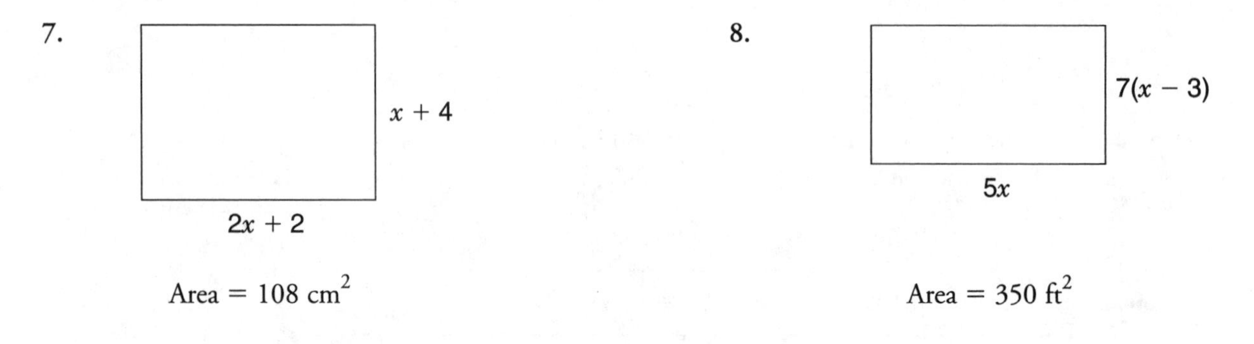

7. Area = 108 cm^2 __________________

8. Area = 350 ft^2 __________________

Solve each equation. Check your solutions.

9. $c^2 + 144 = 24c$ ____________

10. $y^2 - 121 = 0$ ____________

11. $n(n - 5) = 36$ ____________

How many unique solutions does the equation have?

12. Solve the equation $4x - 7 = 13$. __________________

13. Solve the equation $x^2 - x - 56 = 0$. __________________

Solve each problem.

14. The cubic equation $x^3 + x^2 - 20x = 0$ can be factored as $x(x + 5)(x - 4) = 0$. What are the solutions to this equation?

____

15. What do you notice about the order of an equation (the highest exponent) and the number of solutions it has?

____

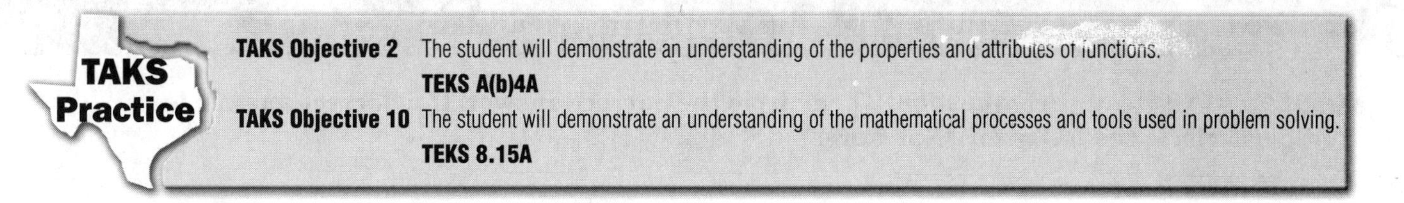

TAKS Objective 2 The student will demonstrate an understanding of the properties and attributes of functions.
TEKS A(b)4A

TAKS Objective 10 The student will demonstrate an understanding of the mathematical processes and tools used in problem solving.
TEKS 8.15A

DIRECTIONS Read each question. Then circle the letter for the correct answer. If a correct answer is not here, circle the letter for "Not Here."

1 What are the solutions to the equation $x^2 + 7x = -12$?

A 3, 4

B −3, 4

C 3, −4

D −3, −4

2 The function $h(t) = 256 - 16t^2$ gives the height of an object in feet, t seconds after it is dropped from a 256-feet tall building. How long does it take for the object to hit the ground?

F 2.5 sec

G 4 sec

H 7 sec

J 12 sec

3 What value of c would produce solutions of $x = 3$ and $x = 6$ in the equation $x^2 - 9x + c = 0$?

A 21

B 18

C −12

D Not Here

4 What is the value of x if the rectangle has an area of 272 square units?

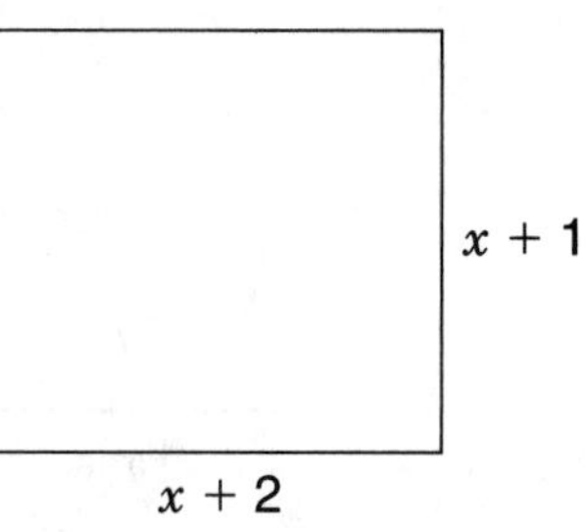

Record your answer and fill in the bubbles on the grid below. Be sure to use the correct place value.

				.			
0	0	0	0		0	0	0
1	1	1	1		1	1	1
2	2	2	2		2	2	2
3	3	3	3		3	3	3
4	4	4	4		4	4	4
5	5	5	5		5	5	5
6	6	6	6		6	6	6
7	7	7	7		7	7	7
8	8	8	8		8	8	8
9	9	9	9		9	9	9

5 In the quadratic function $f(x) = 2(x + 1)^2$, which domain value will NOT produce a range value of 32?

A −5

B 1

C 3

D Not Here

DIRECTIONS Read each question. Then circle the correct answer. If a correct answer is not here, circle the letter for "Not Here."

1 Which of the following situations would produce the graph shown?

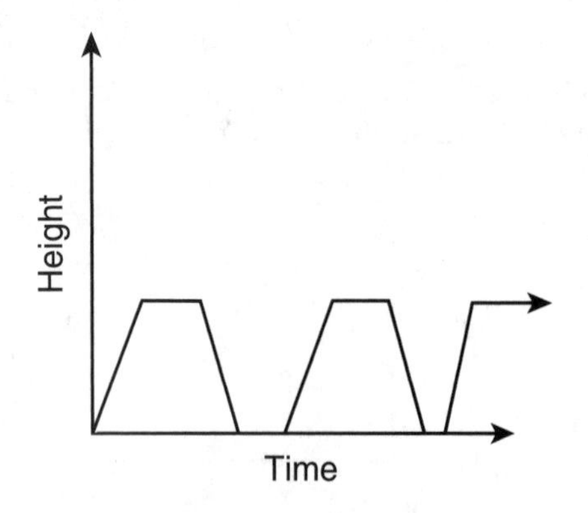

A A reading of a weather balloon's altitude after being released

B A neighbor using a ladder to hang holiday lights from his roof

C The height of a tree t years after it was planted

D Not Here

2 What is the result if the polynomial function $h(x)$ is formed by subtracting $g(x) = 3(x^2 - 4x) + 1$ from $f(x) = 2x^2 + 3(x + 2)$?

F $h(x) = x^2 - 13x - 6$

G $h(x) = 3x^2 + 10x + 2$

H $h(x) = -2x^2 - 4x + 15$

J $h(x) = -x^2 + 15x + 5$

3 Which family of functions would produce the data in the table?

x	0	1	2	3	4	5	6
y	1	−1	1	−1	1	−1	1

A The family of constant functions

B The family of linear functions

C The family of quadratic functions

D Not Here

4 According to the line of best fit, $y = 8.35x - 41$, in which set of range values is y most likely to be if $x = 24$?

F $\{y: 0 \leq y < 65\}$

G $\{y: 65 \leq y < 130\}$

H $\{y: 130 \leq y < 190\}$

J $\{y: 190 \leq y < 250\}$

5 What is the range of $f(x) = 8(4 - x) + 3$ when the domain is $\{-2, 0\ 2\}$?

A $\{51, 35, 19\}$

B $\{14, 22, 30\}$

C $\{-22, -6, 10\}$

D $\{6, 12, 18\}$

6 Which of the following values is not a member of the domain of the scatterplot shown?

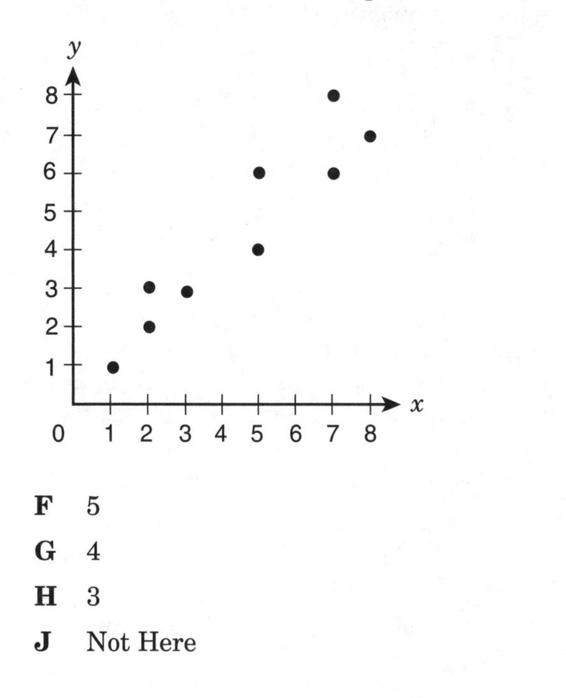

F 5

G 4

H 3

J Not Here

7 The length of a rectangular swimming pool is 10 feet longer than twice the width. The area of the pool is 2,800 feet^2. Which of the following equations will determine the width, x, of the pool?

A $x(2x - 10) = 2{,}800$

B $2x^2 + 10x = 1{,}400$

C $x^2 + 5x - 1{,}400 = 0$

D $x^2 + 10x - 2{,}800 = 0$

8 For which of the sets of data shown below is there a positive correlation between the two variables?

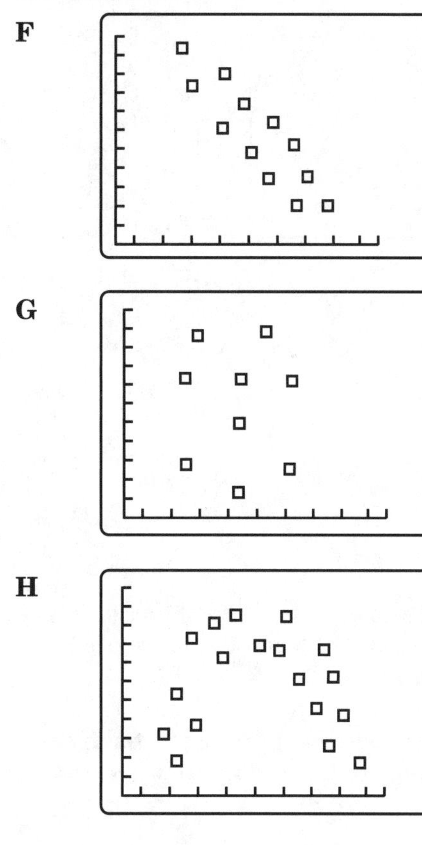

J Not Here

9 What is the range of the quadratic parent function $y = x^2$?

A All real numbers greater than or equal to 0

B All real numbers

C All integers greater than or equal to 0

D All whole numbers

10 Which expression gives the area of the rectangle shown?

$\frac{x-3}{3}$

$3(x+7)$

F $x^2 - 21$

G $3x^2 + 8x + 6$

H $x^2 + 4x - 21$

J $x^2 + 7x - 14$

11 What is the range value of the function $f(x) = 2x^2 + 4x - 12$ when it is evaluated at the point where $x = 3$?

Record your answer and fill in the bubbles on the grid below. Be sure to use the correct place value.

				.			
0	0	0	0		0	0	0
1	1	1	1		1	1	1
2	2	2	2		2	2	2
3	3	3	3		3	3	3
4	4	4	4		4	4	4
5	5	5	5		5	5	5
6	6	6	6		6	6	6
7	7	7	7		7	7	7
8	8	8	8		8	8	8
9	9	9	9		9	9	9

12 What are the solutions to the equation $2x(x + 10) = -32$?

F 2, 8

G −2, 8

H 2, −8

J −2, −8

13 If the area of a triangle is 15 square centimeters and its base is 6 centimeters long, what is the height of the triangle?

A 10 cm

B 8 cm

C 7 cm

D 5 cm

14 A graph shows the cost of an item depending on how many are purchased. Which of the following would be the most appropriate domain for the graph?

F $\{x: x = 1, 2, 3, ...\}$

G $\{x: -10 \leq x \leq 10\}$

H The set of all integers

J The set of all positive rational numbers

15 Which of the following equations does NOT represent a quadratic function?

A $y = \frac{1}{3}(x + 2) - 3x$

B $y = -4x^2 + 12$

C $y = 2x(1 - x) + 15$

D $y = -\frac{1}{2}(x + 4)(x - 7)$

16 A function produces the following values: $(-35, 122)$, $(-21, 66)$, $(-42, 118)$, and $(-9, 32)$. A student needs to resize the window on her calculator to view the graph of the function. Which is the best window for the range?

F ymin $= -100$, ymax $= 100$

G ymin $= 0$, ymax $= 150$

H xmin $= -65$, xmax $= 65$

J xmin $= -50$, xmax $= 0$

17 Which of the following is a simplified expression for the area of the shaded region of the rectangle?

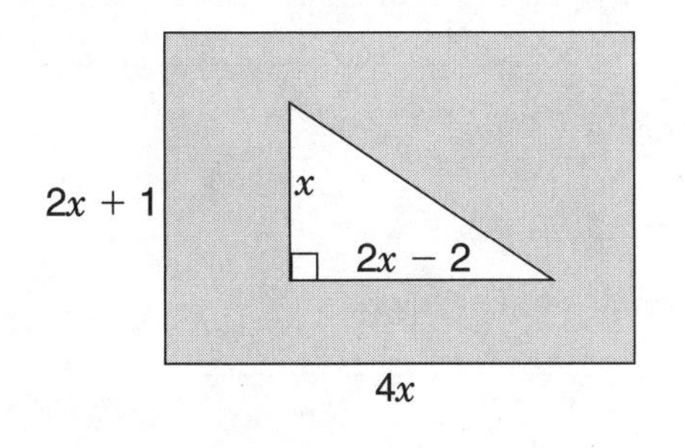

A $8x^2 + 4x$

B $6x^2 + x$

C $10x^2 - 3x$

D $7x^2 + 5x$

18 Financial analysts have modeled the expected profit of a company with the quadratic function $P(h) = 22{,}500 - (4.6h - 80)^2$. In the function, h is the number of advertising hours purchased each month by the company. What is the company's expected profit if they purchase 45 hours of advertising this month?

Record your answer and fill in the bubbles on the grid below. Be sure to use the correct place value.

				•			
0	0	0	0		0	0	0
1	1	1	1		1	1	1
2	2	2	2		2	2	2
3	3	3	3		3	3	3
4	4	4	4		4	4	4
5	5	5	5		5	5	5
6	6	6	6		6	6	6
7	7	7	7		7	7	7
8	8	8	8		8	8	8
9	9	9	9		9	9	9

19 Which of the following linear functions would produce the ordered pairs shown in the graph?

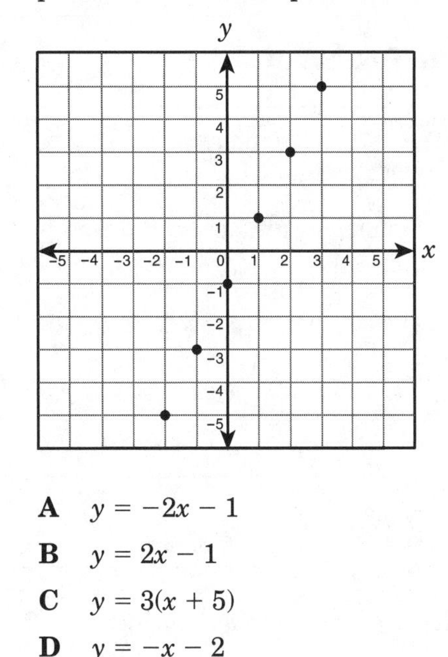

A $y = -2x - 1$

B $y = 2x - 1$

C $y = 3(x + 5)$

D $y = -x - 2$

Focus on TEKS

Lesson 12 Representing and Describing Linear Functions

TEKS A(c)1A Determine whether or not given situations can be represented by linear functions.
TEKS A(c)1B Determine the domain and range values for which linear functions make sense for given situations.
TEKS A(c)1C Translate among and use algebraic, tabular, graphical, or verbal descriptions of linear functions.
TEKS 8.15A Communicate mathematical ideas using language, efficient tools, appropriate units, and graphical, numerical, physical, or algebraic mathematical models.

A linear function can be represented and described in a variety of ways, such as tables, graphs, or equations. Once you determine if a function is linear, you can determine its domain and range.

A **linear function** is a function that can be defined by a linear equation.

A **linear equation** is an equation for which the graph is a straight line.

Problem 1

The data in the table represents the distance Michael biked after a given amount of time. Determine whether the data represents a linear function.

Time (min)	Distance biked (mi)
10	3
20	6
30	10
40	14
50	17
60	19

(Time changes: +10, +10, +10, +10, +10; Distance changes: +3, +4, +4, +3, +2)

Data in a table represents a linear function if the data has a constant rate of change.

Step 1 Check the rate of change in the time. The rate of change is constant, every 10 minutes.

Step 2 Check the rate of change in distance. The rate of change is not constant.

Solution Since the rate of change is not constant for both variables, the data does not represent a linear function.

More Problems

Problem 2 Determine whether $4y = 7x - 6$ represents a linear function.

An equation represents a linear function if the equation can be written in standard form, $Ax + By = C$, where A, B, and C are real numbers, and A and B are not both zero.

Rewrite the equation in the form $Ax + By = C$.

$$\begin{aligned} 4y &= 7x - 6 \\ -7x &= -7x \\ \hline -7x + 4y &= -6 \end{aligned}$$

Solution Since $A = -7$, $B = 4$, and $C = -6$, each a real number, the equation represents a linear function.

Problem 3 Determine whether $y^2 = 9$ represents a linear function.

Solution Since the exponent of y is not 1, the equation does not represent a linear function.

Guided Instruction

Problem 4

Max earns $6.00 per hour working at a concession stand. He is saving his earnings to buy a DVD player with a total price of $190. How many hours must Max work in order to have enough money to buy the DVD player?

Step 1 Make a table to represent the number of hours worked and the amount earned.

Hours Worked	Amount Earned
1	$6
2	$12
3	$18
4	$24

Step 2 Since the domain values are only increasing by 1, the table will need many entries. Use more reasonable domain values in the table, perhaps multiples of 5 to help determine the number of hours Max must work.

Hours Worked	Amount Earned
5	$30
10	$60
15	$90
20	$120
25	$150
30	$180
35	$210

Step 3 Max must work between 30 and 35 hours. Take a closer look at the domain values between 30 and 35.

Hours Worked	Amount Earned
31	$186
32	$192
33	$198
34	$204

Solution

At 31 hours Max will not have earned enough money yet. At 32 hours he will have earned $192, which will be enough money to buy the DVD player.

Problem 5

Name the domain and range of the set of ordered pairs. Then graph the ordered pairs to determine if they represent a linear function.
$(-6, -4), (-3, -2), (0, 0), (3, 2), (6, 4)$

Solution

Domain: $\{x: x = -6, -3, 0, 3, 6\}$
Range: $\{y: y = -4, -2, 0, 2, 4\}$

A graph represents a linear function if it is a nonvertical straight line. Since these points lie on a nonvertical straight line, they represent a linear function.

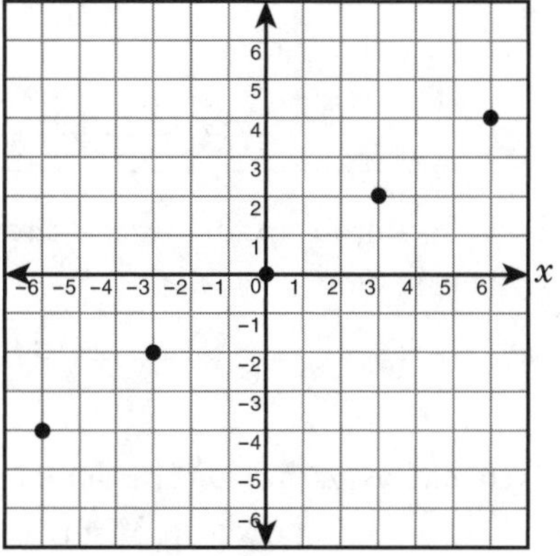

Apply the TEKS Determine whether the data in each table represents a linear function.

1.

Hours Worked	Amount Earned
10	$80
20	$160
30	$240
40	$320
50	$440

____

2.

Miles Walked	Calories Burned
1	89
2	178
3	267
4	356
5	445

____

Determine whether each equation represents a linear function. If so, write the equation in the form $Ax + By = C$.

3. $-2y = 3 - x$ __________

4. $10 + y = 9x$ __________

5. $x^2 - y = 14$ __________

6. $x = -6y$ __________

7. $8 + 3x^2 = y^2$ __________

8. $11 = -3y$ __________

Name the domain and range of each set of ordered pairs. Then graph the ordered pairs on the coordinate plane and determine if they represent a linear function.

9. $(-2, 6), (-1, 1), (0, -1), (1, 1), (2, 6)$

Domain: __________

Range: __________

Linear function: __________

y

−6 −5 −4 −3 −2 −1 0 1 2 3 4 5 6 x

6 5 4 3 2 1 −1 −2 −3 −4 −5 −6

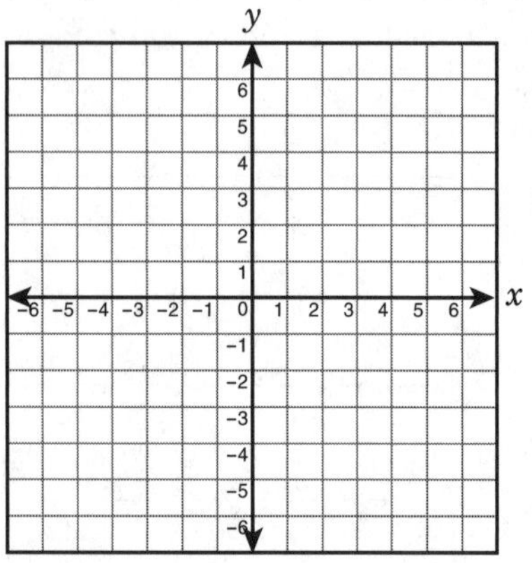

10. $(-5, 1), (-3, 0), (-1, -1), (1, -2), (3, -3)$

Domain: __________

Range: __________

Linear function: __________

y

−6 −5 −4 −3 −2 −1 0 1 2 3 4 5 6 x

6 5 4 3 2 1 −1 −2 −3 −4 −5 −6

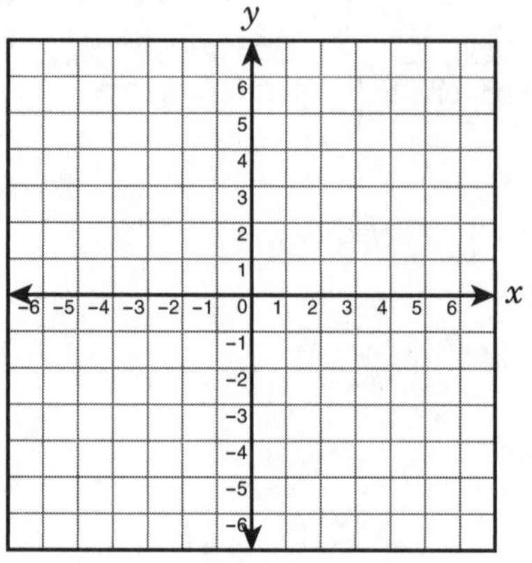

11. Write a problem for either Exercise 9 or 10 where the restrictions on the domain and range make sense to the situation.

____

Given each equation and its domain, find its range.

12. $y = 5x - 7$; $\{x: x = -3, -1, 1, 3, 5\}$

Range: __________

13. $x^2 - y = 3$; $\{x: x = -4, -2, 0, 2, 4\}$

Range: __________

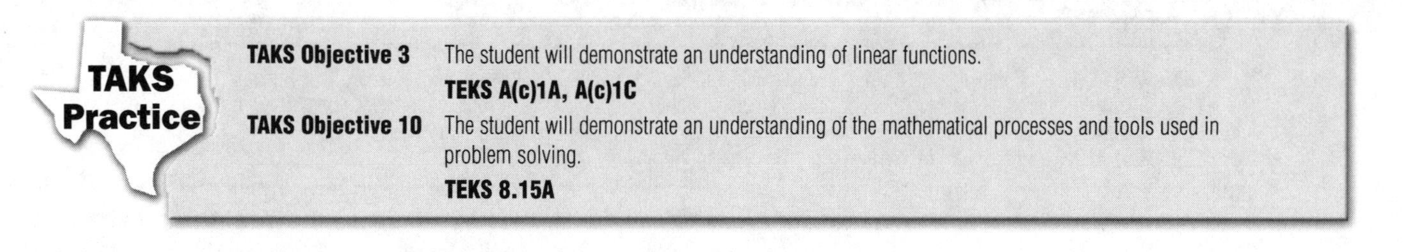

TAKS Practice

TAKS Objective 3 The student will demonstrate an understanding of linear functions.
TEKS A(c)1A, A(c)1C

TAKS Objective 10 The student will demonstrate an understanding of the mathematical processes and tools used in problem solving.
TEKS 8.15A

DIRECTIONS Read each question. Then circle the letter for the correct answer. If a correct answer is not here, circle the letter for "Not Here."

1 Name a reason that both equations $4y + 2x^2 = 20$ and $x^2 + y = -9$ do not represent linear functions.

A Because $A = 4$ and $B = 2$, both real numbers

B Because the exponent of x is 2

C Because A, B, and C are not zero

D Because the data can be represented on a graph

2 Which set of ordered pairs represents the function $2x - 4y = 8$?

F $(0, -2), (2, -3), (4, 1), (8, 2)$

G $(-2, 3), (0, -2), (2, -1), (-4, -4)$

H $(1, -\frac{3}{2}), (2, -1), (3, -\frac{1}{2}), (4, 0)$

J $(-2, -3), (-1, -\frac{5}{2}), (0, 2), (1, -\frac{3}{2})$

3 Mr. Meeker put a deposit on a family vacation. He is also saving \$150 every week to pay for the rest of the vacation. The total cost will be \$3,500. Which linear equation represents this situation?

A $150x - y = 3{,}500$

B $150x + y = 3{,}500$

C $3{,}500x - y = 150$

D $y = 3{,}500x - 150$

4 Which of the following does NOT represent the linear function $6x - 2y = 10$?

F

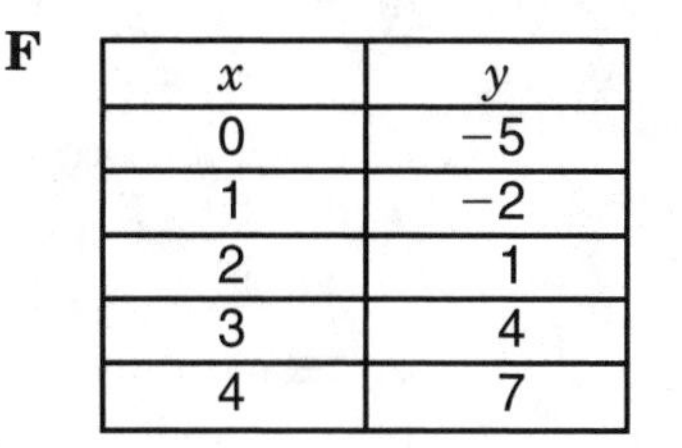

x	y
0	−5
1	−2
2	1
3	4
4	7

G

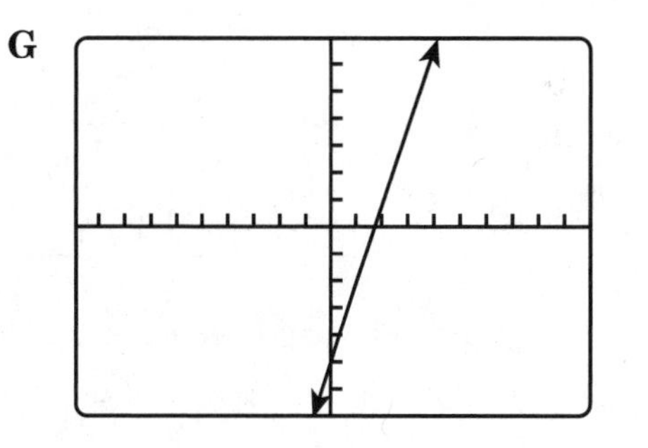

H $(-2, -11), (0, -5), (2, 1), (4, 7), (6, 13)$

J Not Here

Focus on TEKS Lesson 13 Slope and Intercepts of Linear Functions

TEKS A(c)2A Develop the concept of slope as a rate of change and determine slopes from graphs, tables, and algebraic representations.
TEKS A(c)2B Interpret the meaning of slope and intercepts in situations using data, symbolic representations, or graphs.
TEKS A(c)2E Determine the intercepts of linear functions from graphs, tables, and algebraic representations.
TEKS 8.16A Make conjectures from patterns or sets of examples and nonexamples.

In many instances, slope and intercepts can be defined in terms of a real-world situation.

Slope represents rate of change.
The slope of a line or line segment is the ratio of the change in y-coordinates compared to the change in x-coordinates. A line that slants upward from the left to right has a positive slope. A line that slants upward from the right to left has a negative slope.
Intercepts describe where a line intersects the axes.

Guided Instruction

Problem 1

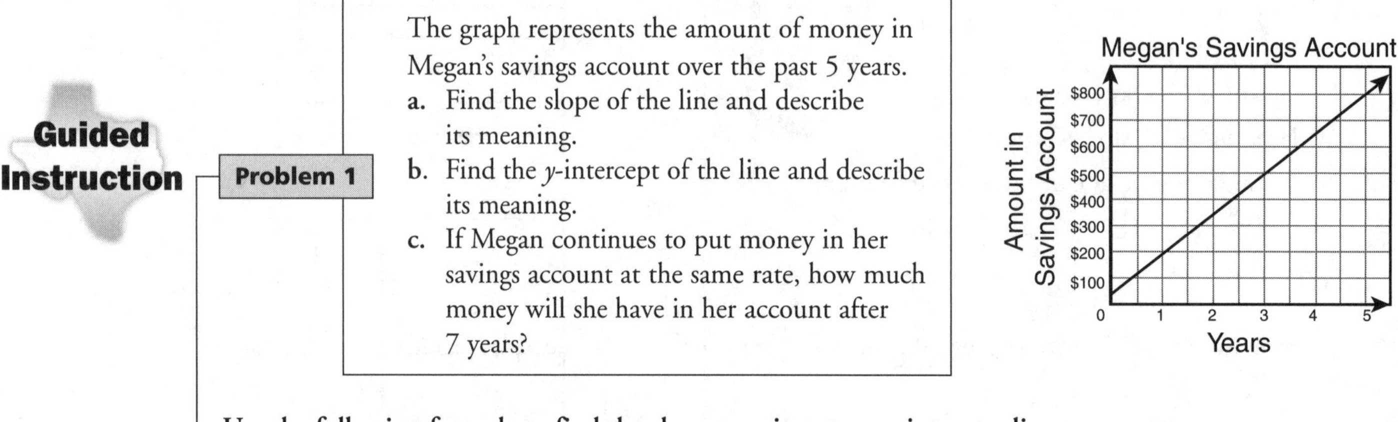

The graph represents the amount of money in Megan's savings account over the past 5 years.

a. Find the slope of the line and describe its meaning.
b. Find the y-intercept of the line and describe its meaning.
c. If Megan continues to put money in her savings account at the same rate, how much money will she have in her account after 7 years?

Use the following formula to find the slope, m, given two points on a line.

$$m = \frac{y_2 - y_1}{x_2 - x_1}, \text{ given } (x_1, y_1) \text{ and } (x_2, y_2)$$

Part a To find the slope of the line, select two points on the line and calculate their slope. Use (1, \$200) and (2, \$350).

$$m = \frac{y_2 - y_1}{x_2 - x_1}$$

$$m = \frac{350 - 200}{2 - 1}$$

$$m = \frac{150}{1} = 150$$

The slope of the line is \$150, which describes the rate of change in the amount of money in the account from year to year.

Part b The y-intercept is \$50, since this is where the line intersects with the y-axis. This represents the amount of money Megan deposited when she first opened the account.

Part c The amount of money in Megan's savings account increases at a rate of \$150 each year.

Year 6: \$800 + \$150 = \$950 Year 7: \$950 + \$150 = \$1,100

Megan will have \$1,100 in her savings account after 7 years.

Solution The slope is \$150 and the y-intercept is \$50. Megan will have \$1,100 after 7 years.

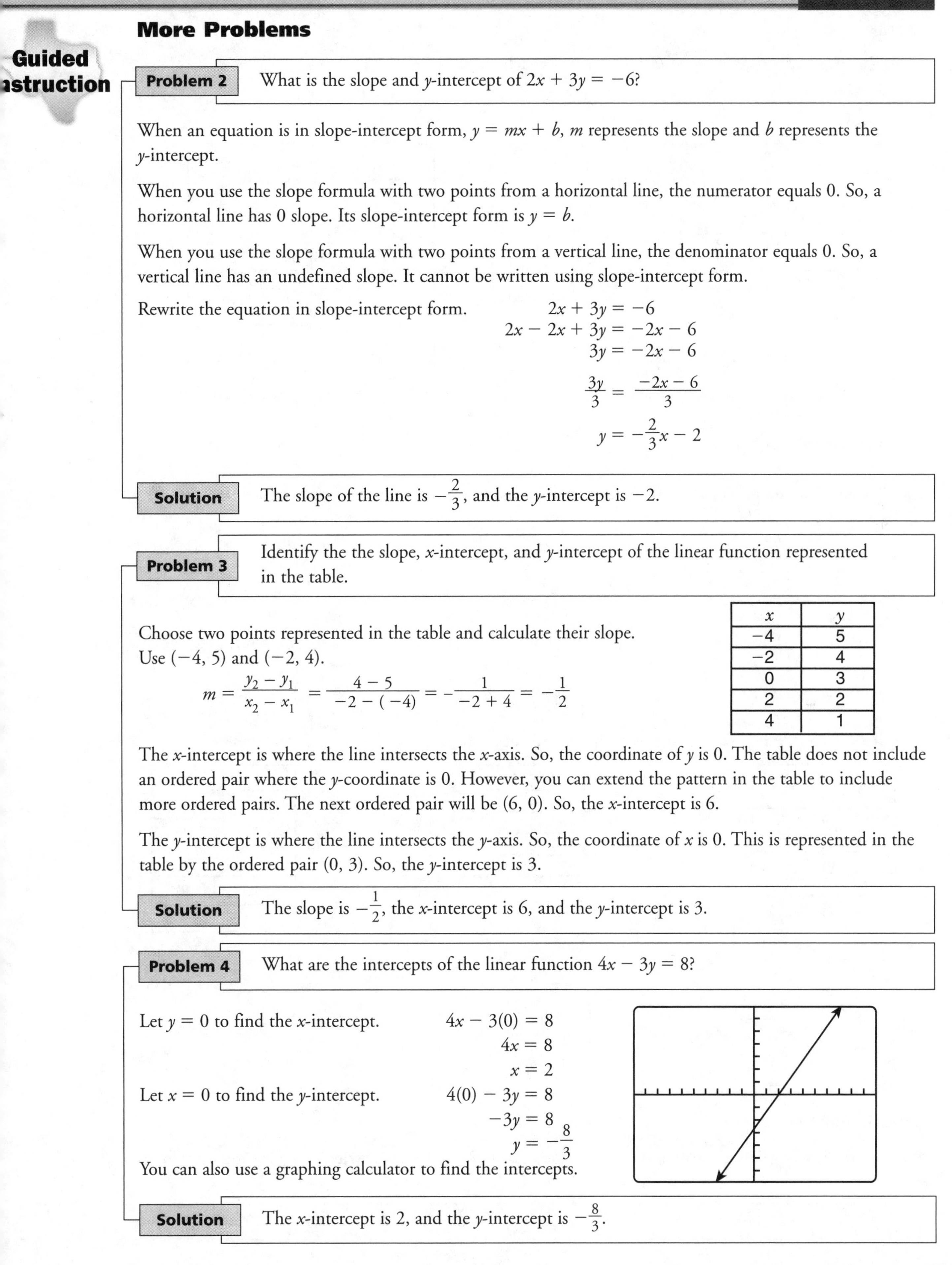

More Problems

Guided Instruction

Problem 2 What is the slope and y-intercept of $2x + 3y = -6$?

When an equation is in slope-intercept form, $y = mx + b$, m represents the slope and b represents the y-intercept.

When you use the slope formula with two points from a horizontal line, the numerator equals 0. So, a horizontal line has 0 slope. Its slope-intercept form is $y = b$.

When you use the slope formula with two points from a vertical line, the denominator equals 0. So, a vertical line has an undefined slope. It cannot be written using slope-intercept form.

Rewrite the equation in slope-intercept form.

$$2x + 3y = -6$$
$$2x - 2x + 3y = -2x - 6$$
$$3y = -2x - 6$$
$$\frac{3y}{3} = \frac{-2x - 6}{3}$$
$$y = -\frac{2}{3}x - 2$$

Solution The slope of the line is $-\frac{2}{3}$, and the y-intercept is -2.

Problem 3 Identify the the slope, x-intercept, and y-intercept of the linear function represented in the table.

x	y
−4	5
−2	4
0	3
2	2
4	1

Choose two points represented in the table and calculate their slope.
Use $(-4, 5)$ and $(-2, 4)$.

$$m = \frac{y_2 - y_1}{x_2 - x_1} = \frac{4 - 5}{-2 - (-4)} = -\frac{1}{-2 + 4} = -\frac{1}{2}$$

The x-intercept is where the line intersects the x-axis. So, the coordinate of y is 0. The table does not include an ordered pair where the y-coordinate is 0. However, you can extend the pattern in the table to include more ordered pairs. The next ordered pair will be $(6, 0)$. So, the x-intercept is 6.

The y-intercept is where the line intersects the y-axis. So, the coordinate of x is 0. This is represented in the table by the ordered pair $(0, 3)$. So, the y-intercept is 3.

Solution The slope is $-\frac{1}{2}$, the x-intercept is 6, and the y-intercept is 3.

Problem 4 What are the intercepts of the linear function $4x - 3y = 8$?

Let $y = 0$ to find the x-intercept.

$$4x - 3(0) = 8$$
$$4x = 8$$
$$x = 2$$

Let $x = 0$ to find the y-intercept.

$$4(0) - 3y = 8$$
$$-3y = 8$$
$$y = -\frac{8}{3}$$

You can also use a graphing calculator to find the intercepts.

Solution The x-intercept is 2, and the y-intercept is $-\frac{8}{3}$.

Apply the TEKS Identify the slope and intercepts of each graph.

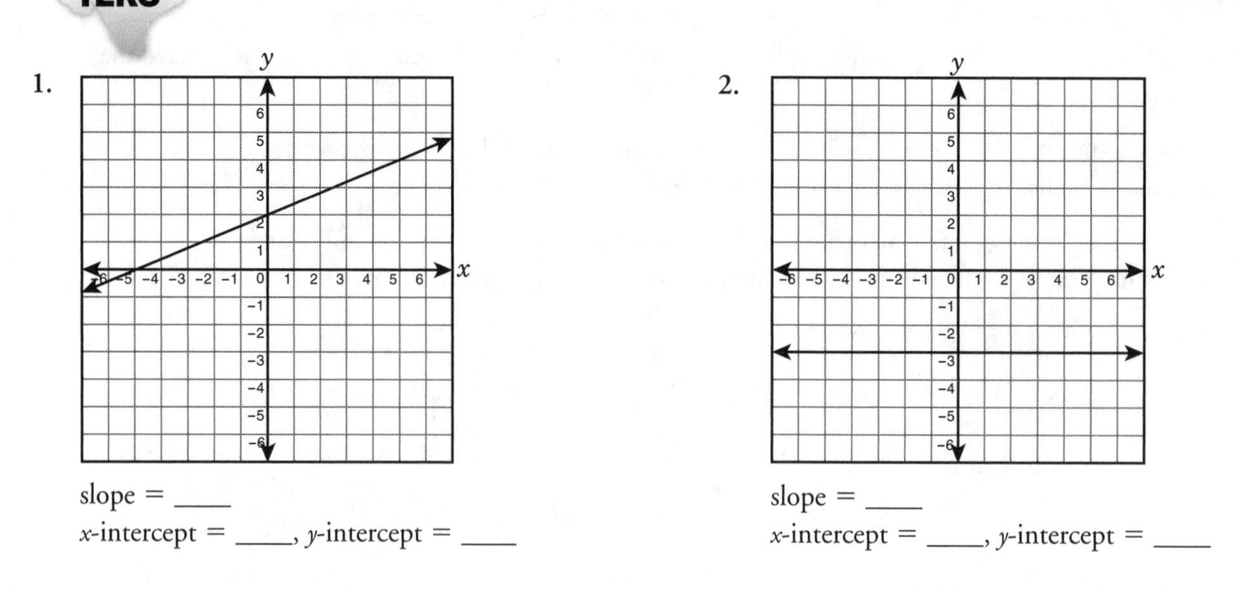

1. slope = ____
   x-intercept = ____, y-intercept = ____

2. slope = ____
   x-intercept = ____, y-intercept = ____

Identify the direction in which the line slants, the slope, and the intercepts of each equation.

3. $5x + y = 4$
   slants ________________
   slope = _____
   x-intercept = _____
   y-intercept = _____

4. $6 - 3y = -4x$
   slants ________________
   slope = _____
   x-intercept = _____
   y-intercept = _____

5. $x = 7$
   slants ________________
   slope = _____
   x-intercept = _____
   y-intercept = _____

Identify the slope, x-intercept, and y-intercept of each linear function represented in each table.

6.

x	y
−2	−3
−1	−2
0	−1
1	0
2	1

slope = _____
x-intercept = _____
y-intercept = _____

7.

x	y
2	2
4	1
6	0
8	−1
10	−2

slope = _____
x-intercept = _____
y-intercept = _____

8.

x	y
0	3
2	$2\frac{1}{2}$
4	2
6	$1\frac{1}{2}$
8	1

slope = _____
x-intercept = _____
y-intercept = _____

Solve the problem.

9. Explain how to take an equation in standard form $Ax + By = C$, and rewrite it in slope-intercept form.

____

____

TAKS Practice

TAKS Objective 3 The student will demonstrate an understanding of linear functions.
TEKS A(c)2A, A(c)2B, A(c)2E

TAKS Objective 10 The student will demonstrate an understanding of the mathematical processes and tools used in problem solving.
TEKS 8.16A

DIRECTIONS Read each question. Then circle the letter for the correct answer. If a correct answer is not here, circle the letter for "Not Here."

1 Which of the following statements is true about the graph shown?

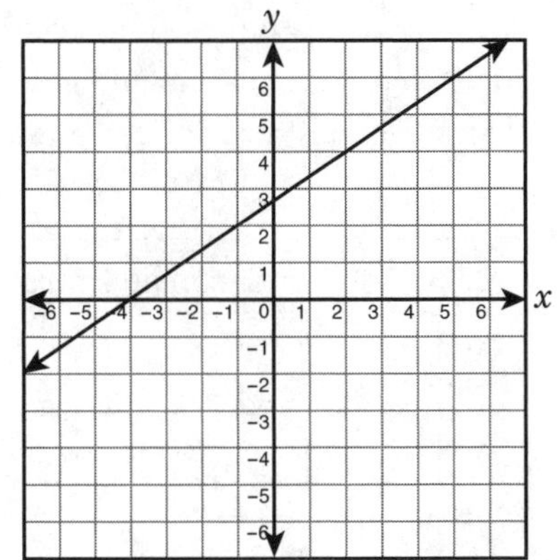

A The slope of the linear function is $\frac{3}{2}$.

B The slope of the linear function is $-\frac{2}{3}$.

C The x-intercept of the linear function is -4.

D The y-intercept of the linear function is -4.

2 What type of slope does a line have that slants upward to the right?

F A slope of 0

G Negative slope

H Undefined slope

J Positive slope

3 Which of the following equations represents a linear function with an x-intercept of -3 and a y-intercept of $\frac{3}{4}$?

A $-2x + 8y = 6$

B $3x - 10y = -9$

C $-4x - 9y = -12$

D $-x + 8y = 3$

4 The cost of ground beef at Humphrey's Meats is a function of the number of pounds purchased. The cost for 1–5 pounds of ground beef is shown in the table.

Pounds	Total Cost
1	$3.25
2	$6.50
3	$9.75
4	$13.00
5	$16.25

If the data are graphed with number of pounds on the horizontal axis and cost on the vertical axis, what does the slope represent?

F The total cost of 2 pounds

G A difference of 1 between the number of pounds purchased

H An average of $9.75 per pound

J A rate of $3.25 per pound

Focus on TEKS

Lesson 14 Effects of Changing Slope and Intercepts

TEKS A(c)2C Investigate, describe, and predict the effects of changes in m and b on the graph of $y = mx + b$.
TEKS A(c)2F Interpret and predict the effects of changing slope and y-intercept in applied situations.
TEKS 8.14A Identify and apply mathematics to everyday experiences, to activities in and outside of school, with other disciplines, and with other mathematical topics.

A line slanting upward to the right has a positive slope, and a line slanting downward to the right has a negative slope. Any change made to the slope of a line affects the graph of that line.

Guided Instruction

Problem 1

Jason McGee is the owner of McGee Landscaping. Last year his equipment expenses (e) were $e = \$100c + \$300$, where c is the number of customers. This year Jason's equipment expenses will increase by 20% due to repairs, replacement, and fuel increases. Describe how this increase will affect the graph for McGee Landscaping's equipment expenses.

Step 1 Graph the equation $e = \$100c + \$300$. Recognize that the equation is in slope-intercept form $y = mx + b$. The y-intercept is \$300, and the slope is \$100.

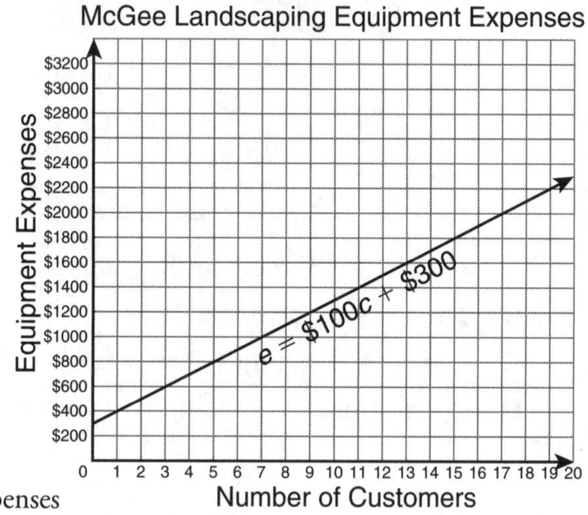

McGee Landscaping Equipment Expenses

Step 2 Calculate the equipment expenses equation for this year. Since the increase is 20%, multiply last year's equipment expense by 100% + 20%, or 120%, or 1.2.

$e = \$100c + \$300$ — last year's equipment expenses

$e = 1.2(\$100c + \$300)$ — this year's equipment expenses
$e = \$120c + \$360$

Step 3 Graph the equation $e = \$120c + \$360$. The y-intercept is \$360, and the slope is \$120.

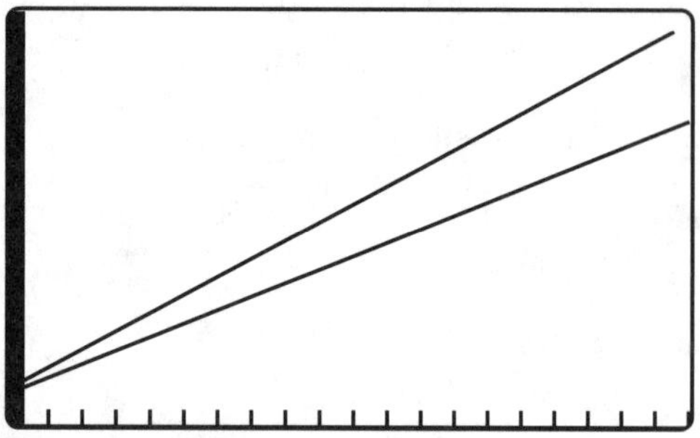

Step 4 Compare the graphs of last year's equipment expenses and this year's equipment expenses.

Solution

The slope has changed from \$100 to \$120. Last year the equipment expenses per customer was \$100; this year it will be \$120. This change in slope alters the graph to slant slightly more upward.
The y-intercept is changed from \$300 to \$360. These values represent the base cost, or minimum expense, for equipment, which was \$300 last year and is \$360 this year. This y-intercept change moves the line so that it crosses the y-axis at a different point.

Graph each set of equations on a graphing calculator. Describe any similarities or differences among the graphs. Then predict how the graph of another equation will look in comparison to the set graphed. Verify by graphing the equation on a graphing calculator.

1. $y = \frac{1}{4}x - 2, y = \frac{1}{2}x - 2, y = \frac{3}{4}x - 2$

   similarities/differences: ____________________

   predict the graph of $y = x - 2$: ____________________

2. $y = x, y = 2x, y = 3x$

   similarities/differences: ____________________

   predict the graph of $y = 4x$: ____________________

3. $y = -2x - 4, y = -2x - 2, y = -2x$

   similarities/differences: ____________________

   predict the graph of $y = -2x + 4$: ____________________

4. $y = \frac{1}{2}x + 3, y = -\frac{1}{2}x + 3, y = \frac{1}{2}x + 5$

   similarities/differences: ____________________

   predict the graph of $y = -\frac{1}{2}x + 5$: ____________________

5. $y = \frac{1}{3}x + 3, y = x + 3, y = \frac{3}{2}x + 3$

   similarities/differences: ____________________

   predict the graph of $y = \frac{7}{4}x + 3$: ____________________

Refer to the equation $y = \frac{3}{5}x - 7$.

6. Will the graph cross the y-axis above or below the origin? ____________________

7. Will the graph slant upward or downward to the right? ____________________

8. Will the graph be more or less steep than the graph of $y = x$? ____________________

Refer to the equation $4x + y = 9$.

9. Will the graph cross the y-axis above or below the origin? ____________________

10. Will the graph slant upward or downward to the right? ____________________

TAKS Objective 3 The student will demonstrate an understanding of linear functions.
TEKS A(c)2C, A(c)2F

TAKS Objective 10 The student will demonstrate an understanding of the mathematical processes and tools used in problem solving.
TEKS 8.14A

DIRECTIONS Read each question. Then circle the letter for the correct answer. If a correct answer is not here, circle the letter for "Not Here."

1 Which of the following equations has a graph that lies between the graphs of $y = -\frac{1}{3}x + 2$ and $y = -\frac{1}{3}x + 5$?

A $y = -\frac{1}{3}x$

B $y = -\frac{1}{3}x + 3$

C $y = \frac{1}{3}x + 6$

D $y = -3x - 4$

2 Mrs. Garcia was driving to an out-of-town business meeting. After driving 20 miles, she stopped for gas. From that point on she drove at a constant rate until she reached her destination at 11:00. This is illustrated in the graph below.

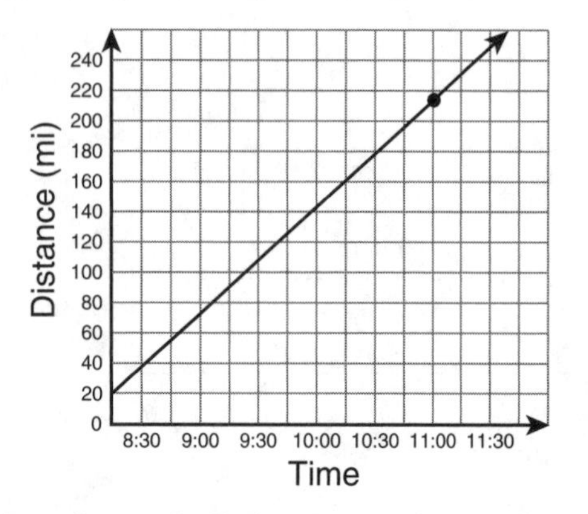

If Mrs. Garcia had driven 5 miles per hour slower from the stop for gas to her destination, about what time would she have arrived?

F 10:45

G 11:05

H 11:15

J 11:30

3 An empty egg carton weighs 0.6 ounce. Each egg placed in the carton weighs an average of 2.3 ounces. The total weight of an egg carton can be represented by the equation $w = 2.3e + 0.6$, where e is the number of eggs in the carton. If the equation were $w = 2.3e + 0.8$, what change would this represent?

A The empty egg carton weighing 0.2 ounce more

B Each egg weighing 0.2 ounce more

C The total weight of two egg cartons

D Not Here

4 When Kim first started baby-sitting, her hourly earnings could be represented by the equation $h = \$0.75c + \$2.00$, where c represents the number of children she was baby-sitting. Since she is more experienced, she changed her hourly earnings to $h = \$2.00c$. Which of the following statements is NOT true?

F When baby-sitting 1 child, Kim earned more money per hour with her old hourly rate.

G The graph of Kim's new hourly rate intersects the y-axis at the origin.

H When graphing each equation, the slope of the new hourly rate is steeper than the slope of the old hourly rate.

J When baby-sitting 4 children, Kim earns twice as much per hour with her new hourly rate than with her old hourly rate.

Focus on TEKS

Lesson 15 Graphing and Writing Equations of Lines

TEKS A(c)2D Graph and write equations of lines given characteristics such as two points, a point and a slope, or a slope and y-intercept.

Many real-world situations that can be represented by a linear function are expressed graphically or by an equation.

The **slope-intercept** form of a line is $y = mx + b$, where m is the slope and b is the y-intercept.

Guided Instruction

Problem 1

The cost of being a member at Macy's Health and Fitness Club is an initial fee of $80 plus a monthly fee of $30. Write an equation to represent the total cost of Macy's Health and Fitness Club based on the number of months as a member. Then graph the line on a coordinate grid.

Step 1 State the given information.

The initial fee is $80, and the monthly fee is $30.

Step 2 Determine if each fee varies or is a set cost.
The initial fee, $80, is a set cost, so it does not vary. Therefore it represents the y-intercept. The monthly fee, $30, varies based on the number of months as a member. This is a rate of change, or the slope of the line.

Step 3 Since we know the slope and y-intercept, write the equation in slope-intercept form.

$y = mx + b$
$y = \$30x + \$80$

Step 4 Before graphing the line, label the axis with reasonable intervals. For this equation, use intervals of 1 month for the x-axis and intervals of $20 for the y-axis.

Step 5 Graph the line by first plotting a point at the y-intercept, $80. Then use the slope of $30, or $\frac{\$30}{1}$ to plot two more points. Draw a line going through the points.

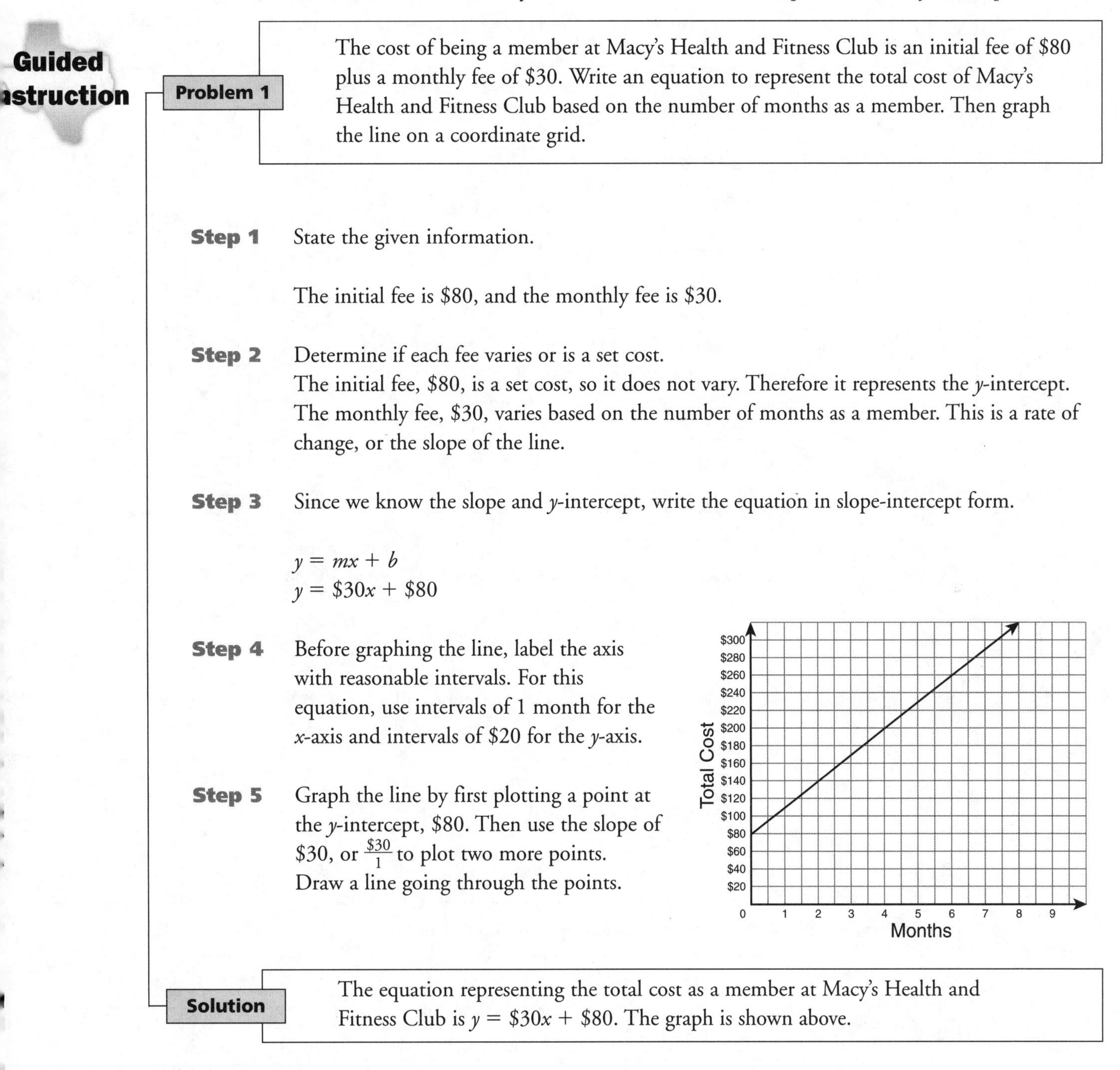

Solution

The equation representing the total cost as a member at Macy's Health and Fitness Club is $y = \$30x + \$80$. The graph is shown above.

Guided Instruction

The point-slope form of a line is $(y - y_1) = m(x - x_1)$, where (x_1, y_1) is a point on the line and m is the slope.

More Problems

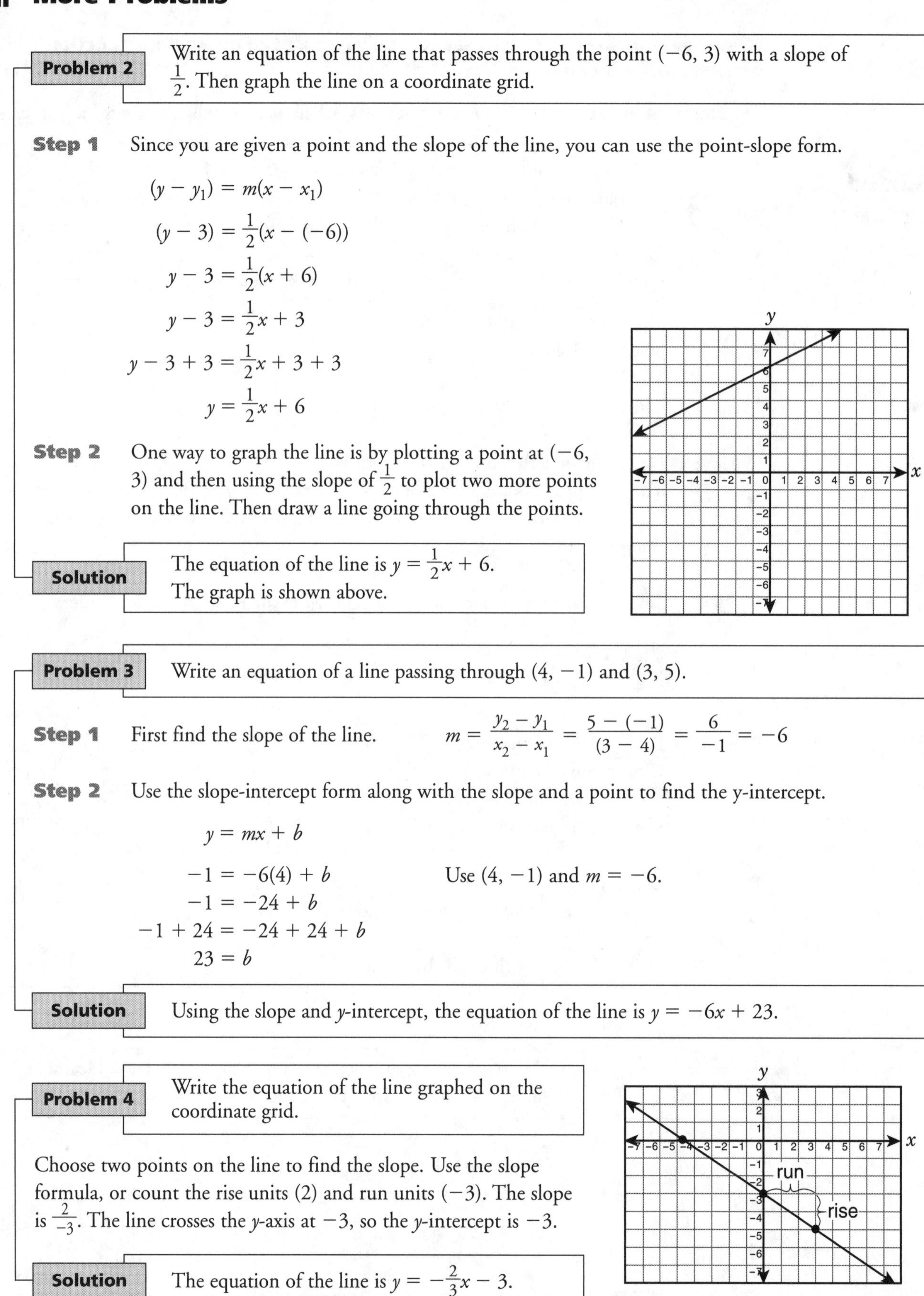

Problem 2 Write an equation of the line that passes through the point $(-6, 3)$ with a slope of $\frac{1}{2}$. Then graph the line on a coordinate grid.

Step 1 Since you are given a point and the slope of the line, you can use the point-slope form.

$$(y - y_1) = m(x - x_1)$$
$$(y - 3) = \frac{1}{2}(x - (-6))$$
$$y - 3 = \frac{1}{2}(x + 6)$$
$$y - 3 = \frac{1}{2}x + 3$$
$$y - 3 + 3 = \frac{1}{2}x + 3 + 3$$
$$y = \frac{1}{2}x + 6$$

Step 2 One way to graph the line is by plotting a point at $(-6, 3)$ and then using the slope of $\frac{1}{2}$ to plot two more points on the line. Then draw a line going through the points.

Solution The equation of the line is $y = \frac{1}{2}x + 6$. The graph is shown above.

Problem 3 Write an equation of a line passing through $(4, -1)$ and $(3, 5)$.

Step 1 First find the slope of the line. $m = \frac{y_2 - y_1}{x_2 - x_1} = \frac{5 - (-1)}{(3 - 4)} = \frac{6}{-1} = -6$

Step 2 Use the slope-intercept form along with the slope and a point to find the y-intercept.

$$y = mx + b$$
$$-1 = -6(4) + b \qquad \text{Use } (4, -1) \text{ and } m = -6.$$
$$-1 = -24 + b$$
$$-1 + 24 = -24 + 24 + b$$
$$23 = b$$

Solution Using the slope and y-intercept, the equation of the line is $y = -6x + 23$.

Problem 4 Write the equation of the line graphed on the coordinate grid.

Choose two points on the line to find the slope. Use the slope formula, or count the rise units (2) and run units (−3). The slope is $\frac{2}{-3}$. The line crosses the y-axis at −3, so the y-intercept is −3.

Solution The equation of the line is $y = -\frac{2}{3}x - 3$.

Apply the TEKS Write the equation of the line graphed on each coordinate grid.

1.

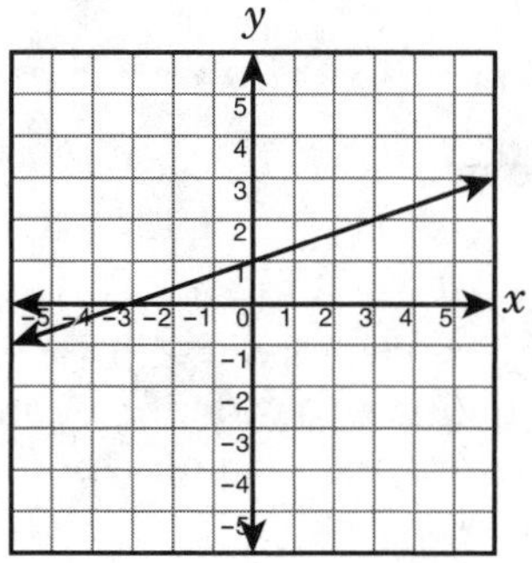

2.

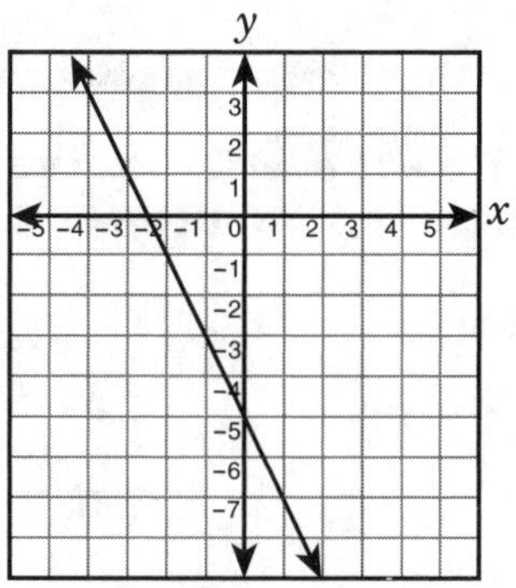

3.

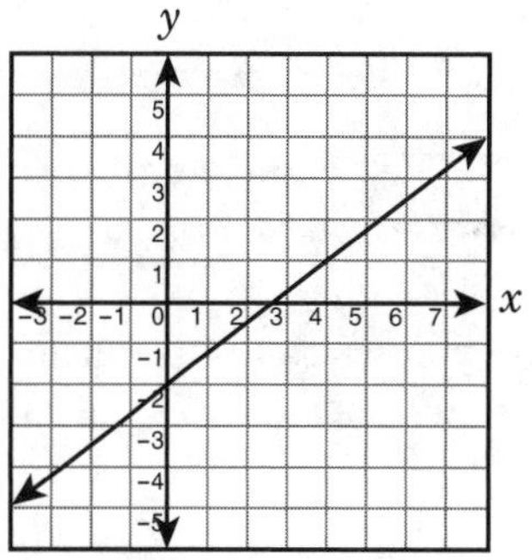

Write the equation of each line given the slope and y-intercept.

4. $m = \frac{3}{4}$; y-intercept $= -1$

5. $m = -4$; y-intercept $= 8$

6. $m = -\frac{1}{4}$; y-intercept $= 0$

Write the equation of each line given a point on the line and the slope.

7. $(0, 7)$, $m = -3$

8. $(-1, -3)$, $m = \frac{2}{3}$

9. $(8, -4)$, $m = -\frac{1}{2}$

Write the equation of each line given two points on the line.

10. $(-5, 0)$, $(-3, 3)$

11. $(2, -1)$, $(8, -7)$

12. $(-2, -5)$, $(-4, 5)$

Graph each line on the coordinate grid.

13. $y = -x + 3$

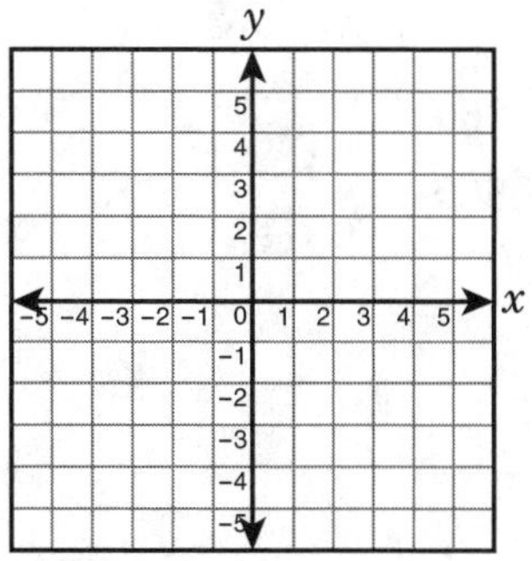

14. $y = \frac{2}{3}x - 4$

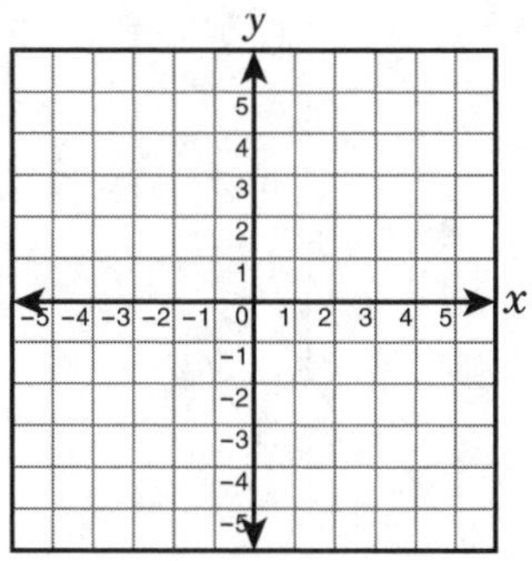

15. $5x + 3y = 12$

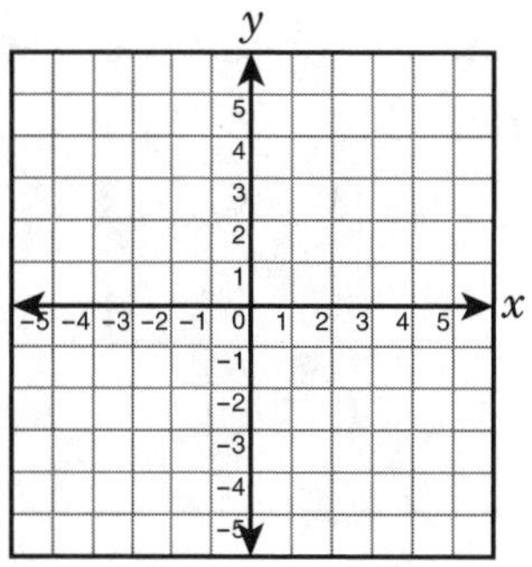

Solve the problem.

16. Given the equation $(y + 6) = -3(x - 10)$, explain what you can determine about the graph of the line.

TAKS Objective 3 The student will demonstrate an understanding of linear functions.
TEKS A(c)2D

DIRECTIONS Read each question. Then circle the letter for the correct answer. If a correct answer is not here, circle the letter for "Not Here."

1 When you write the equation $6x - 5y = -10$ in slope-intercept form, what is the value of m?

A -6

B -2

C $\frac{5}{6}$

D $\frac{6}{5}$

2 Which line is the graph of $3x + 2y = 8$?

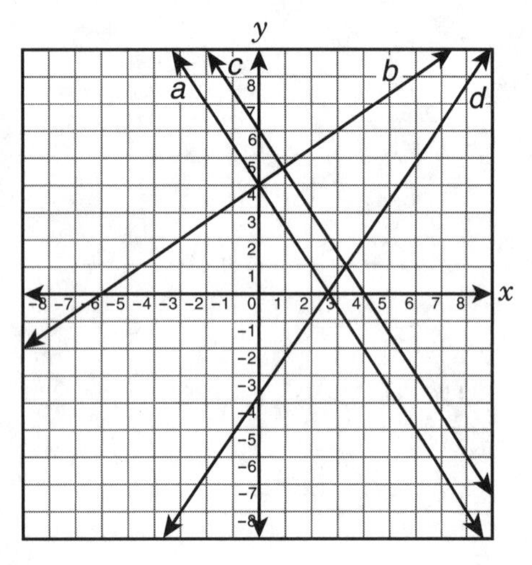

F Line a

G Line b

H Line c

J Line d

3 Mitchel has $3.15 in quarters and dimes. Which equation represents this situation if q equals the number of quarters and d equals the number of dimes Mitchel has?

A $0.10q + 0.25d = 3.15$

B $0.25q + 0.10d = 3.15$

C $25q + 10d = 3.15$

D Not Here

4 The slope of a line is $\frac{3}{4}$, and a point on the line is $(-3, -9)$. Where does the graph of this line cross the x-axis?

F $(-7, 0)$

G $(3.5, 0)$

H $(-15, 0)$

J $(9, 0)$

5 An airplane is flying at an altitude a of 2,660 feet. It is descending 280 feet each minute. Which of the following equations represents the altitude of the plane in terms of elapsed minutes?

A $a = 2{,}660 - 280m$

B $a = 2{,}660 + 280m$

C $a - 280m = 2{,}660$

D $a = 280m - 2{,}660$

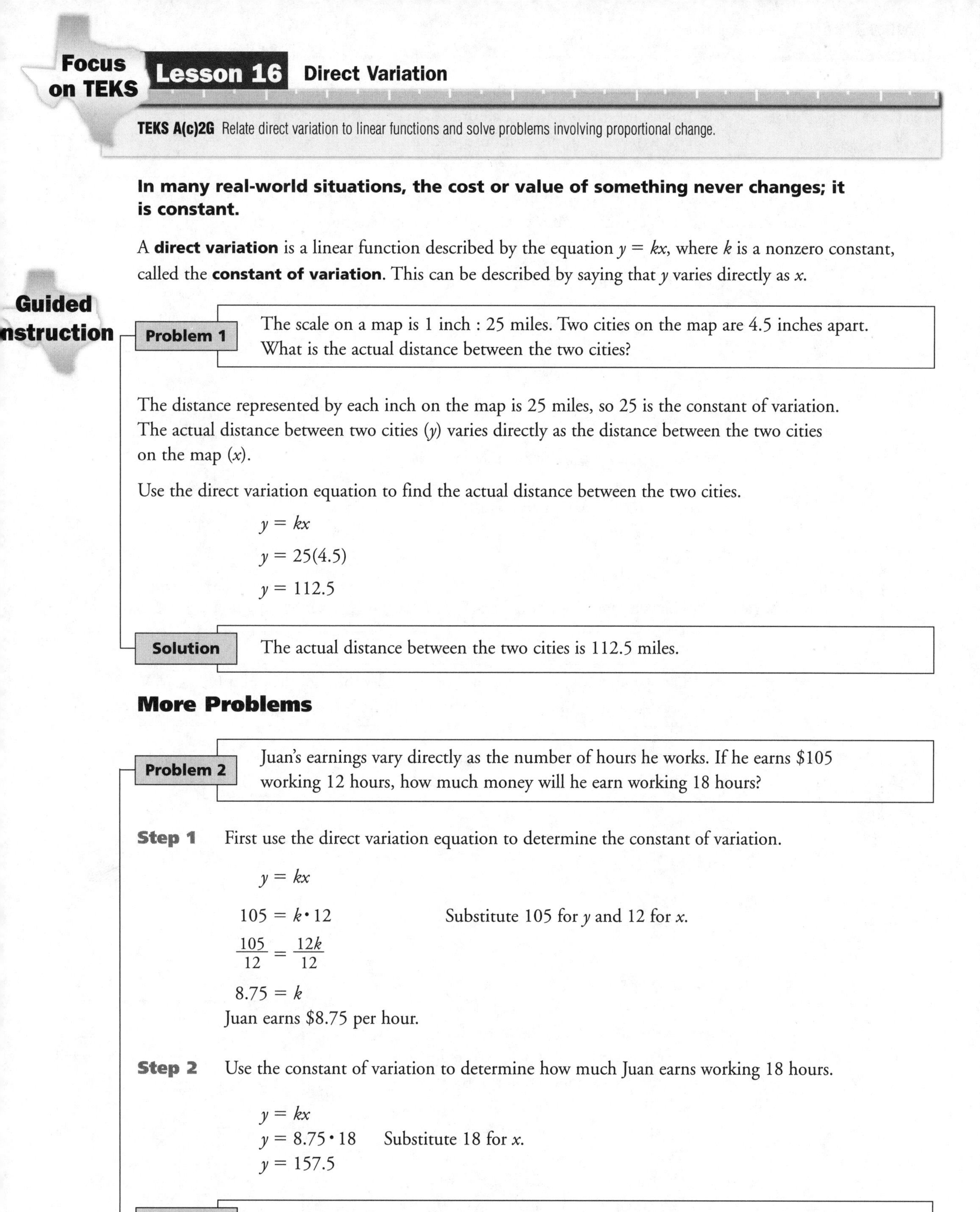

Focus on TEKS

Lesson 16 Direct Variation

TEKS A(c)2G Relate direct variation to linear functions and solve problems involving proportional change.

In many real-world situations, the cost or value of something never changes; it is constant.

A **direct variation** is a linear function described by the equation $y = kx$, where k is a nonzero constant, called the **constant of variation**. This can be described by saying that y varies directly as x.

Guided Instruction

Problem 1 The scale on a map is 1 inch : 25 miles. Two cities on the map are 4.5 inches apart. What is the actual distance between the two cities?

The distance represented by each inch on the map is 25 miles, so 25 is the constant of variation. The actual distance between two cities (y) varies directly as the distance between the two cities on the map (x).

Use the direct variation equation to find the actual distance between the two cities.

$y = kx$

$y = 25(4.5)$

$y = 112.5$

Solution The actual distance between the two cities is 112.5 miles.

More Problems

Problem 2 Juan's earnings vary directly as the number of hours he works. If he earns $105 working 12 hours, how much money will he earn working 18 hours?

Step 1 First use the direct variation equation to determine the constant of variation.

$y = kx$

$105 = k \cdot 12$ Substitute 105 for y and 12 for x.

$\frac{105}{12} = \frac{12k}{12}$

$8.75 = k$

Juan earns $8.75 per hour.

Step 2 Use the constant of variation to determine how much Juan earns working 18 hours.

$y = kx$

$y = 8.75 \cdot 18$ Substitute 18 for x.

$y = 157.5$

Solution Juan earns $157.50 working 18 hours.

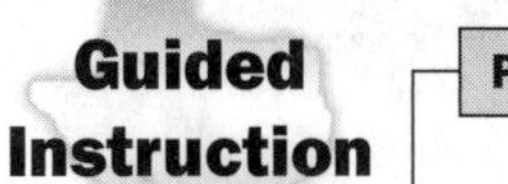

Problem 3

Determine whether the values in the table represent a direct variation function. If so, determine the constant of variation, and write the direct variation equation.

x	y
1.2	3.96
2.7	8.91
4.1	13.53
5.3	17.49

When given a table of values or a group of ordered pairs, you can determine if the data represents a direct variation function by determining if the ratio $\frac{y}{x}$ is the same constant for each row of the table or each ordered pair.

Step 1 Calculate the ratio $\frac{y}{x}$ for each row of the table.

$\frac{3.96}{1.2} = 3.3$ $\quad$ $\frac{8.91}{2.7} = 3.3$

$\frac{13.53}{4.1} = 3.3$ $\quad$ $\frac{17.49}{5.3} = 3.3$

Since the ratio of $\frac{y}{x}$ is 3.3 for each row of the table, the data represents a direct variation function, and the constant of variation is 3.3.

Step 2 Write the direct variation equation.

$y = kx$

$y = 3.3x$

Solution The constant of variation is 3.3, and the direct variation equation is $y = 3.3x$.

Problem 4

The graph of a direct variation function goes through the point $(4, -3)$. Write the direct variation equation, and graph it on the coordinate grid.

Step 1 To write the direct variation equation, find the constant of variation by using the given point.

$$y = kx$$

$$-3 = k \cdot 4$$

$$\frac{-3}{4} = \frac{4k}{4}$$

$$-\frac{3}{4} = k$$

The direct variation equation is $y = -\frac{3}{4}x$.

Step 2 Since all direct variations are in the form $y = kx$, the y-intercept is always 0. Therefore, the line goes through the origin. Plot a point at $(0, 0)$ and $(4, -3)$. Then draw a line going through the points. Verify that the slope of the line is $-\frac{3}{4}$.

Solution The direct variation equation is $y = -\frac{3}{4}x$. The graph is shown at the right.

Apply the TEKS State whether the graph of each line on the coordinate grid is a direct variation.

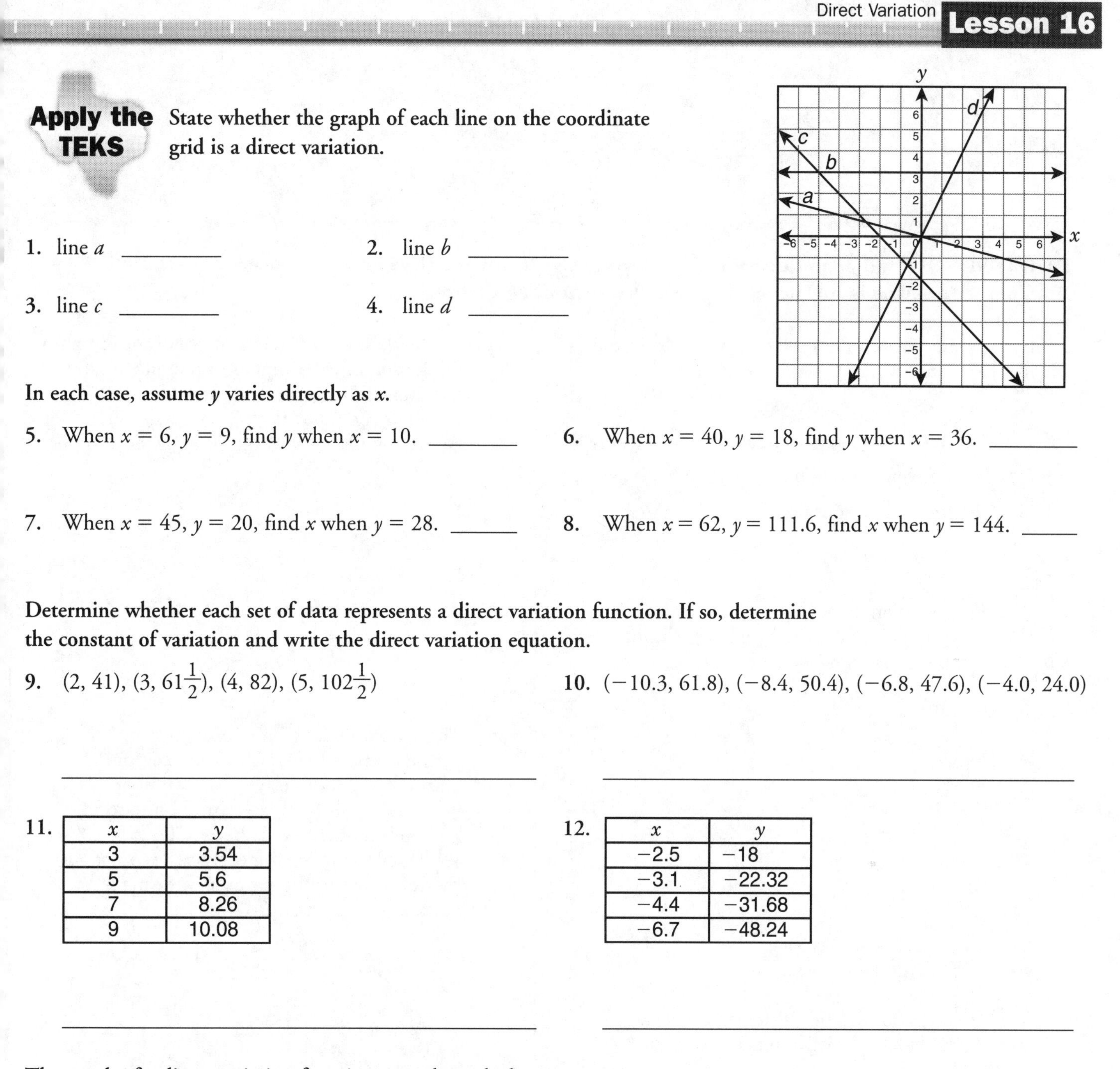

1. line a ________ 2. line b ________

3. line c ________ 4. line d ________

In each case, assume y varies directly as x.

5. When $x = 6$, $y = 9$, find y when $x = 10$. ________

6. When $x = 40$, $y = 18$, find y when $x = 36$. ________

7. When $x = 45$, $y = 20$, find x when $y = 28$. ______

8. When $x = 62$, $y = 111.6$, find x when $y = 144$. _____

Determine whether each set of data represents a direct variation function. If so, determine the constant of variation and write the direct variation equation.

9. $(2, 41), (3, 61\frac{1}{2}), (4, 82), (5, 102\frac{1}{2})$

____

10. $(-10.3, 61.8), (-8.4, 50.4), (-6.8, 47.6), (-4.0, 24.0)$

____

11.

x	y
3	3.54
5	5.6
7	8.26
9	10.08

____

12.

x	y
−2.5	−18
−3.1	−22.32
−4.4	−31.68
−6.7	−48.24

____

The graph of a direct variation function goes through the given point. Write the direct variation equation and graph it on the coordinate grid.

13. $(-6, 2)$ ________________

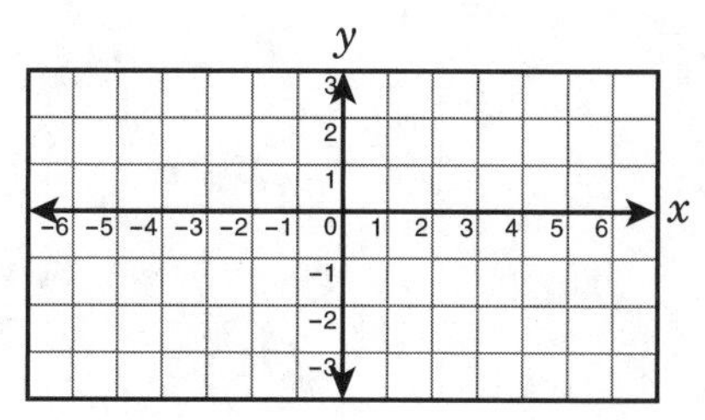

Solve the problem.

14. The amount of Ph balancer needed in an aquarium increases proportionally as the amount of water increases. If 3 units of Ph balancer is the amount needed for 48 gallons of water, what function represents the amount of Ph balancer for x gallons of water?

____

TAKS Objective 3 The student will demonstrate an understanding of linear functions.
TEKS A(c)2G

DIRECTIONS Read each question. Then circle the letter for the correct answer. If a correct answer is <u>not here</u>, circle the letter for "Not Here."

1 By looking at a graph of a line, how can you tell if it is a direct variation?

A The line has a positive slope.

B The line has a negative slope.

C The line goes through the origin.

D The line is horizontal.

2 When graphed on a coordinate grid, which of the following points does the direct variation $y = -\frac{5}{3}x$ pass through?

F $(9, -15)$

G $(6, 10)$

H $(2, -\frac{7}{3})$

J $(-3, -5)$

3 Assume f varies directly as g. When $f = 216$, $g = 48$. Find g when $f = 99$.

Record your answer and fill in the bubbles on the grid below. Be sure to use the correct place value.

				.			
0	0	0	0		0	0	0
1	1	1	1		1	1	1
2	2	2	2		2	2	2
3	3	3	3		3	3	3
4	4	4	4		4	4	4
5	5	5	5		5	5	5
6	6	6	6		6	6	6
7	7	7	7		7	7	7
8	8	8	8		8	8	8
9	9	9	9		9	9	9

4 At the deli, the total cost of an order of ham is a function of the number of pounds of ham purchased. If 2 pounds of ham costs $9.58, which of the following direct variation equations represents the total order of ham at the deli?

F $y = 4.79x$

G $y = 4.99x$

H $y = 9.58x$

J $y = 19.16x$

5 The Witskens hired a painter to paint three rooms of their house. The total cost for the painter varies directly as the number of hours he spends painting. He painted a total of 16 hours and charged the Witskens $520. Which of the following correctly represents the total cost of the painter in terms of hours spent painting?

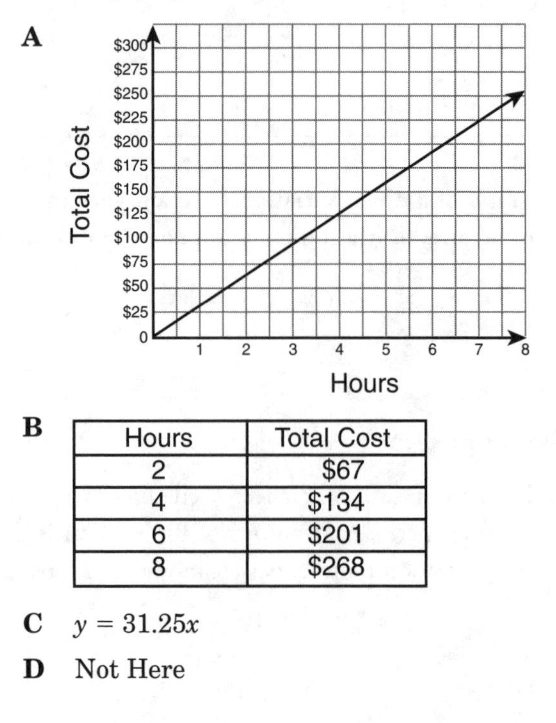

Hours	Total Cost
2	$67
4	$134
6	$201
8	$268

C $y = 31.25x$

D Not Here

Building Stamina™

DIRECTIONS Read each question. Then circle the letter for the correct answer. If a correct answer is not here, circle the letter for "Not Here."

1 A line has x-intercept 6 and y-intercept -4. Which of the following is the equation of the line?

A $y = \frac{3}{2}x - 4$

B $y = \frac{2}{3}x + 6$

C $y = \frac{2}{3}x - 4$

D $y = -\frac{3}{2}x - 4$

2 The sales tax rate in some states is 6%, or $0.06 per $1 of purchase. Which of the following direct variation equations represents the total cost of a purchase where p represents the purchase price and c represents the total cost?

F $c = 0.06p$

G $c = 1.06p$

H $c = 0.06p + 1$

J $c = 0.94p$

3 In Hooperville, the sales tax rate is 6.25%. If the total cost of an item is $42.50, what was the price of the item before taxes?

Record your answer and fill in the bubbles on the grid below. Be sure to use the correct place value.

				.			
0	0	0	0		0	0	0
1	1	1	1		1	1	1
2	2	2	2		2	2	2
3	3	3	3		3	3	3
4	4	4	4		4	4	4
5	5	5	5		5	5	5
6	6	6	6		6	6	6
7	7	7	7		7	7	7
8	8	8	8		8	8	8
9	9	9	9		9	9	9

4 The data in the table represents the distance Patrick had biked after a given amount of time.

Elapsed Time (min)	Distance Biked (mi)
30	4.5
60	9
90	13.5
120	18

Determine whether the data represents a linear function. If so, find the slope of the line.

F Yes, the slope is 4.5.

G No.

H Yes, the slope is $\frac{20}{3}$.

J Yes, the slope is 0.15.

5 The cost of a large pizza at Pizza Express is $8.00 plus $1.50 for each topping. If Pizza Express increases the base cost of a large pizza by $0.50, what change, if any, will this have on the graph of the equation that represents the cost of a large pizza at Pizza Express?

A The slope of the line will change from $1.50 to $2.00.

B The y-intercept of the line will change from $8.00 to $8.50.

C The y-intercept of the line will change from $8.00 to $7.50.

D The slope of the line will change from $8.00 to $8.50.

6 A line has slope $-\frac{3}{4}$ and y-intercept 5. How will the graph of the line change if the slope becomes $\frac{3}{4}$ and what is the new equation of the line?

F The line will cross the y-axis at $\frac{3}{4}$ instead of $-\frac{3}{4}$. The new equation is $y = 5x + \frac{3}{4}$.

G The graph of the line will slant upward to the right instead of downward to the right. The new equation is $y = \frac{3}{4}x + 5$.

H The graph will slant downward to the right instead of upward to the right. The new equation is $y = \frac{3}{4}x - 5$.

J The graph and equation of the line will not change.

7 A line contains the points $(-4, 4)$ and $(8, 1)$. What are the intercepts of the equation of this line?

A (5, 0) and (0, 20)

B (3, 0) and (0, 12)

C (20, 0) and (0, 5)

D (12, 0) and (0, 3)

8 The total cost of renting a midsize car at Rentals, Inc., varies directly as the number of days the car is rented. If it costs $199.50 to re[illegible] a midsize car for 7 days, how much does it cos[illegible] to rent a midsize car for 4 days?

F $140.35

G $114.00

H $85.50

J $28.50

9 Which of the following statements is NOT tru[illegible] about the graph shown below?

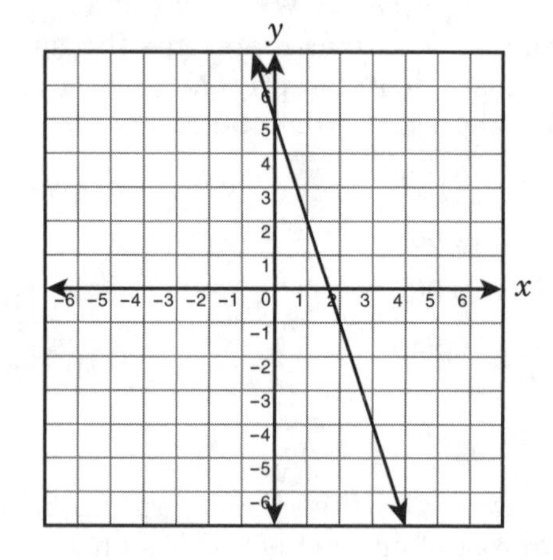

A The equation of the line is $y = -3x + 5$.

B The intercepts of the line are $(\frac{5}{3}, 0)$ and $(0, 5)$

C The line has a negative slope.

D Not Here

10 Which of the following tables represents a linear function?

F

x	y
2	6
4	−6
6	−26
8	−54

G

x	y
−3	−14.2
0	5
3	−14.2
6	−33.4

H

x	y
3.5	−17.5
9.75	−48.75
16	−80
22.25	−111.25

J

x	y
−12	5
−6	10
−3	15
−1.5	20

11 Paula has her own business making cakes for special occasions. The total price (p) of one of Paula's cakes is represented by the equation $p = 0.65s + 15$, where s is the number of people the cake serves. What does 15 represent in this situation?

A The slope, or rate of change per serving

B The y-intercept, or base cost of each cake

C The x-intercept, or base cost of each cake

D The total price of a cake that serves 20

12 Which of the following ordered pairs lie on the graph of the line represented by the equation $3x + 4y = -8$?

F $(-2, 0)$ and $(4, -5)$

G $(-8, 4)$ and $(8, -8)$

H $(-3, 0)$ and $(0, -2)$

J $(-6, 3)$ and $(2, -4)$

13 Jamall bought a sweater that was on sale for 33% off the regular price p. Which of the following direct variation equations represents the sale price s of the sweater?

A $s = 0.33p$

B $s = 0.67p$

C $s = 1.33p$

D $s = 1.67p$

14 Do the data below represent a linear function? If so, what is the rate of change?

(12, \$13.80), (27, \$31.05),
(42, \$48.30), (57, \$65.55)

F No.

G Yes, the rate of change is 15.

H Yes, the rate of change is \$17.25.

J Yes, the rate of change is \$1.15.

15 Two lines are shown on the coordinate grid. The two lines pass through $(5, -3)$. One line passes through the origin, and the other passes through the point $(-1, -1)$.

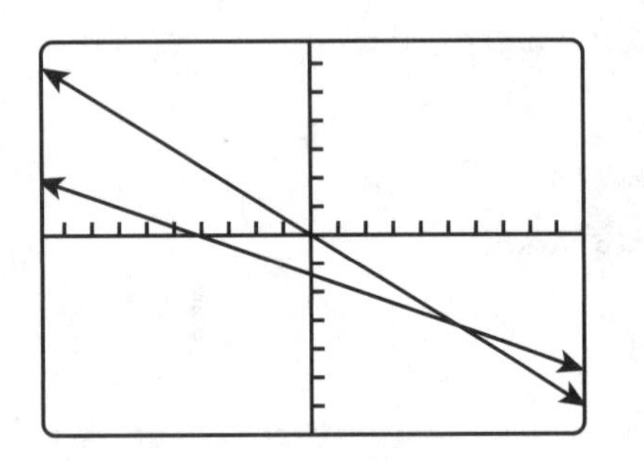

Which pair of equations below identifies these lines?

A $y = -\frac{3}{5}x$ and $y = -\frac{1}{3}x - \frac{4}{3}$

B $y = -\frac{3}{5}x$ and $y = -\frac{1}{3}x$

C $y = -2x$ and $y = -\frac{1}{3}x - 1$

D $y = -\frac{3}{5}x$ and $y = -\frac{1}{3}x - 4$

16 The slope of a line is $-\frac{3}{2}$. The points $A(x, -1)$ and $B(-2, 8)$ lie on the line. What is the value of x?

F -4

G 2

H 4

J 10

17 How will the graph of the line $y = 3x - 7$ change if the y-intercept is changed to -5?

A The line will slant downward to the right instead of upward to the right.

B The line will cross the y-axis at -5 instead of -7.

C The line will have a negative slope instead of a positive slope.

D The line will cross the x-axis at -5 instead of 3.

18 The equation $c = \$0.06m + \$0.50$ represents the cost (c) of a long distance call with a phone company based on the number of minutes (m) of the call. If the company increases the per minute charge to \$0.08, how much more will a 22-minute phone call cost?

Record your answer and fill in the bubbles on the grid below. Be sure to use the correct place value.

				.			
0	0	0	0		0	0	0
1	1	1	1		1	1	1
2	2	2	2		2	2	2
3	3	3	3		3	3	3
4	4	4	4		4	4	4
5	5	5	5		5	5	5
6	6	6	6		6	6	6
7	7	7	7		7	7	7
8	8	8	8		8	8	8
9	9	9	9		9	9	9

Focus on TEKS

Lesson 17 Linear Equations

TEKS A(c)3A Analyze situations involving linear functions and formulate linear equations to solve problems.
TEKS A(c)3B Investigate methods for solving linear equations using graphs and the properties of equality.
TEKS 8.14A Identify and apply mathematics to everyday experiences, to activities in and outside of school, with other disciplines, and with other mathematical topics.
TEKS 8.14B Use a problem-solving model that incorporates understanding the problem, making a plan, carrying out the plan, and evaluating the solution for reasonableness.
TEKS 8.14C Select or develop an appropriate problem-solving strategy from a variety of different types to solve a problem.

Now that you can recognize a linear equation, you need to be able to formulate and solve a linear equation that represents a given situation.

Guided Instruction

Problem 1 One number is three times another number. What is the sum of the two numbers?

You cannot find the exact sum because you are not even given two specific numbers to add. However, you can make a general description of the situation by formulating a linear equation.

A linear equation is often written in one of these common forms:

standard form:	$Ax + By = C$	A, B, and C are real numbers, and A and B are not both zero.
slope-intercept form:	$y = mx + b$	m is the slope, and b is the y-intercept.
point-slope form:	$(y - y_1) = m(x - x_1)$	m is the slope, and (x_1, y_1) is a point.

Formulate a linear equation that represents the sum of the two numbers.

Step 1 Assign a variable to represent the first number. $x =$ first number

This is the independent variable.

Step 2 Since the second number is described in terms of the first number, you can write an expression, using the variable x, that represents the second number. $3x =$ three times the first number

Step 3 Assign a variable to represent the sum of the two numbers. $y =$ the sum of the two numbers

This is the dependent variable.

Step 4 Set up an equation based on what you know. $y = x + 3x$

Step 5 Simplify to get the equation in a common form. $y = 4x$

Solution The equation $y = 4x$ represents the sum of two numbers, one of which is three times the other.

The equation $y = 4x$ means that if you are given a number x, the sum of that number and three times that number is $4x$. In this situation the sum of the two numbers depends on what number is chosen for x. The sum is a function of the number.

So far you have formulated the general equation for the sum of two numbers, one of which is three times the other. Once you choose or are given a value for x, you can then use the equation to find the sum.

More Problems

Guided Instruction

Problem 2 What is the sum of the two numbers when $x = 1$? What are the two numbers?

Step 1 Write the equation. $y = 4x$

Step 2 Substitute 1 for x. $y = 4 \cdot 1 = 4$

Step 3 Verify your answer by substituting 1 for x in the expressions for each number. first number $= x = 1$
second number $= 3x = 3 \cdot 1 = 3$

Then add the two numbers. $1 + 3 = 4$

Solution The sum of two numbers, one of which is three times the other, is 4 when the first number is 1. The other number is 3.

This solution written as an ordered pair is (1, 4). The ordered pair (1, 4) is not the only solution to the equation $y = 4x$. Many more solutions exist.

Problem 3 What are the solutions to $y = 4x$ for $x = 2, 4.5, 0$, and -3?

Make a table to list the solutions.

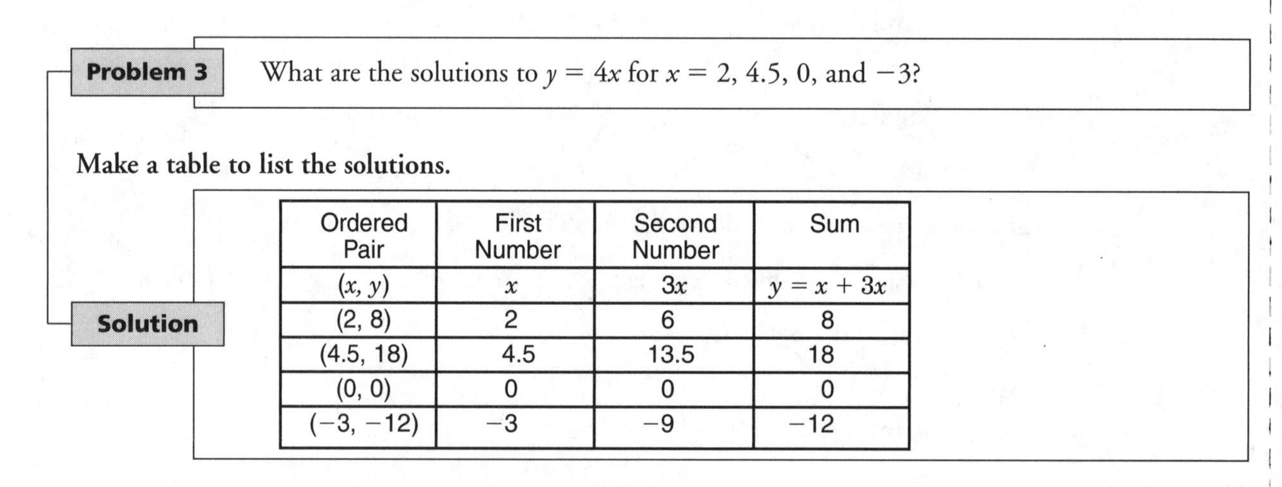

Solution

Ordered Pair	First Number	Second Number	Sum
(x, y)	x	$3x$	$y = x + 3x$
(2, 8)	2	6	8
(4.5, 18)	4.5	13.5	18
(0, 0)	0	0	0
(−3, −12)	−3	−9	−12

How many solutions are there? The number of solutions is infinite. However, you can represent all the solutions by graphing a line. All of the solutions of a linear equation are on that line.

Problem 4 What is the solution of the equation $y = 4x$?

Since it is impossible to compute and list *every* solution, make a graph to represent *every* solution.

Solution You can either graph the line using what you know about the slope-intercept formula, or you can plot the points given in the table above and draw a line through the points.

Apply the TEKS Tell if each equation is a linear equation. For each linear equation, identify the form.

1. $y = x^2 + 8$
____

2. $8x + 5y = 15$
____

3. $y = -\frac{2}{3}x$
____

Solve each equation. If you cannot find a specific solution because the equation has two unknown variables, give the linear equation in slope-intercept form.

4. $2y + x = 10$
____

5. $\frac{3}{4}x + 9 = 1.5x - 12$
____

6. $3x + 4y = 32, x = 12$
____

7. $8x + 11 = 3x - 4$
____

8. $5x + 10y = 40$
____

9. $-2x + \frac{2}{3}y = 4 - 2x$
____

Formulate a linear equation to represent each situation. Find one ordered pair that is a solution to the equation. Represent all the solutions by graphing the line.

10. One number is 6 times another number. What is the sum of the two numbers?
____
____

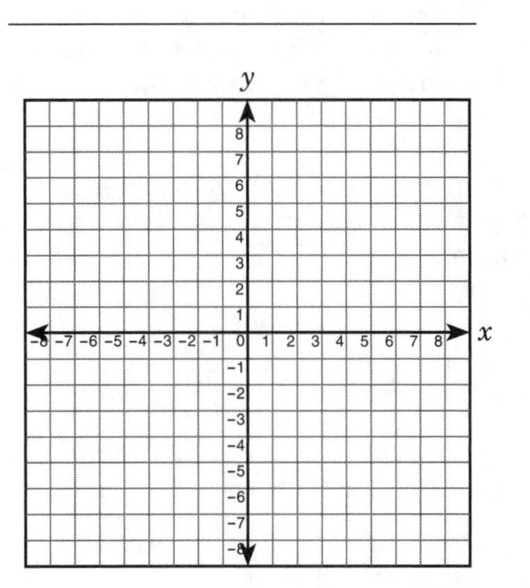

11. Joe is 5 years older than Maurice. What is the sum of their ages?
____
____

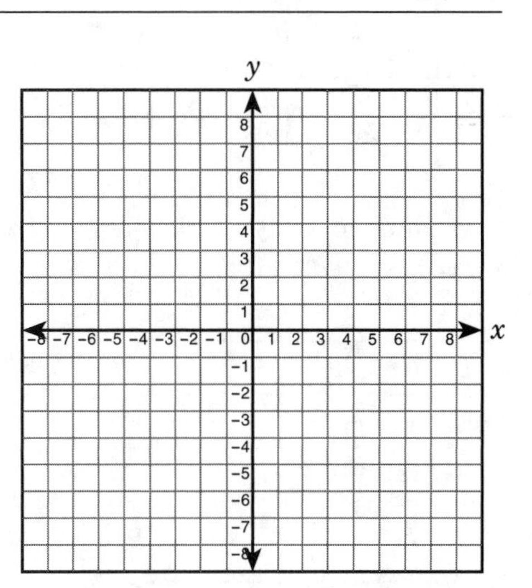

12. Explain how you would use the equation and graph in Exercise 11 to find Joe's age if you knew that the sum of the ages of Joe and Maurice was 29. Explain what an x-value of -1 means.

____

____

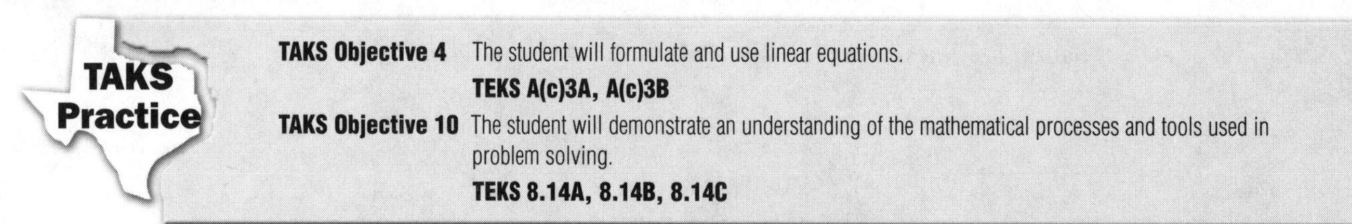

TAKS Objective 4 The student will formulate and use linear equations.
TEKS A(c)3A, A(c)3B

TAKS Objective 10 The student will demonstrate an understanding of the mathematical processes and tools used in problem solving.
TEKS 8.14A, 8.14B, 8.14C

DIRECTIONS Read each question. Then circle the letter for the correct answer. If a correct answer is not here, circle the letter for "Not Here."

1 The sum of two numbers is 65. One number is four times the other number. What is the larger number?

A 13

B 16.25

C 48.75

D 52

2 One number is nine times greater than another number x. Which of these best represents all solutions of the sum y of these two numbers and the number 3?

F $y = 10x$

G

x	y
−1	−7
0	3
1	13
2	23

H If the first number is 1, then the sum of the numbers is $1 + 9 + 3 = 13$.

J

3 Kate is driving on the highway on a cross-country trip. Her average highway speed is 60 miles per hour. Today she drove on the highway 2 more hours than yesterday. If x represents how many hours she drove on the highway yesterday, which equation represents how far Kate drove on the highway over the last two days?

A $y = 60(2x + 2)$

B $y = 60(x^2 + 2)$

C $y = 60(x + 2)$

D Not Here

4 The variable y represents the sum of two numbers. The variable x represents the first number. The second number is c times larger than the first number. If (4, 24) and (9, 54) are two ordered pairs (x, y), then what is the value of c?

Record your answer and fill in the bubbles on the grid below. Be sure to use the correct place value.

Focus on TEKS

Lesson 18 Linear Inequalities

TEKS A(c)3A Analyze situations involving linear functions and formulate linear inequalities to solve problems.
TEKS A(c)3B Investigate methods for solving linear inequalities using graphs and the properties of equality.
TEKS 8.14A Identify and apply mathematics to everyday experiences, to activities in and outside of school, with disciplines, and with other mathematical topics.
TEKS 8.14B Use a problem-solving model that incorporates understanding the problem, making a plan, carrying out the plan, and evaluating the solution for reasonableness.
TEKS 8.14C Select or develop an appropriate problem-solving strategy from a variety of different types.

Some situations are best represented by linear inequalities.

In a **linear inequality**, the equals sign in a linear equation is replaced with $<$, $>$, $\leq$, $\geq$, or $\neq$.

Guided Instruction

Problem 1

Adrian is competing in a 4-round golf tournament. His goal is to have an average score per round of less than or equal to 75. In his first three rounds he shot 76, 83, and 74. What score must he shoot in the fourth round to achieve his goal?

Formulate a linear inequality to represent the situation. Then solve the problem.

Step 1 Formulate an inequality.

$$\frac{\text{sum of the scores}}{\text{number of rounds}} \leq 75$$

x represents Adrian's 4th-round score.

$$\frac{76 + 83 + 74 + x}{4} \leq 75$$

Step 2 Solve the inequality for x.

$$76 + 83 + 74 + x \leq 300$$
$$233 + x \leq 300$$
$$x \leq 67$$

Solution

Adrian must shoot a 67 or lower in the 4th round of the tournament to achieve his goal.

More Problems

Problem 2

Cliff is buying ingredients to make tacos. He picks up a head of lettuce for \$0.99, taco seasoning for \$0.50, taco shells for \$1.89, taco sauce for \$1.75, and shredded cheese for \$2.49. Ground beef costs \$2.69 per pound. If Cliff wants to spend less than \$15, how much ground beef can he buy?

Formulate a linear inequality to represent the situation. Then solve the problem.

Step 1 Add the prices of the other ingredients. $\$0.99 + \$0.50 + \$1.89 + \$1.75 + \$2.49 = \$7.62$

Step 2 Formulate an inequality.

other ingredients	+	ground beef	≤	15.00
7.62	+	$2.69x$	≤	15.00

Step 3 Solve the inequality for x.

$$2.69x \leq 7.38$$
$$x \leq 2.74$$

Solution

Cliff can buy no more than 2.74 pounds of ground beef.

Guided Instruction

Problem 3

This weekend Winona is going to a department store clearance sale in which every item in the store is at least 30% off the original price. Formulate an inequality to represent the sale price of each item.

Formulate a linear inequality to represent the situation.

Step 1 Assign variable expressions.

original price $= x$
30% discount $= 0.30x$
sale price $= y$

Step 2 Formulate an inequality.

sale price	$\leq$	original	$-$	30% discount
y	$\leq$	x	$-$	$0.30x$

Solution

For any item in the store, Winona can use the inequality $y \leq x - 0.30x$ to find its sale price. Since the discount may be more than 30%, y represents the greatest amount that the sale price will be, given the original price x.

Problem 4

Graph the inequality: $y \leq x - 0.30x$

Step 1 Simplify by combining the x terms. $y \leq 0.70x$

Step 2 Identify the slope and y-intercept.

$m = 0.70$
$b = 0$

Solution

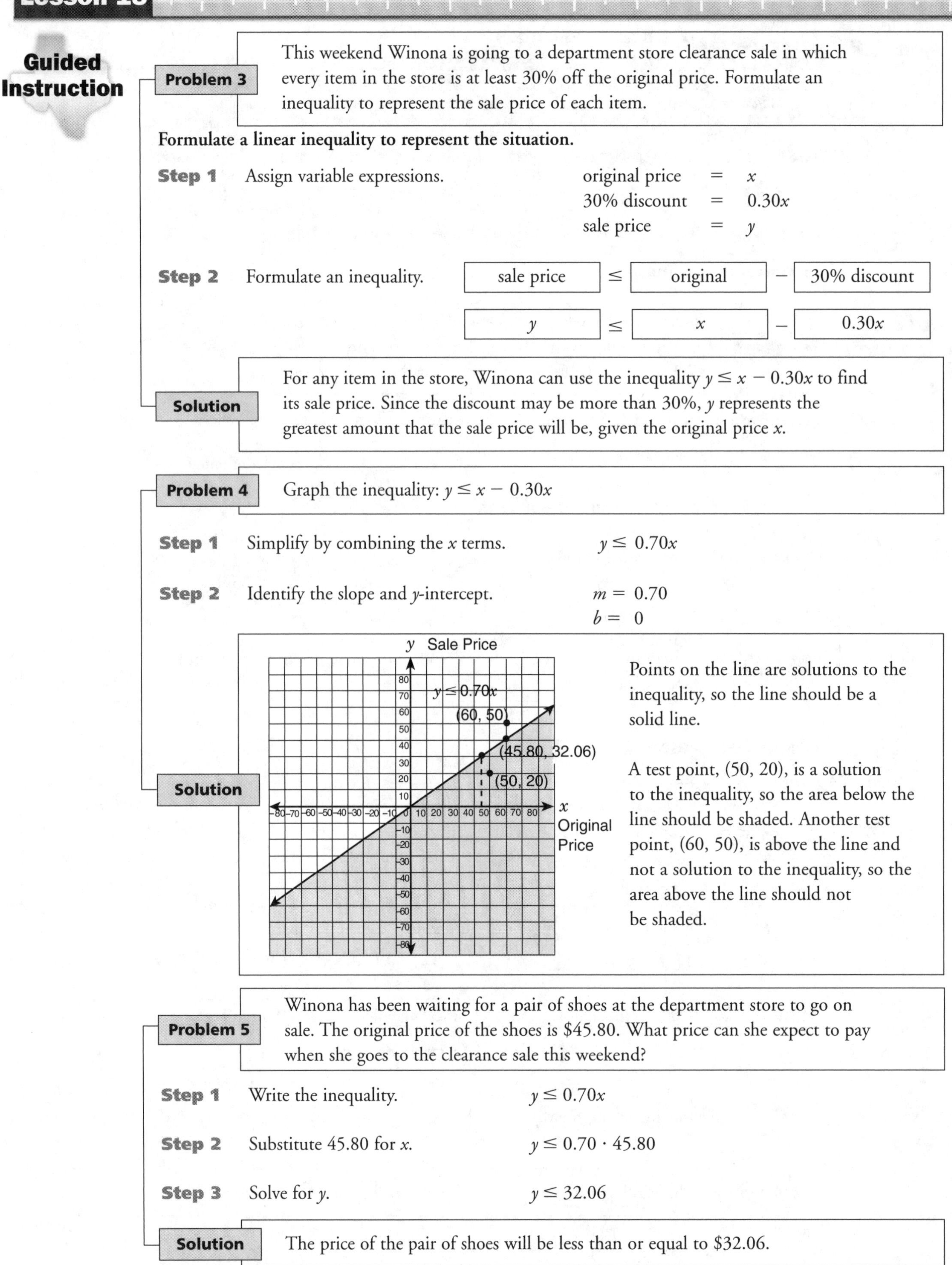

Points on the line are solutions to the inequality, so the line should be a solid line.

A test point, (50, 20), is a solution to the inequality, so the area below the line should be shaded. Another test point, (60, 50), is above the line and not a solution to the inequality, so the area above the line should not be shaded.

Problem 5

Winona has been waiting for a pair of shoes at the department store to go on sale. The original price of the shoes is \$45.80. What price can she expect to pay when she goes to the clearance sale this weekend?

Step 1 Write the inequality. $y \leq 0.70x$

Step 2 Substitute 45.80 for x. $y \leq 0.70 \cdot 45.80$

Step 3 Solve for y. $y \leq 32.06$

Solution

The price of the pair of shoes will be less than or equal to \$32.06.

Graph each linear inequality. Check your answer by finding a test point that is on the shaded side of the graph.

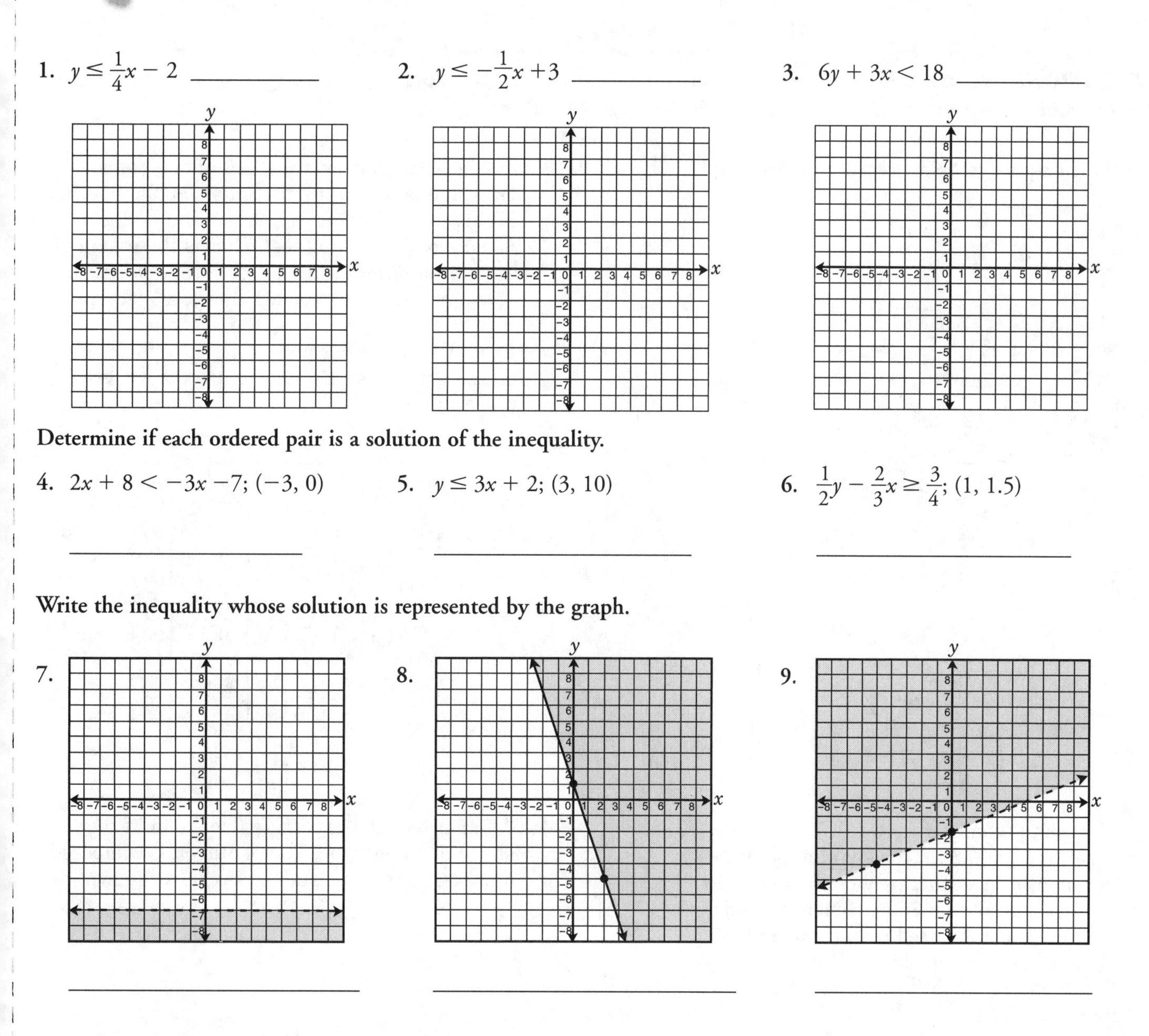

1. $y \leq \frac{1}{4}x - 2$ __________

2. $y \leq -\frac{1}{2}x + 3$ __________

3. $6y + 3x < 18$ __________

Determine if each ordered pair is a solution of the inequality.

4. $2x + 8 < -3x - 7$; $(-3, 0)$

____

5. $y \leq 3x + 2$; $(3, 10)$

____

6. $\frac{1}{2}y - \frac{2}{3}x \geq \frac{3}{4}$; $(1, 1.5)$

____

Write the inequality whose solution is represented by the graph.

7. __________

8. __________

9. __________

Formulate a linear inequality for each situation. Then solve the problem.

10. Before Stephanie leaves the athletic club, she wants to swim for 20 minutes and work at 8 different weight-lifting stations. The time now is 5:44 P.M., and Stephanie has to be home no later than 7:00 P.M. How much time does she have to spend equally at each weight-lifting station? She must allow 10 minutes to get from the club to her house.

____

11. The sum of Tim's and Amy's ages is less than 52 years. If Tim is 17, what is the oldest that Amy can be?

____

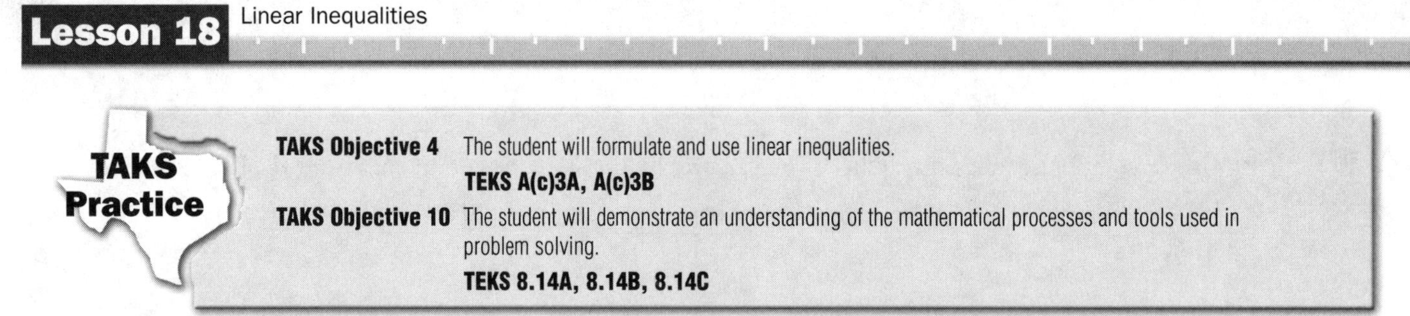

TAKS Practice

TAKS Objective 4 The student will formulate and use linear inequalities.
TEKS A(c)3A, A(c)3B

TAKS Objective 10 The student will demonstrate an understanding of the mathematical processes and tools used in problem solving.
TEKS 8.14A, 8.14B, 8.14C

DIRECTIONS Read each question. Then circle the letter for the correct answer. If a correct answer is not here, circle the letter for "Not Here."

1 Which equation below represents the graph?

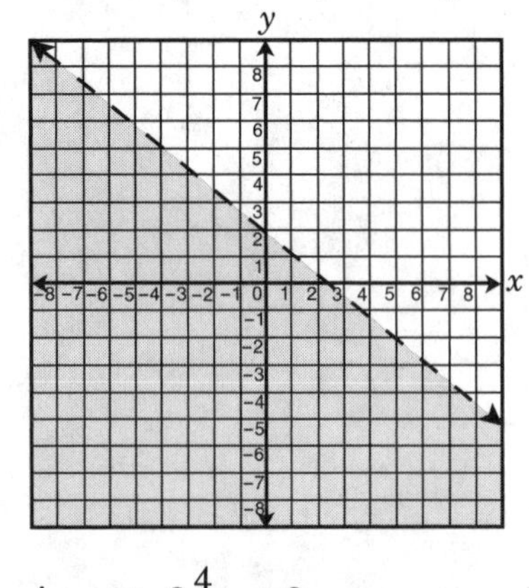

A $y > 2\frac{4}{5}x + 2$

B $y \leq 2\frac{4}{5}x + 2$

C $5y - 4x < 10$

D $5y + 4x < 10$

2 Kenesha is comparing two DSL services. One service charges $300 for installation and $45 per month. The other service charges $150 for installation and $55 per month. Which inequality can be used to find the number of months m for which Kenesha must subscribe to the $45-per-month service in order to save money in the long run?

F $45m < 55m$

G $100m < 450$

H $300 + 45m < 150 + 55m$

J $300 + 45m \geq 150 + 55m$

3 Jessie is comparing two 10-10 phone plans. One plan is 3.9¢ a minute plus a $3.95 monthly billing fee. The other is 2.9¢ a minute plus a $5.95 monthly billing fee. What is the maximum amount of minutes Jessie could talk before the 3.9¢-a-minute plan becomes the more costly plan?

Record your answer and fill in the bubbles on the grid below. Be sure to use the correct place value.

				.			
0	0	0	0		0	0	0
1	1	1	1		1	1	1
2	2	2	2		2	2	2
3	3	3	3		3	3	3
4	4	4	4		4	4	4
5	5	5	5		5	5	5
6	6	6	6		6	6	6
7	7	7	7		7	7	7
8	8	8	8		8	8	8
9	9	9	9		9	9	9

4 An architect is designing a floor plan in the shape of a pentagon. The pentagon is composed of a 14-inch square and a triangle as shown.

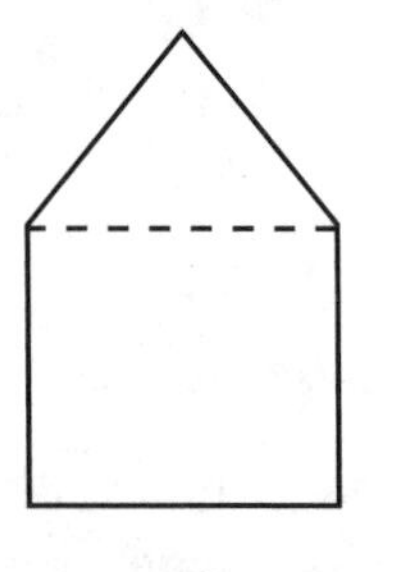

The area of the pentagon must be less than or equal to 231 square feet. What is the height of the triangle?

F $0 \leq h \leq 2.5$

G $0 < h \leq 5$

H $0 \leq h \leq 5$

J Not Here

Focus on TEKS

Lesson 19 Systems of Linear Equations

TEKS A(c)4A Analyze situations and formulate systems of linear equations to solve problems.
TEKS 8.14A Identify and apply mathematics to everyday experiences, to activities in and outside of school, with other disciplines, and with other mathematical topics.

The situations you have analyzed so far could be adequately described with one linear equation. Other situations require that you formulate more than one linear equation.

A **system of linear equations** is a set of two or more linear equations.

Guided Instruction

Problem 1

Roberto and Mia are in the United States. They are each buying postage for postcards to send to their friends outside of the United States. The U.S Postal Service has two different postage rates for postcards sent out of the country. The rate to Mexico and Canada is less than the rate to all other countries. Mia spends $6.10 on postage to send 8 postcards to Mexico and Canada and 3 postcards to other countries. Roberto spends $10.90 on postage to send 5 postcards to Mexico and Canada and 12 postcards to other countries. Formulate a system of linear equations that can be used to find the two different rates.

Step 1 Assign a variable letter for the different postage rates.

Let m = postage rate for postcards to Mexico and Canada.
Let c = postage rate for postcards to all other countries.

Step 2 Write two equations to represent the amount each person spent on postage.

Mia: $8m + 3c = \$6.10$
Roberto: $5m + 12c = \$10.90$

Solution

The two equations $8m + 3c = 6.10$ and $5m + 12c = 10.90$ represent a system of linear equations that can be used to find both U.S. postcard postage rates.

More Problems

Problem 2

Charlie pays $5.95 plus $0.05 a minute for his long-distance phone service. Mary Beth pays $4.95 plus $0.07 a minute for her long-distance phone service.
Formulate a system of linear equations that can be used to find the number of long-distance minutes at which the two plans will cost the same amount.

Step 1 Write the equation for Charlie's plan. $y = 5.95 + 0.05x$

Step 2 Write the equation for Mary Beth's plan. $y = 4.95 + 0.07x$

Solution

The two equations $y = 5.95 + 0.05x$ and $y = 4.95 + 0.07x$ represent a system of linear equations that can be used to find the number of long-distance minutes at which both plans will cost the same amount.

Guided Instruction

Problem 3

Two runners are training for a marathon. Angela tells Brent to go on ahead and that she will catch up with him. Brent takes off and runs at 6 miles per hour. After 20 minutes, Angela takes off and runs at 10 miles per hour. Formulate a system of linear equations to find the number of minutes it will it take for Angela to catch up with Brent.

Formulate a system of linear equations to solve the problem.

Step 1 Assign a variable to represent how many minutes have passed since Angela started running.

Let x = minutes that Angela has been running.

Step 2 Since the question is asked in terms of minutes, convert hours to minutes.

$$6 \text{ mph} = \frac{6}{60} = \frac{1}{10} \text{ mi per min}$$

$$10 \text{ mph} = \frac{10}{60} = \frac{1}{6} \text{ mi per min}$$

Step 3 Write an equation for how far Brent has run after x minutes.

$y = 2 + \frac{1}{10}x$ He had been running for 20 minutes at $\frac{1}{10}$ mile a minute. So, he had a 2-mile head start.

Step 4 Write an equation for how far Angela has run after x minutes.

$y = \frac{1}{6}x$

Solution

The two equations $y = \frac{1}{10}x + 2$ and $y = \frac{1}{6}x$ represent a system of linear equations that can be used to find how many minutes it will take Angela to catch up with Brent.

Problem 4

Stacy has 19 coins in quarters and dimes in her pocket. The value of the coins is \$2.35. Formulate a system of linear equations to find the number of quarters q and dimes d Stacy has.

Formulate a system of linear equations to solve the problem.

Step 1 Write an equation that represents that the sum of the number of quarters and dimes is 19.

$q + d = 19$

Step 2 Write an equation that represents that the value of q quarters and d dimes is \$2.35.

$0.25q + 0.10d = 2.35$

Solution

The two equations $q + d = 19$ and $0.25q + 0.10d = 2.35$ represent a system of linear equations that can be used to find how many quarters and dimes Stacy has.

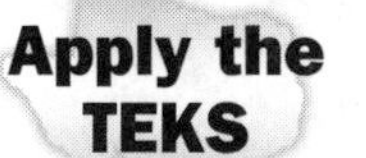

For each situation, formulate a system of linear equations to solve the problem.

1. At a baseball game, Lynn spent \$18.50 on 3 cotton candies and 5 soft drinks for her children. Another parent spent \$17.00 on 6 cotton candies and 2 soft drinks. What is the price of 1 cotton candy and 1 soft drink?

____

2. A local charity is hosting a fund-raising dinner. They have sold 368 tickets. Premium tickets cost \$50, and regular tickets cost \$25. Altogether the ticket sales have been \$12,000. How many premium tickets have they sold?

____

3. The grass in Tony's yard is 3 inches tall and grows $\frac{1}{4}$ inch a day. The grass in Sara's yard is 2 inches tall and grows $\frac{2}{5}$ inch a day. When will the grass in Tony's yard be the same height as the grass in Sara's yard?

____

4. Serenity has \$3.40 in dimes d and nickels n. She has 47 coins that are either dimes or nickels. How many of each coin does she have?

____

5. The sum of two numbers is 300. One number is 44 greater than the other number. What are the two numbers?

____

6. Two friends are riding their bikes. Tom tells Latrice to go on ahead and that he will catch up with her. Latrice takes off and rides at 12 miles per hour. After 10 minutes, Tom takes off and rides 15 miles per hour. How many minutes will it take Tom to catch up with Latrice?

____

7. Cecilia bought 8 symphony tickets for \$240. Floor level tickets cost \$35 and balcony level tickets cost \$25. How many balcony level tickets did she buy?

____

8. A rectangle is 7 feet longer than it is wide. It has a perimeter of 34 feet. What is the length l and width w of the rectangle?

____

9. Explain how you could represent the perimeter of the rectangle in Exercise 8 by using one equation instead of a system of equations.

____

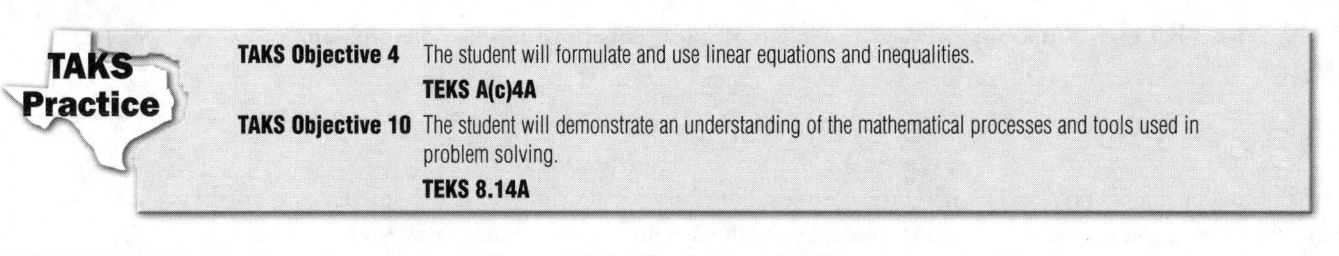
TAKS Practice

TAKS Objective 4 The student will formulate and use linear equations and inequalities.
TEKS A(c)4A
TAKS Objective 10 The student will demonstrate an understanding of the mathematical processes and tools used in problem solving.
TEKS 8.14A

DIRECTIONS Read each question. Then circle the letter for the correct answer. If a correct answer is not here, circle the letter for "Not Here."

1 The sum of Scott's and Kylie's ages is 64. Scott is 32 years older than Kylie. Which of these systems of equations best describes Scott's and Kylie's ages?

A $s + k = 64$
$s = 32$

B $s + k = 64$
$s - k = 32$

C $s + k = 64$
$k - s = 32$

D $s + k = 64$
$k = 32 + s$

2 Jacob has a jar of 538 pennies and nickels. The total value of the coins is \$20.94. Which system of equations would be the best to use for finding how many pennies and nickels Jacob has?

F $p + n = 538$
$0.01p + 0.05n = 20.94$

G $p + n = 538$
$1p + 5n = 20.94$

H $p + n = 20.94$
$0.01p + 0.05n = 538$

J Not Here

3 Luis is making a rectangular picture frame. The height of the frame is 9 inches longer than its width. The perimeter of the frame is 82 inches. Which of these systems of equations best describes the dimensions of the picture frame?

A $h + w = 9$
$h + w = 82$

B $h - w = 9$
$2h + 2w = 82$

C $h + w = 9$
$2h + 2w = 82$

D $h - w = 9$
$h \cdot w = 82$

4 An electronics store advertised a 19-inch model television for \$349 and a 25-inch model television for \$469. During one month they sold 44 of the two models for total sales of \$17,516. Which system of equations best describes this situation?

F $19x + 25y = 44$
$349x + 469y = 17{,}516$

G $19x + 25y = 17{,}516$
$x + y = 44$

H $349x + 469y = 44$
$x + y = 17{,}516$

J $x + y = 44$
$349x + 469y = 17{,}516$

Focus on TEKS

Lesson 20 Solutions of Systems of Linear Equations

TEKS A(c)4B Solve systems of linear equations using models, graphs, tables, and algebraic methods.
TEKS 8.14A Identify and apply mathematics to everyday experiences, to activities in and outside of school, with other disciplines, and with other mathematical topics.
TEKS 8.14B Use a problem-solving model that incorporates understanding the problem, making a plan, carrying out the plan, and evaluating the solution for reasonableness.
TEKS 8.14C Select or develop an appropriate problem-solving strategy from a variety of different types.

Use systems of linear equations that you have formulated to solve problems.

The solution of a system of linear equations can be categorized in one of these ways:

Many
Each line in the system is the same line.
They have infinite points in common.
Therefore their solution is a linear equation.

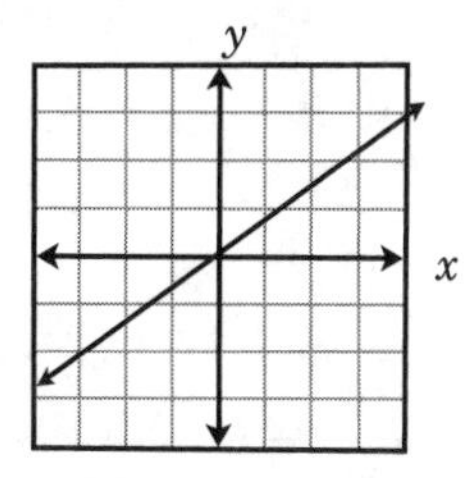

One
Every line in the system intersects at one point.
They have only one point in common.
Therefore their solution is one ordered pair.

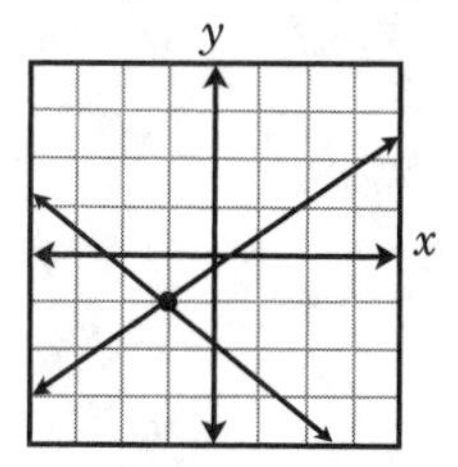

None
The lines do not all intersect at one point.
They have no points in common.
Therefore no solution exists

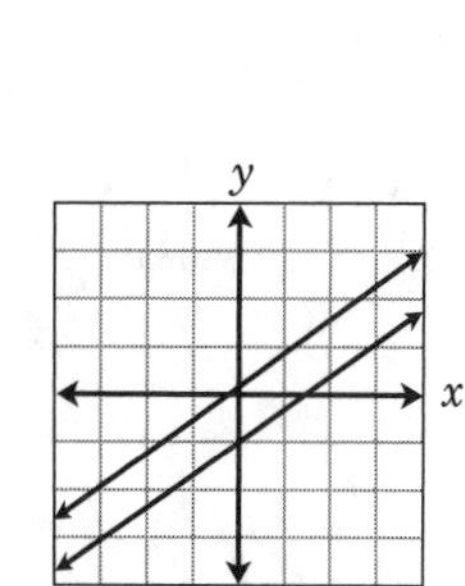

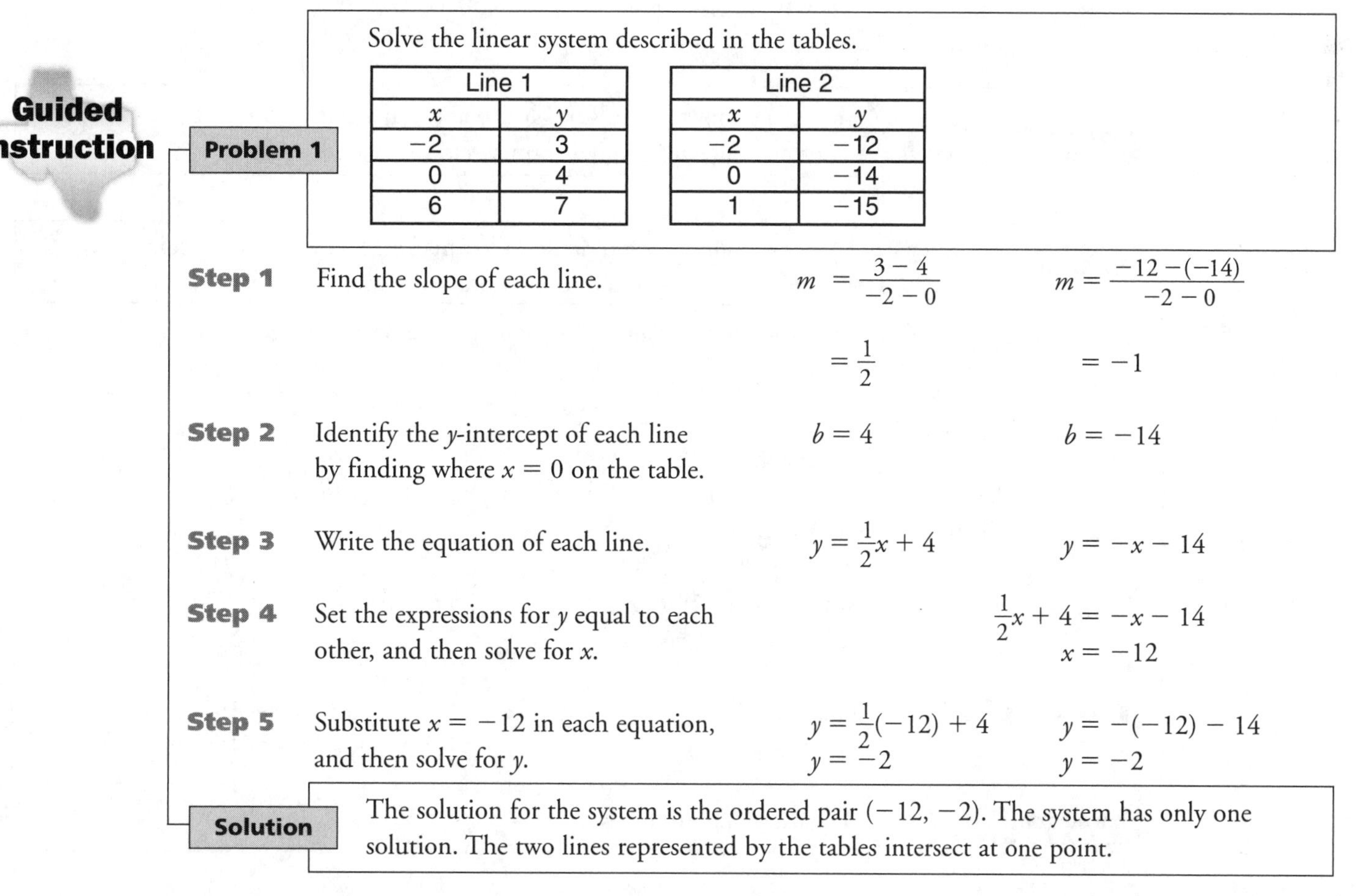

Guided Instruction

Problem 1

Solve the linear system described in the tables.

Line 1	
x	y
−2	3
0	4
6	7

Line 2	
x	y
−2	−12
0	−14
1	−15

Step 1 Find the slope of each line.

$m = \frac{3-4}{-2-0} = \frac{1}{2}$ $\quad$ $m = \frac{-12-(-14)}{-2-0} = -1$

Step 2 Identify the y-intercept of each line by finding where $x = 0$ on the table.

$b = 4$ $\quad$ $b = -14$

Step 3 Write the equation of each line.

$y = \frac{1}{2}x + 4$ $\quad$ $y = -x - 14$

Step 4 Set the expressions for y equal to each other, and then solve for x.

$\frac{1}{2}x + 4 = -x - 14$
$x = -12$

Step 5 Substitute $x = -12$ in each equation, and then solve for y.

$y = \frac{1}{2}(-12) + 4$ $\quad$ $y = -(-12) - 14$
$y = -2$ $\quad$ $y = -2$

Solution The solution for the system is the ordered pair $(-12, -2)$. The system has only one solution. The two lines represented by the tables intersect at one point.

More Problems

Guided Instruction

Problem 2

Roberto and Mia are traveling in the United States. They are each buying postage for postcards to send to their friends outside of the United States. The U.S Postal Service has two different postage rates for postcards sent out of the country. The rate to Mexico and Canada is less than the rate to all other countries. Mia spends \$6.10 on postage to send 8 postcards to Mexico and Canada and 3 postcards to other countries. Roberto spends \$10.90 on postage to send 5 postcards to Mexico and Canada and 12 postcards to other countries. What is the postage rate for postcards to Mexico and Canada?

Use the system of linear equations $8m + 3c = 6.10$ and $5m + 12c = 10.90$ to solve the problem.

Step 1 Write the equations.

$$8m + 3c = 6.10$$
$$5m + 12c = 10.90$$

Step 2 Multiply the first equation by 4 so that the variable c has the same coefficient in both equations.

$$4(8m + 3c = 6.10) \rightarrow 32m + 12c = 24.40$$

Step 3 Subtract one equation from the other to eliminate one of the variables.

$$\begin{array}{r} 32m + 12c = 24.40 \\ -\ \underline{5m + 12c = 10.90} \\ 27m \qquad = 13.50 \end{array}$$

Step 4 Solve for m.

$$m = 0.50$$

Step 5 Substitute $m = 0.50$ in an original equation and solve for c.

$$8(0.50) + 3c = 6.10$$
$$c = 0.70$$

Solution The U.S. postage rate for postcards to Mexico and Canada is \$0.50, and the postage rate for postcards to all other countries is \$0.70.

Problem 3

Stacy has 19 coins in quarters and dimes in her pocket. The value of the coins is \$2.35. How many quarters q and dimes d does Stacy have?

Use the system of linear equations $q + d = 19$ and $0.25q + 0.10d = 2.35$ to solve the problem.

Step 1 Solve the first equation for q or d.

$$d = 19 - q$$

Step 2 Substitute the expression for d in the second equation so that the equation has only one variable.

$$0.25q + 0.10(19 - q) = 2.35$$

Step 3 Solve for q. First multiply by 100 to eliminate the decimal.

$$25q + 10(19 - q) = 235$$
$$q = 3$$

Step 4 Substitute $q = 3$ in an original equation and solve for d.

$$3 + d = 19$$
$$d = 16$$

Solution Stacy has 3 quarters and 16 dimes.

Apply the TEKS For each linear system described in the tables, write the equations of the two lines and find the solution of the system.

1.

Line 1	
x	y
−4	19
0	3
8	−29

Line 2	
x	y
−5	21
0	−9
11	−75

2.

Line 1	
x	y
10	$\frac{1}{2}$
5	0
0	$-\frac{1}{2}$

Line 2	
x	y
−5	5
0	4
2	$3\frac{3}{5}$

______________________ ______________________

Tell if each linear system has an infinite number of solutions, one solution, or no solution.

3. $y = \frac{1}{3}x + 25$
   $y = -3x - 17$

____

4. $10x + 2y = 90$
   $45x + 9y = 405$

____

5. $y = 2x + 5$
   $y = 2x - 5$

____

Solve each system of linear equations.

6. $y = 4x + 8$
   $y = -x - 2$

____

7. $x + 2y = 1$
   $6x + 12y = 3$

____

8. $4a + 5b = 11$
   $2a - 6b = 31$

____

9. $x + y = 12$
   $x - y = 3$

____

10. $18m = 10n - 4$
    $3m = 2n - 2$

____

11. $0.2x + 0.3y = 2.4$
    $0.8x + 1.2y = 9.6$

____

For each situation, formulate a system of linear equations. Then solve the problem.

12. Josh and Caleb take their cars to the gas station to fill each of their gas tanks. Josh has 2.4 gallons in his tank. The pump he is at pumps gas at a rate of 0.2 gallon per second. Caleb has 1.6 gallons in his tank. His pump pumps at a rate of 0.3 gallon per second. After how many seconds will each tank have the same amount of gas?

____

13. The sum of two numbers is 532. One number is 216 greater than the other number. What are the two numbers?

____

14. Tina has 98 coins consisting of only dimes and nickels. The total value of the coins is $6.45. How many of each coin does she have?

____

TAKS Objective 4 The student will formulate and use linear equations and inequalities.
TEKS A(c)4B

TAKS Objective 10 The student will demonstrate an understanding of the mathematical processes and tools used in problem solving.
TEKS 8.14A, 8.14B, 8.14C

DIRECTIONS Read each question. Then circle the letter for the correct answer. If a correct answer is not here, circle the letter for "Not Here."

1 Which of these represents the solution of the system of linear equations described by the tables?

Line 1	
x	y
−4	70
0	2
2	−32

Line 2	
x	y
−12	206
−1	19
0	2

A (0, 0)

B (0, 2)

C $y = -17x + 2$

D Not Here

2 Where do these two lines intersect?

$$2y + 2x = -6$$
$$6y - 3x = 18$$

F (0, 0)

G (−4, 1)

H They are the same line.

J They do not intersect.

3 The sum of two numbers is 953. The difference of the two number is 281. Which of these equations describes the two numbers?

A $x + y = 281$

B $x - y = 953$

C $953 - x + y = 281$

D $953 - 2y = 281$

4 The width of a rectangle is 12 centimeters shorter than its length. The perimeter of the rectangle is 52 centimeters. What is the area of the rectangle in square centimeters?

Record your answer and fill in the bubbles on the grid below. Be sure to use the correct place value.

				.			
0	0	0	0		0	0	0
1	1	1	1		1	1	1
2	2	2	2		2	2	2
3	3	3	3		3	3	3
4	4	4	4		4	4	4
5	5	5	5		5	5	5
6	6	6	6		6	6	6
7	7	7	7		7	7	7
8	8	8	8		8	8	8
9	9	9	9		9	9	9

5 Bobby has 42 dimes and quarters. The total value of the coins is $9.60. What is the value of Bobby's dimes?

A $3.80

B $3.60

C $2.40

D $0.60

6 Camille and Duane bought some shares of stock. Camille bought 120 shares of company A and 180 shares of company B for a total of $9,660. Duane bought 150 shares of company A and 150 shares of company B for a total of $9,450. What is the price of one share of company B's stock?

F $28

G $31.50

H $35

J $150

Focus on TEKS

Lesson 21 Reasonableness of Solutions

TEKS A(c)3C Interpret and determine the reasonableness of solutions to linear equations and inequalities.
TEKS A(c)4C Interpret and determine the reasonableness of solutions to systems of linear equations.
TEKS 8.14B Use a problem-solving model that incorporates understanding the problem, making a plan, carrying out the plan, and evaluating the solution for reasonableness.
TEKS 8.14C Select or develop an appropriate problem-solving strategy from a variety of different types.

Make sure that your interpretation of the solution of an equation, inequality, or system of equations is a correct interpretation.

Guided Instruction

Problem 1

An MD-88 commercial aircraft is traveling from Seattle to Dallas at a cruising speed of 509 miles per hour. A Fairchild-Dornier 328 takes off from the Dallas-Fort Worth (DFW) Airport at 7:30 A.M. and travels at 397 miles per hour toward New York. The distance from Dallas to New York is about 1,565 miles. At 7:30 A.M., the MD-88 is 1,909 miles from DFW. Do the graphs accurately represent the situation? Describe any changes that are needed.

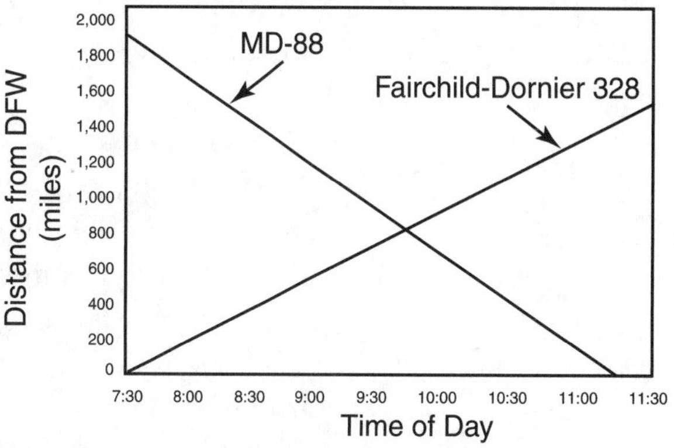

MD-88
Fairchild-Dornier 328
Distance from DFW (miles)
2,000
1,800
1,600
1,400
1,200
1,000
800
600
400
200
0
7:30 8:00 8:30 9:00 9:30 10:00 10:30 11:00 11:30
Time of Day

Step 1 Consider questions as you decide if the graphs are representative or if changes are needed.

1. What does each graph represent?
2. What is represented at the point of intersection of the two graphs?
3. How far is each plane from DFW at 11:30 A.M.?
4. For what domain values are the graphs reasonable representations of the situation?

Step 2 Evaluate and answer each question posed in Step 1.

1. The graph with a positive slope represents how far the Fairchild-Dornier 328 is from DFW at any given time. The graph with a negative slope represents how far the MD-88 is from DFW at any given time.

2. This point is the solution of the system of linear equations represented by the graphs shown. It represents the time when both planes are the same distance from DFW. At about 9:36 A.M. both planes are about 830 miles from DFW.

3. The MD-88 is 0 miles from DFW, and the Fairchild Dornier is 1,565 from DFW. Both planes have arrived at their destinations.

4. The graph representing the MD-88 is reasonable from 7:30 A.M. $\leq x \leq$ 11:15 A.M. The graph representing the Fairchild-Dornier 328 is reasonable from 7:30 A.M. $\leq x \leq$ 11:27 A.M. The MD-88 lands at about 11:15 A.M., and the Fairchild-Dornier lands at about 11:27 A.M.

Solution

The graph does accurately represent the situation, with one exception. The graph for the Fairchild-Dornier 328 should not extend past 11:27 A.M.

Guided Instruction

Another Problem

Problem 2

Michelle pays \$39.99 a month for her cellular phone service. With this plan she receives 500 free minutes. She is billed an additional 30 cents for each minute over 500. Can Michelle use the equation $y = 39.99 + 0.30(x - 500)$ to figure her bill for any reasonable number of minutes? If not, how should the equation be changed?

Step 1 Graph the equation.

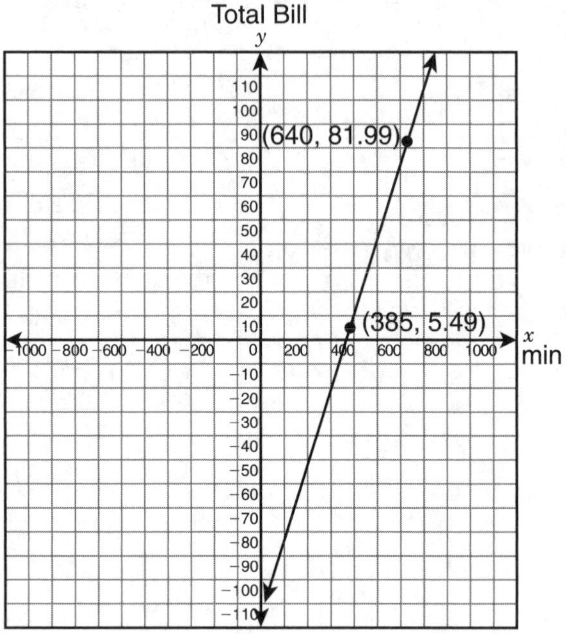

Total Bill

Step 2 Consider a couple different minutes of usage and see if the graph provides a reasonable answer.

Test 640 minutes.
When $x = 640$, $y = 81.99$. The amount \$81.99 is reasonable in this situation. Michelle knows that if she uses more than 500 minutes she will be charged extra.

Test 385 minutes.
When $x = 385$, $y = 5.49$. The amount \$5.49 is not reasonable in this situation. Michelle knows that her minimum bill will be \$39.99.

Step 3 Consider if the equation with restrictions on the domain will better represent the situation algebraically.

$$y = 39.99 + 0.30(x - 500),\ x > 500$$

Step 4 Determine how can you represent this problem graphically using a system that includes a linear equation and a linear inequality.

Total Bill

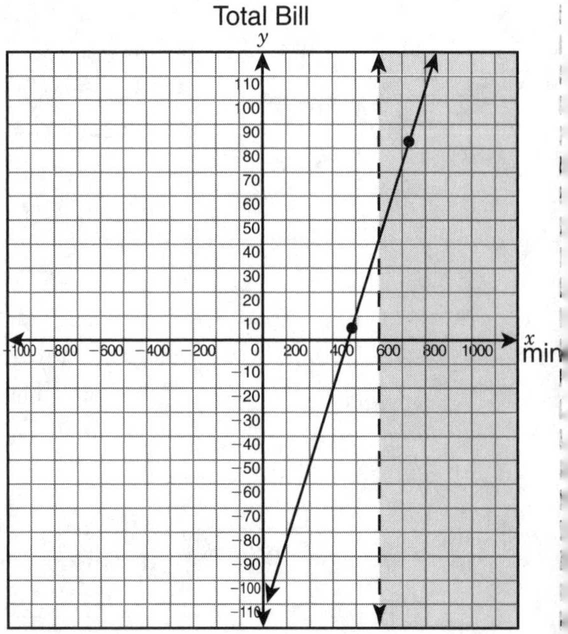

The solution of the system is the intersection of the line with the shaded area, which is the same solution given by the algebraic solution

$$y = 39.99 + 0.30(x - 500),\ x > 500.$$

Solution

Michelle cannot always use the equation to figure her bill. She needs to use a system of a linear equation and a linear inequality to account for the fact that her bill cannot be less than \$39.99. She must use:

$y = 39.99 + 0.30(x - 500)$
$x > 500$

Apply the TEKS **Represent each situation algebraically. If necessary, restrict the domain so the solution is reasonable.**

1. Rita is making a rectangular dog pen with exactly 40 feet of fencing. Formulate an equation representing the length of one side y of the rectangle in terms of the length of its other side x.

____

____

2. If done individually, an assigned paper must be 8 pages minimum. The paper can be done as a group. For each person 4 pages need to be added to the minimum. How many pages are in a paper?

____

____

Represent each situation graphically. Create the graph to represent only reasonable solutions.

3. From last night's dinner, 52 ounces of pasta are left over. To reheat up to 8 ounces, microwave for 50 seconds. For each additional ounce add 4 seconds. How long should this leftover pasta be microwaved?

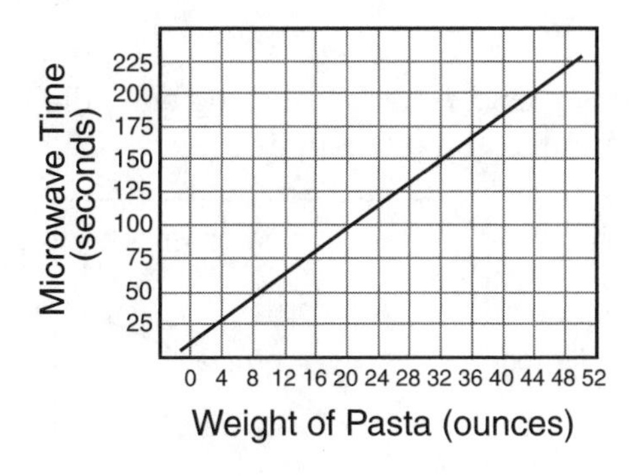

4. Trey is buying a floral arrangement of gerbera daisies and/or roses for Mother's Day. Daisies are \$2 each, and roses are \$3 each. How many of each flower can be in the arrangement if Trey wants to spend \$10 to \$15?

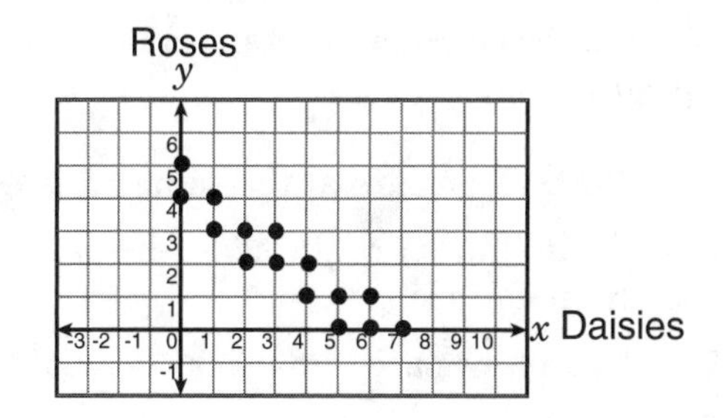

Answer the question for each situation.

5. A baseball card collector has 5 Barry Bonds and 8 Ichiro Suzuki cards from this year's set worth \$7.30. His friend has 10 Bonds cards and 3 Suzuki cards worth \$6.80. What does the point of intersection represent? What are the coordinates of the point?

____

____

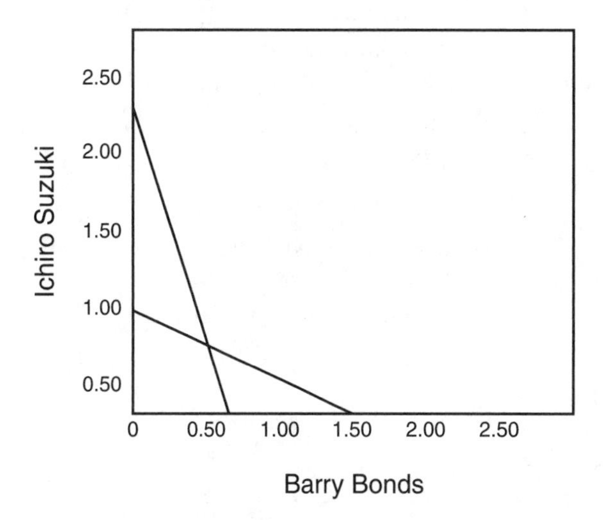

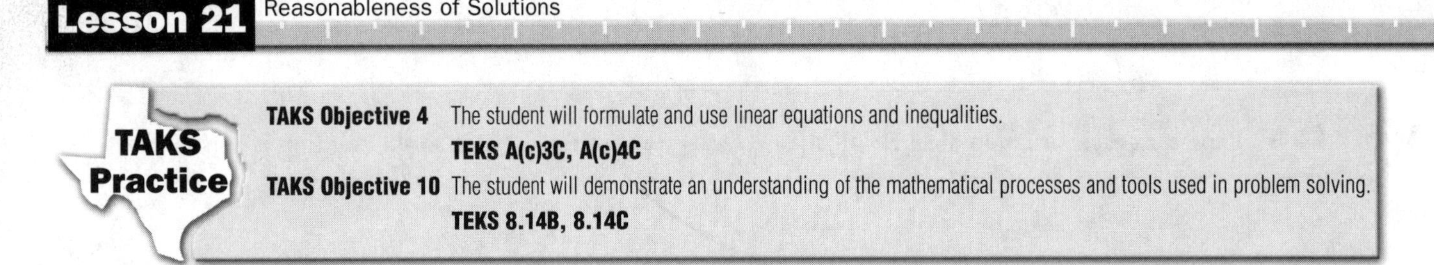

DIRECTIONS Read each question. Then circle the letter for the correct answer. If a correct answer is not here, circle the letter for "Not Here."

1 One plane is taking off from Chicago's O'Hare Airport, and another is coming toward O'Hare.

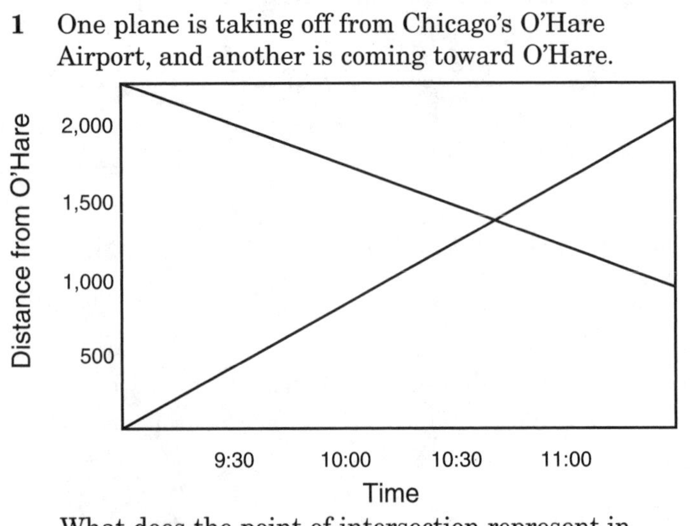

What does the point of intersection represent in the situation?

A Both planes are at the same altitude.

B Both planes are the same distance from O'Hare.

C The planes are in danger of colliding.

D Both planes are traveling at the same speed.

2 Tickets to a concert cost \$24, and a parking pass costs \$15. Is the line $y = 24x + 15$ the best solution for how much Jake will spend for x number of tickets and one parking pass?

F No, x should be restricted to integers greater than 0.

G No, the equation should be $y = 39x$.

H No, y should be an inequality.

J Yes

3 A country's population is shown in the table for every 250 years.

Year	1000	1250	1500	1750	2000
Population	48,600	52,400	56,300	60,300	185,300

Which statement best describes the reasonableness of the equation $y = 15.6x + 33{,}000$ for the data, where y represents the population for the given year x?

A It is reasonable for each year in the table.

B It is reasonable for each year except 2000.

C It is reasonable for each year except 1250.

D Not Here

4 Lori's record time for running one mile is 6 minutes and 30 seconds.

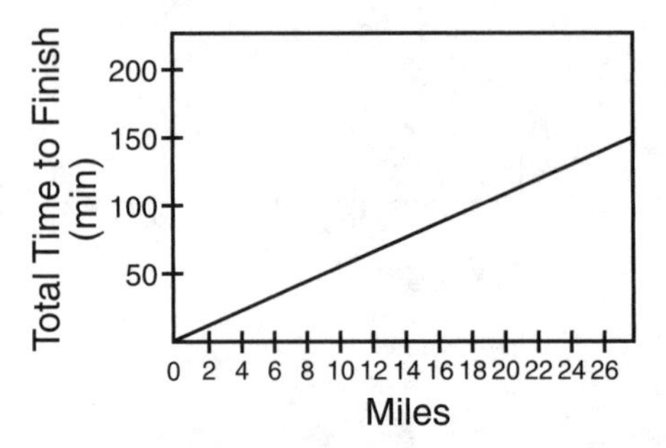

If Lori is graphing the solution of an equation that represents the time it will take her to finish a race of x miles, should she shade below or above the line?

F Above, because the line represents her fastest possible time

G Below, because the line represents her fastest possible time

H Above, but the line should be dashed

J Below, but the line should be dashed

Building Stamina™

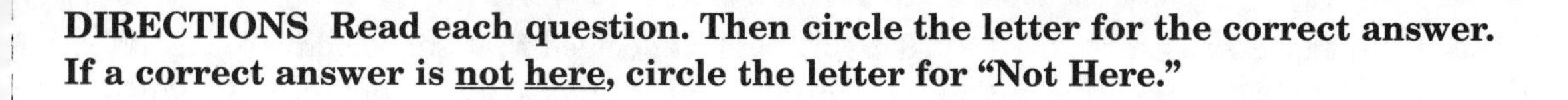

DIRECTIONS Read each question. Then circle the letter for the correct answer. If a correct answer is <u>not here</u>, circle the letter for "Not Here."

1 The sum of two numbers is 123. One number is three times the other number. Which equation best describes the situation?

A $x = 41$

B $3x = 123$

C $x + y = 123$

D $x + 3x = 123$

2 John is traveling in Mexico. He has a pocketful of 1-peso coins and 2-peso coins worth 43 pesos. Altogether he has 27 coins. Which of the equations below can be used to find the number of 1-peso coins x and 2-peso coins y that John has in his pocket?

F $x + y = 43$

G $x + y = 27$

H $x + 2y = 43$

J Both G and H

3 Which inequality belongs with the graph?

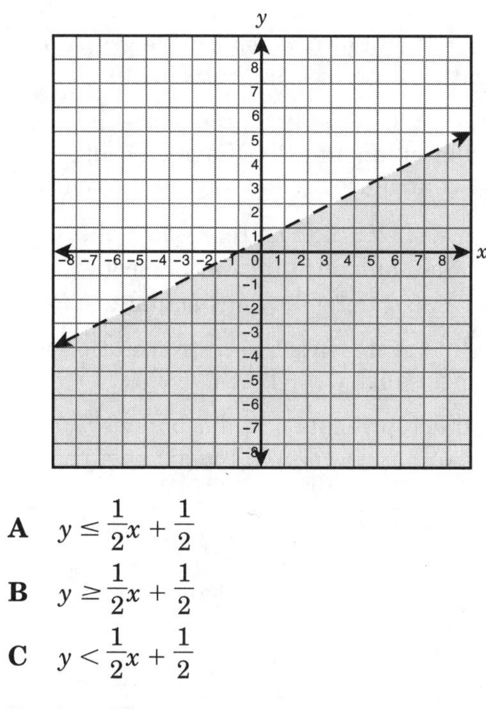

A $y \leq \frac{1}{2}x + \frac{1}{2}$

B $y \geq \frac{1}{2}x + \frac{1}{2}$

C $y < \frac{1}{2}x + \frac{1}{2}$

D Not Here

4 At Sean's house in Colorado, the snow is 2.5 inches deep. At Kelly's house in Wyoming the snow is 6.25 inches deep. At 5:00 P.M. a snow storm began over the Rocky Mountains. The snow at Sean's house increased in depth by 0.75 inch per hour, and the snow at Kelly's house increased in depth by 0.25 inch per hour. At what time was the snow at Sean's house the same depth as the snow at Kelly's house?

F 7:30 P.M.

G 7:50 P.M.

H 12:30 A.M.

J 2:30 A.M.

5 The sum of two numbers is 16.34. One number is four times the other number. What is the smaller number?

Record your answer and fill in the bubbles on the grid below. Be sure to use the correct place value.

				.			
0	0	0	0		0	0	0
1	1	1	1		1	1	1
2	2	2	2		2	2	2
3	3	3	3		3	3	3
4	4	4	4		4	4	4
5	5	5	5		5	5	5
6	6	6	6		6	6	6
7	7	7	7		7	7	7
8	8	8	8		8	8	8
9	9	9	9		9	9	9

6 Where do these two lines intersect?

$$2x + 3y = 54$$
$$6x + 9y = -54$$

F $(18, -6)$

G $(18, 30)$

H $(0, 0)$

J Not Here

7 In baseball, an RBI is a run that scores as a result of a player's at-bat. The most RBIs that a player can have in one at bat is four. This occurs, when a player hits a grand slam—a home run that is hit when a runner is on every base. In his last game, George had four at-bats.

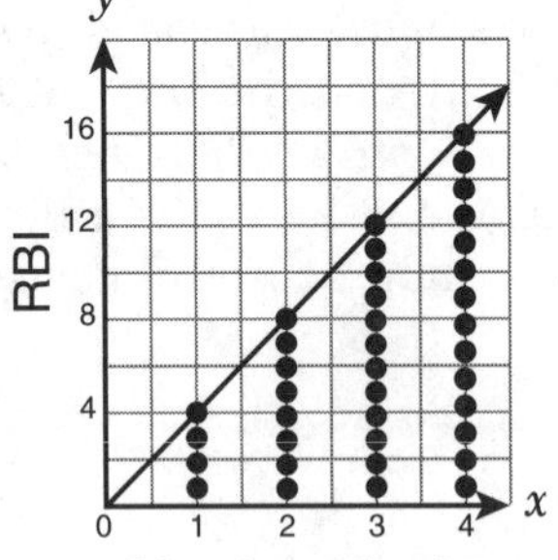

What do the plotted points along the line $y = 4x$ represent?

A George's total number of at bats

B The number of RBIs George got per at bat

C The maximum number of home runs George could have had after each at bat

D The maximum number of RBIs George could have had after each at bat

8 Ethan already owes the library \$3.75. He currently has three overdue CDs on loan from the library. The fine for overdue CDs is \$0.25 per day per CD. Which of these equations best describes how much Ethan will owe the library when he finally returns the CDs to the library?

F $y = 3.75 + 0.25x$

G $y = 3.75 + 0.75x$

H $y = 11.25 + 0.75x$

J Not Here

9 Solve the inequality $4x - 18 \geq 6x - 16$.

A $x \leq -1$

B $x \geq -1$

C $x \leq -\frac{17}{5}$

D $x \geq \frac{1}{5}$

10 Carmen has decided that she is going to pay off her debts and start saving money. She currently is \$2,164 in debt, and her goal is to save at least \$500 a month. Until the debt is paid off she will put all savings toward the debt. Once the debt is paid off she will begin contributing to a savings account.

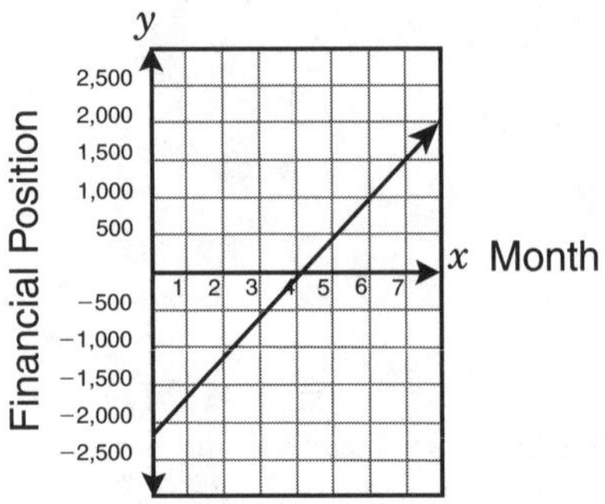

If she achieves her goal of saving at least \$500 a month, what is the least amount she should have contributed to the savings account in 6 months?

F \$4.34

G \$836

H After 6 months the debt will not be paid yet.

J Not Here

11 What does the line represent in the graph of the situation described in Problem 10?

A For $x > 4.328$, the line represents the maximum amount that Carmen could have contributed to her savings account.

B For $x > 4.328$, the line represents the minimum amount that Carmen could have contributed to her savings account.

C The line represents the entire solution for the inequality $y \geq -2,164 + 500x$.

D The line represents how much money Carmen has saved up through any given day.

12 Leonard works in a grocery store. Tonight he is responsible for mopping the aisles. The store has 33 aisles that are either one of two different lengths. The aisles to the right of the checkout lanes are shorter than the other aisles. It takes Leonard 5 minutes to mop each shorter aisle and 8 minutes to mop each longer aisle. It takes him 3 hours and 57 minutes to mop all of the aisles. Which system of equations can be used to find how many long aisles and how many short aisles are in the store?

F $x + y = 33$
$5x + 8y = 357$

G $x + y = 237$
$5x + 8y = 33$

H $x + y = 33$
$5x + 8y = 237$

J Not Here

13 When x is 3, what is y?

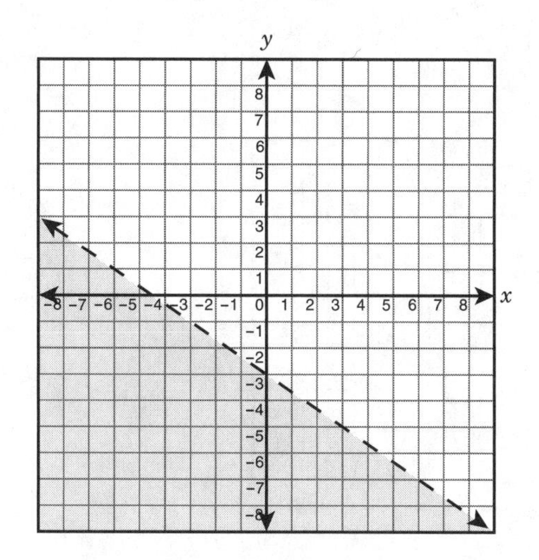

A $y = -3$

B $y = 0$

C $y < -5$

D $y \leq -5$

14 What is the solution of the system of equations?

Line 1	
x	y
$-\frac{1}{12}$	$\frac{3}{2}$
0	$-\frac{1}{2}$
$\frac{1}{24}$	0

Line 2	
x	y
−8	4
0	6
16	10

F (0, 0)

G $(-\frac{1}{2}, 6)$

H $(-\frac{26}{5}, \frac{47}{10})$

J $(\frac{26}{27}, \frac{1,345}{194})$

15 Kaitlyn is riding her bike around the block, which is in the shape of a rectangle. She rides around the block two times for a total of 7,640 feet. The block is 110 feet longer than it is wide. She uses the two equations $2l + 2w = 3,820$ and $l - w = 110$ to make the graph below.

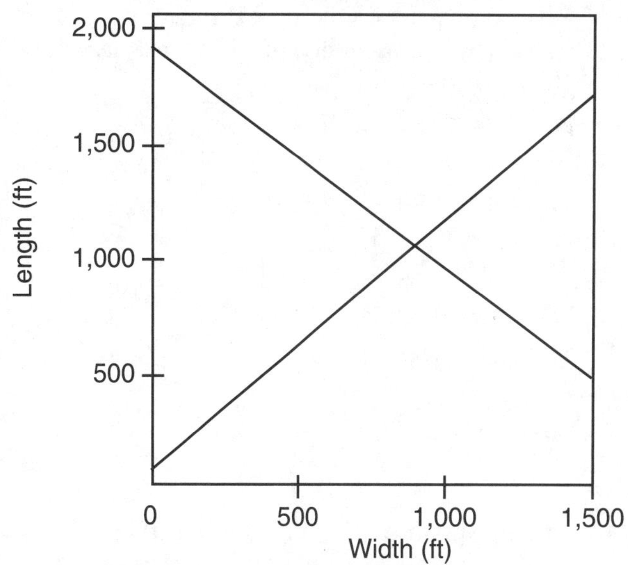

What is represented by the intersection of the two lines?

A The time it takes Kaitlyn to go once around the block

B The dimensions of the block

C The area of the block

D Not Here

16 Samantha is paid \$6.25 an hour. She receives a paycheck every two weeks. In the two weeks of the current pay period she worked 4 fewer hours the second week than she did the first week. If she earned \$425 for the two-week pay period, how many hours did she work the second week?

Record your answer and fill in the bubbles on the grid below. Be sure to use the correct place value.

				.			
0	0	0	0		0	0	0
1	1	1	1		1	1	1
2	2	2	2		2	2	2
3	3	3	3		3	3	3
4	4	4	4		4	4	4
5	5	5	5		5	5	5
6	6	6	6		6	6	6
7	7	7	7		7	7	7
8	8	8	8		8	8	8
9	9	9	9		9	9	9

17 Craig has eleven bills in his wallet that total \$80. Some are \$5 bills, and the rest are \$10 bills. Which system of equations best describes this situation?

A $5x + 10y = 80$
$x + y = 11$

B $x + y = 80$
$5x + 10y = 11$

C $x + y = 15$
$5x + 10y = 11$

D Not Here

18 At what point do the lines intersect?

$$-2x + 5y = 25$$
$$6x - 3y = -3$$

F $(2.5, -6)$

G $(-2.5, -6)$

H $(2.5, 6)$

J $(-2.5, 6)$

19 Noah and Jackie start jogging around a track from the same spot at the same time. Noah jogs $\frac{1}{5}$ of the track per minute, and Jackie runs $\frac{1}{4}$ of the track per minute. How long will it take Jackie to lap Noah?

A 0 min

B 4 min

C 20 min

D 1 hr, 40 min

20 Which of these graphs represents a solution set that includes the solution of the system of equations $\frac{2}{3}x - y = 4$ and $-x + \frac{1}{4}y = \frac{3}{2}$?

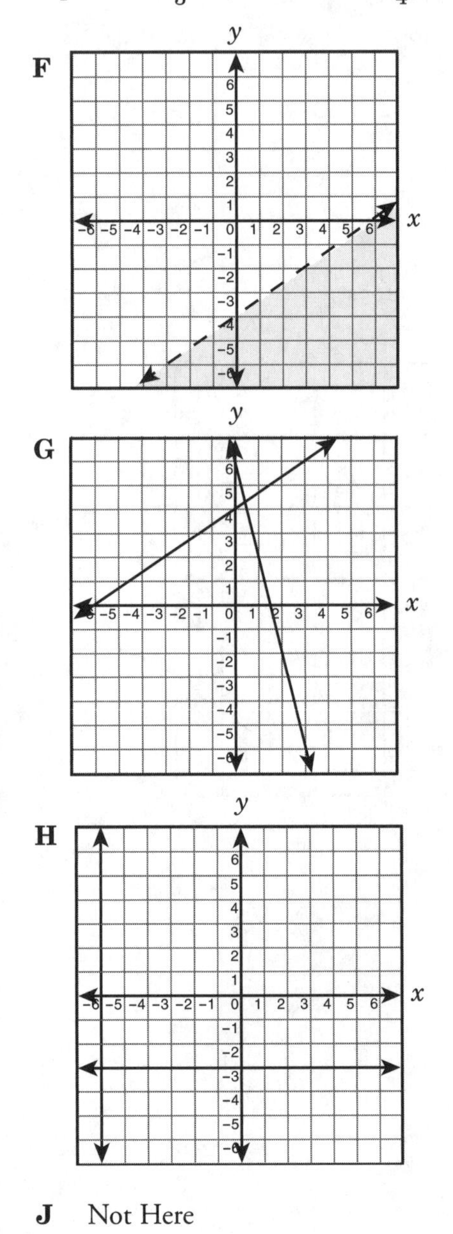

J Not Here

Focus on TEKS Lesson 22 Describe and Predict Effects of Changes on the Parent Function

TEKS A(b)2A Identify and sketch the general forms of quadratic ($y = x^2$) parent functions.
TEKS A(d)1A Determine the domain and range values for which quadratic functions make sense for given situations.
TEKS A(d)1B Investigate, describe, and predict the effects of changes in *a* on the graph of $y = ax^2$.
TEKS A(d)1C Investigate, describe, and predict the effects of changes in *c* on the graph of $y = x^2 + c$.

Previously, you learned that in quadratic functions there is an x-term with an exponent of 2. Therefore, the parent function for the family of quadratic functions is $y = x^2$.

A **quadratic function** is a function in the form $y = ax^2 + bx + c$, where a, b, and c are real numbers, and $a \neq 0$. The graph of a quadratic function is a U-shaped curve, called a **parabola**.

Guided Instruction

Problem 1

A ball is thrown straight up into the air with an initial velocity of 48 feet per second. The height of the ball (h) is represented by the function $h = 48t - 16t^2$, where t is the time in seconds. How high is the ball at 2 seconds? What is a reasonable domain and range for this situation?

Step 1 To find the height of the ball at 2 seconds, substitute 2 for t in the function $h = 48t - 16t^2$.

$h = 48t - 16t^2$
$h = 48(2) - 16(2)^2$
$h = 96 - 64$
$h = 32$

Step 2 To determine reasonable domain and range values, graph the function by making a table of values. Since t represents time, only 0 and positive numbers will be used for the domain.

t	$48t - 16t^2$	h
0	$48(0) - 16(0)^2$	0
0.5	$48(0.5) - 16(0.5)^2$	20
1	$48(1) - 16(1)^2$	32
1.5	$48(1.5) - 16(1.5)^2$	36
2	$48(2) - 16(2)^2$	32
2.5	$48(2.5) - 16(2.5)^2$	20
3	$48(3) - 16(3)^2$	0

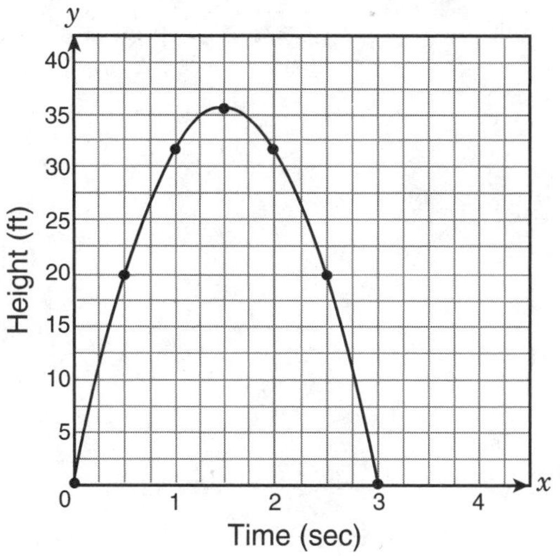

y
40
35
30
25
20
15
10
5
0
1
2
3
4
x
Height (ft)
Time (sec)

Step 3 Plot the points on the coordinate grid, and draw the curve.

Step 4 State the domain and range values by referring to the graph of the function.

Domain: $\{t: 0 \leq t \leq 3\}$
Range: $\{h: 0 \leq h \leq 36\}$

Solution

At 2 seconds the ball is 32 feet high. Reasonable domain values are between 0 and 3. Reasonable range values are between 0 and 36.

More Problems

Guided Instruction

Problem 2

Graph the equations $y = x^2$, $y = -x^2$, and $y = 2x^2$ on a graphing calculator. Then predict what the graph of $y = -2x^2$ will look like. Verify by graphing the equation on a graphing calculator.

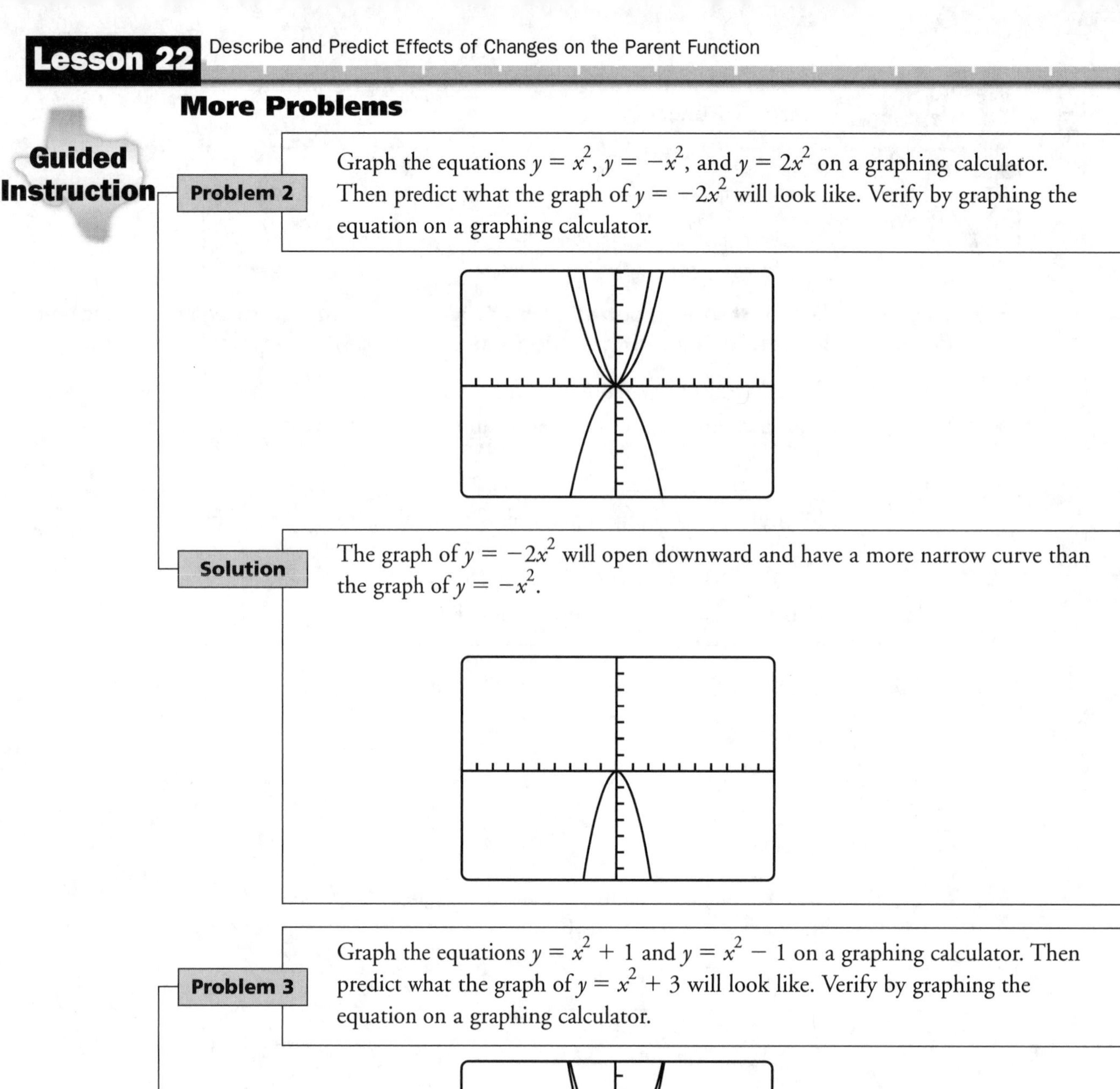

Solution

The graph of $y = -2x^2$ will open downward and have a more narrow curve than the graph of $y = -x^2$.

Problem 3

Graph the equations $y = x^2 + 1$ and $y = x^2 - 1$ on a graphing calculator. Then predict what the graph of $y = x^2 + 3$ will look like. Verify by graphing the equation on a graphing calculator.

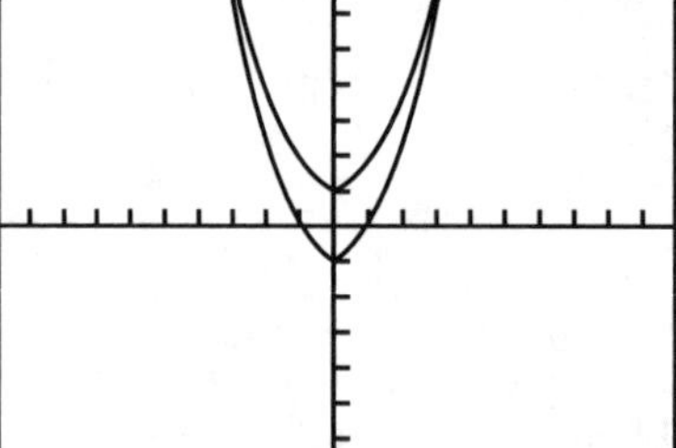

Solution

The graph of $y = x^2 + 3$ will be the graph of $y = x^2$ shifted 3 units up on the y-axis.

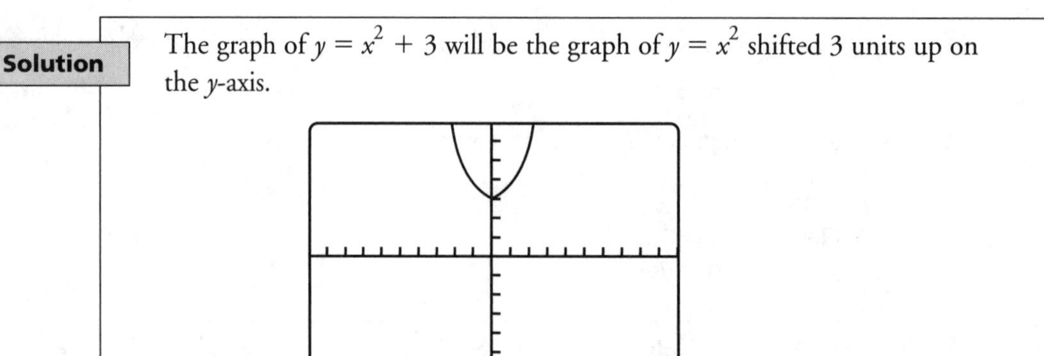

Apply the TEKS Match each equation with its graph.

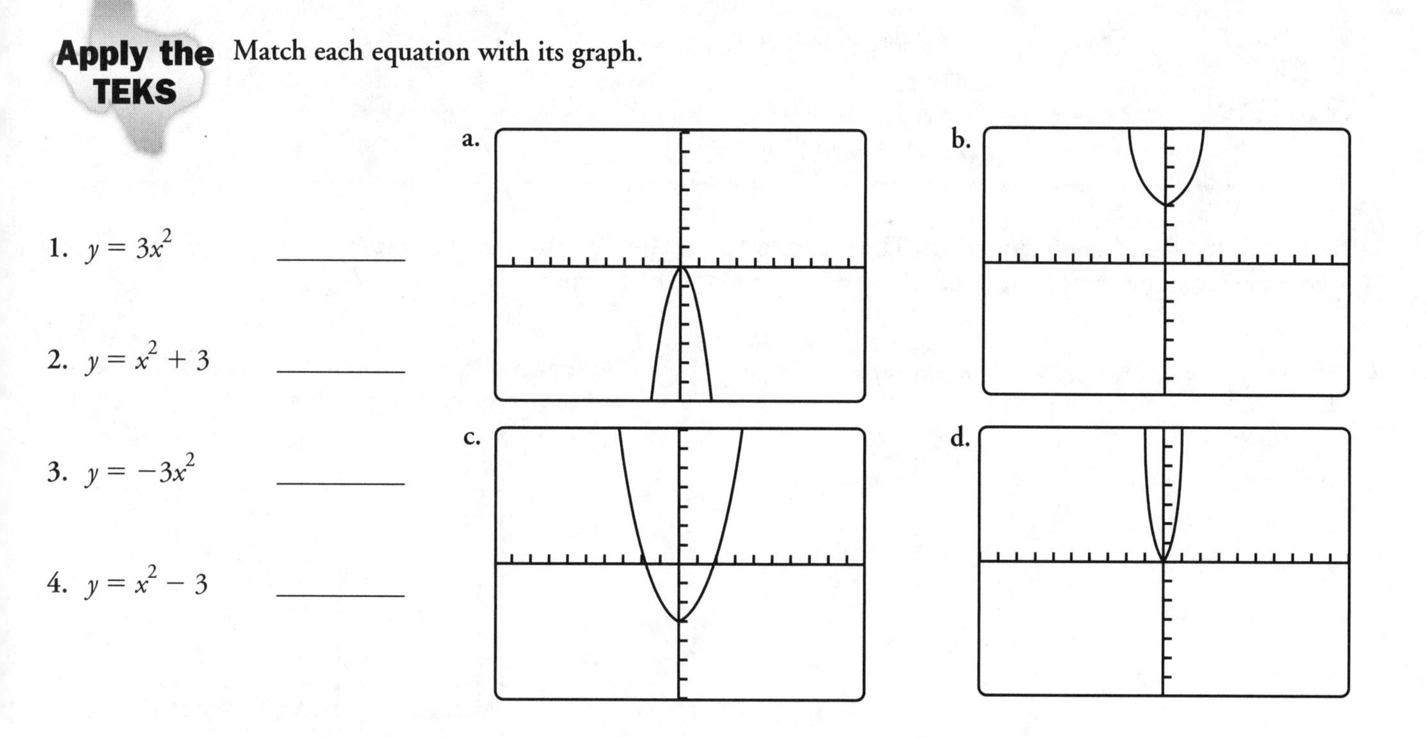

1. $y = 3x^2$ ________

2. $y = x^2 + 3$ ________

3. $y = -3x^2$ ________

4. $y = x^2 - 3$ ________

Determine whether the graph of each equation will open *upward* or *downward*.

5. $y = -6x^2 + 5$ ________

6. $y = 8x^2 - 3x - 10$ ________

7. $y = -3x^2 - 6x + 1$ ________

Describe how the graph of each equation will differ from the graph of $y = x^2$.

8. $y = \frac{1}{2}x^2$ ________

9. $y = -6x^2$ ________

10. $y = x^2 - 5$ ________

11. $y = 2x^2 + 3$ ________

Solve the problem.

12. A ball is thrown straight up into the air with an initial velocity of 66 feet per second. The height of the ball *(h)* is represented by the function $h = 66t - 16t^2$, where t is the time in seconds.
    a. How high is the ball at 3 seconds? ________

    b. What is a reasonable domain and range for this situation?

    Domain: ________

    Range: ________

TAKS Practice

TAKS Objective 2 The student will demonstrate an understanding of the properties and attributes of functions.
TEKS A(b)2A

TAKS Objective 5 The student will demonstrate an understanding of quadratic and other nonlinear functions.
TEKS A(d)1B, A(d)1C

DIRECTIONS Read each question. Then circle the letter for the correct answer. If a correct answer is not here, circle the letter for "Not Here."

1 Which of the following functions represents the graph of $y = x^2 + 5$ shifted down 8 units on the y-axis?

A $y = x^2 - 3$

B $y = x^2 + 13$

C $y = x^2 - 8$

D Not Here

2 What is the effect on the graph of the equation $y = 2x^2$ when the equation is changed to $y = \frac{1}{2}x^2$?

F The y values for any given x value are closer to the y-axis.

G The graph intersects the y-axis at $\frac{1}{2}$ instead of 2.

H The graph opens downward instead of upward.

J The y values for any given x value are farther from the y-axis.

3 Which of the following quadratic functions has the narrowest graph?

A $y = \frac{1}{3}x^2 - 4$

B $y = -4x^2 + 10$

C $y = 5x^2 + 1$

D $y = \frac{5}{2}x^2 - 7$

4 What is the equation of the quadratic function graphed on the coordinate grid?

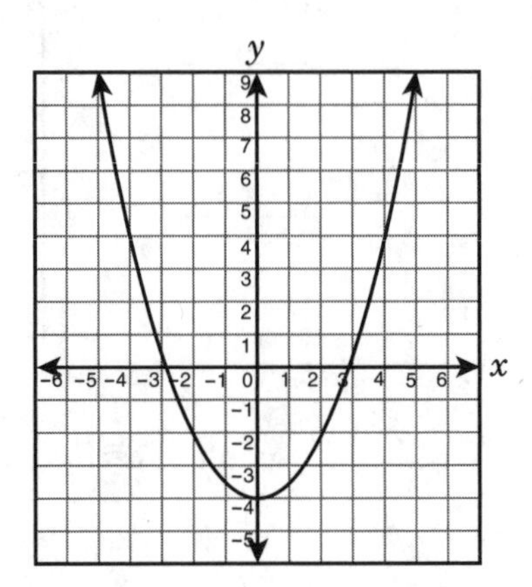

F $y = 2x^2 - 4$

G $y = \frac{1}{2}x^2 - 4$

H $y = 2x^2 + 4$

J $y = \frac{1}{4}x^2 + 4$

5 In the general form $y = ax^2 + c$ of a quadratic function, which of the following statements will result in a graph opening downward?

A $|c| < 0$

B $a < 0$

C $|a| > 0$

D $a > 0$

Focus on TEKS **Lesson 23**

Analyze Graphs of Quadratic Functions

TEKS A(d)1D For problem situations, analyze graphs of quadratic functions and draw conclusions.
TEKS 8.16B Validate conclusions using mathematical properties and relationships.

The parabolic graphs of quadratic functions often are used to represent the height of rising and falling objects, such as a ball.

The **vertex** of a parabola is the highest or lowest point of the graph.

When the value of a is positive in a quadratic function ($y = ax^2 + bx + c$), the parabola opens upward and the vertex is the **minimum value**. The minimum value is identified by the y-coordinate of the vertex.

When the value of a is negative in a quadratic function, the parabola opens downward and the vertex is the **maximum value**. The maximum value is identified by the y-coordinate of the vertex.

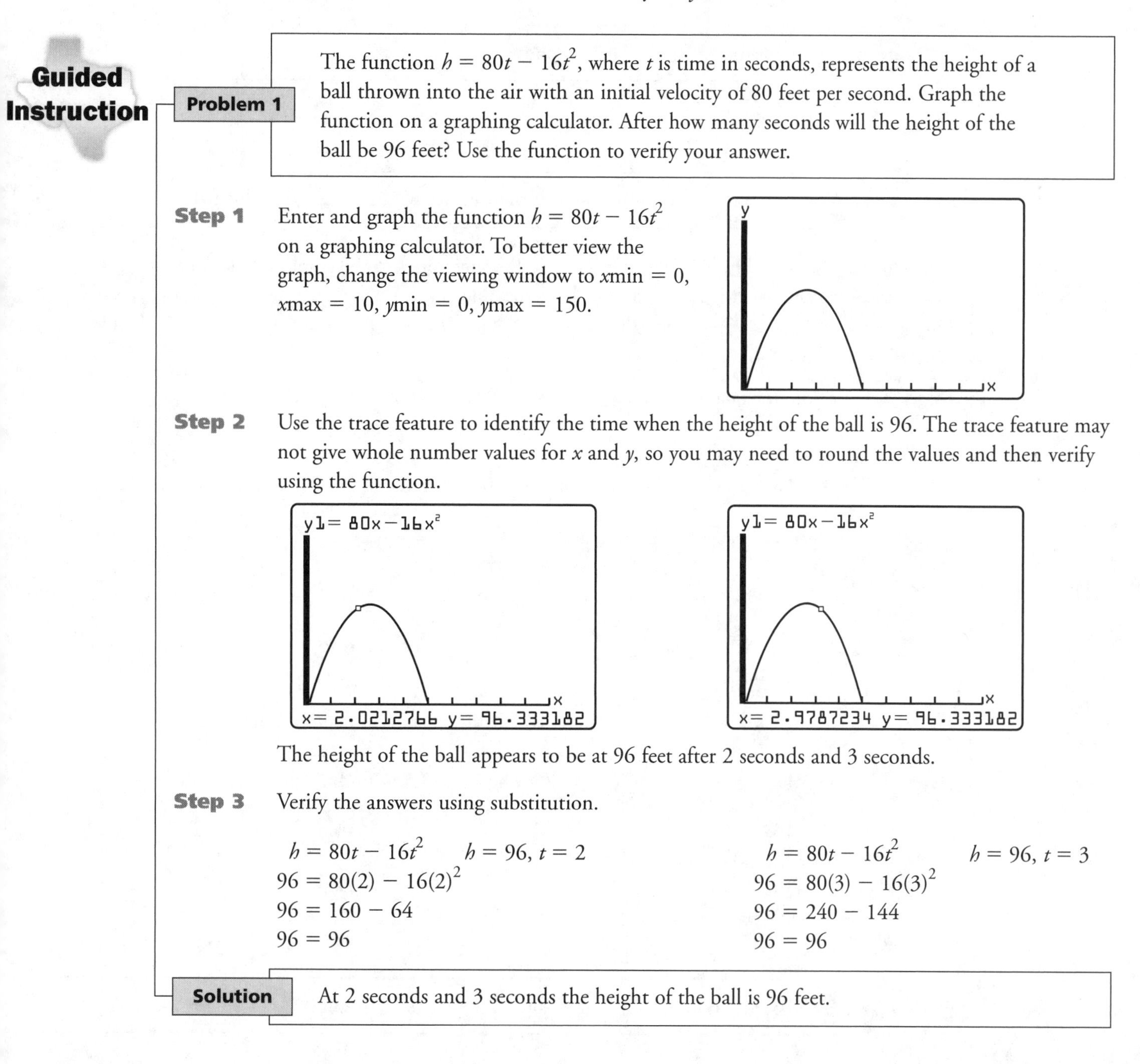

Guided Instruction

Problem 1

The function $h = 80t - 16t^2$, where t is time in seconds, represents the height of a ball thrown into the air with an initial velocity of 80 feet per second. Graph the function on a graphing calculator. After how many seconds will the height of the ball be 96 feet? Use the function to verify your answer.

Step 1 Enter and graph the function $h = 80t - 16t^2$ on a graphing calculator. To better view the graph, change the viewing window to $x$min = 0, $x$max = 10, $y$min = 0, $y$max = 150.

Step 2 Use the trace feature to identify the time when the height of the ball is 96. The trace feature may not give whole number values for x and y, so you may need to round the values and then verify using the function.

The height of the ball appears to be at 96 feet after 2 seconds and 3 seconds.

Step 3 Verify the answers using substitution.

$h = 80t - 16t^2 \qquad h = 96, t = 2$
$96 = 80(2) - 16(2)^2$
$96 = 160 - 64$
$96 = 96$

$h = 80t - 16t^2 \qquad h = 96, t = 3$
$96 = 80(3) - 16(3)^2$
$96 = 240 - 144$
$96 = 96$

Solution At 2 seconds and 3 seconds the height of the ball is 96 feet.

More Problems

Guided Instruction

Problem 2 How many seconds is the ball in the air in Problem 1?

Step 1 Use the graph to determine when the ball reaches the ground. The graph appears to intersect the horizontal axis at (5, 0), so 5 seconds could represent the time when the ball hits the ground.

Step 2 Verify using the function.

$h = 80t - 16t^2$
$0 = 80(5) - 16(5)^2$
$0 = 400 - 400$

Solution The ball is in the air for 5 seconds.

Problem 3 What is the maximum height of the ball thrown in the air in Problem 1?

The ball is at its maximum height at the vertex of the function. On the graphing calculator you may not be able to determine the exact value at the vertex. However, when a quadratic function is in the form $y = ax^2 + bx + c$, you can use the equation $x = \frac{-b}{2a}$ to find the x-value of the vertex. Then you can substitute to find the y-value.

Step 1 Rewrite the quadratic function $h = 80t - 16t^2$ in the form $y = ax^2 + bx + c$. Let $h = y$ and $t = x$.

$y = -16x^2 + 80x$ The value of a is -16, the value of b is 80, and the value of c is 0.

Step 2 Find the value of x at the vertex.

$x = \frac{-b}{2a}$

$x = \frac{-80}{2(-16)} = \frac{-80}{-32} = 2.5$

This represents the time (2.5 seconds) when the ball is at its maximum height.

Step 3 Solve the equation $y = -16x^2 + 80x$ when $x = 2.5$ to find the maximum height.

$y = -16x^2 + 80x$
$y = -16(2.5)^2 + 80(2.5)$
$y = -100 + 200$
$y = 100$

Solution The maximum height of the ball is 100 feet at 2.5 seconds.

Apply the TEKS Name the values of a, b, and c for each quadratic function.

1. $y = -7x^2 + 9x - 2$

   $a =$ _____, $b =$ _____, $c =$ _____

2. $y = 12x^2 + 15$

   $a =$ _____, $b =$ _____, $c =$ _____

3. $y = -3 + x^2 - 9x$

   $a =$ _____, $b =$ _____, $c =$ _____

Identify the coordinates of the vertex of each graph. State whether the vertex is the *maximum* or *minimum* value.

4. 5. 6.

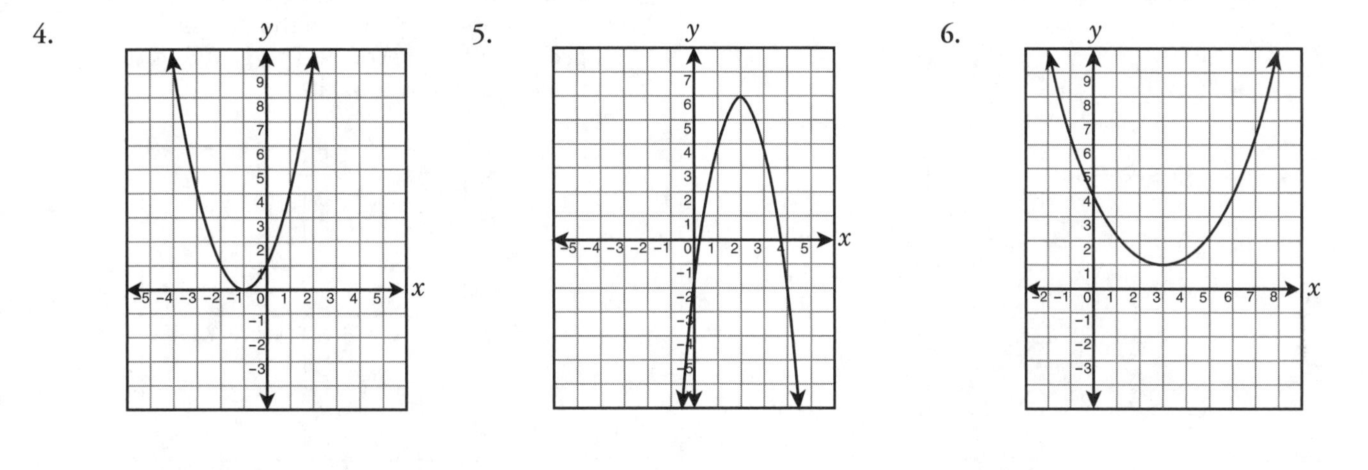

_______________ _______________ _______________

Name the coordinates of the vertex of each quadratic function.

7. $y = 4x^2 - 8x + 10$

   ____

8. $y = -6x^2 + 36x - 12$

   ____

9. $y = -45x + 5x^2 + 15$

   ____

Solve each problem.

10. The function $h = 96t - 16t^2$, where t is time in seconds, represents the height of a ball thrown into the air with an initial velocity of 96 feet per second. Verify your estimated answer using the function.

    a. Using a graphing calculator, determine and verify how many seconds it will take for the height of the ball to be 128 feet. __________

    b. How many seconds is the ball in the air? __________

    c. What is the maximum height of the ball? __________

11. Give an example of a quadratic function that opens downward and has a vertex of (0, 6). __________

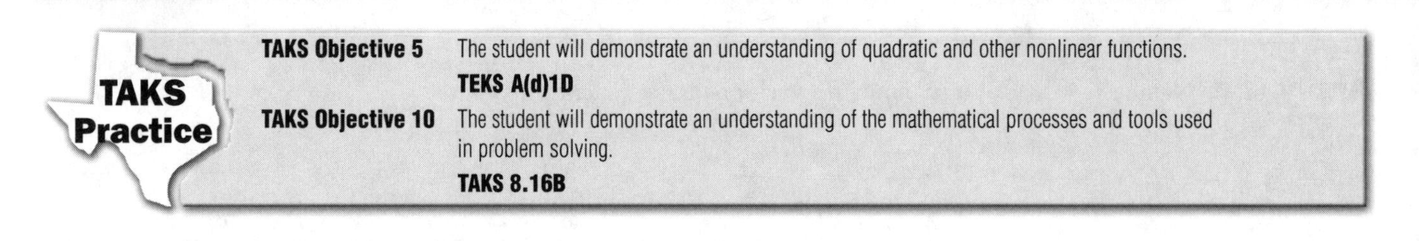

DIRECTIONS Read each question. Then circle the letter for the correct answer. If a correct answer is <u>not here</u>, circle the letter for "Not Here."

1 What is the vertex of the graph of the quadratic function $y = \frac{1}{2}x^2 - 4x + 3$?

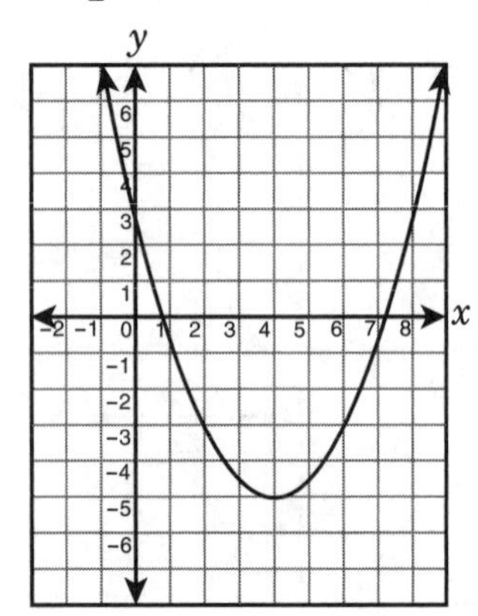

A (0, 3)

B (2, −3)

C (1, 0)

D (4, −5)

2 The function $h = 112t - 16t^2$, where t equals time in seconds, represents the height of an object thrown upward with a given velocity of 112 feet per second. In terms of this situation, what can one conclude from the ordered pair (3.5, 196)?

F The maximum height of the object is 196 feet.

G The height of the object at 3.5 seconds is 196 feet.

H (3.5, 196) is the vertex of the function.

J All of these

3 A ball is dropped from the top of a building that is 260 feet high. The function $d = -16t^2 + 260$ represents the distance the ball is from the ground after t seconds. The graph of the function is shown below.

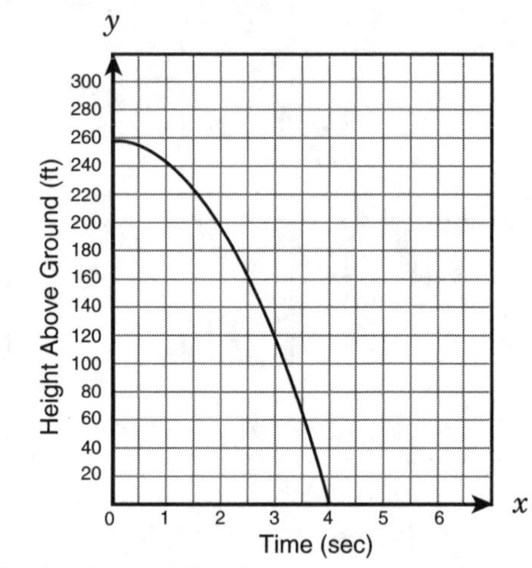

Which of the following statements is true?

A It takes the ball about 5 seconds to reach the ground.

B After 2 seconds the ball is about 60 feet from the ground.

C After 2 seconds the ball is about halfway to the ground.

D The ball is about 20 feet from the top of the building after 1 second.

4 Which of the following quadratic functions has a maximum point at (3, 8)?

F $y = -2x^2 + 10x - 8$

G $y = -2x^2 + 12x - 10$

H $y = x^2 - 6x + 1$

J $y = -3x^2 - 6x + 8$

Focus on TEKS

Lesson 24 Solutions of Quadratic Equations

TEKS A(d)2A Solve quadratic equations using models, tables, graphs, and algebraic methods.
TEKS A(d)2B Relate the solutions of quadratic equations to the roots of their functions.
TEKS 8.15A Communicate mathematical ideas using language, efficient tools, appropriate units, and graphical, numerical, physical, or algebraic mathematical models.

A quadratic equation may have one, two, or no solutions. A quadratic equation can be solved using graphs, roots, or the quadratic formula.

A quadratic equation in the form $d = ax^2 + bx + c$ is in **standard form** when $d = 0$.
The **solutions of a quadratic equation** are the values where the graph crosses the x-axis, or the x-intercepts of the graph. These solutions are called the **roots** of the equation.

If the graph of a quadratic equation crosses the x-axis at two points, then the equation has two solutions. If the graph touches the x-axis at only one point, then the equation has one solution. If the graph does not cross or touch the x-axis, then the equation has no real solutions.

Guided Instruction

Problem 1 Use a graphing calculator to graph and solve the quadratic equation $0 = x^2 - 6x + 5$.

Step 1 Enter and graph the equation $y = x^2 - 6x + 5$ on a graphing calculator.

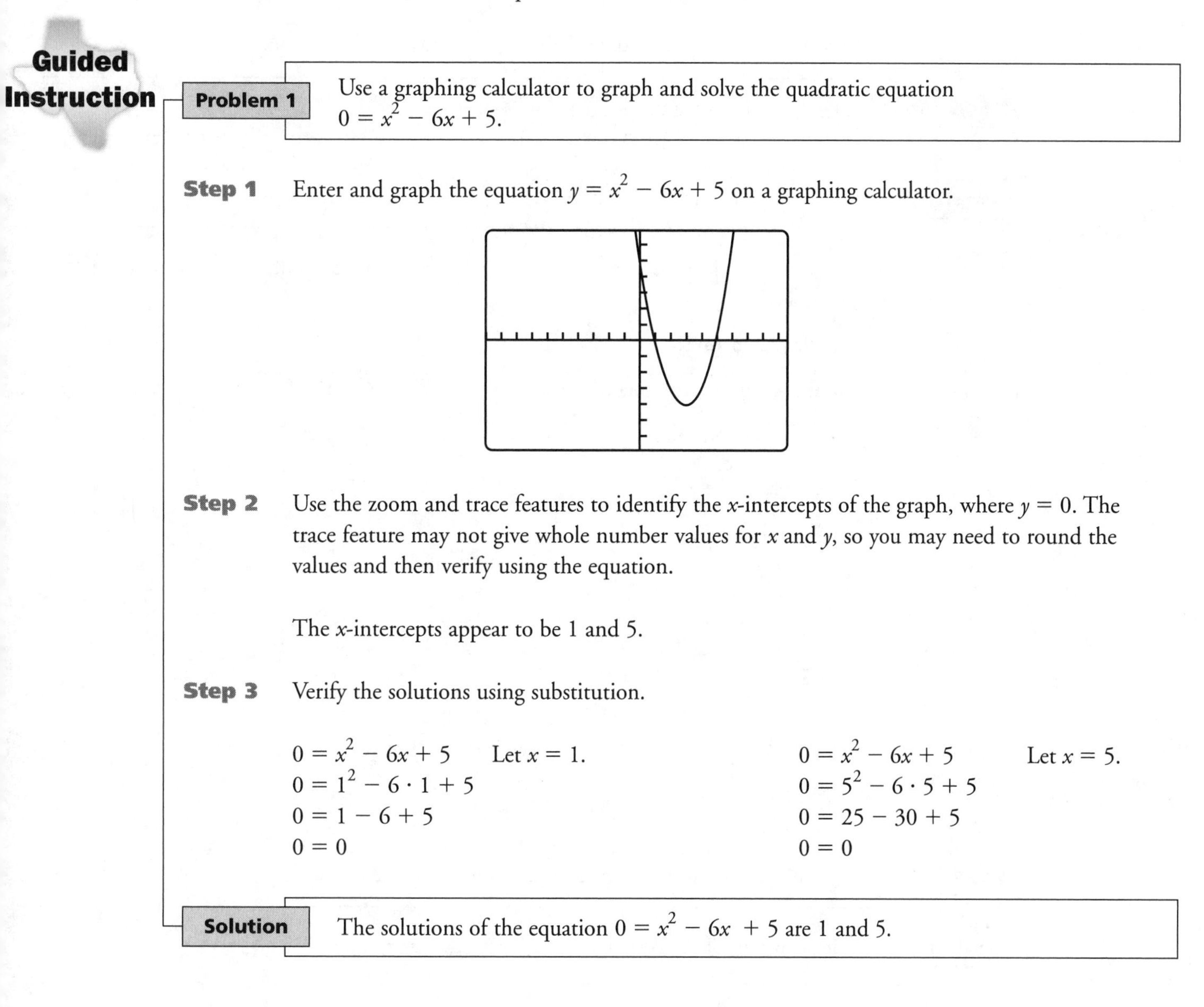

Step 2 Use the zoom and trace features to identify the x-intercepts of the graph, where $y = 0$. The trace feature may not give whole number values for x and y, so you may need to round the values and then verify using the equation.

The x-intercepts appear to be 1 and 5.

Step 3 Verify the solutions using substitution.

$0 = x^2 - 6x + 5$ Let $x = 1$.
$0 = 1^2 - 6 \cdot 1 + 5$
$0 = 1 - 6 + 5$
$0 = 0$

$0 = x^2 - 6x + 5$ Let $x = 5$.
$0 = 5^2 - 6 \cdot 5 + 5$
$0 = 25 - 30 + 5$
$0 = 0$

Solution The solutions of the equation $0 = x^2 - 6x + 5$ are 1 and 5.

More Problems

Guided Instruction

Problem 2 Solve the equation $3x^2 + 7 = 250$.

When a quadratic equation is in the form $ax^2 + b = c$, you can use the square root method to solve the equation. First solve for x^2, and then take the square root of both sides of the equation.

Step 1 Solve for x^2.

$$3x^2 + 7 = 250$$
$$3x^2 + 7 - 7 = 250 - 7$$
$$3x^2 = 243$$
$$\frac{3x^2}{3} = \frac{243}{3}$$
$$\sqrt{x^2} = \pm\sqrt{81}$$
$$x = \pm 9$$

Step 2 Check both solutions in the original equation using substitution.

Solution The solutions of the equation $3x^2 + 7 = 250$ are 9 and −9.

Problem 3 Solve the equation $2x^2 - 7 = -4x$.

For a quadratic equation in the form $ax^2 + bx + c = 0$, you can use the quadratic formula to find the solutions of the equation.

Quadratic formula: $x = \frac{-b \pm \sqrt{b^2 - 4ac}}{2a}$

Step 1 Rewrite the equation in standard form. $2x^2 + 4x - 7 = 0$

Step 2 Use the quadratic formula.

$$x = \frac{-b \pm \sqrt{b^2 - 4ac}}{2a}$$

$$x = \frac{-4 \pm \sqrt{4^2 - 4(2)(-7)}}{2(2)}$$ $a = 2$, $b = 4$, and $c = -7$

$$x = \frac{-4 \pm \sqrt{16 + 56}}{4}$$

$$x = \frac{-4 \pm \sqrt{72}}{4}$$

$$x = \frac{-4 \pm 6\sqrt{2}}{4}$$ Simplify under the radical symbol.

$$x = \frac{-2 \pm 3\sqrt{2}}{2}$$ Divide each term by 2.

Step 3 Check both solutions in the original equation using substitution.

Solution The solutions of the equation $2x^2 - 7 = -4x$ are $\frac{-2 + 3\sqrt{2}}{2}$ and $\frac{-2 - 3\sqrt{2}}{2}$.

Apply the TEKS Rewrite each equation in the form $ax^2 + bx + c = 0$.

1. $3x^2 + 6x - 3 = 8$
2. $-2x^2 = 12 - 9x$
3. $4x - 11 = -3x^2 - 19$

Use a graphing calculator to determine the number of solutions for each equation.

4. $x^2 - 4x - 8 = 0$
5. $0 = 6x^2 - x + 6$
6. $\frac{1}{3}x^2 + 2x = 0$

Use a graphing calculator to graph and solve each equation.

7. $x^2 - 7x + 6 = 0$
8. $x^2 + 4x - 12 = 0$
9. $3x^2 + 9x = 12$

Use the square root method to solve each equation.

10. $x^2 = 169$
11. $x^2 + 8 = 57$
12. $4x^2 - 7 = 93$
13. $\frac{1}{2}x^2 + 13 = 45$
14. $82 = 6x^2 - 14$
15. $\frac{1}{4}x^2 - 14 = 50$

Use the quadratic formula to solve each equation.

16. $x^2 - 9x + 8 = 0$
17. $6x^2 - 3x - 5 = 0$
18. $0 = -4x^2 - 5x + 10$
19. $x^2 - 30 = 7x$
20. $3x^2 - 7x - 6 = 0$
21. $9 = 5x^2 - 2x$

Write and solve an equation for the expression.

22. Three times the square of a number increased by 8 is 35.

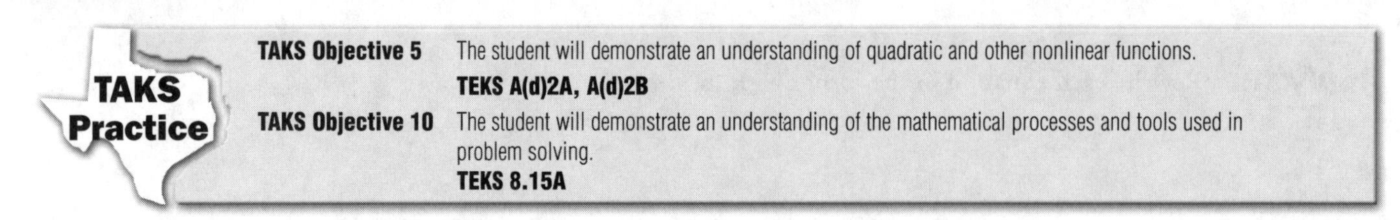

DIRECTIONS Read each question. Then circle the letter for the correct answer. If a correct answer is not here, circle the letter for "Not Here."

1 What are the roots of the equation $5x^2 + 14 = 419$?

A -8 and 8

B -20 and 20

C -6 and 6

D Not Here

2 Which of the following equations is NOT equivalent to $6x^2 - 9x = -15$?

F $6x^2 - 9x + 15 = 0$

G $2x^2 - 3x - 5 = 0$

H $2x^2 - 3x = -5$

J $2x^2 - 3x + 5 = 0$

3 Which of the following explains the roots of a quadratic equation in terms of its graph?

A The x-coordinates of the points where the graph crosses the x-axis

B The y-coordinates of the points where the graph crosses the x-axis

C The x-coordinates of the points where the graph crosses the y-axis

D The y-coordinates of the points where the graph crosses the y-axis

4 Which of the following quadratic equations has no solutions?

F $0 = 3x^2 - 4x + 5$

G $\frac{1}{2}x^2 + 2x - 3 = 0$

H $2x^2 + x = 9$

J $18 = 12x^2 - 6x$

5 What are the roots of the equation $4(x + 5)^2 = 144$?

A -6 and 6

B -1 and 11

C -11 and 1

D Not Here

6 The sum of two numbers is 8. The product of the same two numbers is -105. Write and solve a quadratic equation to find the two numbers. What are the numbers?

F -5 and 21

G -2 and 10

H -15 and 7

J -7 and 15

Focus on TEKS

Lesson 25 Laws of Exponents

TEKS A(d)3A Use patterns to generate the laws of exponents and apply them in problem-solving situations.

The laws of exponents can be examined and defined by evaluating patterns among a series of numbers.

A power is an expression in the form x^n, where x is the base and n is the exponent.

Guided Instruction

Problem 1

Find the value of each product in the table. Then examine the pattern and make a conjecture from the pattern you observe.

Product	Value
$2^2 \cdot 2^5$	
$2^3 \cdot 2^4$	
$2^4 \cdot 2^3$	
$2^5 \cdot 2^2$	
$2^6 \cdot 2^1$	

Step 1 Find the value of each product.

$2^2 \cdot 2^5 = (2 \cdot 2) \cdot (2 \cdot 2 \cdot 2 \cdot 2 \cdot 2) = 4 \cdot 32 = 128$

$2^3 \cdot 2^4 = (2 \cdot 2 \cdot 2) \cdot (2 \cdot 2 \cdot 2 \cdot 2) = 8 \cdot 16 = 128$

$2^4 \cdot 2^3 = (2 \cdot 2 \cdot 2 \cdot 2) \cdot (2 \cdot 2 \cdot 2) = 16 \cdot 8 = 128$

$2^5 \cdot 2^2 = (2 \cdot 2 \cdot 2 \cdot 2 \cdot 2) \cdot (2 \cdot 2) = 32 \cdot 4 = 128$

$2^6 \cdot 2^1 = (2 \cdot 2 \cdot 2 \cdot 2 \cdot 2 \cdot 2) \cdot (2) = 128$

Step 2 Look for a pattern in the table.

Each product is 128.

The sum of the exponents in each product is 7.

Product	Value
$2^2 \cdot 2^5$	128
$2^3 \cdot 2^4$	128
$2^4 \cdot 2^3$	128
$2^5 \cdot 2^2$	128
$2^6 \cdot 2^1$	128

Step 3 Make a conjecture.

The product of two powers with the same base is the base raised to the sum of the exponents.

Solution

Product of Powers: For any real number a and all positive integers m and n,
$a^m \cdot a^n = a^{m+n}$.

Below are two other laws of exponents that can be discovered through patterns.

Power of a Power: For any real number a and all positive integers m and n, $(a^m)^n = a^{mn}$.

Power of a Product: For any real numbers a and b and positive integer m, $(ab)^m = a^m b^m$.

Problem 2

Simplify each expression using the laws of exponents.

a. $x^3 \cdot x^5$ b. $(3y)^3$ c. $(4^2)^3$

Solution

a. $x^3 \cdot x^5$
x^{3+5}
x^8

b. $(3y)^3$
3^3y^3
$27y^3$

c. $(4^2)^3$
$4^{2 \cdot 3}$
$4^6 = 4096$

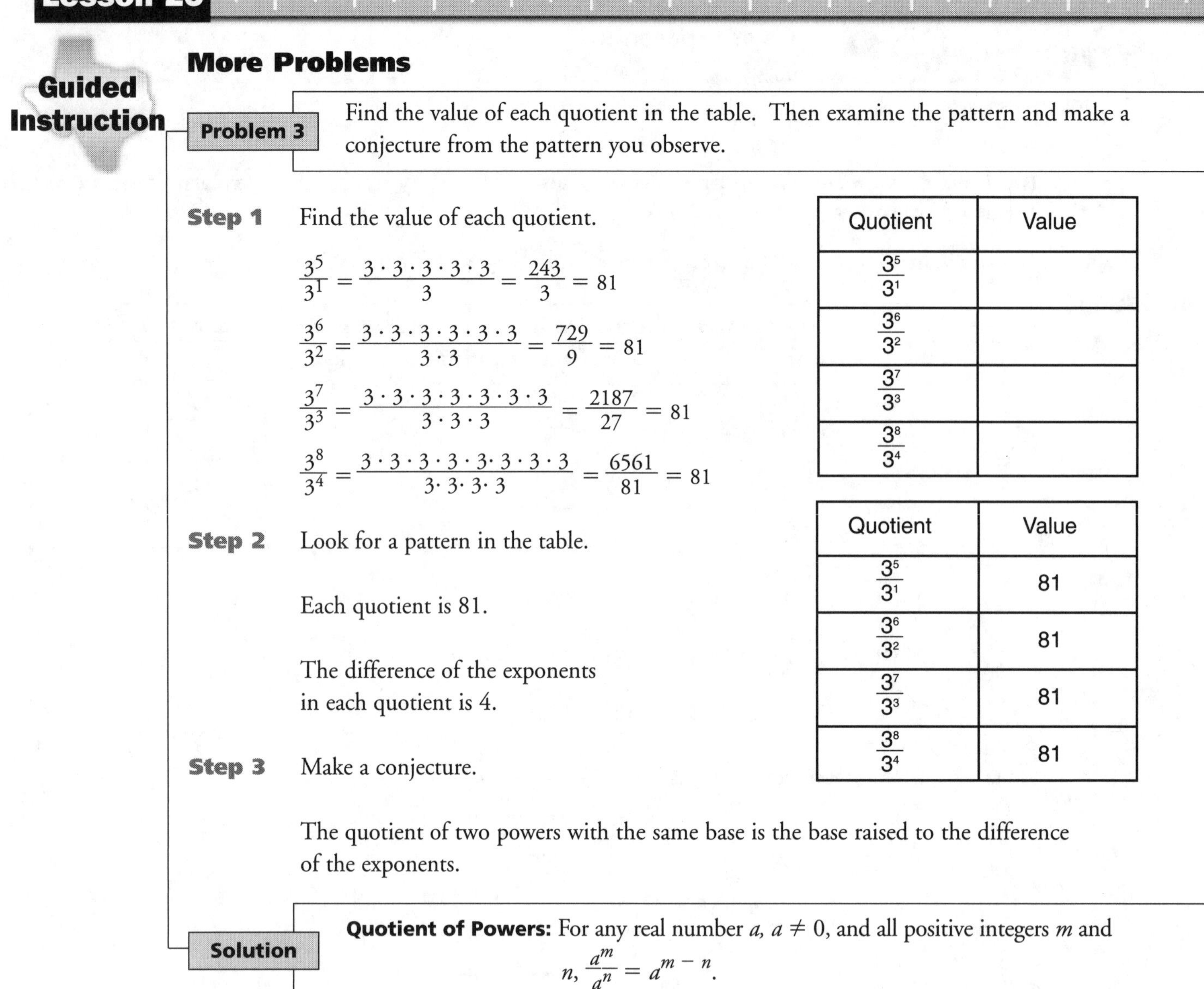

Guided Instruction

More Problems

Problem 3

Find the value of each quotient in the table. Then examine the pattern and make a conjecture from the pattern you observe.

Step 1 Find the value of each quotient.

$$\frac{3^5}{3^1} = \frac{3 \cdot 3 \cdot 3 \cdot 3 \cdot 3}{3} = \frac{243}{3} = 81$$

$$\frac{3^6}{3^2} = \frac{3 \cdot 3 \cdot 3 \cdot 3 \cdot 3 \cdot 3}{3 \cdot 3} = \frac{729}{9} = 81$$

$$\frac{3^7}{3^3} = \frac{3 \cdot 3 \cdot 3 \cdot 3 \cdot 3 \cdot 3 \cdot 3}{3 \cdot 3 \cdot 3} = \frac{2187}{27} = 81$$

$$\frac{3^8}{3^4} = \frac{3 \cdot 3 \cdot 3 \cdot 3 \cdot 3 \cdot 3 \cdot 3 \cdot 3}{3 \cdot 3 \cdot 3 \cdot 3} = \frac{6561}{81} = 81$$

Quotient	Value
$\frac{3^5}{3^1}$	
$\frac{3^6}{3^2}$	
$\frac{3^7}{3^3}$	
$\frac{3^8}{3^4}$	

Step 2 Look for a pattern in the table.

Each quotient is 81.

The difference of the exponents in each quotient is 4.

Quotient	Value
$\frac{3^5}{3^1}$	81
$\frac{3^6}{3^2}$	81
$\frac{3^7}{3^3}$	81
$\frac{3^8}{3^4}$	81

Step 3 Make a conjecture.

The quotient of two powers with the same base is the base raised to the difference of the exponents.

Solution

Quotient of Powers: For any real number a, $a \neq 0$, and all positive integers m and n, $\frac{a^m}{a^n} = a^{m-n}$.

Below are three other laws of exponents which can be discovered through patterns.

Power of a Quotient: For all real numbers a and b, $b \neq 0$, and any positive integer m, $\left(\frac{a}{b}\right)^m = \frac{a^m}{b^m}$.

Zero Exponent: For any real number a, $a \neq 0$, $a^0 = 1$.

Negative Exponent: For any real number a, $a \neq 0$, and any positive integer n, $a^{-n} = \frac{1}{a^n}$.

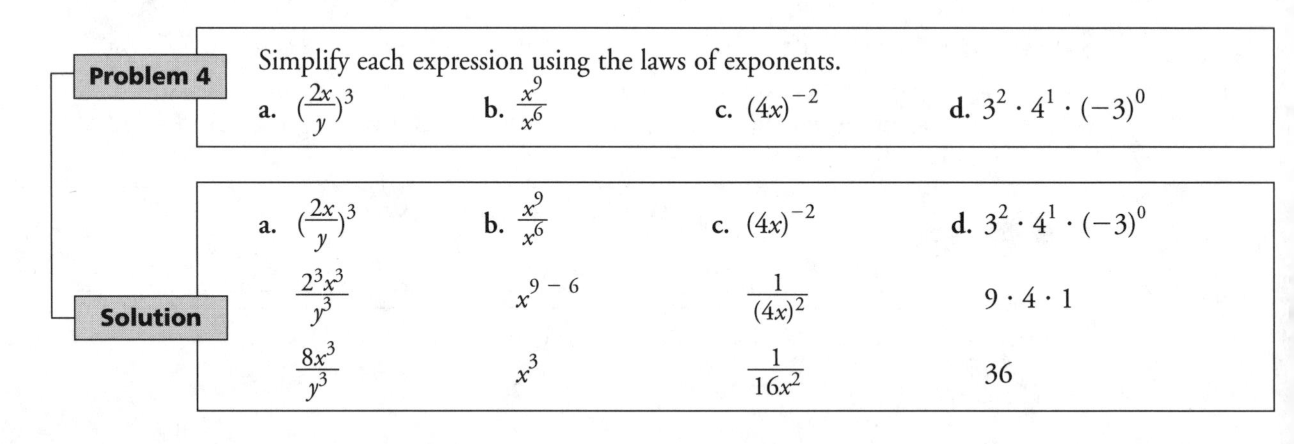

Problem 4

Simplify each expression using the laws of exponents.

a. $\left(\frac{2x}{y}\right)^3$ b. $\frac{x^9}{x^6}$ c. $(4x)^{-2}$ d. $3^2 \cdot 4^1 \cdot (-3)^0$

Solution

a. $\left(\frac{2x}{y}\right)^3$ b. $\frac{x^9}{x^6}$ c. $(4x)^{-2}$ d. $3^2 \cdot 4^1 \cdot (-3)^0$

a. $\frac{2^3x^3}{y^3}$ b. x^{9-6} c. $\frac{1}{(4x)^2}$ d. $9 \cdot 4 \cdot 1$

a. $\frac{8x^3}{y^3}$ b. x^3 c. $\frac{1}{16x^2}$ d. 36

Apply the TEKS State the value of a that makes each statement true.

1. $x^7 \cdot x^5 = x^a$ ______ 2. $\frac{y^a}{y^3} = y^5$ ______ 3. $(x^a)^6 = x^{18}$ ______

4. $(x^2y)^a = 1$ ______ 5. $\left(\frac{3x^2}{2y}\right)^3 = \frac{27x^a}{8y^3}$ ______ 6. $(5y^3)^a = 625y^{12}$ ______

State whether each pair of expressions is equivalent.

7. $\frac{-18a^2b^5}{2ab^3}$ and $-9ab^2$ ______ 8. $(2x^4)^{-2}$ and $\frac{1}{4x^8}$ ______

9. $(3x)^4 + (x^3y)^5$ and $3x^4 + x^{15}y^5$ ______ 10. $\left(\frac{24m^5n^9}{6m^5n^3}\right)^3$ and $64n^{18}$ ______

Simplify each expression using the laws of exponents. Write all answers with positive exponents.

11. $q^5 \cdot q^6$ ______ 12. $\frac{w^8}{w}$ ______ 13. $(h^5k^2)^4$ ______

14. $(a^2b)^{-3}$ ______ 15. $(7c^2d^2)^0$ ______ 16. $\left(\frac{5w^6}{2v^8}\right)^2$ ______

17. $(x^3y^6z)^4$ ______ 18. $\frac{m^9n^5}{m^7n^2}$ ______ 19. $(x^3y^5)(x^2)$ ______

20. $\frac{-30a^4b}{5a^3}$ ______ 21. $(3a^3b^7c^5)^4$ ______ 22. $x^{-4} \cdot x^7$ ______

23. $\frac{-3w^4x^8}{9w^9x^7}$ ______ 24. $p^6 \cdot p^0 \cdot p^{-10}$ ______ 25. $\left(\frac{a^6b^8c^4}{a^5b^{10}c^2}\right)^3$ ______

Solve each problem.

26. Are -3^4 and $(-3)^4$ equivalent? Explain.

______

27. The formula for the volume of a rectangular prism is $V = l \cdot w \cdot h$. Find an expression for the volume of a rectangular prism that has a length of $3x$ feet, a width of $8x$ feet, and a height of $2x$ feet.

______

TAKS Objective 5 The student will demonstrate an understanding of quadratic and other nonlinear functions.
TEKS A(d)3A

DIRECTIONS Read each question. Then circle the letter for the correct answer. If a correct answer is not here, circle the letter for "Not Here."

1 What is the exponent of the product $5x^7 \cdot 3x^3$?

A 21

B 15

C 10

D Not Here

2 When a power is raised to a power, what operation is performed on the exponents?

F Addition

G Subtraction

H Multiplication

J Division

3 Which value of n will make the statement $12x^8 \cdot 6x^n = 72x^{24}$ true?
Record your answer and fill in the bubbles on the grid below. Be sure to use the correct place value.

				.			
0	0	0	0		0	0	0
1	1	1	1		1	1	1
2	2	2	2		2	2	2
3	3	3	3		3	3	3
4	4	4	4		4	4	4
5	5	5	5		5	5	5
6	6	6	6		6	6	6
7	7	7	7		7	7	7
8	8	8	8		8	8	8
9	9	9	9		9	9	9

4 Which of the following equations is NOT true?

F $(4x^3y^0)^4 = 256x^{12}$

G $(a^5b^3)^{-2} = \frac{1}{a^7b^5}$

H $x^0 \cdot x^4 \cdot x^{-1} = x^3$

J $\left(\frac{7m^3}{9n^8}\right)^2 = \frac{49m^6}{81n^{16}}$

5 Which of the following expressions is equivalent to $x^{2a} \cdot x^a \cdot x^{-4a}$?

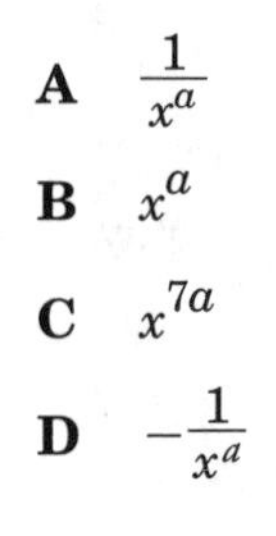

A $\frac{1}{x^a}$

B x^a

C x^{7a}

D $-\frac{1}{x^a}$

6 For which of the following expressions would you use the product of a power rule and the power of quotients rule?

F $(n^3)^2 \cdot (n^7)^4$

G $\left(\frac{n^4 \cdot n^3}{m^8 \cdot m^3}\right)^5$

H $\left(\frac{n^{11}}{n^7}\right)^3$

J $(6n^5)^{-2}$

7 The volume of a rectangular prism is $168x^2y^2$. The length is $7xy$ and the width is $3y$. What is the height of the rectangular prism?

A $8y$

B $7x$

C $8x$

D $16.8xy$

Focus on TEKS

Lesson 26 Inverse Variation

TEKS A(d)3B Analyze data and represent situations involving inverse variation using concrete models, tables, graphs, or algebraic methods.
TEKS 8.14A Identify and apply mathematics to everyday experiences, to activities in and outside of school, with other disciplines, and with other mathematical topics.

In real-world situations, the cost of something may remain constant while a cost per person varies.

An **inverse variation** is a function described by the equation $y = \frac{k}{x}$, where k is a nonzero constant, called the **constant of variation**. This can be described by saying that *y varies inversely as x*.

For example, the cost of playing recreation volleyball may cost \$275 per team. The price p per player is a function of the number of players n on the team, or $p = \frac{275}{n}$. This is an example of an inverse variation function.

Guided Instruction

Problem 1

The Cort family is renting a picnic area at a park for a family reunion. It costs \$185 to rent the picnic area, which will be split evenly among the families attending.

a. Write an equation representing the cost per family in terms of the number of families attending.
b. Make a table representing the cost per family based on up to 7 families attending.
c. How much is the cost per family if 6 families attend?
d. How many families must attend to keep the cost below \$20 per family?

Part a. Write the inverse variation equation. The cost per family varies inversely as the number of families attending the reunion. Let x represent the number of families attending and let y represent the cost per family.

$$y = \frac{185}{x}$$

Part b. Use the inverse variation equation to complete the table.

Number of Families	1	2	3	4	5	6	7
Cost per Family	\$185.00	\$92.50	\$61.67	\$46.25	\$37.00	\$30.83	\$26.43

Part c. Use the table to find the cost per family if 6 families attend.
The cost will be \$30.83 per family.

Part d. Let $y = 20$ and solve for x to find the number of families that must attend to keep the cost below \$20 per family.

$$20 = \frac{185}{x}$$
$$x \cdot 20 = \frac{185}{x} \cdot x$$
$$20x = 185$$
$$\frac{20x}{20} = \frac{185}{20}$$
$$x = 9.25$$

Since the number of families must be a whole number, 10 families must attend to keep the cost below \$20 per family.

Solution Using the table or inverse variation equation, the cost per family is \$30.83 if 6 families attend. To keep the cost below \$20 per family, 10 families must attend the reunion.

Guided Instruction

If (x_1, y_1) and (x_2, y_2) are both solutions of an inverse variation equation, then you can relate the two solutions using either a product or a proportion.

Product Rule for Inverse Variation: $x_1y_1 = x_2y_2$

Proportion Rule for Inverse Variation: $\frac{x_1}{x_2} = \frac{y_2}{y_1}$

More Problems

Problem 2 If y varies inversely as x, and $y = 8$ when $x = 38$, find x when $y = 16$.

Step 1 Write the points as (x_1, y_1) and (x_2, y_2) to determine which value you are looking for.

(38, 8) and $(x_2, 16)$.

Step 2 Use the product rule or proportion rule for inverse variation.

product rule:	proportion rule:
$x_1y_1 = x_2y_2$	$\frac{x_1}{x_2} = \frac{y_2}{y_1}$
$38 \cdot 8 = x_2 \cdot 16$	$\frac{38}{x_2} = \frac{16}{8}$
$304 = 16x_2$	$304 = 16x_2$
$19 = x_2$	$19 = x_2$

Solution When y is 16, x is 19.

The amount of weight needed to balance a lever is an example of an inverse variation. A lever is balanced when $w_1d_1 = w_2d_2$, where w_1 and w_2 are the respective weights on the lever and d_1 and d_2 are the respective distances from the fulcrum.

Problem 3 If Sam weighs 130 pounds and is sitting 7 feet from the fulcrum on a seesaw, how far from the fulcrum should Tyrell sit to balance the seesaw if he weighs 140 pounds?

Step 1 Use the equation for a balanced lever.

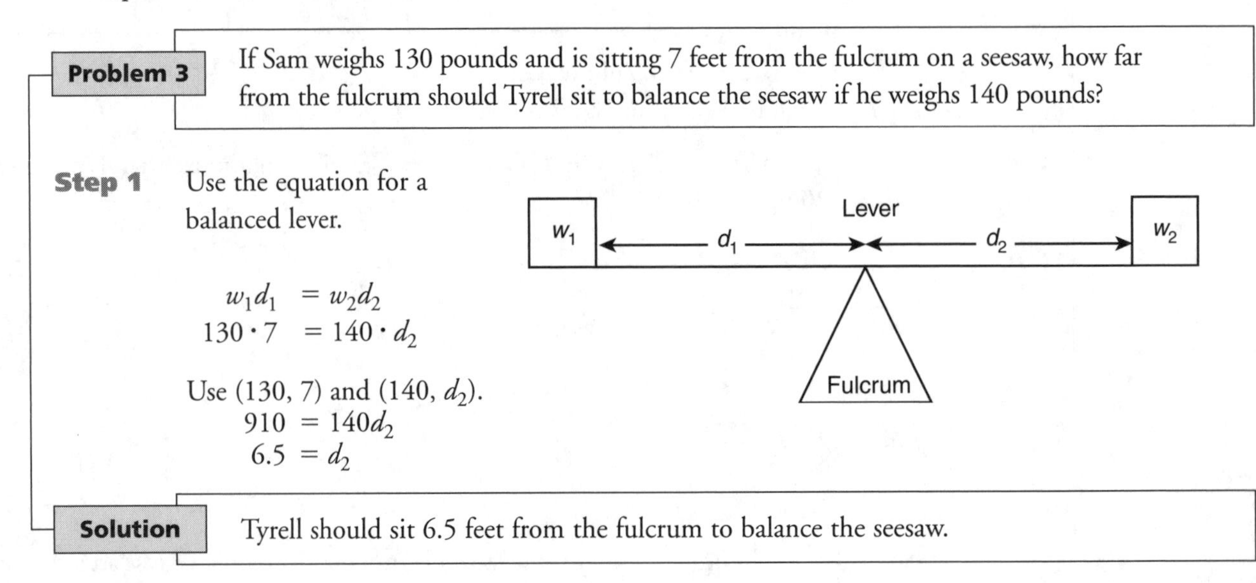

$w_1d_1 = w_2d_2$

$130 \cdot 7 = 140 \cdot d_2$

Use (130, 7) and $(140, d_2)$.

$910 = 140d_2$

$6.5 = d_2$

Solution Tyrell should sit 6.5 feet from the fulcrum to balance the seesaw.

Apply the TEKS Find k, the constant of variation, for each inverse variation.

1. $y = 12$ when $x = 3$ ____________
2. $x = \frac{2}{3}$ when $y = 9$ ____________
3. $x = 7$ when $y = 12$ ____________
4. $y = 8.5$ when $x = 35$ ____________
5. $y = 22$ when $x = 13$ ____________
6. $x = 40$ when $y = 7.5$ ____________

In each case, assume y varies inversely as x.

7. When $x = 3$, $y = 8$. Find x when $y = 4$. ________
8. When $x = 18$, $y = 5$. Find y when $x = 15$. ________
9. When $x = 4.5$, $y = 24$. Find y when $x = 27$. ________
10. When $x = \frac{5}{8}$, $y = 72$. Find x when $y = 9$. ________
11. When $x = 23$, $y = 4$. Find x when $y = \frac{5}{8}$. ________
12. When $x = 46$, $y = 58$. Find y when $x = 92$. ________

Find the missing value for each pair of points, which form an inverse variation.

13. $(a, 12)$ and $(3, 8)$ ____________
14. $(6, 8)$ and $(4, n)$ ____________
15. $(11, 6)$ and $(w, 4)$ ____________
16. $(\frac{3}{4}, 16)$ and $(\frac{1}{3}, m)$ ____________
17. $(4, p)$ and $(6.2, 20)$ ____________
18. $(d, 10.4)$ and $(12.8, 6.5)$ ____________

Solve each problem.

19. Some students are sharing the cost of a birthday cake for their teacher. The cost of the cake is \$36.
    a. Write an equation for the cost of the cake per student based on the number of students chipping in for the cake. ________________
    b. If 15 students chip in for the cake, how much will it cost each student? ________________

20. Jack and Morgan are on a seesaw. If Jack weighs 115 pounds and is sitting 9 feet from the fulcrum on the seesaw, how far from the fulcrum should Morgan sit to balance the seesaw if she weighs 90 pounds? ________________

21. Rosa and Carlos are on a seesaw. If Rosa weighs 125 pounds and is sitting 6 feet from the fulcrum on the seesaw, how much does Carlos weigh if he is sitting 5 feet from the fulcrum and the seesaw is balanced? ________________

TAKS Objective 10 The student will demonstrate an understanding of the mathematical processes and tools used in problem solving.
TEKS 8.14A

DIRECTIONS Read each question. Then circle the letter for the correct answer. If a correct answer is not here, circle the letter for "Not Here."

1 Aneesa and Tricia are on a seesaw. Tricia weighs 106 pounds and is 8 feet from the fulcrum. Aneesa weighs 128 pounds. If the seesaw is balanced, which equation can be used to find the distance Aneesa is from the fulcrum?

A $106 \cdot d = 128 \cdot 8$

B $\frac{108}{6} = \frac{128}{d}$

C $106 \cdot 128 = 8 \cdot d$

D $106 \cdot 8 = 128 \cdot d$

2 The area of a rectangle is 36 square feet. Which of the following inverse variation equations represents the length of the rectangle in terms of the width?

F $l \cdot 36 = w$

G $l = \frac{36}{w}$

H $\frac{l}{w} = 36$

J $l = \frac{w}{36}$

3 Mrs. Carlisle hires high school students from her neighborhood to place mulch around the landscaping in her yard. If she has 3 students working it will take 7 hours. How long will it take if 5 students work?

A 2.1 h

B 3.5 h

C 4.2 h

D 11.6 h

4 The time it takes to travel a certain distance is inversely proportional to the speed at which one travels. Mr. Fenster is driving 260 miles to visit a relative. He usually drives at a constant rate of 65 miles per hour. However, due to construction he will have to drive at a constant rate of 55 miles per hour. About how much longer will the drive take Mr. Fenster?

F About 25 min

G About 45 min

H About 75 min

J About 90 min

5 Which of the following situations does NOT represent an inverse variation relationship?

A The cost per person of renting a limousine $350 divided evenly among a group of friends

B The total cost of buying ground beef that costs $3.29 per pound

C The time it takes to run a marathon (approximately 26 miles) based on the speed of the runner

D The time it takes to paint a house based on the number of painters

Focus on TEKS

Lesson 27 Exponential Growth and Decay

TEKS A(d)3C Analyze data and represent situations involving exponential growth and decay using concrete models, tables, graphs, or algebraic methods.

TEKS 8.14A Identify and apply mathematics to everyday experiences, to activities in and outside of school, with other disciplines, and with other mathematical topics.

Two examples of functions that are neither linear nor quadratic are exponential growth functions and exponential decay functions.

The general form of an **exponential growth function** is $y = C(1 + r)^t$, where C is the starting amount, r is the percent increase, and t is the time. The quantity $(1 + r)$ is called the growth factor. Compound interest is an example of exponential growth, and the half-life of a substance is an example of exponential decay.

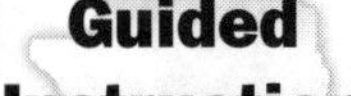

Guided Instruction

Problem 1 Nakesha deposited \$2,000 into a savings account that pays 6% interest, compounded semi-annually. Find the amount of money in Nakesha's savings account after 5 years.

Interest rates are sometimes compounded more than once a year. The table illustrates the rate of interest for each period based on the method of compounding.

Compounded	Periods per Year	Rate each Period
Annually	1	6%
Semi-annually	2	$\frac{6\%}{2}$ or 3%
Quarterly	4	$\frac{6\%}{4}$ or 1.5%
Monthly	12	$\frac{6\%}{12}$ or 0.5%

Step 1 Determine which values in the problem represent each variable in the exponential growth function.

y = amount in account after 5 years
C = starting amount = \$2,000
r = percent increase = 3% = 0.03
t = number of times = 2 times every 5 years = 10

Step 2 Substitute the values in the equation and solve for y.

$y = 2{,}000(1 + 0.03)^{10}$
$y = 2{,}000(1.03)^{10}$
$y = 2{,}000(1.3439)$
$y = 2{,}687.80$

Solution After 5 years, Nakesha will have \$2,687.80 in her savings account.

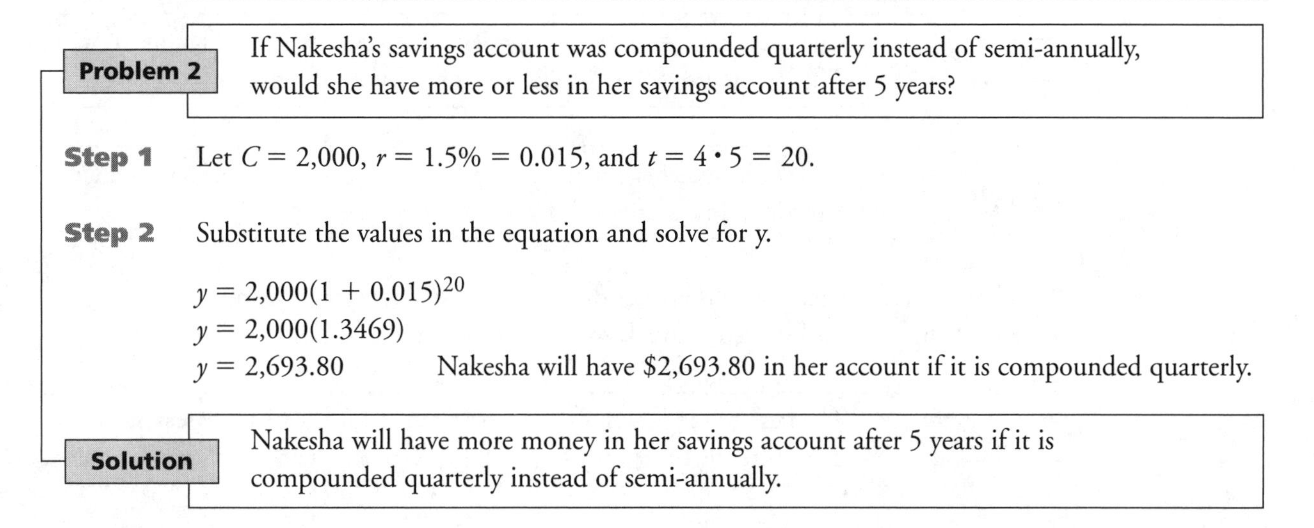

Problem 2 If Nakesha's savings account was compounded quarterly instead of semi-annually, would she have more or less in her savings account after 5 years?

Step 1 Let $C = 2{,}000$, $r = 1.5\% = 0.015$, and $t = 4 \cdot 5 = 20$.

Step 2 Substitute the values in the equation and solve for y.

$y = 2{,}000(1 + 0.015)^{20}$
$y = 2{,}000(1.3469)$
$y = 2{,}693.80$ Nakesha will have \$2,693.80 in her account if it is compounded quarterly.

Solution Nakesha will have more money in her savings account after 5 years if it is compounded quarterly instead of semi-annually.

Guided Instruction

The general form of an exponential decay function is $y = C(1 - r)^t$, where C is the starting amount, r is the percent decrease, and t is the time. The quantity $(1 - r)$ is called the decay factor.

More Problems

Problem 3

Radioactive elements decay according to a process called *half-life*, or the amount of time it takes for half of the initial quantity to decay. The half-life of sodium-24 is 15 hours. This means that half of the remaining substance decays every 15 hours.

a. Write an equation to represent the decay of 60 milligrams of sodium-24.

b. Use a graphing calculator to graph the equation in Part a. Describe the graph.

c. How much of the substance will remain after 90 hours?

Part a. Determine which values in the problem represent each variable in the exponential growth function.

y = amount of substance remaining after t half-lives
C = starting amount = 60 mg
r = percent decrease = 50% = 0.5
t = number of half-lives

$y = 60(1 - 0.5)^t$
$y = 60(0.5)^t$

Part b. Enter and graph the equation $y = 60(0.5)^t$ on a graphing calculator. To better view the graph, change the viewing window to $x$min = 0, $x$max = 10, $y$min = 0, $y$max = 20.

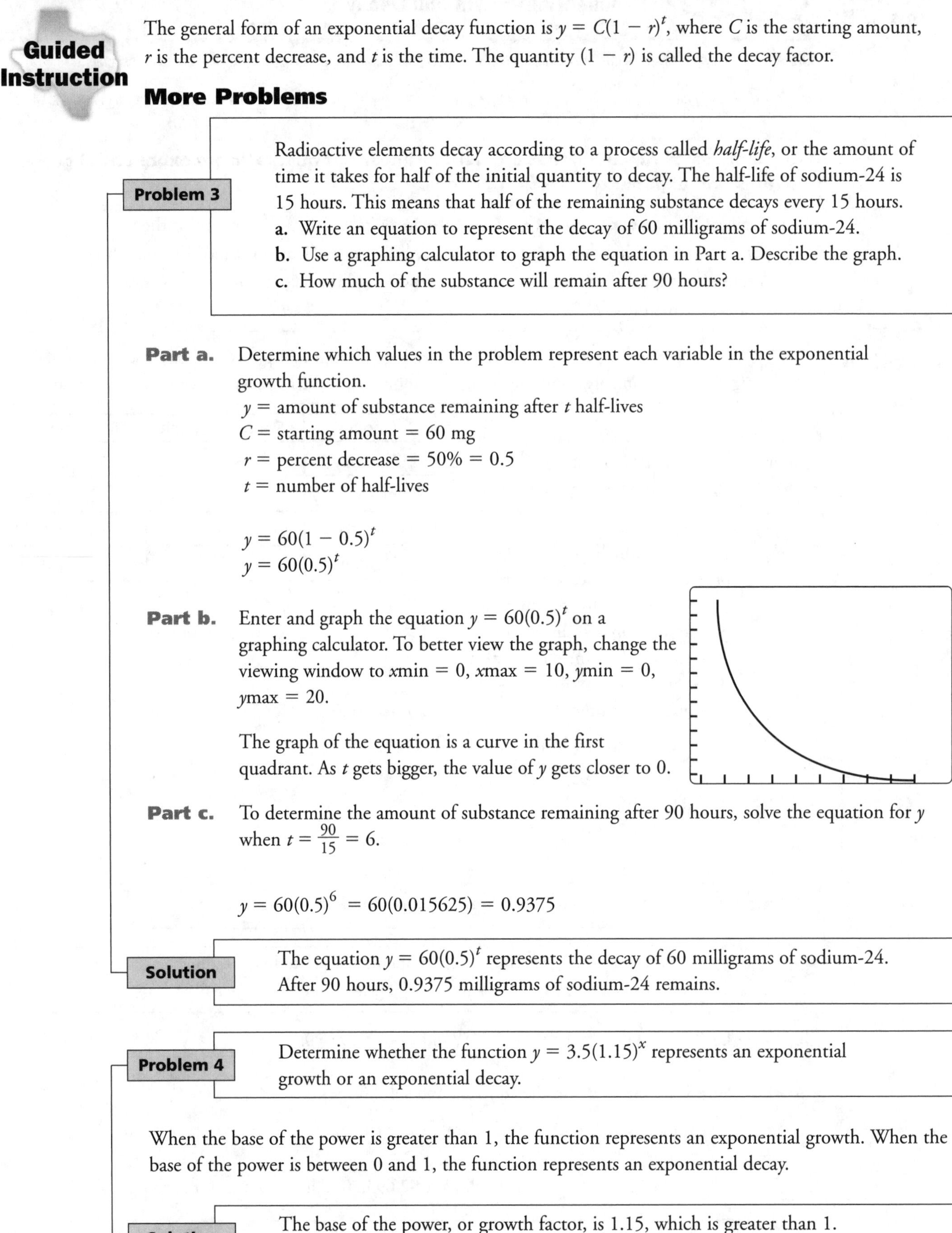

The graph of the equation is a curve in the first quadrant. As t gets bigger, the value of y gets closer to 0.

Part c. To determine the amount of substance remaining after 90 hours, solve the equation for y when $t = \frac{90}{15} = 6$.

$y = 60(0.5)^6 = 60(0.015625) = 0.9375$

Solution

The equation $y = 60(0.5)^t$ represents the decay of 60 milligrams of sodium-24. After 90 hours, 0.9375 milligrams of sodium-24 remains.

Problem 4

Determine whether the function $y = 3.5(1.15)^x$ represents an exponential growth or an exponential decay.

When the base of the power is greater than 1, the function represents an exponential growth. When the base of the power is between 0 and 1, the function represents an exponential decay.

Solution

The base of the power, or growth factor, is 1.15, which is greater than 1. Therefore the function $y = 3.5(1.15)^x$ represents an exponential growth.

Apply the TEKS Identify the growth factor or decay factor of each exponential function in simplified form.

1. $y = 2(1.06)^t$ ________

2. $y = 18(1 + 0.85)^x$ ________

3. $y = (1 - 0.22)^x(315)$ ________

State whether each equation represents an *exponential growth* or an *exponential decay*.

4. $y = 18(1 - 0.25)^x$ ________

5. $y = 0.6(1 + 0.1)^t$ ________

6. $y = 3(1.27)^x$ ________

7. $y = 1.7(0.7)^t$ ________

8. $y = 128(1.004)^x$ ________

9. $y = (1 - 0.009)^x(1.38)$ ________

Identify the percent of increase or decrease of each exponential function.

10. $y = 95(1.097)^x$ ________

11. $y = 1.35(0.45)^t$ ________

12. $y = 2{,}000(1.0125)^x$ ________

Solve each problem.

13. Gabe invested $6200 into a CD (certificate of deposit). The CD pays 7% interest compounded annually.

 a. Write an equation to represent the value of the CD after t years. ________

 b. What will be the value of the CD after 6 years? ________

 c. What would be the value of the CD after 6 years if was compounded semi-annually? ________

 d. What would be the value of the CD after 6 years if it was compounded quarterly? ________

 e. Complete the following statement with the word *more* or *less*.

 The value of money invested will grow ________ rapidly the more times it is compounded.

14. In 1990, the population of Alabama was 4,040,587. Since then the population of Alabama has increased by about 1% each year.

 a. Write an equation to represent the population of Alabama since 1990. ________

 b. What was the approximate population of Alabama in 1995? ________

 c. If the current rate of increase continues, what will be the estimated population of Alabama in 2008? ________

TAKS Objective 10 The student will demonstrate an understanding of the mathematical processes and tools used in problem solving.
TEKS 8.14A

DIRECTIONS Read each question. Then circle the letter for the correct answer. If a correct answer is not here, circle the letter for "Not Here."

1 Madison invested $1,600 into a savings account that pays 3% interest compounded semi-annually. How much money will be in the account after 2 years? Round your answer to the nearest cent.

Record your answer and fill in the bubbles on the grid below. Be sure to use the correct place value.

				.			
0	0	0	0		0	0	0
1	1	1	1		1	1	1
2	2	2	2		2	2	2
3	3	3	3		3	3	3
4	4	4	4		4	4	4
5	5	5	5		5	5	5
6	6	6	6		6	6	6
7	7	7	7		7	7	7
8	8	8	8		8	8	8
9	9	9	9		9	9	9

2 A ball is dropped from a ladder that is 12 feet high. Each bounce is half the height of its previous bounce. How high will the ball bounce on the fifth bounce?

F $1\frac{1}{2}$ ft

G $\frac{3}{4}$ ft

H $\frac{3}{8}$ ft

J $\frac{3}{16}$ ft

3 If the population of a city began decreasing in 1985 at a steady pace of 1.25% each year, which equation represents the population of the city in 2001. Let c represent the population of the city in 1985.

A $y = c(0.9875)^{16}$

B $y = c(1.0125)^{16}$

C $y = c(0.9875)^{15}$

D $y = c(0.875)^{16}$

4 Niko started a job earning an annual salary of $27,800. As long as Niko's annual performance evaluation is positive, Niko will receive an annual raise of 3%. If Niko receives the 3% raise each year, what can Niko expect his annual salary to be after 7 years?

F $29,544.41

G $30,046.19

H $34,190.49

J $35,216.21

5 The half life of oxygen-15 is 2 minutes. How long will it take 100 milligrams of oxygen-15 to decay to 6.25 milligrams?

A 4 min

B 6 min

C 8 min

D 16 min

Building Stamina™

DIRECTIONS Read each question. Then circle the letter for the correct answer. If a correct answer is not here, circle the letter for "Not Here."

1 Josh, Kim, and Dante each predicted how the graph of $y = \frac{1}{4}x^2$ will look compared to the graph of $y = x^2$. Josh said the graph will be more narrow than the graph of $y = x^2$. Kim said the graph will open in the opposite direction of the graph of $y = x^2$. Dante said the graph will be wider than the graph of $y = x^2$. Who is correct?

A Josh

B Kim

C Dante

D Not Here

2 Below is the graph of the quadratic function $y = \frac{1}{2}x^2 - 5$.

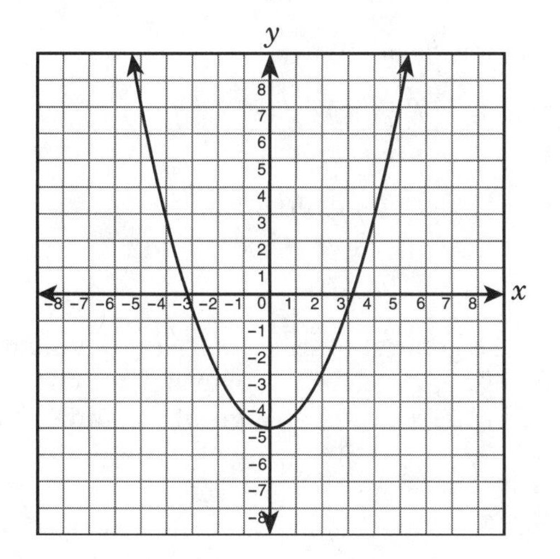

What is the range of the function?

F $\{y: y = \text{all real numbers}\}$

G $\{y: y \geq -5\}$

H $\{x: x = \text{all real numbers}\}$

J $\{x: -8 < x < 8\}$

3 The function $h = 76t - 16t^2$, where t is time in seconds, represents the height of a ball thrown into the air with an initial velocity of 76 feet per second. How would the graph of this function change if the ball was thrown into the air with an initial velocity of 95 feet per second?

A The graph will have a greater maximum value.

B The graph will intersect the x-axis closer to the origin.

C The graph will have a smaller minimum value.

D The graph will remain the same.

4 How can the graph of $y = 5x^2 - 2x + 7$ help you solve the equation $0 = 5x^2 - 2x + 7$?

F The solutions, or roots, of the equation are the points where the graph intersects the y-axis.

G The solutions, or roots, of the equation are the points where the graph intersects the x-axis.

H The solution is the vertex of the graph.

J The solution is the entire parabola graphed.

5 Which value of n will make the statement $(\frac{25x^n}{5x^4})^3 = 125x^9$ true?

A 3

B 5

C 7

D 10

6 Which of the following functions represents the graph of $y = x^2 - 6$ shifted up 9 units on the y-axis?

F $y = x^2 - 9$

G $y = x^2 + 3$

H $y = x^2 - 15$

J $y = x^2 - 3$

7 The equation $h = 128t - 16t^2$ represents the height (h) of a rocket shot into the air after t seconds. After how many seconds will the rocket return to the ground?

A 7 sec

B 7.5 sec

C 8 sec

D 9 sec

8 The graph represents the height of a ball thrown into the air after t seconds.

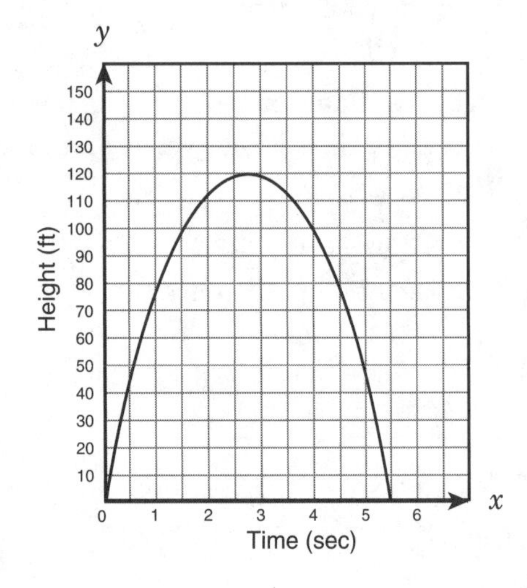

Which equation represents this situation?

F $h = 44t - 16t^2$

G $h = 88t - 16t^2$

H $h = 176t - 16t^2$

J $h = 90t^2 - 16^t$

9 Which of the following quadratic functions has the narrowest graph?

A $y = \frac{1}{7}x^2 - 5$

B $y = 3x^2 + 12$

C $y = \frac{1}{2}x^2 + 7$

D $y = 6x^2 - 4$

10 Which exponent law is illustrated in the table?

$\frac{4^4}{4^1}$	64
$\frac{4^5}{4^2}$	64
$\frac{4^6}{4^3}$	64
$\frac{4^7}{4^4}$	64
$\frac{4^8}{4^5}$	64

F Power of a power

G Quotient of powers

H Power of a product

J Power of a quotient

11 In the general form $y = ax^2 + c$ of a quadratic function, which of the following statements will always result in a graph opening upward?

A $|c| > 0$

B $a < 0$

C $a > 0$

D $|a| > 0$

12 What is the effect on the graph of the equation $y = 6x^2$ when it is changed to $y = -6x^2$?

F The graph of $y = -6x^2$ is a reflection of $y = 6x^2$ across the x-axis.

G The vertex of the graph is at (26, 0), instead of (6, 0).

H The graph is rotated 90° counterclockwise.

J Not Here

13 A ball was thrown into the air with an initial velocity of 72 feet per second. The height of the ball after t seconds is represented by the equation $h = 72t - 16t^2$. The graph of the function is shown below.

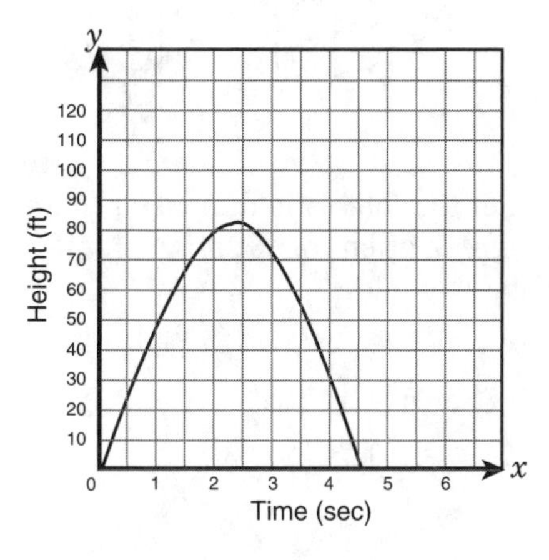

What is the best conclusion you can reach about the ball's action from the graph?

A The ball reached a maximum height of 72 feet.

B The ball was in the air for less than 4 seconds.

C It took the ball longer to reach its maximum height than it did to return to the ground.

D It took slightly more than 2 seconds for the ball to reach its maximum height.

14 What is the exponent of z in the product $(12x^3y^6z^5)(5x^9y^7z^{12})$?

Record your answer and fill in the bubbles on the grid below. Be sure to use the correct place value.

				.			
0	0	0	0		0	0	0
1	1	1	1		1	1	1
2	2	2	2		2	2	2
3	3	3	3		3	3	3
4	4	4	4		4	4	4
5	5	5	5		5	5	5
6	6	6	6		6	6	6
7	7	7	7		7	7	7
8	8	8	8		8	8	8
9	9	9	9		9	9	9

15 What is the vertex of the graph of the quadratic function $y = 2x^2 + 4x - 6$?

A $\left(-\frac{1}{2}, -7\frac{1}{2}\right)$

B (1, 0)

C (0, 26)

D (−1, −8)

16 What are the roots of the equation $-3(x - 5)^2 = -147$?

F −2 and 12

G −7 and 7

H 44 and 54

J −12 and 2

17 Which of the following calculator screens represents the graph of the equation $y = 3x^2 + 6x - 5$?

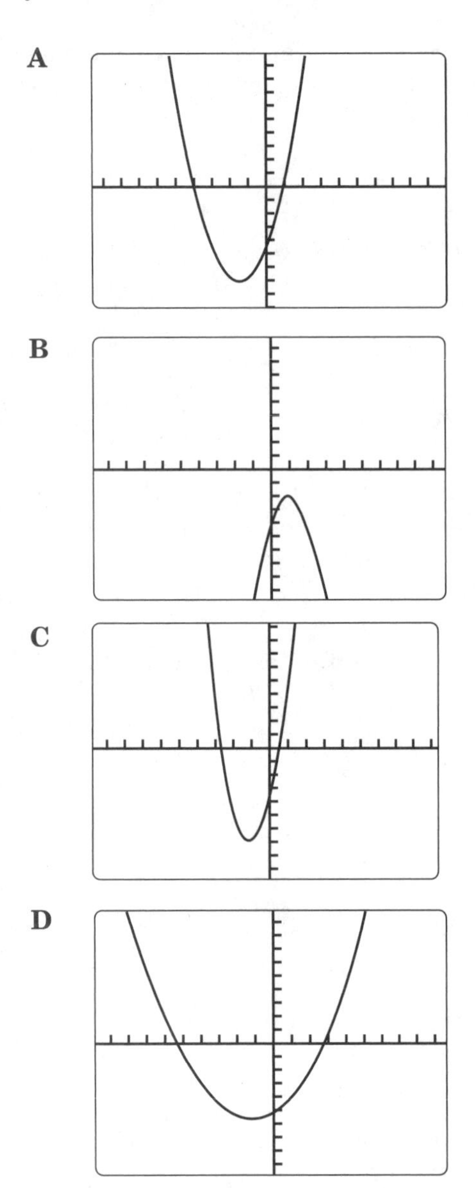

18 Which of the following functions has a minimum or maximum point $(-2, 2)$?

F $y = -8x^2 - 2x - 30$

G $y = -3x^2 - 12x - 10$

H $y = 3x^2 + 6x + 2$

J Not Here

19 What is the coefficient when the following expression is simplified?

$$\left(\frac{56a^9b^5c^2}{8a^4b^3c}\right)^4$$

Record your answer and fill in the bubbles on the grid below. Be sure to use the correct place value.

				.			
0	0	0	0		0	0	0
1	1	1	1		1	1	1
2	2	2	2		2	2	2
3	3	3	3		3	3	3
4	4	4	4		4	4	4
5	5	5	5		5	5	5
6	6	6	6		6	6	6
7	7	7	7		7	7	7
8	8	8	8		8	8	8
9	9	9	9		9	9	9

20 Which of the following dimensions of a rectangular prism result in a volume of $540x^4y^5$?

F $5x^2y$ by $9x^3y$ by $12xy^2$

G $6xy^3$ by $5xy$ by $18x^2y$

H $15x^4y^2$ by $6x^3y$ by $8xy^3$

J $4x^4y$ by $18x^3y$ by $8x^4y$

21 The equation $p = 0.08t(1000 - t)$ represents the profit of a company that makes T-shirts, where t represents the number of T-shirts sold. What is the maximum profit the company can make on the sale of the T-shirts?

A \$500

B \$10,000

C \$20,000

D \$40,000

PART 1 Building Stamina™

DIRECTIONS Read each question. Then circle the letter for the correct answer. If a correct answer is not here, circle the letter for "Not Here."

1 Which represents a function?

I

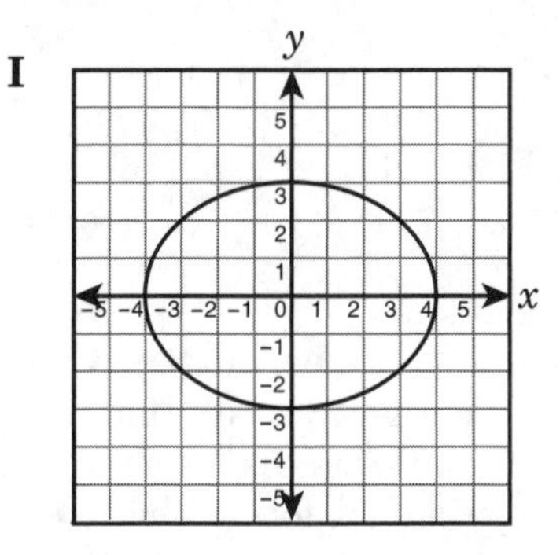

II

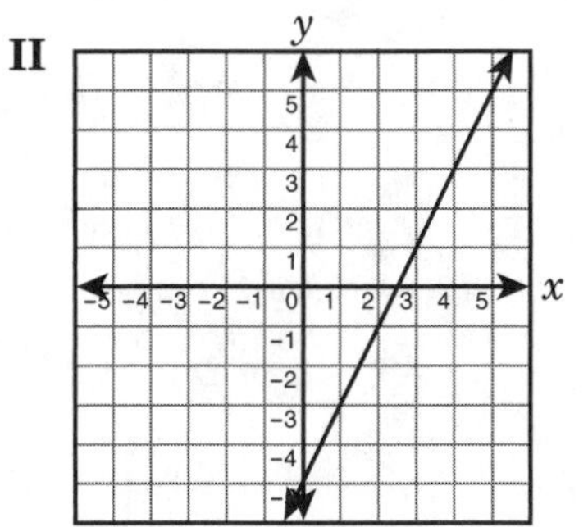

III

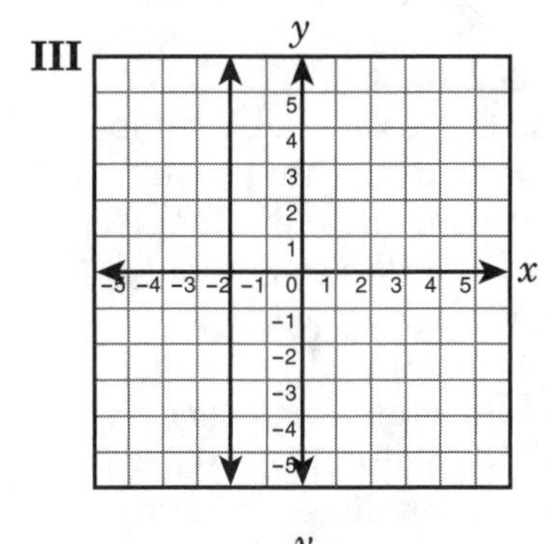

IV

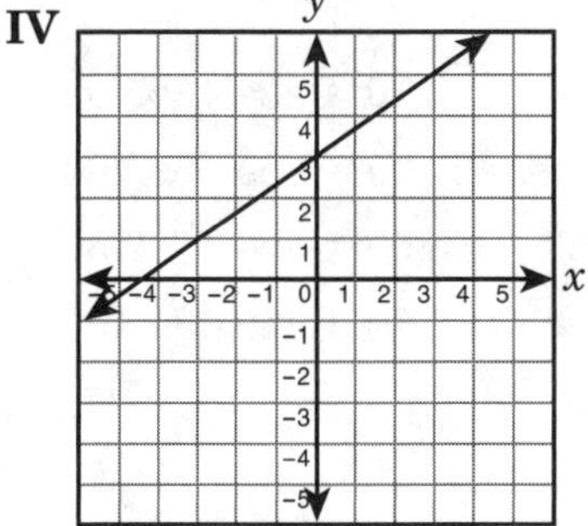

A I only

B Both I and II

C II only

D Both II and IV

Use the following scenario to answer Questions 2–3.

Jeremy's cell phone company charges a flat rate of \$19.95 per month with 150 free airtime minutes. Additional minutes are billed at 25 cents per minute. Michael's company charges \$24.95 per month and an additional 20 cents per minute after the first 200 free airtime minutes.

2 Which of the following equations can be used to find the cost of Jeremy's bill if he used x minutes more than 150?

F $y = 19.95 + 150x$

G $y = 19.95 - 0.25x$

H $y = 19.95 + 0.25x$

J $y = 19.95 - 25x$

3 Both Jeremy and Michael used 300 minutes last month. What was the difference between Jeremy's bill and Michael's bill?

Record your answer and fill in the bubbles on the grid below. Be sure to use the correct place value.

				.			
0	0	0	0		0	0	0
1	1	1	1		1	1	1
2	2	2	2		2	2	2
3	3	3	3		3	3	3
4	4	4	4		4	4	4
5	5	5	5		5	5	5
6	6	6	6		6	6	6
7	7	7	7		7	7	7
8	8	8	8		8	8	8
9	9	9	9		9	9	9

4 Determine which of the following relations are functions.

I {(4,5), (4,9), (4,13)}

II {(0,0), (1,5), (2,10)}

III {(1,4), (2,4), (3,4)}

IV {(0,6), (0,8), (0,10)}

F I only

G I and II only

H II only

J II and III only

5 The graph of the two equations $y = \frac{3}{4}x + 2$ and $4y - 3x - 8 = 0$ would show —

A the same line

B parallel lines

C perpendicular lines

D Different lines

6 A coin collector has 85 coins in dimes and quarters with a total value of \$16.15. How many of each type of coin does she have?

F 25 dimes, 60 quarters

G 34 dimes, 51 quarters

H 42 dimes, 43 quarters

J 60 dimes, 25 quarters

7 Square *ABCD* is shown below.

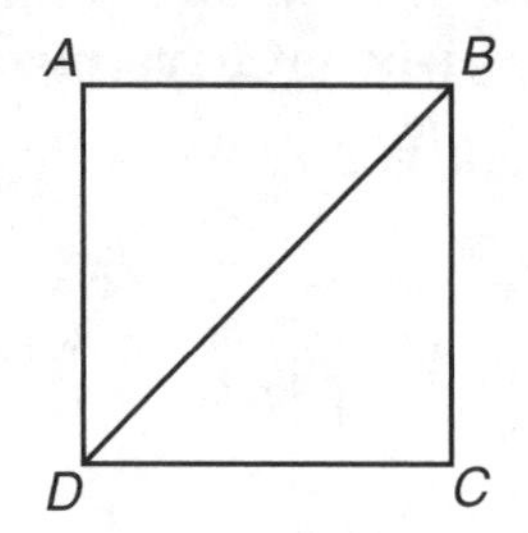

If the length of one side is equal to $x + 4$, then the area of the square can be written as $(x + 4)^2$. Write an equation to verify that the area of square *ABCD* is equal to the sum of the areas of the two triangles formed by diagonal $\overline{BD}$.

A $(x - 2)(x + 2) = x^2 + 4$

B $(x + 4)^2 = 2x + 8$

C $(x + 4)^2 = \frac{1}{2}(x + 4)^2 + \frac{1}{2}(x + 4)^2$

D $(x + 4) + (x^2 - 4) = (2x - 8)^2$

8 Tod, Gabe, and Mike decided to share the cost of a limo for the prom. Since they all lived in different areas, they agreed that they would each pay a \$60 flat rate and an additional fee for mileage from their homes to the prom site. Gabe lives twice as far away as Tod, who lives 3 miles farther than Mike. Mike lives only 2 miles from the location where the prom was being held. If their additional mileage fee was 50 cents per mile, how much did each have to pay?

F Mike - \$65.00, Tod - \$62.50, Gabe - \$61.00

G Mike - \$62.50, Tod - \$61.00, Gabe - \$65.00

H Mike - \$61.00, Tod - \$65.00, Gabe - \$62.50

J Mike - \$61.00, Tod - \$62.50, Gabe - \$65.00

9 Look at the table below.

x	1	2	3	6	10
y	3	6	9	18	30

Which statement is true, based on the data in the table?

A y does not vary directly with x, and $y = 3x$.

B y varies directly with x, and $y = x + 2$.

C y varies directly with x, and $y = 3x$.

D y does not vary directly with x, and $y = \frac{x}{2} - 1$.

10 The sum of two numbers is 100. Their difference is 10. What is the value of the smaller number?

Record your answer and fill in the bubbles on the grid below. Be sure to use the correct place value.

				.			
0	0	0	0		0	0	0
1	1	1	1		1	1	1
2	2	2	2		2	2	2
3	3	3	3		3	3	3
4	4	4	4		4	4	4
5	5	5	5		5	5	5
6	6	6	6		6	6	6
7	7	7	7		7	7	7
8	8	8	8		8	8	8
9	9	9	9		9	9	9

11 Mr. Adams needs 6 gallons of a 50% alcohol solution. Which is NOT a reasonable combination to give him the result that he needs?

A 4 gal of a 40% solution and 2 gal of a 70% solution

B 4 gal of a 60% solution and 2 gal of a 30% solution

C 3 gal of a 30% solution and 3 gal of a 70% solution

D 3 gal of a 50% solution and 3 gal of a 70% solution

12 Which is an equation of the line in standard form with slope 3 that passes through the point (2, −5)?

F $y = 3x + 11$

G $3x - y = 11$

H $y = 3x + 3$

J $3x - y = 3$

13 What will happen to the graph of $y = 5x^2 + 3$ if the coefficient of x^2 is decreased by 3 and the constant is increased by 1?

A The parabola will become narrower and shift to the left one unit.

B The parabola will become narrower and shift to the right one unit.

C The parabola will become wider and shift down one unit.

D The parabola will become wider and shift up one unit.

14 Tamara has $250 to spend on her dress, shoes, and accessories for the prom. If Tamara spent $142.50 for her dress, and s represents the amount she can spend on shoes and accessories, which statement is true?

F $142.50 - s \leq 250$

G $142.50 - s = 250$

H $s + 142.50 \leq 250$

J $s - 142.50 > 250$

Use the information in the following scenario to answer Questions 15–18.

The car manufacturer Nologo has an SUV that sells for $22,000 and depreciates by $1,500 per year. A competitor's SUV sells for $19,500 and depreciates by $1,250 per year.

15 Which of the following statements is true about the relationship between the age of the vehicle and the value of the vehicle?

A It is a function only for Nologo's SUV.

B It is a function only for the competitor's SUV.

C The relationship is a function for both Nologo's SUV and the competitor's SUV.

D Neither relationship can be expressed as a function.

16 Which equation expresses the relationship of a Nologo SUV's value y and its age in years x in standard form?

F $x + 1{,}500y = 22{,}000$

G $1{,}250x + y = 19{,}500$

H $x + 1{,}250y = 19{,}500$

J $1{,}500x + y = 22{,}000$

17 How many years would it take for the two SUVs to be equal in value?

Record your answer and fill in the bubbles on the grid below. Be sure to use the correct place value.

				.			
0	0	0	0		0	0	0
1	1	1	1		1	1	1
2	2	2	2		2	2	2
3	3	3	3		3	3	3
4	4	4	4		4	4	4
5	5	5	5		5	5	5
6	6	6	6		6	6	6
7	7	7	7		7	7	7
8	8	8	8		8	8	8
9	9	9	9		9	9	9

18 If Nologo raises its price by $3,000 next year, and the competitor raises its price by $1,000, how many years will it take for the two SUV's to be of equal value?

Record your answer and fill in the bubbles on the grid below. Be sure to use the correct place value.

				.			
0	0	0	0		0	0	0
1	1	1	1		1	1	1
2	2	2	2		2	2	2
3	3	3	3		3	3	3
4	4	4	4		4	4	4
5	5	5	5		5	5	5
6	6	6	6		6	6	6
7	7	7	7		7	7	7
8	8	8	8		8	8	8
9	9	9	9		9	9	9

19 Which description is true about solutions of equations and solutions of systems of equations?

A A solution to an equation is the same as a solution to a system of equations.

B A solution to an equation is an ordered pair or a number that satisfies that equation. A solution to a system of equations is an ordered pair that satisfies both equations.

C A solution to an equation is always a single number. A solution to a system of equations is an ordered pair that satisfies one of the equations.

D A solution to an equation is always positive. A solution to a system of equations is always negative.

20 The formula for the perimeter of a square is $P = 4s$. If you use a given value for s to find a perimeter P, which is the independent variable?

F P

G s

H Both P and s

J Not Here

21 What are the domain and the range of the function graphed?

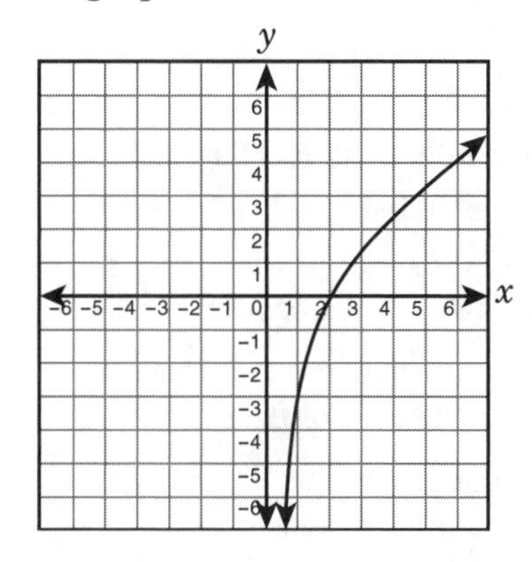

A Domain = {all real numbers}
Range = {all real numbers}

B Domain = $\{x: x > 0\}$
Range = {all real numbers}

C Domain = {all real numbers}
Range = $\{y: y = 0\}$

D Domain = $\{x: x = 0\}$
Range = $\{y: y = 0\}$

22 A contractor is building a wheelchair ramp to doorway that is elevated 24 inches. If the maximum slope allowed is $\frac{1}{12}$, how far away from the wall must the ramp begin? Give your answer in inches.

Record your answer and fill in the bubbles on the grid below. Be sure to use the correct place value.

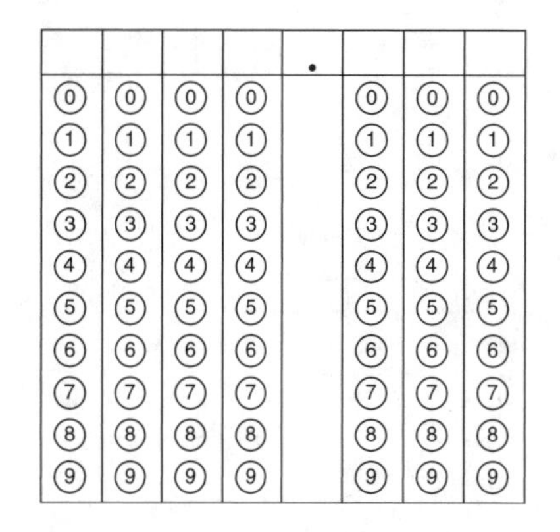

23 Write a function rule to describe the change $f(x)$ from a 10-dollar bill when buying x hot dogs at 90 cents each.

A $f(x) = 0.90x$

B $f(x) = 90x - 10$

C $f(x) = 10 + 0.90x$

D $f(x) = 10 - 0.90x$

24 Which of the following statements is true for direct variation?

F The graph of a direct variation may be a vertical line.

G A direct variation has no constant of variation.

H The graph of a direct variation will not pass through the origin.

J A direct variation is always a function.

25 Kaitlyn's car has a 20-gallon fuel tank. Her car gets 30 miles per gallon. Which graph shows the number of gallons y of gas left in the car as a function of the number of miles x driven?

A

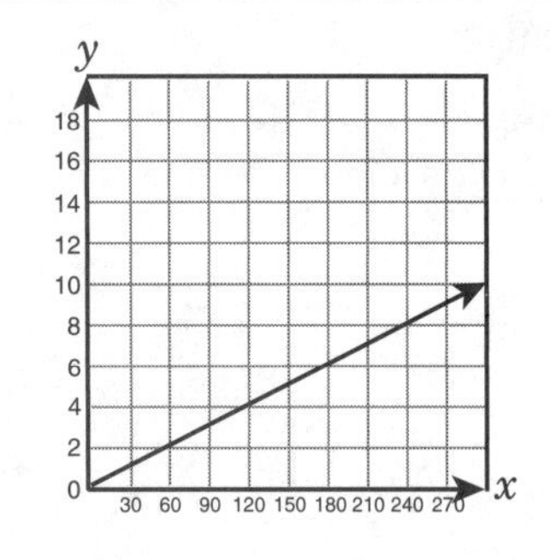

B

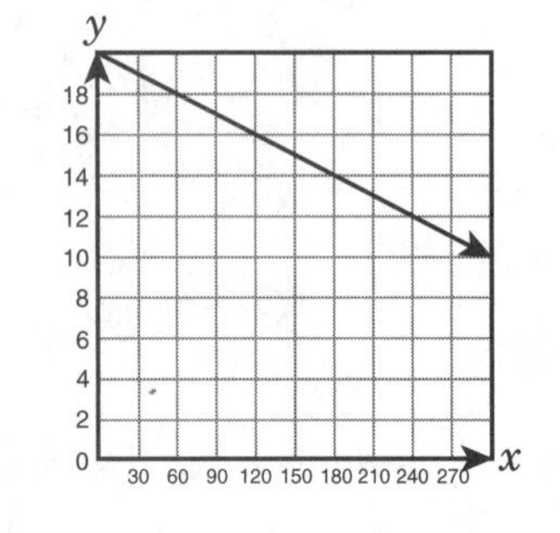

C

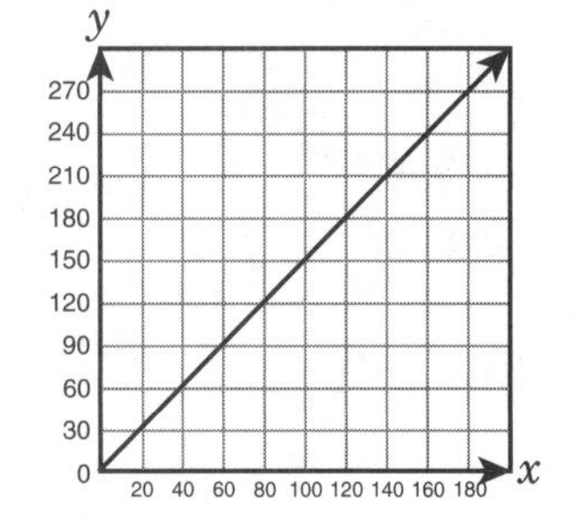

D

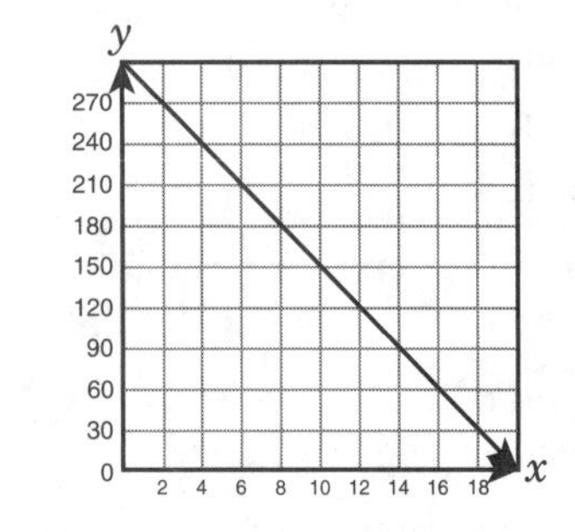

26 Solve the system of equations.

$$\begin{cases} 7x - 6y = 2 \\ 6x - 5y = 1 \end{cases}$$

What is the absolute value of y?

Record your answer and fill in the bubbles on the grid below. Be sure to use the correct place value.

				.			
0	0	0	0		0	0	0
1	1	1	1		1	1	1
2	2	2	2		2	2	2
3	3	3	3		3	3	3
4	4	4	4		4	4	4
5	5	5	5		5	5	5
6	6	6	6		6	6	6
7	7	7	7		7	7	7
8	8	8	8		8	8	8
9	9	9	9		9	9	9

27 Find the range of the function $f(x) = x^2$ when the domain is {0, 1, 2, 3} and determine whether the function is linear or quadratic.

A {0, 1, 4, 9}; quadratic

B {0, 1, 4, 9}; linear

C {0, 2, 4, 6}; quadratic

D {0, 2, 4, 6}; linear

28 Which statement is NOT true for a quadratic equation?

F A quadratic equation may have two real number solutions.

G A quadratic equation may have only one real number solution.

H A quadratic equation may have no real number solutions.

J A quadratic equation may have an infinite number of real number solutions.

29 Raven has q quarters and d dimes. Altogether, she has 41 coins and $8.00. Which system of equations can be used to find the number of quarters and dimes Raven has?

A $q + 41 = d$
$0.25q + 0.10d = 8$

B $q + d = 41$
$0.25q + 0.10d = 8$

C $q - d = 41$
$0.25d + 0.10q = 8$

D $0.25d - d = 41$
$0.10q - q = 8$

30 Compare the sums of the quantities in Column A and Column B.

Column A	Column B
$f(2)$ for $f(x) = 3x^2 - 1$	$f(2)$ for $f(x) = 6x + 1$
$f(0)$ for $f(x) = 5x - 7$	$f(0)$ for $f(x) = x^2 + 5$
$f(1)$ for $f(x) = -3x + 6$	$f(1)$ for $f(x) = x - 9$

F The sum in column A is greater.

G The sum in column B is greater.

H The sums in the columns are equal.

J Not Here

31 The cells of a strand of bacteria regenerate by splitting in two every 30 minutes. If Jamie begins with one cell of the bacteria and observes it 6 hours later, how many cells will there be?

Record your answer and fill in the bubbles on the grid below. Be sure to use the correct place value.

				.			
0	0	0	0		0	0	0
1	1	1	1		1	1	1
2	2	2	2		2	2	2
3	3	3	3		3	3	3
4	4	4	4		4	4	4
5	5	5	5		5	5	5
6	6	6	6		6	6	6
7	7	7	7		7	7	7
8	8	8	8		8	8	8
9	9	9	9		9	9	9

32 Daphne has money invested in two different mutual funds. The first pays 14% per year, while the other pays 12%. If her total investment is $25,000 and one year's interest on the accounts is $3,260, how much interest did she earn at 14%?

Record your answer and fill in the bubbles on the grid below. Be sure to use the correct place value.

				.			
0	0	0	0		0	0	0
1	1	1	1		1	1	1
2	2	2	2		2	2	2
3	3	3	3		3	3	3
4	4	4	4		4	4	4
5	5	5	5		5	5	5
6	6	6	6		6	6	6
7	7	7	7		7	7	7
8	8	8	8		8	8	8
9	9	9	9		9	9	9

33 Solve the quadratic equation $x^2 + 3x + 2 = 0$ for x.

A $\{5, 6\}$

B $\{1, -3\}$

C $\{0, \frac{2}{3}\}$

D $\{-1, -2\}$

34 Which expression will always result in the sum of 3 consecutive odd integers if x is any integer?

F $(2x + 1) + (2x + 3) + (2x + 5)$

G $(x + 1) + (x + 3) + (x + 5)$

H $x^2 + x^3 + x^4$

J $x + (x + 2) + (x + 4)$

Use the graph to answer Questions 35–42.

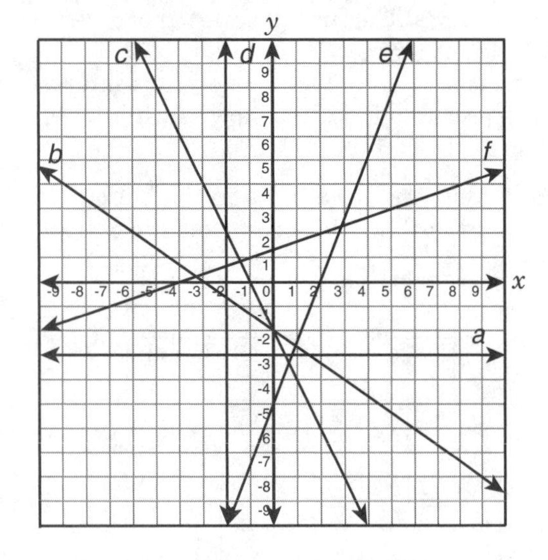

35 Which line has an undefined slope?

A a

B d

C e

D Both a and d

36 Which lines have negative slope?

F a

G Both b and c

H d

J Both e and f

37 Which lines have positive slope?

A a

B Both b and c

C d

D Both e and f

38 Which line has a slope of 0?

F a

G b

H d

J f

39 Which line has the greatest slope?

A a

B b

C e

D f

40 What is the sum of the slopes of lines a, b, c, e and f? Round your answer to the nearest hundredth.

Record your answer and fill in the bubbles on the grid below. Be sure to use the correct place value.

				.			
0	0	0	0		0	0	0
1	1	1	1		1	1	1
2	2	2	2		2	2	2
3	3	3	3		3	3	3
4	4	4	4		4	4	4
5	5	5	5		5	5	5
6	6	6	6		6	6	6
7	7	7	7		7	7	7
8	8	8	8		8	8	8
9	9	9	9		9	9	9

41 $y = \frac{1}{3}x + \frac{4}{3}$ is the equation of which line?

A b

B f

C d

D e

42 Which ordered pairs contain the intercepts of line c?

F (0, 0), (2, 0)

G (−1, 0), (0, −2)

H (−1, −2), (0, −1)

J (−2, 0), (0, −1)

43 Which is the graph of the equation $y = 2x^2$?

A

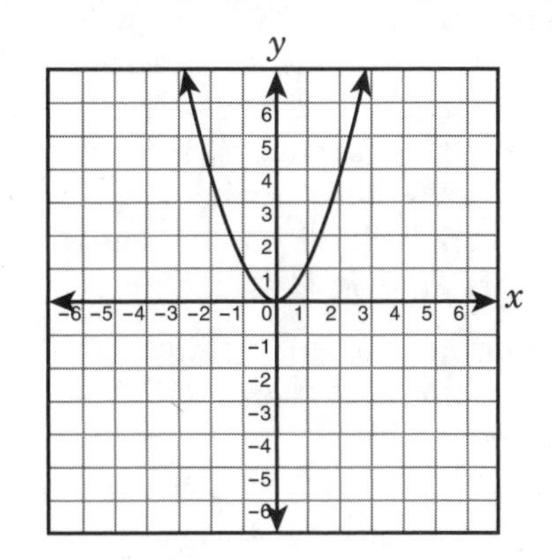

B

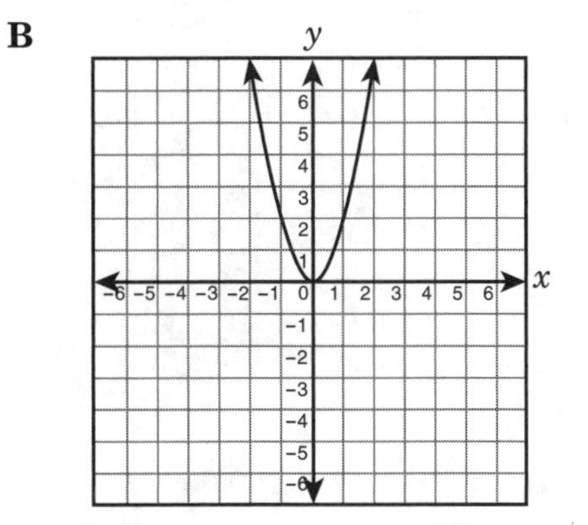

C

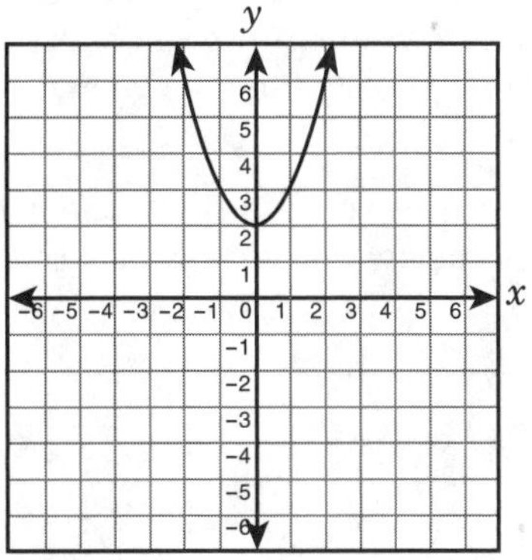

D

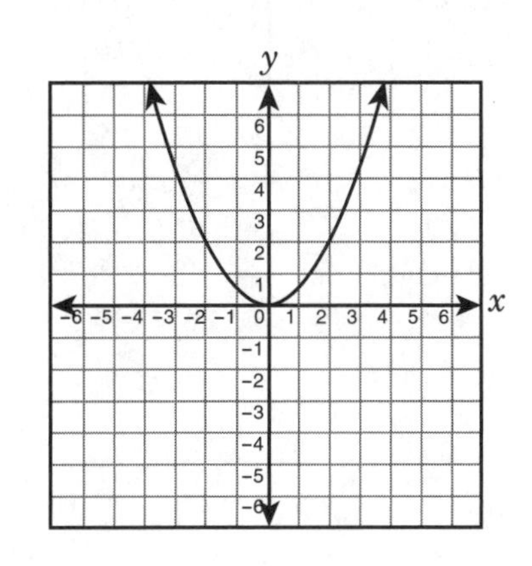

44 Which is an algebraic expression for the sum of the squares of three consecutive integers?

F $(x + x + 1 + x + 2)^2$

G $x^2 + (x + 1)^2 + (x + 2)^2$

H $(x + 1)^2 + (x + 3)^2 + (x + 5)^2$

J Not Here

45 A rectangular garden has a perimeter of 125 feet. If its length is 4 times its width, what is the width of the garden?

Record your answer and fill in the bubbles on the grid below. Be sure to use the correct place value.

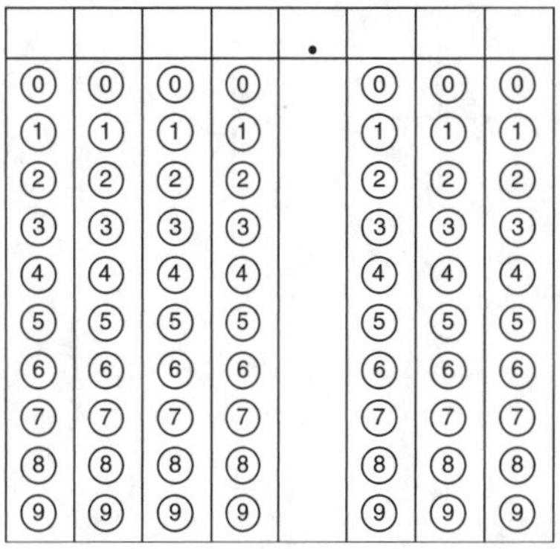

				.			
0	0	0	0		0	0	0
1	1	1	1		1	1	1
2	2	2	2		2	2	2
3	3	3	3		3	3	3
4	4	4	4		4	4	4
5	5	5	5		5	5	5
6	6	6	6		6	6	6
7	7	7	7		7	7	7
8	8	8	8		8	8	8
9	9	9	9		9	9	9

46 Look at the scatterplot below.

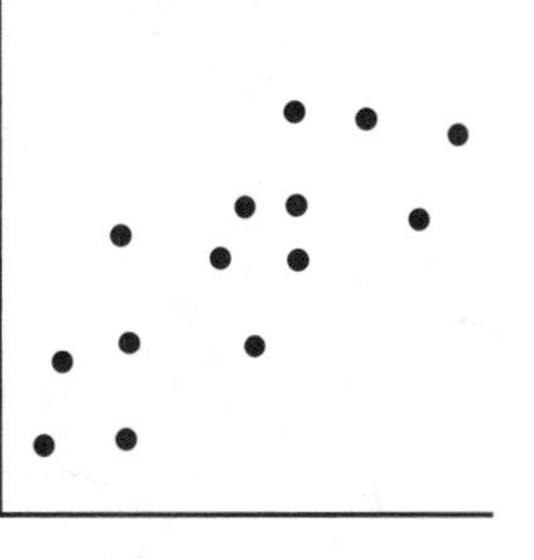

Which describes the correlation for the data in the scatterplot?

F Positive correlation

G Negative correlation

H No correlation

J Not Here

Use the information below to answer Questions 47–48.

The pitch of a roof is a slope. A roof with a pitch of $\frac{6}{12}$ has 6 inches of rise for every 12 inches of run.

47 Which graph displays a pitch of $\frac{6}{12}$?

A

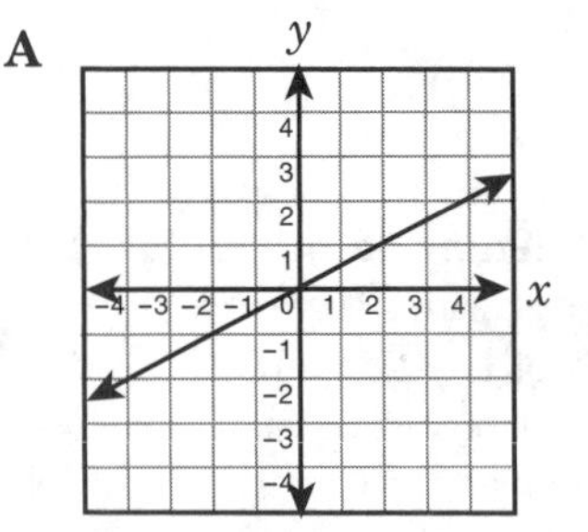

B

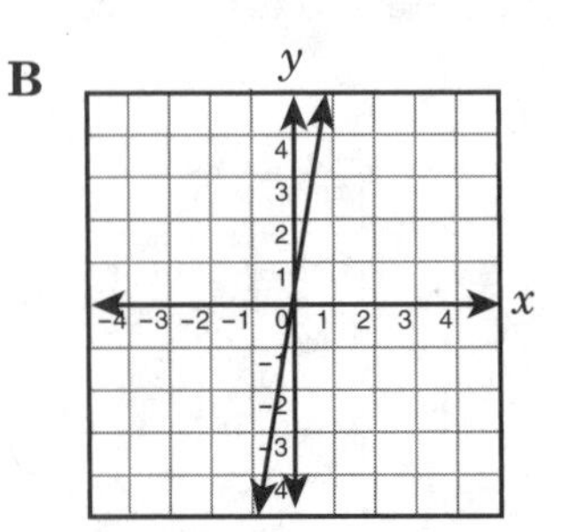

C

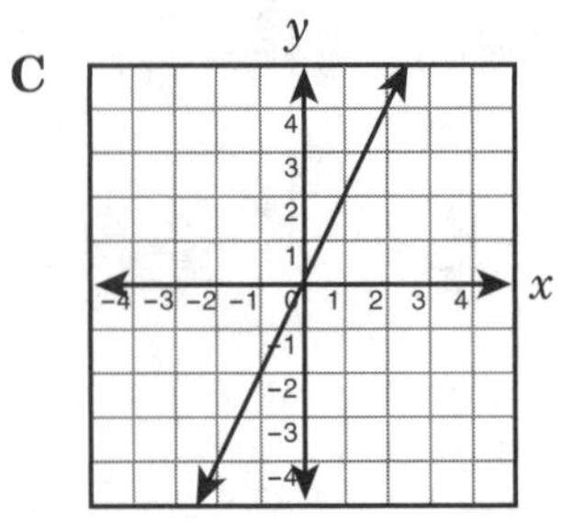

D

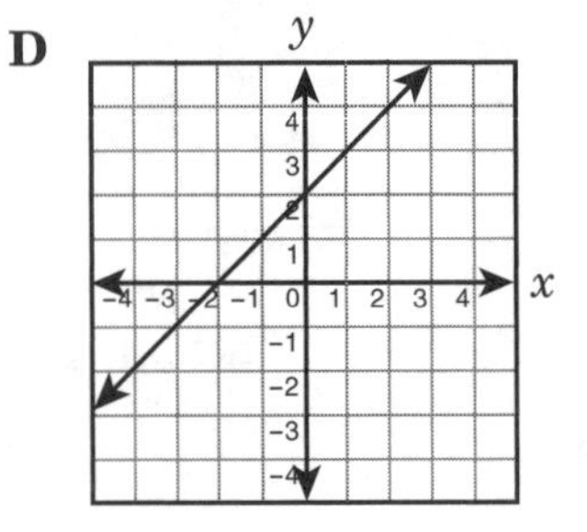

48 Which equation could represent the slanted portion of a roof with a pitch of $\frac{6}{12}$?

F $y = x + \frac{1}{2}$

G $y = 2x$

H $y = \frac{1}{2}x$

J $y = 6x$

49 When investigating an accident, police may use the formula $d = 0.05x^2 + x$, where d is the braking distance in feet and x is the speed in miles per hour that a car was traveling. According to this formula, if a car is traveling at a speed of 25 miles per hour when the brakes are applied, how many feet will it travel before stopping?

Record your answer and fill in the bubbles on the grid below. Be sure to use the correct place value.

				.			
0	0	0	0		0	0	0
1	1	1	1		1	1	1
2	2	2	2		2	2	2
3	3	3	3		3	3	3
4	4	4	4		4	4	4
5	5	5	5		5	5	5
6	6	6	6		6	6	6
7	7	7	7		7	7	7
8	8	8	8		8	8	8
9	9	9	9		9	9	9

50 Maria's parents invested \$60,000 in two accounts for her college fund. If they invested part at 6% and part at 8% and earned \$4,400 in interest, how much interest was earned at the 8% rate? Determine your answer in dollars and cents.

Record your answer and fill in the bubbles on the grid below. Be sure to use the correct place value.

				.			
0	0	0	0		0	0	0
1	1	1	1		1	1	1
2	2	2	2		2	2	2
3	3	3	3		3	3	3
4	4	4	4		4	4	4
5	5	5	5		5	5	5
6	6	6	6		6	6	6
7	7	7	7		7	7	7
8	8	8	8		8	8	8
9	9	9	9		9	9	9

51 What is the value of x in the solution to the system shown?

$$\begin{cases} x - y = 2 \\ 6x + 2y = -1 \end{cases}$$

A -2

B $-\frac{1}{2}$

C $-\frac{3}{8}$

D $\frac{3}{8}$

Use the graph below to answer Questions 52–55.

The graph below shows that the enrollment at two high schools is increasing.

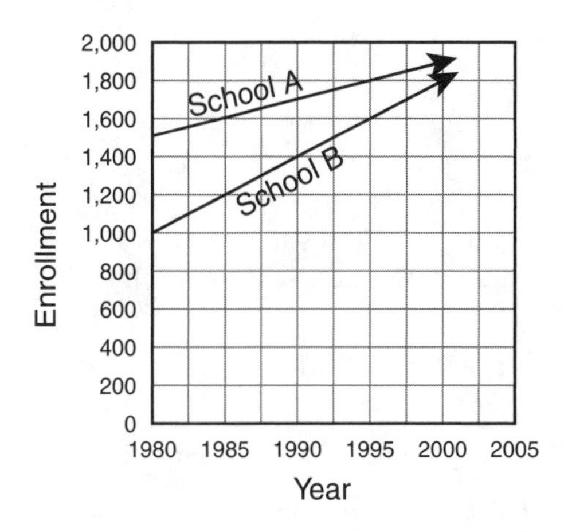

52 If the trends continue, how will the enrollments compare in the year 2010?

F School A will have a greater enrollment.

G School B will have a greater enrollment.

H The enrollments will be equal.

J It cannot be determined.

53 If the trend continues, which is the best estimate for the enrollment of school A in 2005?

A 1,900

B 2,000

C 2,100

D 2,200

54 What is the average annual increase in student enrollment for school B?

Record your answer and fill in the bubbles on the grid below. Be sure to use the correct place value.

				.			
0	0	0	0		0	0	0
1	1	1	1		1	1	1
2	2	2	2		2	2	2
3	3	3	3		3	3	3
4	4	4	4		4	4	4
5	5	5	5		5	5	5
6	6	6	6		6	6	6
7	7	7	7		7	7	7
8	8	8	8		8	8	8
9	9	9	9		9	9	9

55 In what year will the enrollments be equal?

A 2000

B 2002

C 2005

D 2010

56 What will be the equation of the function graphed if each point is moved two units down?

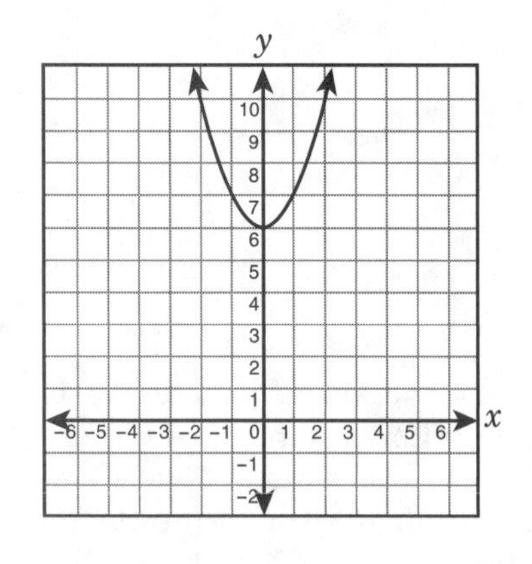

F $2x^2 + 6x = 0$

G $x^2 - 2 = 0$

H $y = 6x^2 - 2$

J $y = x^2 + 4$

57 A video rental store allows customers the first 5 videos free after paying a $25 membership fee. After the first 5 videos, the cost to rent each video is $1.75. Sue paid the membership fee and got x videos altogether, including the 5 free videos. Which equation can be used to find her total cost y, if she rented more than 5 videos?

A $y = 1.75x + 8.75$

B $y = 1.75x + 16.25$

C $y = 1.75x + 20$

D $y = 1.75x + 25$

58 The basketball team manager ordered replacement jerseys and new balls. The balls cost $26 each, and the jerseys cost $38 each. Part of the invoice was not legible, but it did state that a total of 16 items were shipped, and the total cost was $488. How many jerseys were ordered?

F 4

G 6

H 10

J 12

59 What is the equation of the line in slope-intercept form?

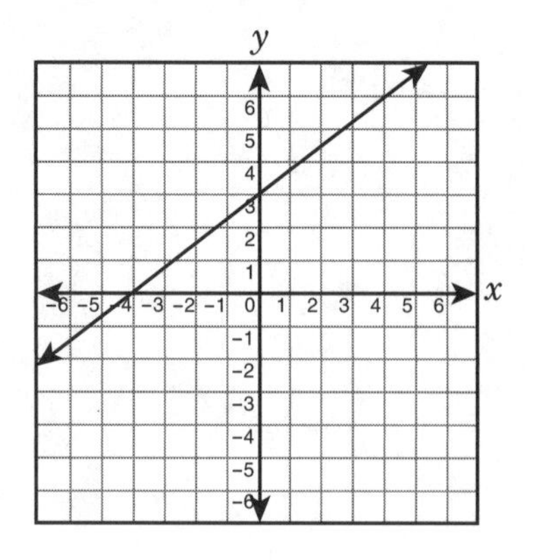

A $y = \frac{3}{4}x - 3$

B $y = \frac{4}{3}x + 3$

C $y = 4x - 3$

D $y = \frac{3}{4}x + 3$

60 If the y-intercept of the equation $y = 4x + 2$ is increased by two, how will the graph be affected?

F The graph will shift two spaces to the right.

G The graph will shift two spaces up.

H The graph will be magnified by a factor of 2.

J Not Here

Chapter 6 Geometric Relationships and Reasoning

In this chapter, you will study and practice:

- how to review Euclidean and Non-Euclidean geometries
- how to illustrate the fundamentals of Euclidean geometry
- how to identify properties of geometric figures
- how to follow guidelines to create transformations
- how to apply the Pythagorean Theorem
- how to analyze conditional statements
- how to reason using deductive and inductive reasoning

★ **Building Stamina™** This section gives you a chance to sharpen your understanding of geometry and reasoning skills and to strengthen your test-taking abilities.

Chapter 7 Two- and Three-Dimensional Representations

In this chapter, you will study and practice:

- how to identify three-dimensional figures
- how to name cross sections and slices of three-dimensional figures
- how to create nets of three-dimensional objects
- how to illustrate different views of three-dimensional objects
- how to represent geometric shapes on the coordinate system
- how to calculate midpoints and distances

★ **Building Stamina™** This section gives you a chance to sharpen your visualization skills and to strengthen your test-taking abilities.

Chapter 8 Geometry of Size and Shape

In this chapter, you will study and practice:

- how to calculate perimeter and area of polygons
- how to identify parts of a circle
- how to name segments relative to a circle
- how to compute volume and surface area of solid figures
- how to determine if triangles are congruent
- how to verify that figures are similar

★ **Building Stamina**™ This section gives you a chance to sharpen your computation skills that relate to size and shape and to strengthen your test-taking abilities.

Chapter 9 Percents, Proportional Relationships, Probability, and Statistics

In this chapter, you will study and practice:

- how to solve problems involving proportions
- how to solve problems involving percents
- how to compute theoretical and experimental probabilities
- how to determine measures of central tendencies
- how to read graphs and histograms
- how to predict based on collected data

★ **Building Stamina**™ This section gives you a chance to sharpen your computation and statistical skills and to strengthen your test-taking abilities.

Focus on TEKS Lesson 28 Euclidean and Non-Euclidean Geometries

TEKS G(b)1B Through the historical development of geometric systems, recognize that mathematics is developed for a variety of purposes.
TEKS G(b)1C Compare and contrast the structures and implications of Euclidean and non-Euclidean geometries.

The type of geometry with which you are probably most familiar is Euclidean geometry, but there are several other systems of non-Euclidean geometries of interest.

Euclidean geometry is the system of geometry based on the postulates, or assumptions, of the Greek mathematician, Euclid, who lived around 300 B.C.
Systems of geometry that do not rely on some or all of Euclid's postulates are referred to as **non-Euclidean geometries**.

Guided Instruction

Problem 1 Refer to the sphere at the right. According to the spherical geometry model, which of the following figures represent lines: $\overleftrightarrow{AB}$, $\overleftrightarrow{CD}$, $\overleftrightarrow{EF}$, or $\overleftrightarrow{AE}$?

E
A
B
D
C
F

In Euclidean geometry, a *line* can be drawn in the coordinate plane by using a straightedge to connect two points. The line is the set of all points between and including the two points and extending in either direction.

In spherical geometry, a *line* is defined to be a *great circle* of the sphere. A great circle is a circle that divides the sphere into two equal halves. A great circle must contain the center of the sphere.

A globe serves as an excellent model for spherical geometry. On a globe the equator and longitude lines are great circles since they divide the earth into two equal halves.

Notice, however, that latitude lines do not divide the earth into two equal halves. So, they are not great circles, and therefore not lines.

N
Line of Longitude
Line of Latitude
W
E
Equator
S

Step 1 Consider the sphere in the original figure. Notice that $\overleftrightarrow{AB}$ is similar to the equator of a globe, and $\overleftrightarrow{EF}$ is like a line of longitude since it intersects the north and south poles of the sphere. Both $\overleftrightarrow{AB}$ and $\overleftrightarrow{EF}$ divide the sphere into two equal halves and contain the center of the sphere.

Step 2 $\overleftrightarrow{CD}$ is a circle on the sphere, but it is not a great circle since it does not cut the sphere into equal halves. $\overleftrightarrow{AE}$ does not even lie on the surface of the sphere. Although it looks more like what is commonly thought of as a line segment, it is not a great circle. So, it is not a line in spherical geometry.

Solution In the spherical geometry model, only $\overleftrightarrow{AB}$ and $\overleftrightarrow{EF}$ represent lines.

The shortest distance between two points on a sphere is along the great circle connecting the points. For this reason, when pilots navigate long distances, they often travel along the lines, or great circles, of spherical geometry.

Guided Instruction

Euclid based his geometry on five assumptions, which are known as postulates. These five postulates are:

1. A straight line may be drawn between any two points.
2. Any terminated straight line may be extended indefinitely.
3. A circle may be drawn with any given point as the center and any given radius.
4. All right angles are equal in measure.
5. If two straight lines lying in a plane are met by another line, and if the sum of the internal angles on one side is less than two right angles, the straight lines will meet.

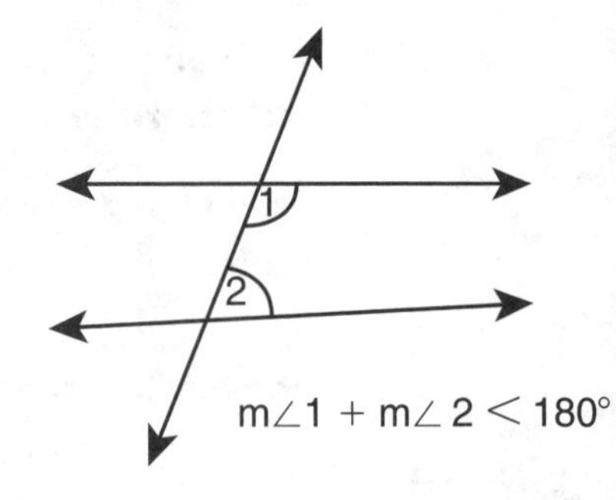

Euclid's fifth postulate is also known as the Parallel Postulate. Today the postulate is commonly stated, "If given a line and a point not on that line in the same plane, then through the point there exists one and only one line parallel to the given line."

If the parallel postulate is assumed not true, then other geometries are formed based on other assumptions or postulates. As explained in Problem 1, spherical geometry is one such geometry. Another geometry, known as hyperbolic geometry, is based on a surface that looks like a saddle.

Another Problem

Problem 2

Thinking of parallel lines as lines that do not intersect, consider a given line (m) and a given point (P) in each of the three geometries described. How many lines can be drawn through P so that each line is parallel to m?

Step 1 Think about the surface of Euclidean geometry: a plane. There is only one line that can be drawn through point P and parallel to line m.

In spherical geometry, recall that a line is a great circle of the sphere.

Step 2 Think about the surface of spherical geometry: a sphere. There is no line that can be drawn through point P and parallel to line m because a line is a great circle and therefore would intersect line m at two points (at the north and south pole of the sphere).

In hyperbolic geometry, a line is the shortest path between two points.

Step 3 Think about the surface of hyperbolic geometry: a hyperbola or "saddle" curve. There is more than one line through point P that is parallel to line m. Actually, there are infinitely many.

Solution

In Euclidean geometry, one line can be drawn parallel to line m through point P.
In spherical geometry, no line can be drawn parallel to line m through point P.
In hyperbolic geometry, an infinite number of lines can be drawn parallel to line m through point P.

Apply the TEKS For each of the following spheres, tell whether the figure drawn represents a line in spherical geometry.

1. 2. 3.

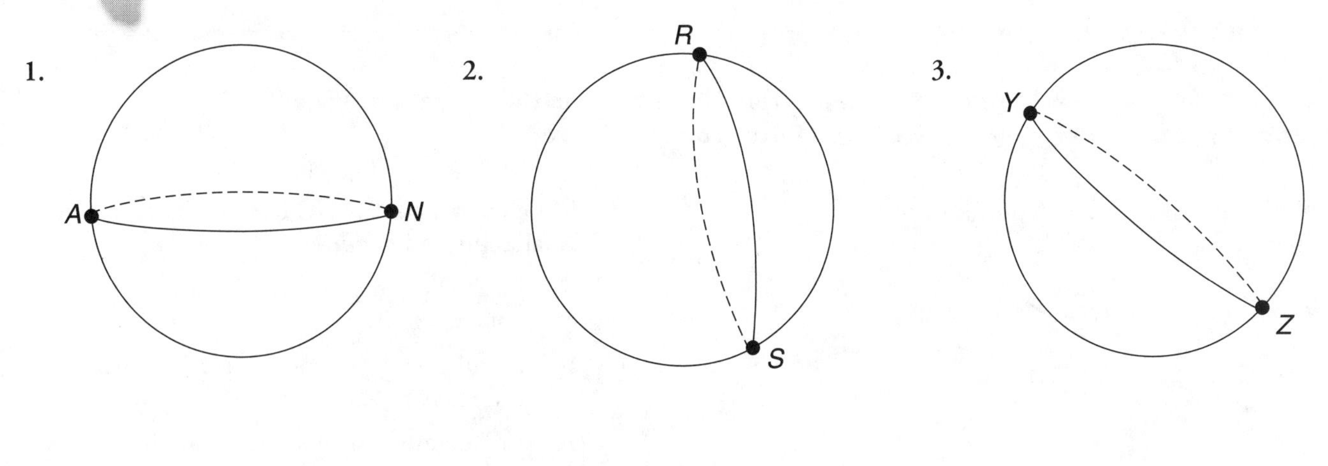

______________ ______________ ______________

For each of the following hyperbolas, tell whether the figure drawn represents a line in hyperbolic geometry.

4. 5. 6.

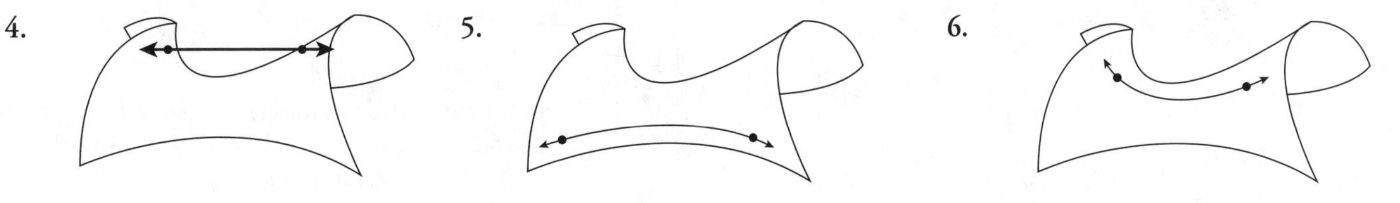

______________ ______________ ______________

Illustrate each of the following situations by sketching an example on the sphere provided.

7. $\overleftrightarrow{CD}$ represents a line in spherical geometry.

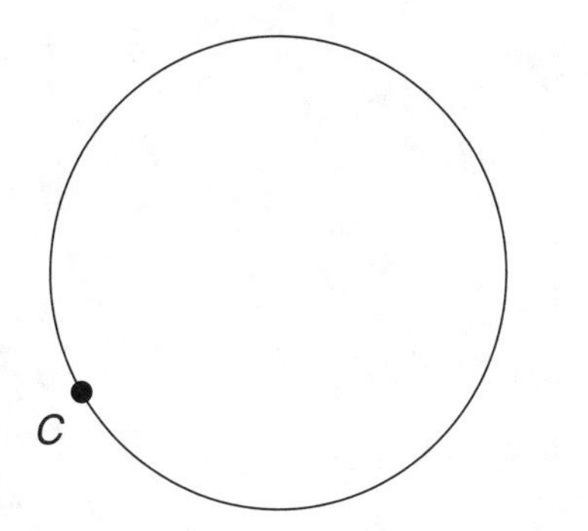

8. Suppose two hot-air balloons start along the equator at points *A* and *B*, respectively, and travel due north along lines defined by spherical geometry. Sketch their paths on the sphere. At what point will the two balloons meet?

____

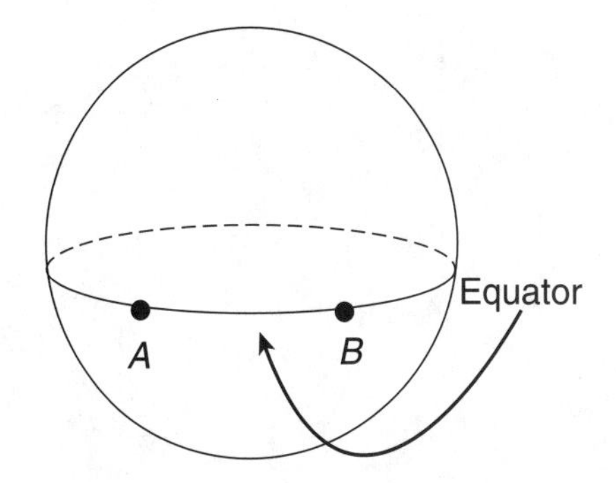

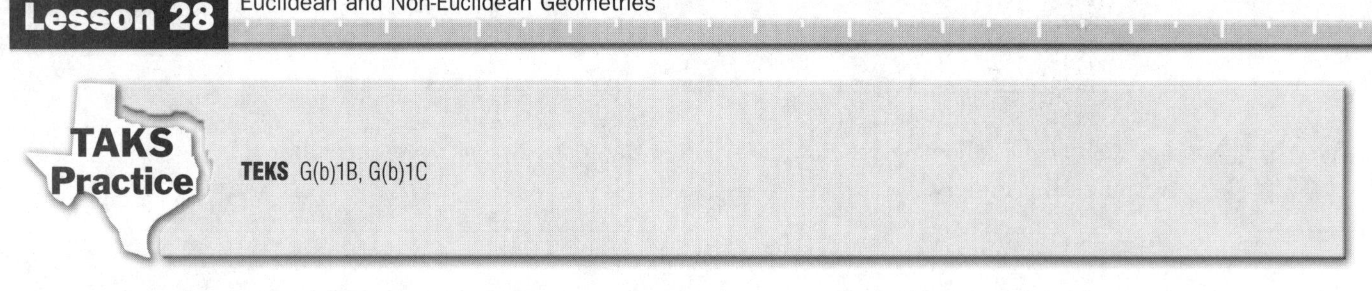

DIRECTIONS Read each question. Then circle the letter for the correct answer. If a correct answer is not here, circle the letter for "Not Here."

1 Which is of the following illustrates hyperbolic geometry?

A

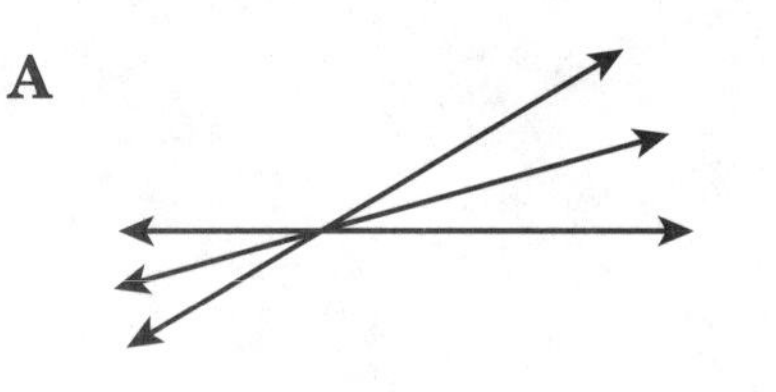

B

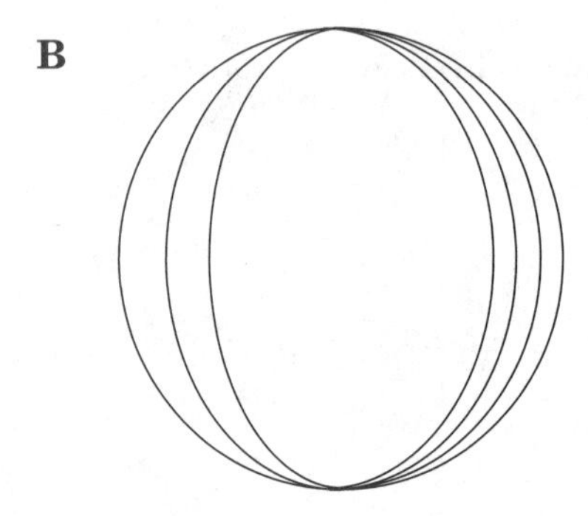

C

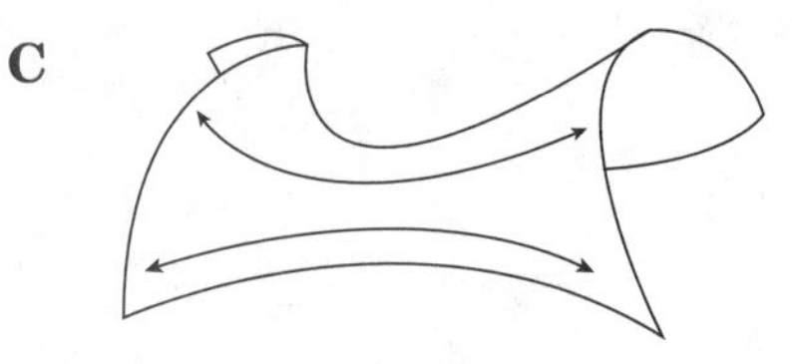

D Not Here

2 Which statement is NOT true about lines in Euclidean and spherical geometries.

F In Euclidean geometry, parallel lines do not intersect.

G In spherical geometry, parallel lines intersect at exactly one point.

H In Euclidean geometry, parallel lines are equidistant from each other.

J In spherical geometry, lines intersect in exactly two points.

3 Which real-world application does NOT use the fundamentals of either a Euclidean or non-Euclidean geometry?

A Architecture

B Art and design

C Landscaping

D Not Here

Focus on TEKS

Lesson 29 Fundamentals of Euclidean Geometry

TEKS G(b)1A Develop an awareness of the structure of a mathematical system, connecting definitions, postulates, logical reasoning, and theorems.
TEKS G(b)2A Use constructions to explore attributes of geometric figures and to make conjectures about geometric relationships.
TEKS G(b)2B Make and verify conjectures about angles and lines.
TEKS G(d)2B Use slopes and equations of lines to investigate geometric relationships, including parallel lines, perpendicular lines, and special segments of triangles and other polygons.
TEKS G(e)2A Formulate and test conjectures about the properties of parallel and perpendicular lines.

Many geometric properties can be explored by making constructions and measurements. You can also apply what you know about linear equations to solve problems involving parallel and perpendicular lines.

Parallel lines are lines that lie in the same plane and do not intersect.

Perpendicular lines are lines that intersect to form right angles.

Guided Instruction

Problem 1 Construct two intersecting lines and use a protractor to reach a conclusion about the resulting angles.

Step 1 Using a straightedge, draw two intersecting lines on a sheet of paper. Label the resulting angles 1, 2, 3, and 4.

When two lines intersect, two pairs of *vertical angles* are formed. In the figure, $\angle 1$ and $\angle 3$ are vertical angles, and $\angle 2$ and $\angle 4$ are vertical angles.

Step 2 Use a protractor to find the measure *m* of each of the four angles you drew. If you measure the angles drawn in this example, you will find that $m\angle 1 = m\angle 3 = 54°$, and that $m\angle 2 = m\angle 4 = 126°$.

Solution When two lines intersect, the resulting pairs of vertical angles have the same measure. Stated differently, if two angles are vertical angles, then they are *congruent*.

More Problems

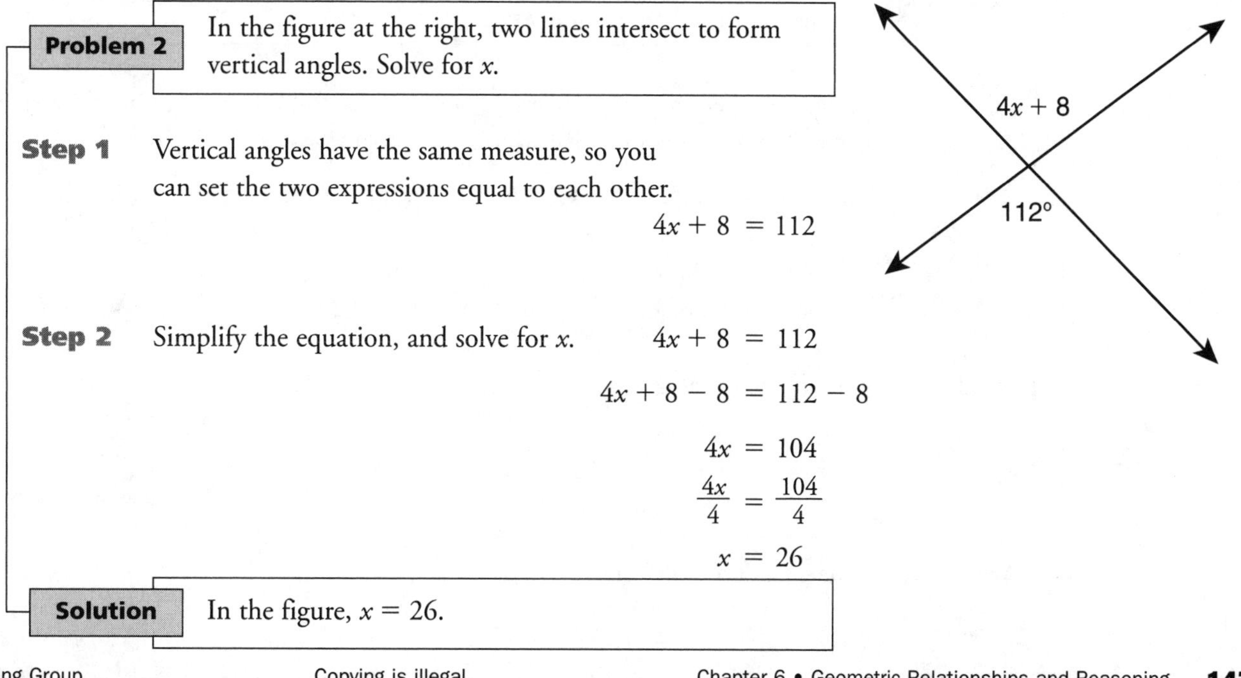

Problem 2 In the figure at the right, two lines intersect to form vertical angles. Solve for *x*.

Step 1 Vertical angles have the same measure, so you can set the two expressions equal to each other.

$$4x + 8 = 112$$

Step 2 Simplify the equation, and solve for *x*.

$$4x + 8 = 112$$
$$4x + 8 - 8 = 112 - 8$$
$$4x = 104$$
$$\frac{4x}{4} = \frac{104}{4}$$
$$x = 26$$

Solution In the figure, $x = 26$.

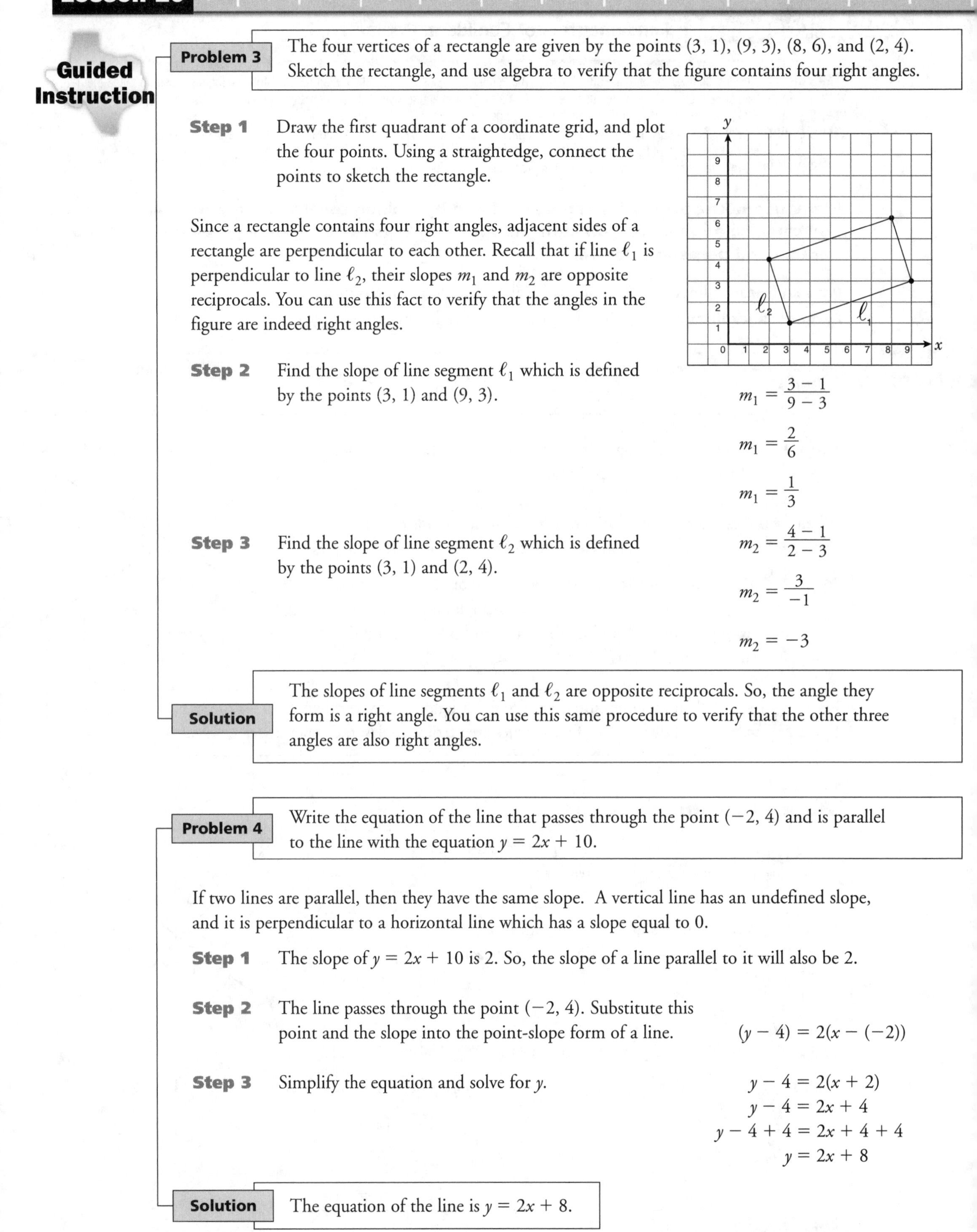

Guided Instruction

Problem 3 The four vertices of a rectangle are given by the points (3, 1), (9, 3), (8, 6), and (2, 4). Sketch the rectangle, and use algebra to verify that the figure contains four right angles.

Step 1 Draw the first quadrant of a coordinate grid, and plot the four points. Using a straightedge, connect the points to sketch the rectangle.

Since a rectangle contains four right angles, adjacent sides of a rectangle are perpendicular to each other. Recall that if line ℓ_1 is perpendicular to line ℓ_2, their slopes m_1 and m_2 are opposite reciprocals. You can use this fact to verify that the angles in the figure are indeed right angles.

Step 2 Find the slope of line segment ℓ_1 which is defined by the points (3, 1) and (9, 3).

$$m_1 = \frac{3 - 1}{9 - 3}$$

$$m_1 = \frac{2}{6}$$

$$m_1 = \frac{1}{3}$$

Step 3 Find the slope of line segment ℓ_2 which is defined by the points (3, 1) and (2, 4).

$$m_2 = \frac{4 - 1}{2 - 3}$$

$$m_2 = \frac{3}{-1}$$

$$m_2 = -3$$

Solution The slopes of line segments ℓ_1 and ℓ_2 are opposite reciprocals. So, the angle they form is a right angle. You can use this same procedure to verify that the other three angles are also right angles.

Problem 4 Write the equation of the line that passes through the point (−2, 4) and is parallel to the line with the equation $y = 2x + 10$.

If two lines are parallel, then they have the same slope. A vertical line has an undefined slope, and it is perpendicular to a horizontal line which has a slope equal to 0.

Step 1 The slope of $y = 2x + 10$ is 2. So, the slope of a line parallel to it will also be 2.

Step 2 The line passes through the point (−2, 4). Substitute this point and the slope into the point-slope form of a line.

$$(y - 4) = 2(x - (-2))$$

Step 3 Simplify the equation and solve for y.

$$y - 4 = 2(x + 2)$$

$$y - 4 = 2x + 4$$

$$y - 4 + 4 = 2x + 4 + 4$$

$$y = 2x + 8$$

Solution The equation of the line is $y = 2x + 8$.

Apply the TEKS Solve for x in each of the following figures.

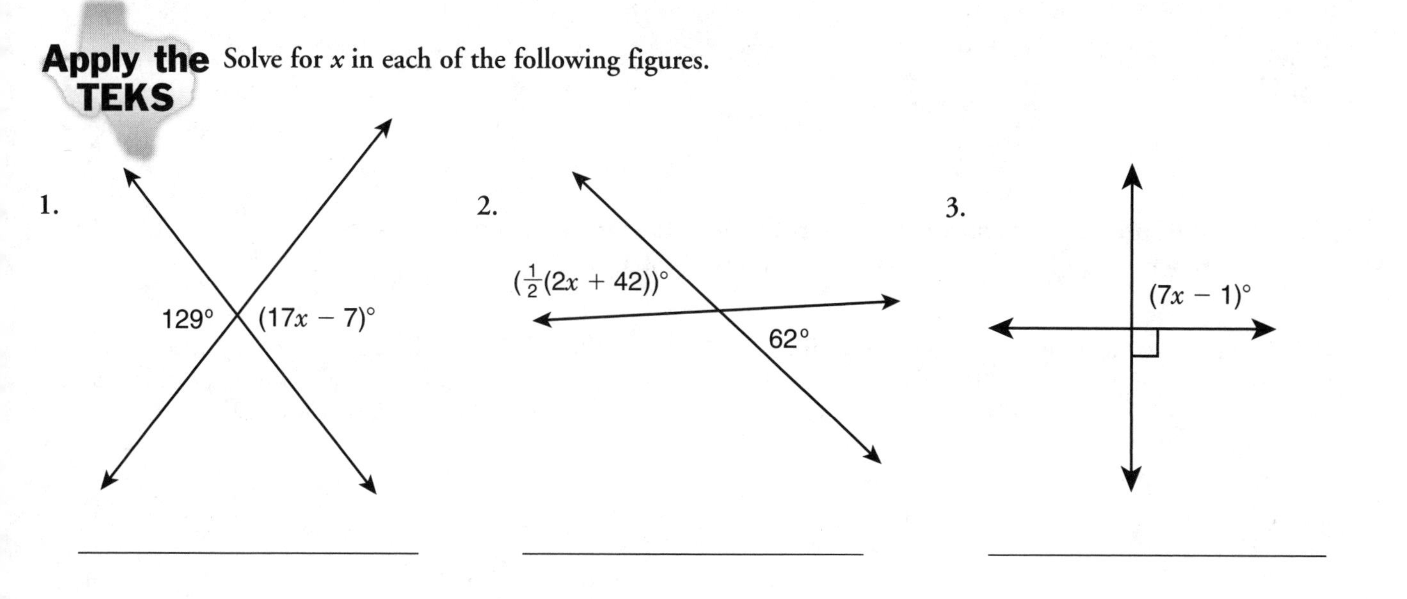

Write the equation for each line described below.

4. The line parallel to $y = 3x + 1$ that passes through the point (5, 1)

5. The line perpendicular to $y = -\frac{1}{4}x - 9$ that passes through the origin

Determine whether each triangle defined by the following vertices is a right triangle. (A right triangle contains one right angle.) Write *yes* or *no*.

6. (−2, 1), (−2, 4), (6, 4)

7. (3, 2), (7, 1), (1, −3)

8. (−2, −2), (1, −6), (9, 0)

Solve each problem.

9. In the figure at the right, line ℓ_1 is parallel to line ℓ_2. Line t is a transversal intersecting the pair of parallel lines. The measure of $\angle 1$ is $(4x - 10)$, and the measure of $\angle 2$ is $(5x - 8)$. Recall that supplemental angles have a sum of 180°. Find the measure m of each of the following angles.

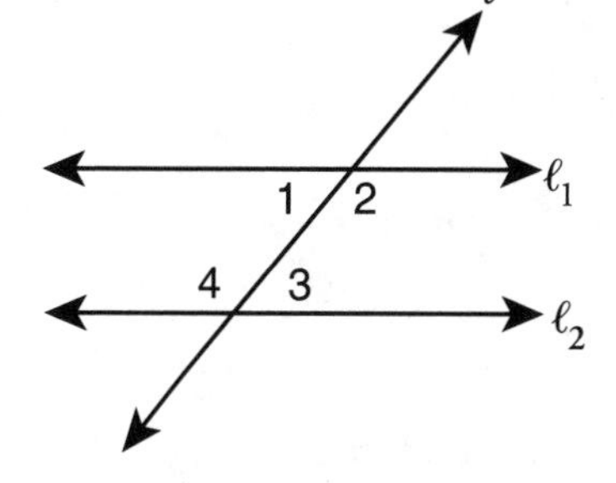

$m\angle 1 =$ ________ $m\angle 2 =$ ________

$m\angle 3 =$ ________ $m\angle 4 =$ ________

10. In the figure, angles 1 and 3 and angles 2 and 4 are called *alternate interior angles*. Based on your results from Exercise 9, complete the following rule.

When two parallel lines are cut by a transversal, ________________________.

TAKS Objective 7 The student will demonstrate an understanding of two-dimensional representations of geometric relationships and shapes.
TEKS G(d)2B

DIRECTIONS Read each question. Then circle the letter for the correct answer. If a correct answer is not here, circle the letter for "Not Here."

1 The base of a rectangle is contained in the line with the equation $y = -\frac{4}{7}x - 10$. One of the sides of the rectangle is contained in the line with the equation $y = mx - 5$. What is the value of m in the second linear equation?

A $-\frac{7}{4}$

B $-\frac{4}{7}$

C $\frac{4}{7}$

D $\frac{7}{4}$

2 What kind of triangle is represented in the figure below?

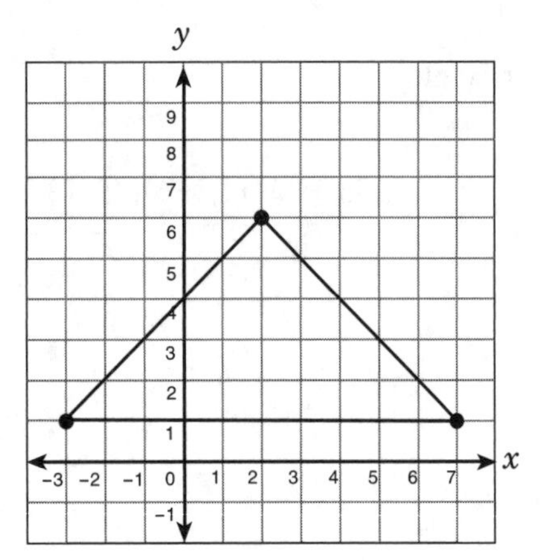

F A right triangle

G An acute triangle

H An obtuse triangle

J Not Here

3 Which of the following linear equations passes through the point (−1, 7) and is parallel to the line with the equation $y = -12x - 1$?

A $y = -12x + 8$

B $y = -12x - 5$

C $y = \frac{1}{12}x - 7$

D $y = \frac{1}{12}x + 4$

4 Which of the following sets of ordered pairs represents the vertices of a right triangle?

F (1, 3), (4, 4), (7, 2)

G (−1, 1), (−1, −3), (4, −1)

H (0, 0), (0, 4), (6, 5)

J Not Here

5 Two points on the line containing a side of a square are (−5, −2) and (4, 6). What is the slope of the line that contains the opposite side of the square?

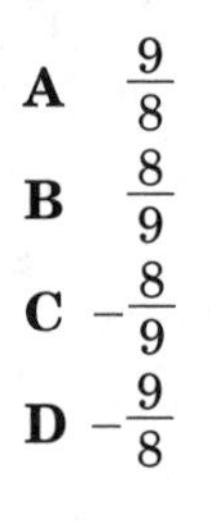

A $\frac{9}{8}$

B $\frac{8}{9}$

C $-\frac{8}{9}$

D $-\frac{9}{8}$

Focus on TEKS **Lesson 30** **Properties of Geometric Figures**

TEKS G(c)1A Use numeric and geometric patterns to make generalizations about geometric properties, including properties of polygons, ratios in similar figures, and angle relationships in polygons.
TEKS G(e)3A Use congruence transformations to make conjectures and justify properties of geometric figures.

In this lesson, you will explore several characteristics and properties of figures in Euclidean geometry.

Two figures are **congruent figures** if they have the same size and shape. **Similar figures** have the same shape but not necessarily the same size.

Guided Instruction

Problem 1 Determine whether the two figures are congruent, similar, or neither.

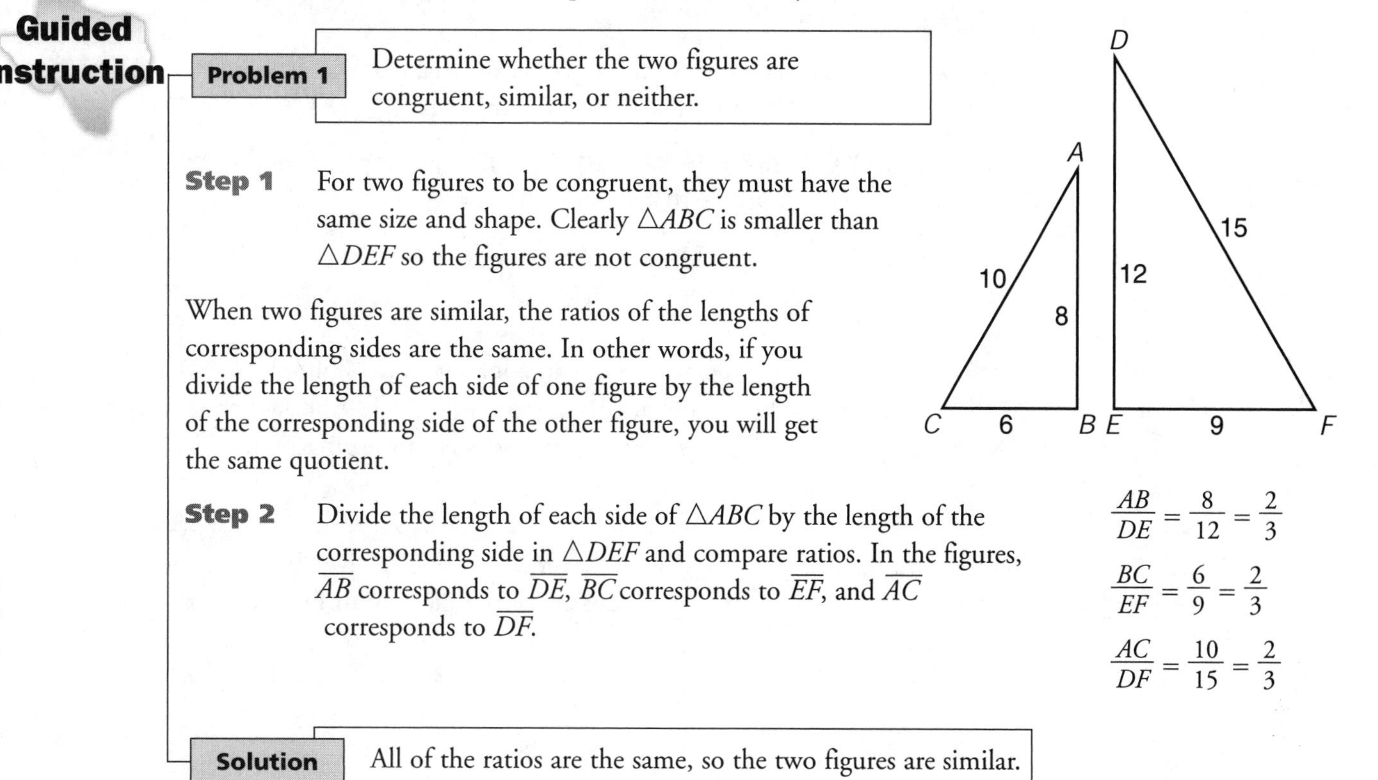

Step 1 For two figures to be congruent, they must have the same size and shape. Clearly $\triangle ABC$ is smaller than $\triangle DEF$ so the figures are not congruent.

When two figures are similar, the ratios of the lengths of corresponding sides are the same. In other words, if you divide the length of each side of one figure by the length of the corresponding side of the other figure, you will get the same quotient.

Step 2 Divide the length of each side of $\triangle ABC$ by the length of the corresponding side in $\triangle DEF$ and compare ratios. In the figures, $\overline{AB}$ corresponds to $\overline{DE}$, $\overline{BC}$ corresponds to $\overline{EF}$, and $\overline{AC}$ corresponds to $\overline{DF}$.

$$\frac{AB}{DE} = \frac{8}{12} = \frac{2}{3}$$

$$\frac{BC}{EF} = \frac{6}{9} = \frac{2}{3}$$

$$\frac{AC}{DF} = \frac{10}{15} = \frac{2}{3}$$

Solution All of the ratios are the same, so the two figures are similar.

More Problems

Problem 2 Rectangle *ABCD* is shown in the figure. Sketch a rectangle that is congruent to *ABCD*.

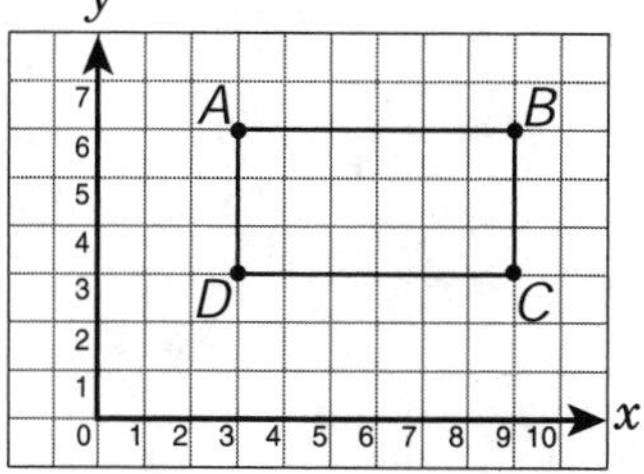

Step 1 The dimensions of *ABCD* are 6 by 3, so the dimensions of the new rectangle must also be 6 by 3.

Step 2 Choose a vertex for the new rectangle. Use the point (2, 7). Extend 3 units to the right and 6 units down to plot two other vertices.

Step 3 Plot the final vertex and label the points *E*, *F*, *G*, and *H*.

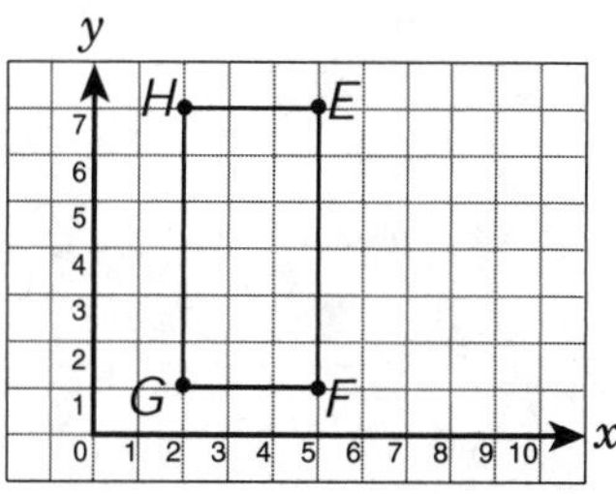

Solution Rectangle *EFGH* has the same size and shape as *ABCD*, so the two rectangles are congruent.

Guided Instruction

Problem 3

Measure the interior angles of each figure. Find the sum of their angles and generalize your results.

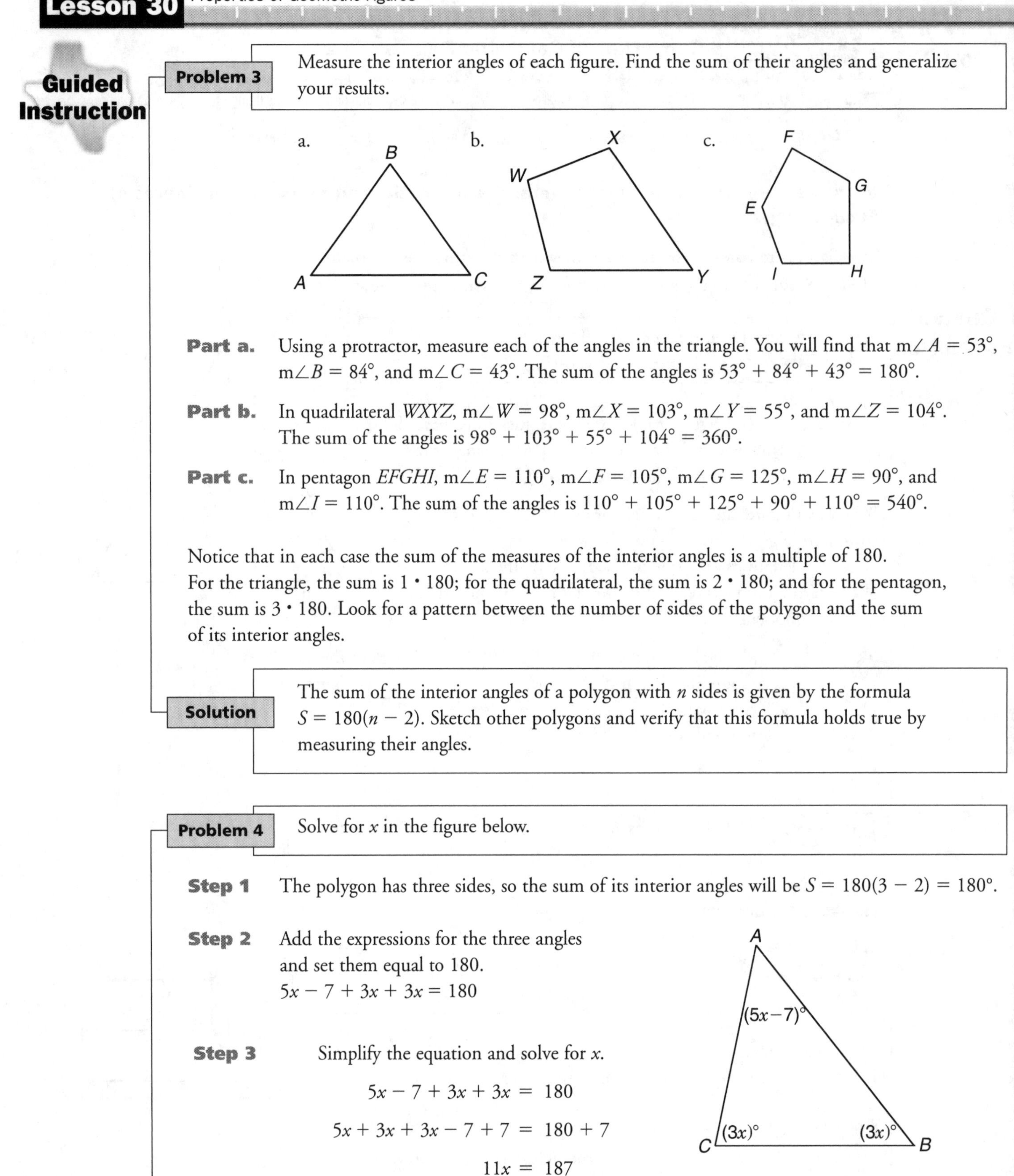

Part a. Using a protractor, measure each of the angles in the triangle. You will find that $m\angle A = 53°$, $m\angle B = 84°$, and $m\angle C = 43°$. The sum of the angles is $53° + 84° + 43° = 180°$.

Part b. In quadrilateral *WXYZ*, $m\angle W = 98°$, $m\angle X = 103°$, $m\angle Y = 55°$, and $m\angle Z = 104°$. The sum of the angles is $98° + 103° + 55° + 104° = 360°$.

Part c. In pentagon *EFGHI*, $m\angle E = 110°$, $m\angle F = 105°$, $m\angle G = 125°$, $m\angle H = 90°$, and $m\angle I = 110°$. The sum of the angles is $110° + 105° + 125° + 90° + 110° = 540°$.

Notice that in each case the sum of the measures of the interior angles is a multiple of 180. For the triangle, the sum is $1 \cdot 180$; for the quadrilateral, the sum is $2 \cdot 180$; and for the pentagon, the sum is $3 \cdot 180$. Look for a pattern between the number of sides of the polygon and the sum of its interior angles.

Solution

The sum of the interior angles of a polygon with n sides is given by the formula $S = 180(n - 2)$. Sketch other polygons and verify that this formula holds true by measuring their angles.

Problem 4

Solve for x in the figure below.

Step 1 The polygon has three sides, so the sum of its interior angles will be $S = 180(3 - 2) = 180°$.

Step 2 Add the expressions for the three angles and set them equal to 180.

$5x - 7 + 3x + 3x = 180$

Step 3 Simplify the equation and solve for x.

$$5x - 7 + 3x + 3x = 180$$

$$5x + 3x + 3x - 7 + 7 = 180 + 7$$

$$11x = 187$$

$$x = 17$$

Solution

In the figure, $x = 17$.

Apply the TEKS Determine whether each pair of figures is similar.

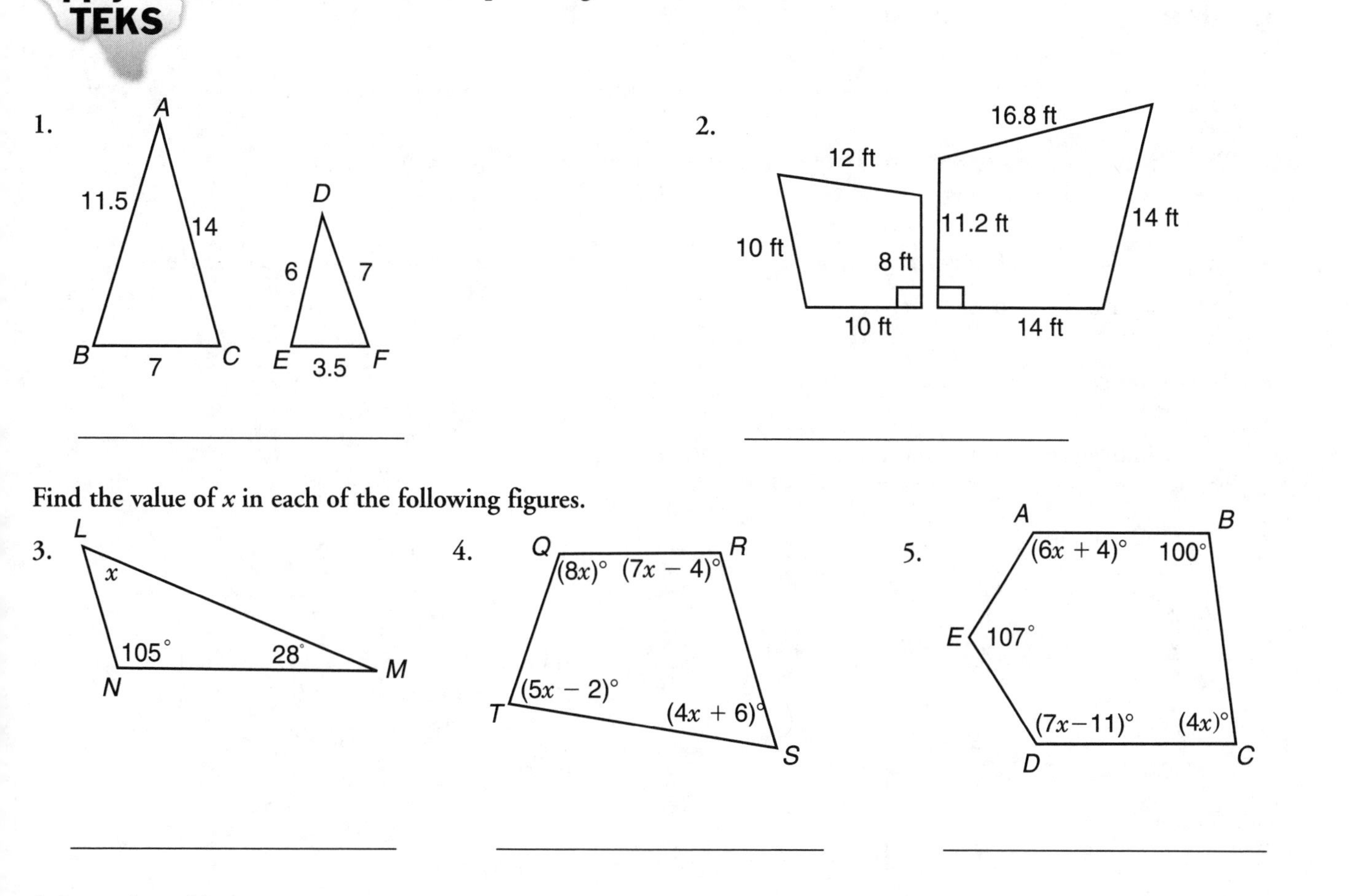

Find the value of x in each of the following figures.

Solve each problem.

6. One angle of a right triangle has a measure of 33°. What is the measure of the third angle?

7. A hexagon is a six-sided polygon. Three of the interior angles of a hexagon have measures of 141°, 126°, and 151°. The other three angles are given by the expressions $(3x + 10)$, $(5x)°$, and $(6x - 44)°$. Solve for x.

8. Determine whether the two quadrilaterals in the figure at the right are *congruent*, *similar*, or *neither*.

9. "If two figures are similar, then they are congruent." Is this statement *true* or *false*? Explain.

TAKS Objective 6 The student will demonstrate an understanding of geometric relationships and spatial reasoning.
TEKS G(c)1A, G(e)3A

DIRECTIONS Read each question. Then circle the letter for the correct answer. If a correct answer is not here, circle the letter for "Not Here."

1 Which of the following statements is true?

A If two figures are similar, then they are congruent.

B If two figures are congruent, then they are similar.

C If two figures are similar, then their corresponding sides have the same lengths.

D Not Here

2 What is the measure of $\angle E$ in the figure below?

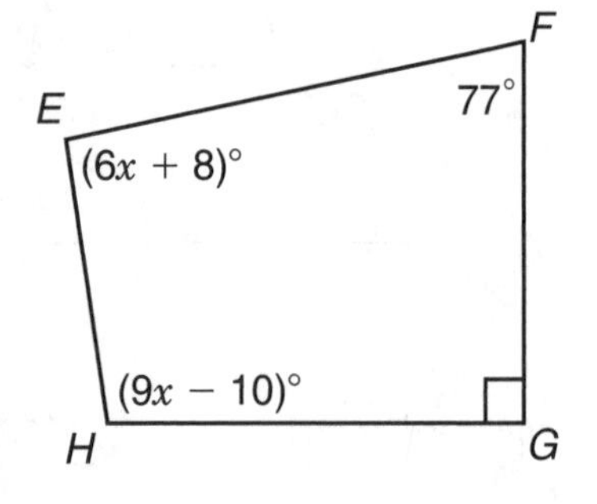

F 13°

G 35°

H 86°

J 107°

3 $\triangle ABC$ is graphed on the coordinate grid.

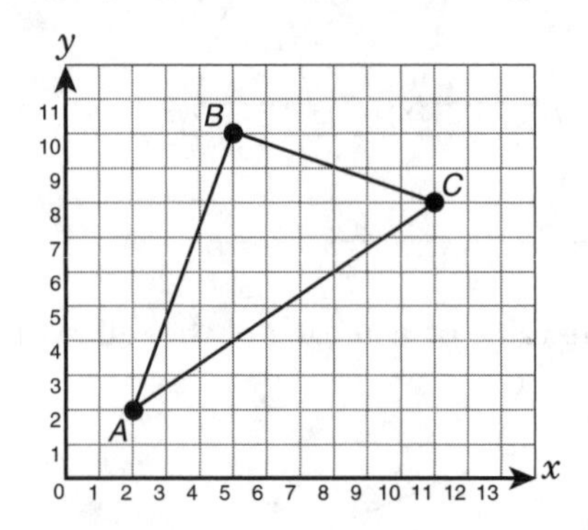

Which set of coordinates represents the vertices of a triangle that is congruent to $\triangle ABC$?

A (4, 9), (13, 3), (10, 11)

B (4, 9), (13, 5), (10, 10)

C (3, 7), (9, 3), (12, 10)

D Not Here

4 The angles of a triangle are in the ratio of 3:4:5. What is the degree measure of the smallest angle of the triangle?

Record your answer and fill in the bubbles on the grid below. Be sure to use the correct place value.

				.			
0	0	0	0		0	0	0
1	1	1	1		1	1	1
2	2	2	2		2	2	2
3	3	3	3		3	3	3
4	4	4	4		4	4	4
5	5	5	5		5	5	5
6	6	6	6		6	6	6
7	7	7	7		7	7	7
8	8	8	8		8	8	8
9	9	9	9		9	9	9

Lesson 31 Transformations

TEKS G(c)1B Use the properties of transformations and their compositions to make connections between mathematics and the real world in applications.
TEKS G(f)1A Use transformations to explore and justify conjectures about geometric figures.

You can apply what you know about coordinate geometry to problems involving geometric figures and their transformations.

A **transformation** is a change in the position, size, or shape of a figure. The original figure is the **preimage**, and the new figure created by the transformation is the **image**.

A **translation** is a transformation in which all of the points in the preimage move the same distance to create the image. This is also called a slide transformation since the points slide across the plane. In a **reflection**, or flip transformation, all of the points of the preimage are flipped across a line to form the image.

This problem deals with a *composition* of transformations since it involves more than one kind of transformation.

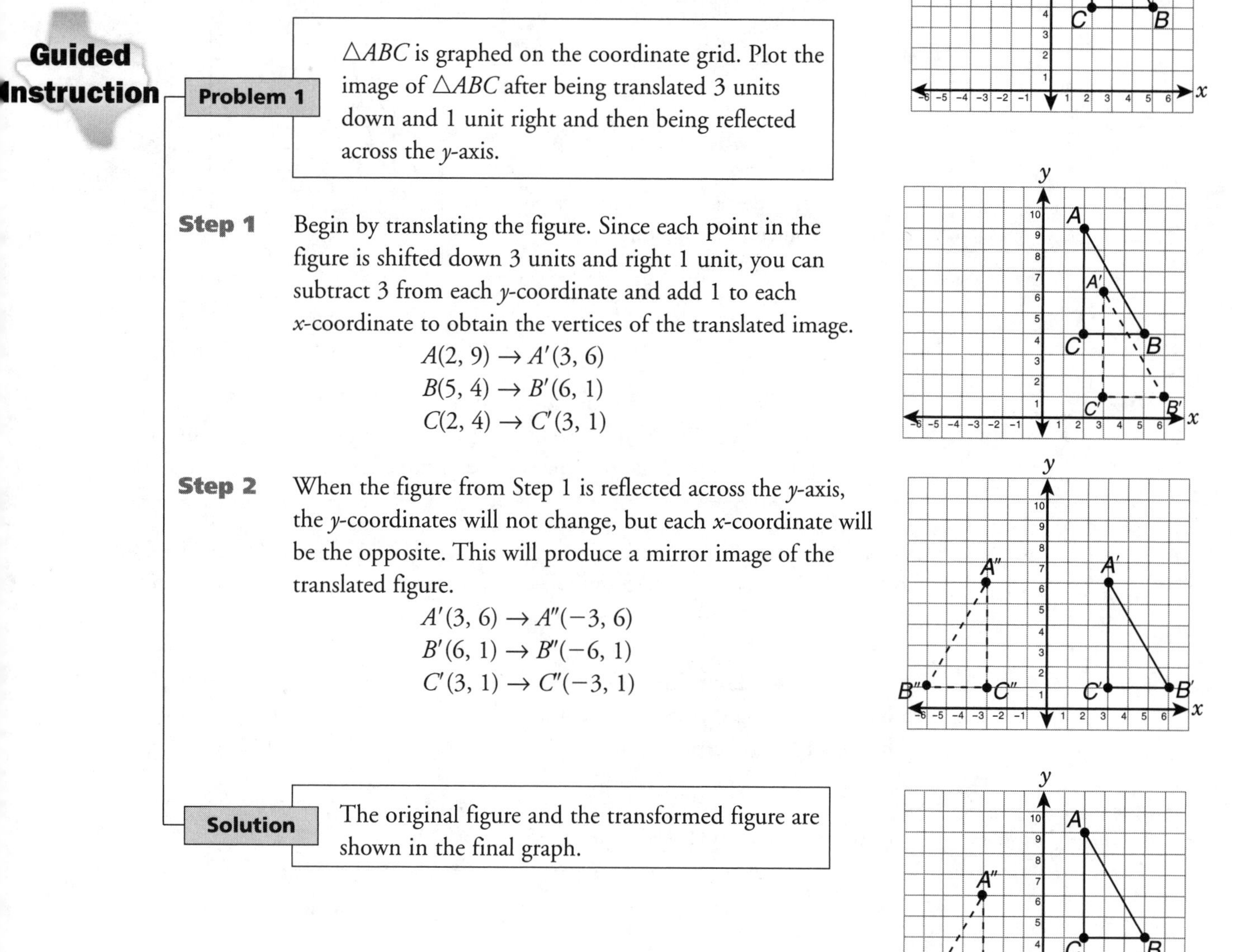

Guided Instruction

Problem 1

$\triangle ABC$ is graphed on the coordinate grid. Plot the image of $\triangle ABC$ after being translated 3 units down and 1 unit right and then being reflected across the y-axis.

Step 1 Begin by translating the figure. Since each point in the figure is shifted down 3 units and right 1 unit, you can subtract 3 from each y-coordinate and add 1 to each x-coordinate to obtain the vertices of the translated image.

$$A(2, 9) \rightarrow A'(3, 6)$$
$$B(5, 4) \rightarrow B'(6, 1)$$
$$C(2, 4) \rightarrow C'(3, 1)$$

Step 2 When the figure from Step 1 is reflected across the y-axis, the y-coordinates will not change, but each x-coordinate will be the opposite. This will produce a mirror image of the translated figure.

$$A'(3, 6) \rightarrow A''(-3, 6)$$
$$B'(6, 1) \rightarrow B''(-6, 1)$$
$$C'(3, 1) \rightarrow C''(-3, 1)$$

Solution

The original figure and the transformed figure are shown in the final graph.

Guided Instruction

A **rotation** is a transformation that involves rotating the preimage about a given point in the plane to create the image. This is also called a turn transformation.

More Problems

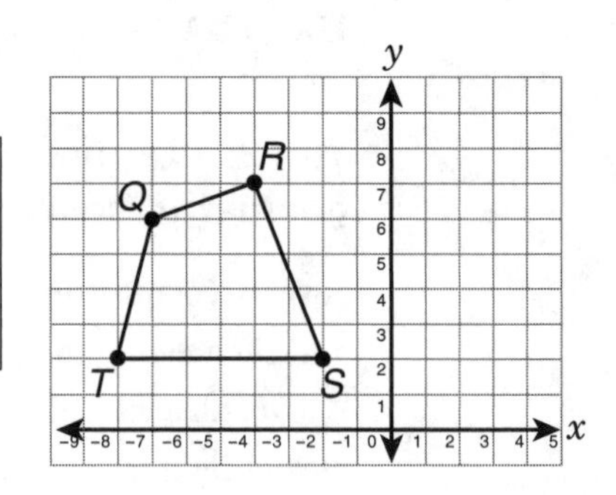

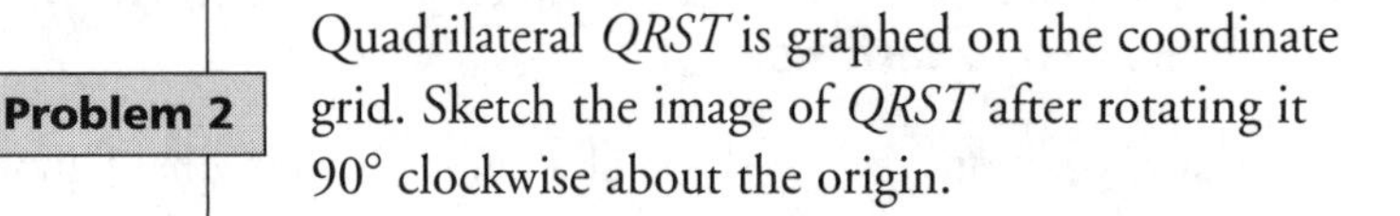

Problem 2

Quadrilateral $QRST$ is graphed on the coordinate grid. Sketch the image of $QRST$ after rotating it 90° clockwise about the origin.

To sketch the image of the rotation, imagine quadrilateral $QRST$ is drawn on a transparency laid over the coordinate grid. If you were to place a compass point at the center of rotation, in this case the origin, and rotate the transparency 90° to the right, you would arrive at the rotated image.

$Q(-7, 6) \rightarrow Q'(6, 7)$
$R(-4, 7) \rightarrow R'(7, 4)$
$S(-2, 2) \rightarrow S'(2, 2)$
$T(-8, 2) \rightarrow T'(2, 8)$

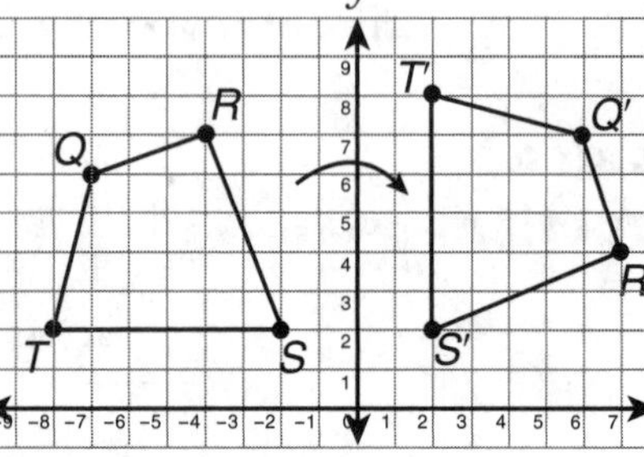

Solution

The original quadrilateral and its rotated image are shown in the graph.

Problem 3

The vertices of a triangle after being transformed are $A'(1, 0)$, $B'(3, -5)$, and $C'(-1, -3)$. If the preimage underwent a translation 5 units down and 3 units right, what were the coordinates of the vertices of the preimage?

Step 1 The preimage was shifted 5 units down. To undo this translation, you must add 5 to the y-coordinates of each vertex.

$A(\_\_, 5) \leftarrow A'(1, 0)$
$B(\_\_, 0) \leftarrow B'(3, -5)$
$C(\_\_, 2) \leftarrow C'(-1, -3)$

Step 2 The preimage was also shifted 3 units to the right. To undo this translation, you must subtract 3 from each of the x-coordinates of the vertices.

$A(-2, 5) \leftarrow A'(1, 0)$
$B(0, 0) \leftarrow B'(3, -5)$
$C(-4, 2) \leftarrow C'(-1, -3)$

Solution The original figure had vertices of $A(-2, 5)$, $B(0, 0)$, and $C(-4, 2)$.

Apply the TEKS Identify the type of transformation. Write *translation*, *reflection*, or *rotation*.

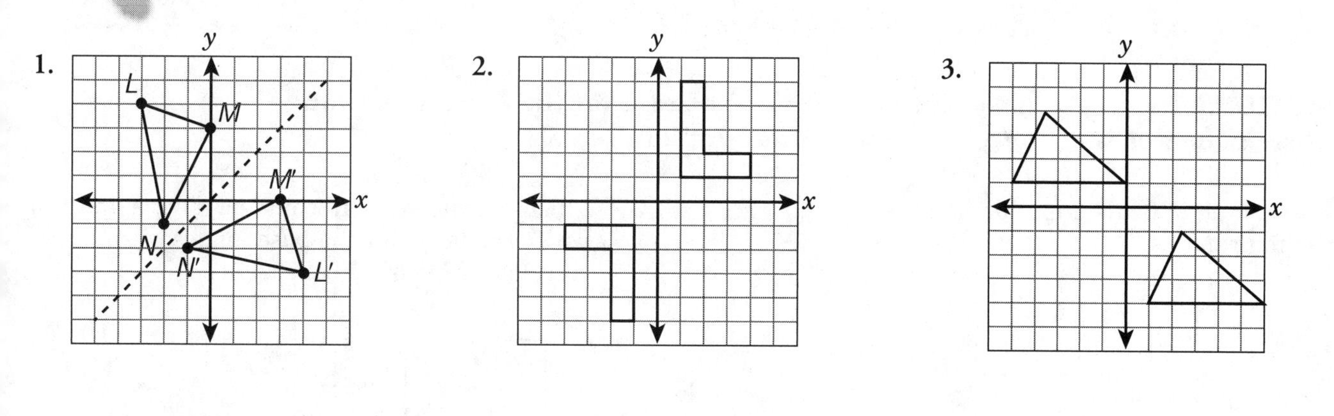

Solve each problem.

4. The endpoints of a line segment are given by the coordinates $A(1, 1)$ and $B(4, 3)$. What coordinates would give the endpoints of the segment's image after being reflected across the x-axis?

____

5. The vertices of a rectangle's image are given by the coordinates $A'(-5, 4)$, $B'(1, 4)$, $C'(1, 1)$, and $D'(-5, 1)$. The vertices of the preimage were $A(-3, 2)$, $B(3, 2)$, $C(3, -1)$, and $D(-3, -1)$. Describe the transformation that was applied to the rectangle.

____

6. A triangle has vertices $A(-2, 4)$, $B(-4, 0)$, and $C(-1, 0)$. After being transformed, its image has vertices $A'(2, -4)$, $B'(4, 0)$, and $C'(1, 0)$. Describe the transformation that was applied to the preimage.

____

Sketch each transformation described below.

7. A translation 6 units right and 3 units up.

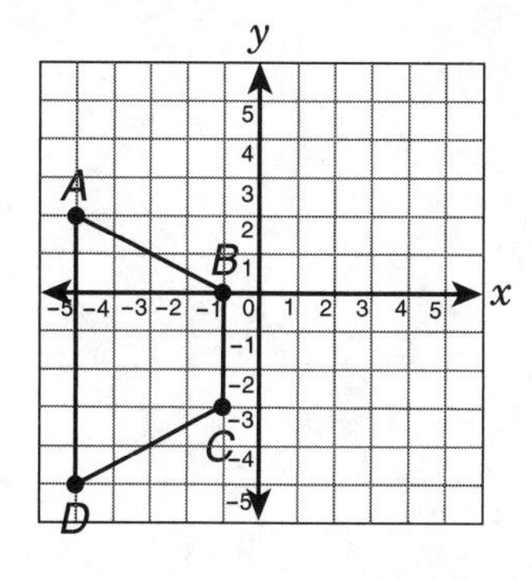

8. A reflection across the line $y = x$.

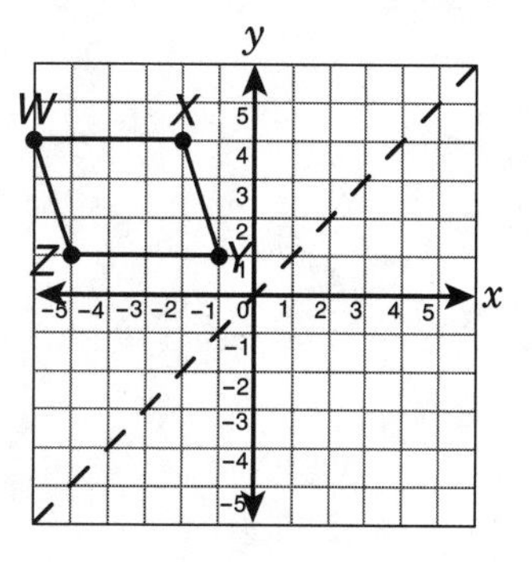

TAKS Practice

TAKS Objective 6 The student will demonstrate an understanding of geometric relationships and spatial reasoning.
TEKS G(c)1B

TAKS Objective 8 The student will demonstrate an understanding of the concepts and uses of measurement and similarity.
TEKS G(f)1A

DIRECTIONS Read each question. Then circle the letter for the correct answer. If a correct answer is not here, circle the letter for "Not Here."

1 Which kind of transformation is shown in the figure?

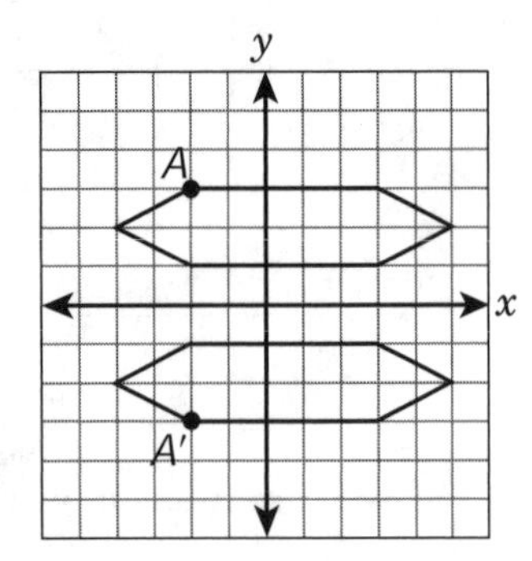

A A reflection

B A translation

C A rotation

D Not Here

2 The endpoints of a line segment have coordinates (−3, 0) and (−3, 4). What are the coordinates of the image of the line segment after being rotated 90° counterclockwise about the origin?

F (0, 3) and (4, 3)

G (0, 3) and (3, 4)

H (0, −3) and (4, −3)

J (0, −3) and (−4, −3)

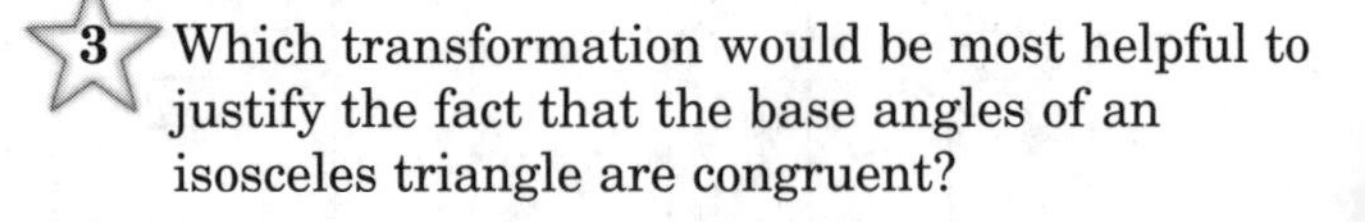

3 Which transformation would be most helpful to justify the fact that the base angles of an isosceles triangle are congruent?

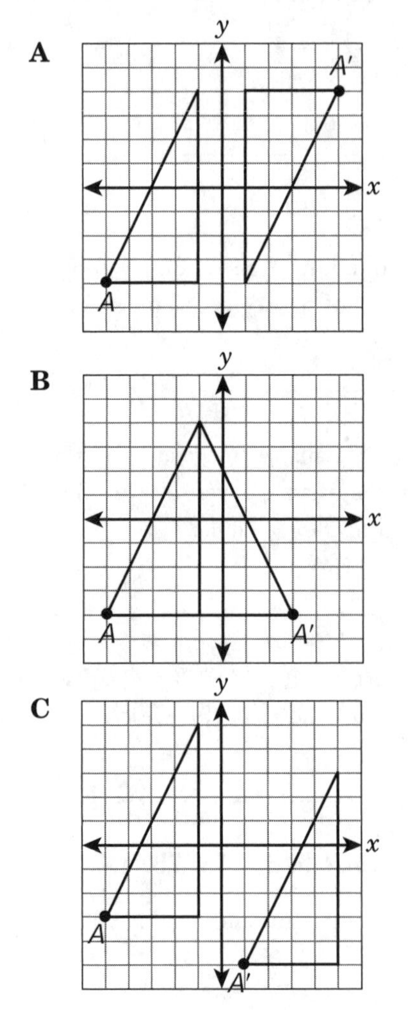

D Not Here

Focus on TEKS

Lesson 32 Applications of Transformations

TEKS G(c)1B Use the properties of transformations and their compositions to make connections between mathematics and the real world in applications such as tessellations or fractals.

Transformations play an important role in many real-world applications such as tessellations and fractals.

A **tessellation** is a repeating pattern of plane figures that completely covers a plane with no gaps and without overlapping any figures. You can find the patterns of tessellations in the work of artists, bricklayers, quilters, fabric designers, and painters, just to name a few.

Problem 1

Sketch a tessellation using the three figures at the right: a square, an equilateral triangle, and a regular hexagon.

A *regular* polygon has all sides and all interior angles congruent to each other. The three figures in this problem are all regular polygons.

Step 1 Begin by sketching the hexagon in the plane. Then, on each side of the hexagon, sketch a square such that the sides of each square completely cover the sides of the hexagon.

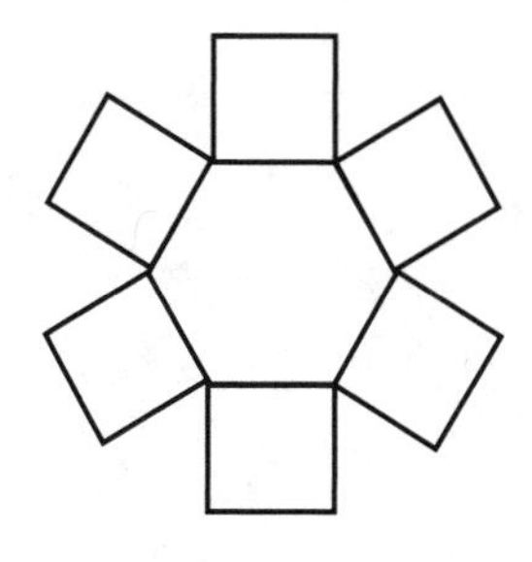

Step 2 Connect neighboring vertices of the squares with a straight line to form the equilateral triangles. The resulting figure is what will be repeated to form the tessellation. It is called the *basic unit* of the tessellation.

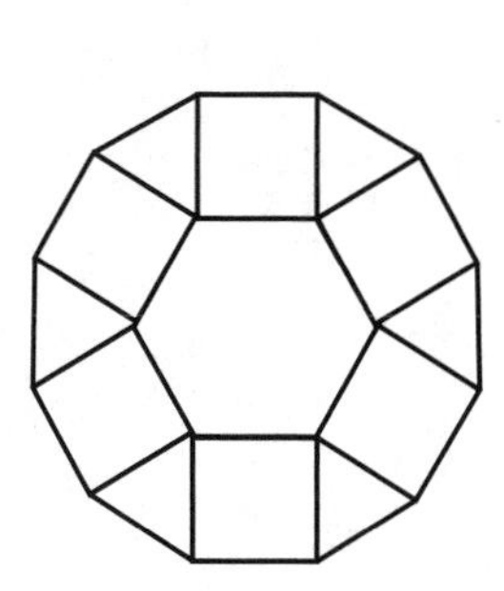

Step 3 Continue the procedure by extending the basic unit of the tessellation until the plane is completely covered.

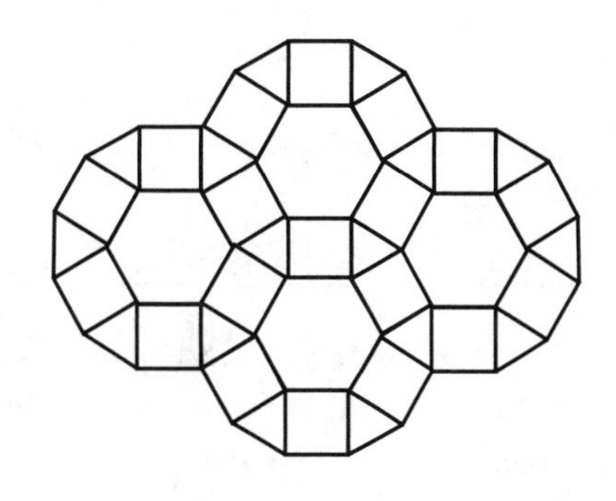

Solution The tessellation is shown above.

Guided Instruction

A **fractal** is a geometric object with repeating patterns containing shapes that are like the whole object but of different sizes.

An iteration is a process in which a certain series of steps is repeated to create a pattern.

A **Koch snowflake** is a fractal formed using multiple iterations of adding equilateral triangles to the center third of each segment of the initial equilateral triangle.

Another Problem

Problem 2 Sketch the first few iterations of the fractal Koch snowflake.

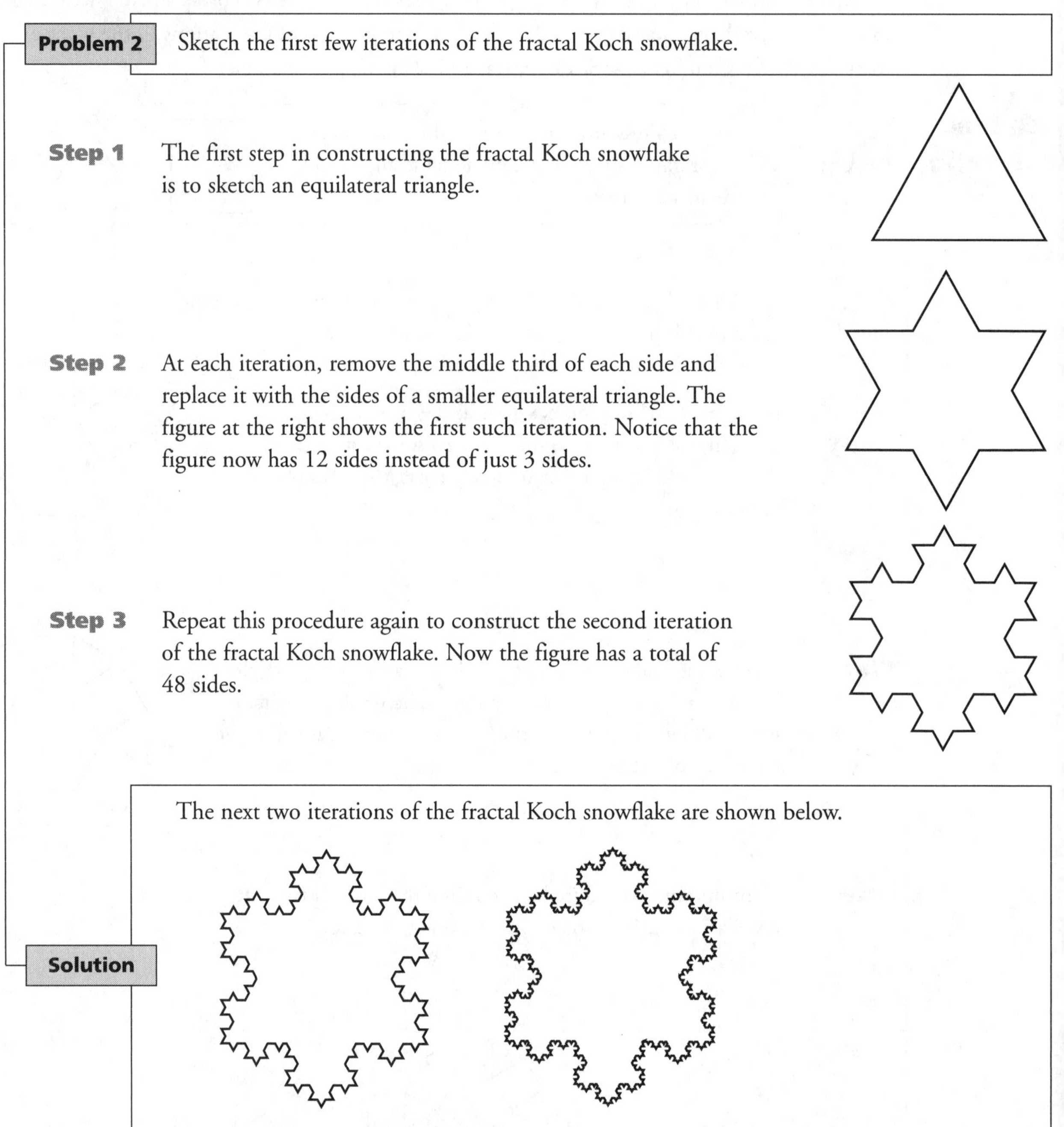

Interestingly, the perimeter of the fractal Koch snowflake grows larger and larger without bound as further iterations are constructed. However, the area of the snowflake cannot grow larger than the area of a circle containing the snowflake. You can imagine a circle enclosing the three vertices of the original triangle. As the snowflake is constructed, it will not grow beyond the bounds of the circle. So, its area will never be greater than the area of the circle even as its perimeter grows infinitely long.

Apply the TEKS Determine whether each figure could be used as a basic unit for a tessellation.

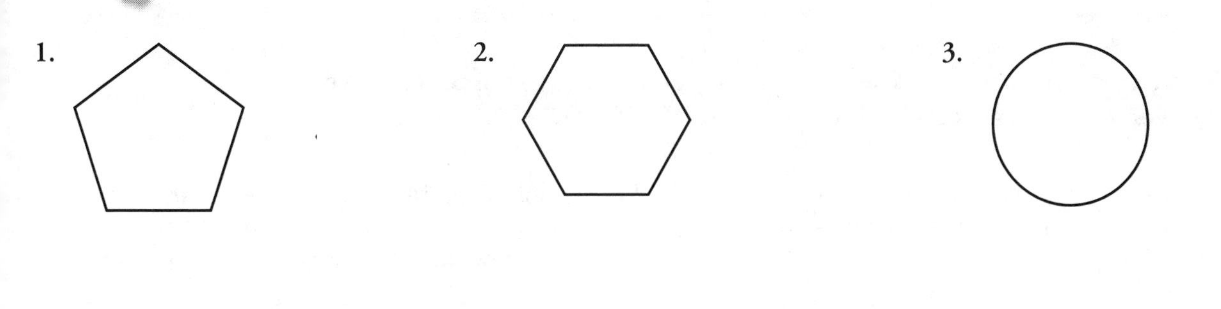

______________ ______________ ______________

Use the figure or pair of figures to sketch a tessellation in the space provided.

4.

5.

The following figures show the first four levels of the fractal called the Sierpinski triangle.

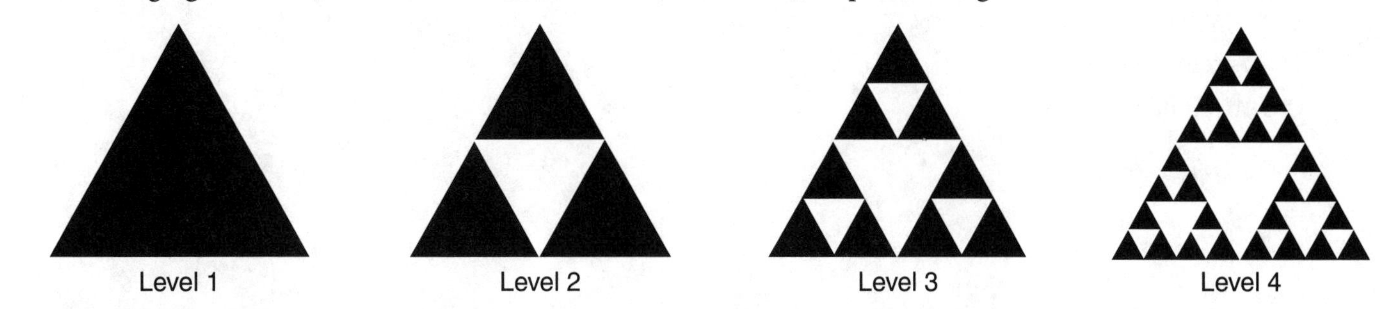

6. How many shaded triangles are contained in each of the first four levels of the Sierpinski triangle?

____

7. How many shaded triangles would you expect the fifth level of the Sierpinski triangle to contain?

____

TAKS Objective 6 The student will demonstrate an understanding of geometric relationships and spatial reasoning.
TEKS G(c)1B

DIRECTIONS Read each question. Then circle the letter for the correct answer. If a correct answer is not here, circle the letter for "Not Here."

1 The honeycomb within a beehive can be modeled by a tessellation of hexagons as shown in the figure below.

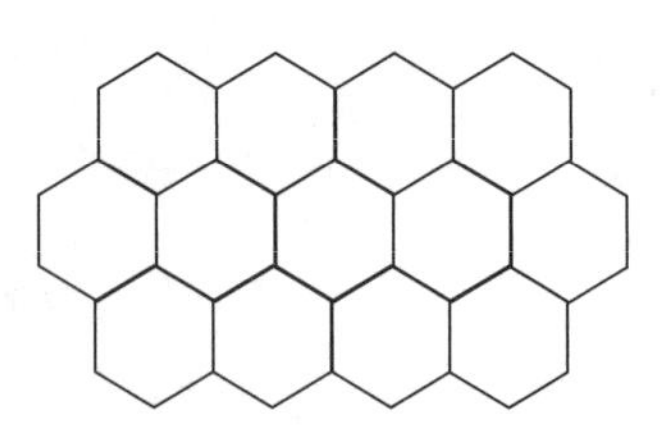

Which kind of transformation was most likely used to create the tessellation?

A Reflections

B Translations

C Rotations

D Dilations

2 Which regular polygon cannot be used to create a tessellation?

F An equilateral triangle

G A square

H A regular pentagon

J A regular hexagon

3 The following table shows the number of sides contained in each level of the fractal Koch snowflake.

Level	Number of sides
1	3
2	12
3	48
4	192

How many sides are contained in the sixth level of the Koch snowflake?

Record your answer and fill in the bubbles on the grid below. Be sure to use the correct place value.

				.			
0	0	0	0		0	0	0
1	1	1	1		1	1	1
2	2	2	2		2	2	2
3	3	3	3		3	3	3
4	4	4	4		4	4	4
5	5	5	5		5	5	5
6	6	6	6		6	6	6
7	7	7	7		7	7	7
8	8	8	8		8	8	8
9	9	9	9		9	9	9

Focus on TEKS

Lesson 33 Pythagorean Theorem

TEKS G(c)1C Identify and apply patterns from right triangles (45-45-90 and 30-60-90) to solve problems, including special right triangles and triangles whose sides are Pythagorean triples.
TEKS G(e)1C Develop, extend, and use the Pythagorean theorem.

You can apply what you have learned about squares and square roots to problems involving right triangles.

A **right triangle** is a triangle with one right angle.
The **hypotenuse** is the side of a right triangle opposite the right angle and is the longest side.
The **legs** are the other two sides of a right triangle.
The **Pythagorean theorem** states that, in a right triangle, the sum of the squares of the lengths of the legs equals the square of the length of the hypotenuse.

Guided Instruction

Problem 1

How could you use the Pythagorean theorem to find the shortest distance between the two docks on opposite sides of the river?

25 ft
15 ft

The Pythagorean theorem is represented by the equation $a^2 + b^2 = c^2$, where a and b are the lengths of the legs of a right triangle and c is the length of the hypotenuse. If you know the lengths of two sides of a right triangle, you can substitute those values in the equation and solve for the length of the third side.

a
c
b

Pythagorean theorem: $a^2 + b^2 = c^2$

Use the Pythagorean theorem to find the length of the hypotenuse of the triangle.

Step 1 Substitute the given lengths in the equation representing the Pythagorean theorem.

$$a^2 + b^2 = c^2$$
$$25^2 + 15^2 = c^2$$

Step 2 Simplify the equation.

$$625 + 225 = c^2$$
$$850 = c^2$$

Step 3 Find the square root in simplest radical form.

$$\sqrt{850} = c$$
$$\sqrt{25(34)} = c$$
$$5\sqrt{34} = c$$

Solution The shortest distance between the docks is $5\sqrt{34}$ or approximately 29.2 feet.

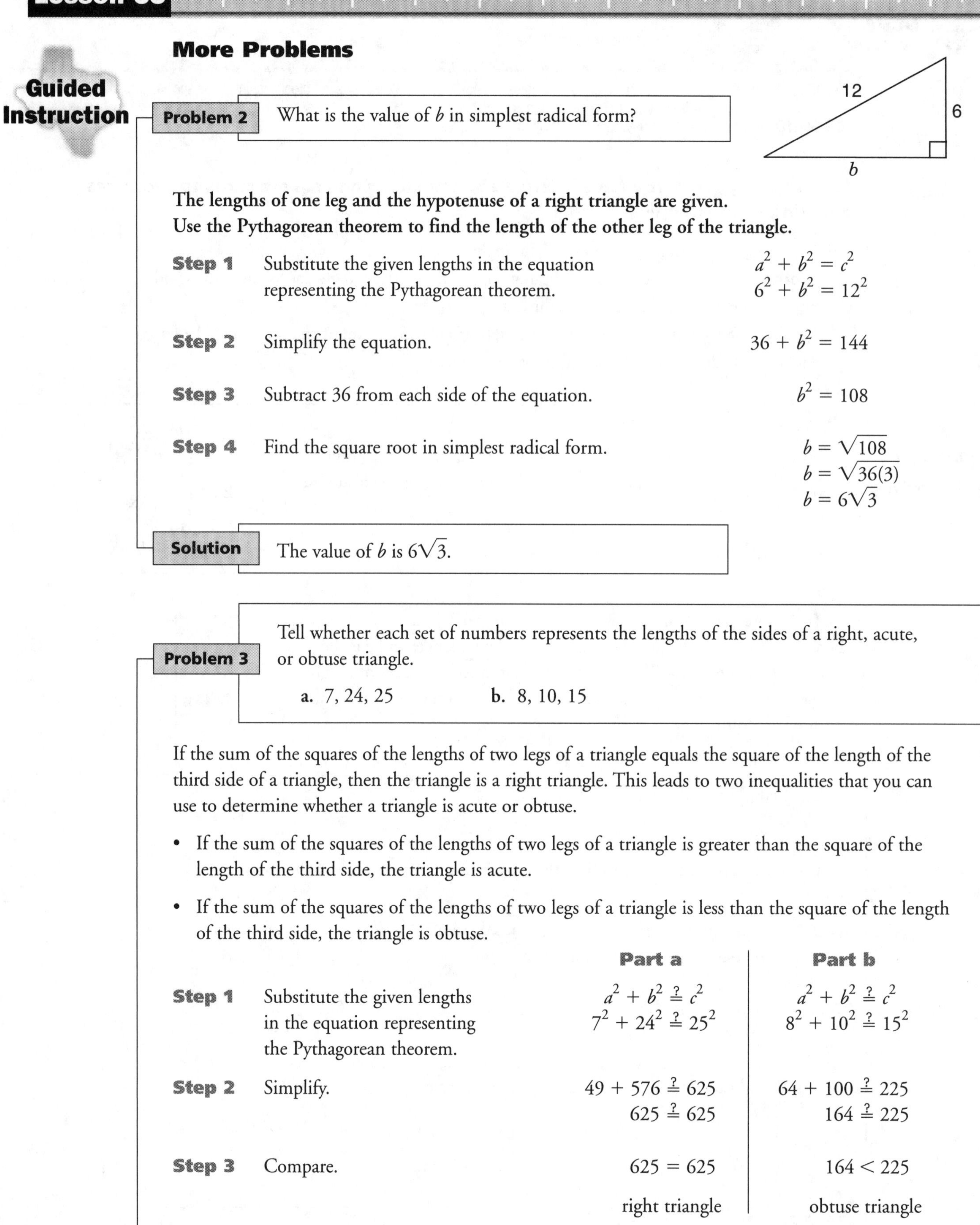

More Problems

Guided Instruction

Problem 2 What is the value of b in simplest radical form?

The lengths of one leg and the hypotenuse of a right triangle are given. Use the Pythagorean theorem to find the length of the other leg of the triangle.

Step 1 Substitute the given lengths in the equation representing the Pythagorean theorem.

$$a^2 + b^2 = c^2$$
$$6^2 + b^2 = 12^2$$

Step 2 Simplify the equation.

$$36 + b^2 = 144$$

Step 3 Subtract 36 from each side of the equation.

$$b^2 = 108$$

Step 4 Find the square root in simplest radical form.

$$b = \sqrt{108}$$
$$b = \sqrt{36(3)}$$
$$b = 6\sqrt{3}$$

Solution The value of b is $6\sqrt{3}$.

Problem 3 Tell whether each set of numbers represents the lengths of the sides of a right, acute, or obtuse triangle.

a. 7, 24, 25 **b.** 8, 10, 15

If the sum of the squares of the lengths of two legs of a triangle equals the square of the length of the third side of a triangle, then the triangle is a right triangle. This leads to two inequalities that you can use to determine whether a triangle is acute or obtuse.

- If the sum of the squares of the lengths of two legs of a triangle is greater than the square of the length of the third side, the triangle is acute.
- If the sum of the squares of the lengths of two legs of a triangle is less than the square of the length of the third side, the triangle is obtuse.

		Part a	Part b
Step 1	Substitute the given lengths in the equation representing the Pythagorean theorem.	$a^2 + b^2 \stackrel{?}{=} c^2$ $7^2 + 24^2 \stackrel{?}{=} 25^2$	$a^2 + b^2 \stackrel{?}{=} c^2$ $8^2 + 10^2 \stackrel{?}{=} 15^2$
Step 2	Simplify.	$49 + 576 \stackrel{?}{=} 625$ $625 \stackrel{?}{=} 625$	$64 + 100 \stackrel{?}{=} 225$ $164 \stackrel{?}{=} 225$
Step 3	Compare.	$625 = 625$ right triangle	$164 < 225$ obtuse triangle

Solution The set of numbers representing Triangle A form a right triangle. The set of numbers representing Triangle B form an obtuse triangle.

Apply the TEKS Using the Pythagorean theorem, complete the following. Give answers in simplest radical form.

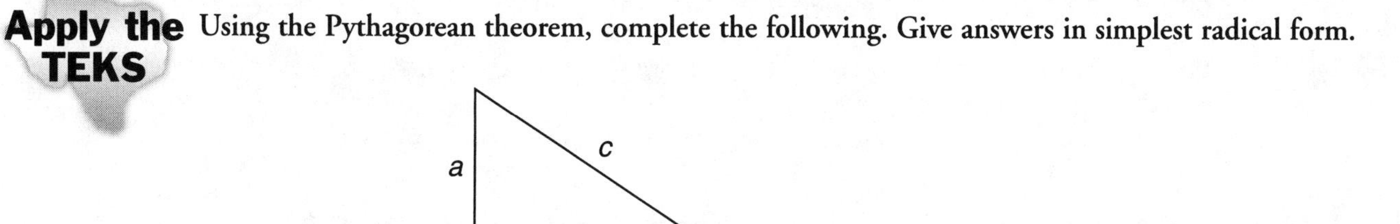

1. $a = 8$ $b = 6$ $c =$ ______
2. $a = 2.1$ $b = 9.7$ $c =$ ______
3. $a = 5$ $b =$ ______ $c = 13$
4. $a =$ ______ $b = 11$ $c = \sqrt{137}$

Find the missing length in each figure. Give answers in simplest radical form.

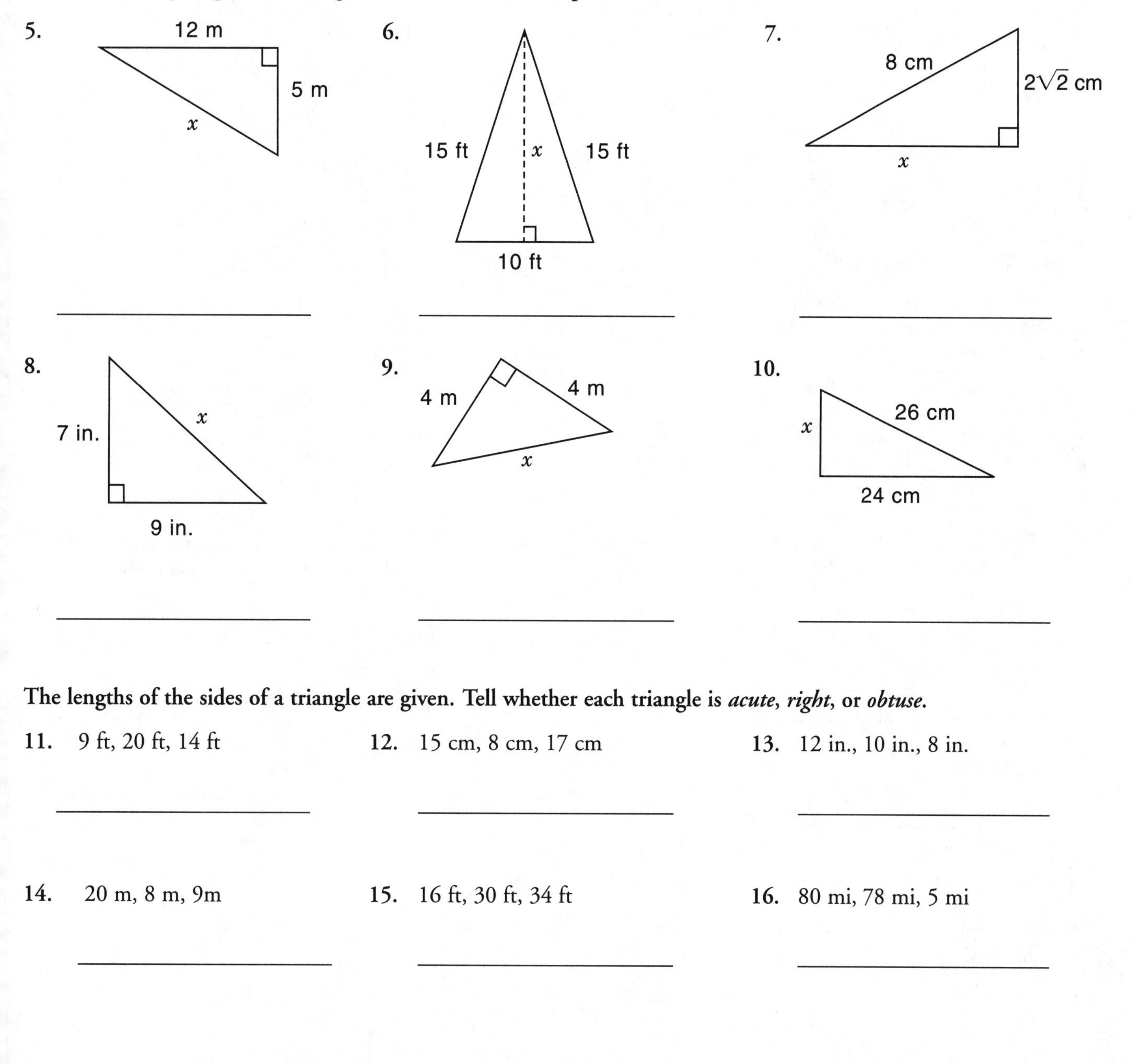

5. ______
6. ______
7. ______
8. ______
9. ______
10. ______

The lengths of the sides of a triangle are given. Tell whether each triangle is *acute*, *right*, or *obtuse*.

11. 9 ft, 20 ft, 14 ft ______
12. 15 cm, 8 cm, 17 cm ______
13. 12 in., 10 in., 8 in. ______
14. 20 m, 8 m, 9m ______
15. 16 ft, 30 ft, 34 ft ______
16. 80 mi, 78 mi, 5 mi ______

TAKS Objective 6 The student will demonstrate an understanding of geometric relationships and spatial reasoning.
TEKS G(c)1C

TAKS Objective 8 The student will demonstrate an understanding of the concepts and uses of measurement and similarity.
TEKS G(e)1C

DIRECTIONS Read each question. Then circle the letter for the correct answer. If a correct answer is not here, circle the letter for "Not Here."

1 The legs of an isosceles right triangle are 5 inches long. What is the length of the hypotenuse of the triangle to the nearest inch?

A 7 in.

B 10 in.

C 25 in.

D 50 in.

2 Mr. Miller has a 20-foot ladder, which he wants to reach 18 feet up the side of his house. To the nearest foot, how far from the base of the house should he place the ladder?

Record your answer and fill in the bubbles on the grid below. Be sure to use the correct place value.

				•			
0	0	0	0		0	0	0
1	1	1	1		1	1	1
2	2	2	2		2	2	2
3	3	3	3		3	3	3
4	4	4	4		4	4	4
5	5	5	5		5	5	5
6	6	6	6		6	6	6
7	7	7	7		7	7	7
8	8	8	8		8	8	8
9	9	9	9		9	9	9

3 What is the height of the triangle?

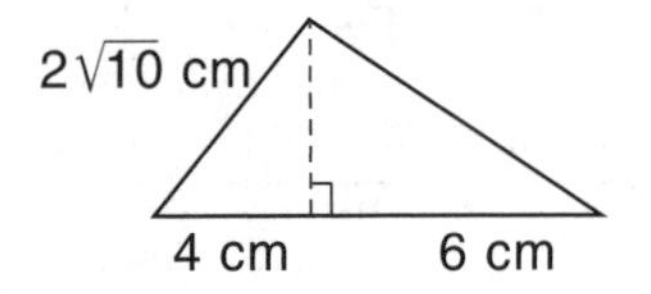

A 2 cm

B $2\sqrt{6}$ cm

C $2\sqrt{14}$ cm

D $3\sqrt{10}$ cm

4 What is the length of the diagonal sidewalk across this rectangular playground?

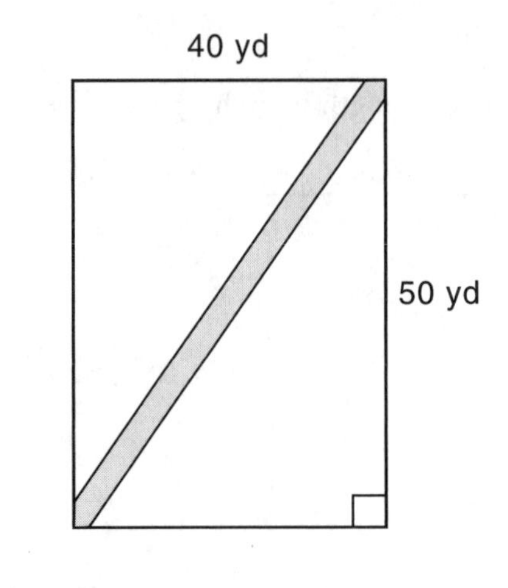

F $3\sqrt{10}$ yd

G $6\sqrt{5}$ yd

H $100\sqrt{41}$ yd

J Not Here

5 Which of the following sets of measurements could be the lengths of the sides of an acute triangle?

A 3 in., 4 in., 5 in.

B 8 ft, 11 ft, 13 ft

C 10 yd, 15 yd, 20 yd

D 12 m, 7 m, 9 m

Focus on TEKS

Lesson 34 Special Right Triangles and Pythagorean Triples

TEKS G(c)1C Identify and apply patterns from right triangles to solve problems, including special right triangles (45-45-90 and 30-60-90) and triangles whose sides are Pythagorean triples.
TEKS 8.14A Identify and apply mathematics to everyday experiences, to activities in and outside of school, with other disciplines, and with other mathematical topics.
TEKS 8.14B Use a problem-solving model that incorporates understanding the problem, making a plan, carrying out the plan, and evaluating the solution for reasonableness.

You can apply what you have learned about right triangles and the Pythagorean theorem to solve problems involving special right triangles.

Guided Instruction

Problem 1 The infield of a professional baseball diamond is a square that measures 90 feet on each side. Use a special triangle relationship to find the distance from home plate to second base.

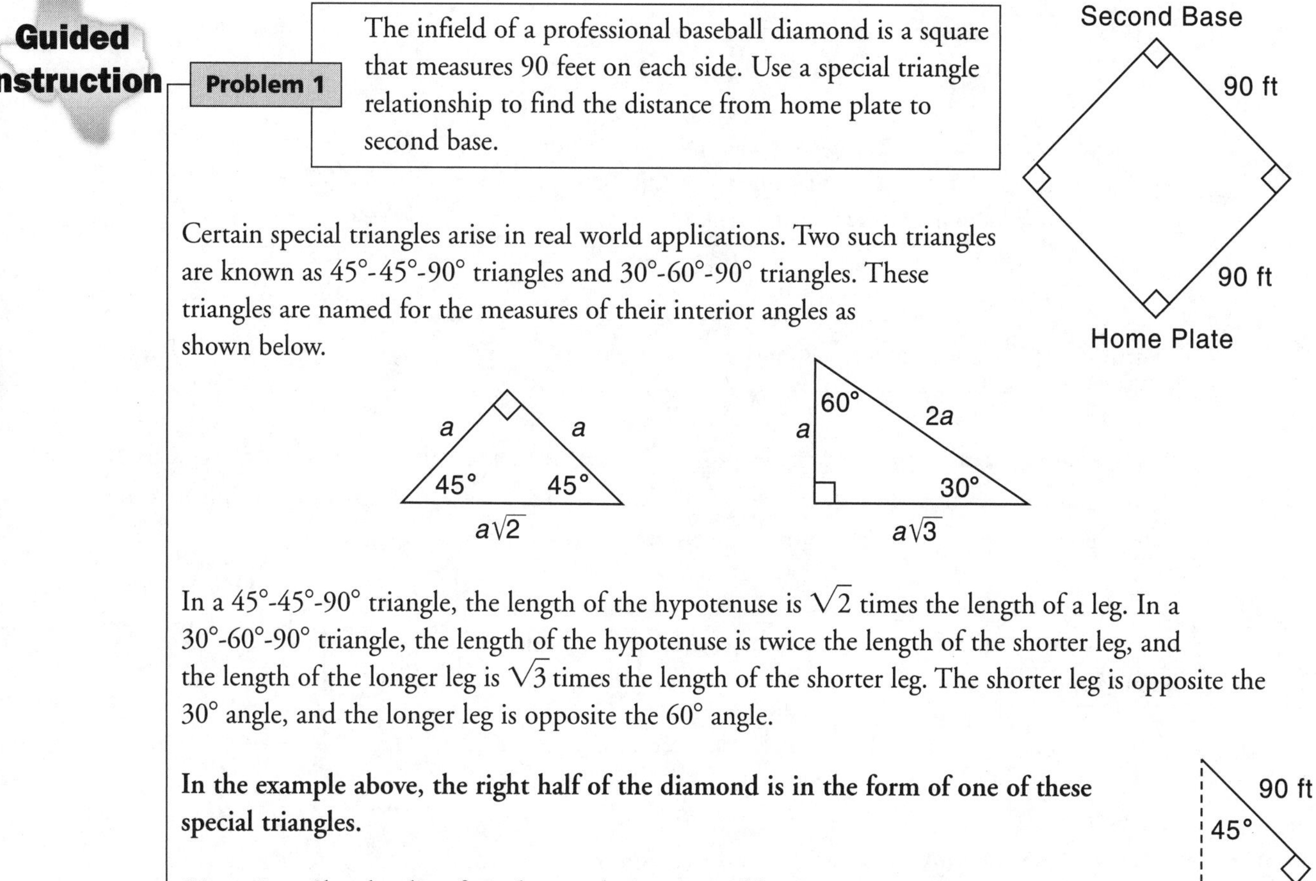

Certain special triangles arise in real world applications. Two such triangles are known as 45°-45°-90° triangles and 30°-60°-90° triangles. These triangles are named for the measures of their interior angles as shown below.

In a 45°-45°-90° triangle, the length of the hypotenuse is $\sqrt{2}$ times the length of a leg. In a 30°-60°-90° triangle, the length of the hypotenuse is twice the length of the shorter leg, and the length of the longer leg is $\sqrt{3}$ times the length of the shorter leg. The shorter leg is opposite the 30° angle, and the longer leg is opposite the 60° angle.

In the example above, the right half of the diamond is in the form of one of these special triangles.

90 ft
45°
45°
90 ft

Step 1 Sketch a line from home plate to second base to create a triangle. Notice that this bisects two right angles to form two 45° angles.

Step 2 The length of the hypotenuse of the 45°-45°-90° triangle will be $\sqrt{2}$ times the length of a leg. Since each of the legs is 90 feet long, the length of the hypotenuse is $90\sqrt{2}$ feet.

Solution The distance from home plate to second base is $90\sqrt{2}$, or approximately 127.3 feet.

You should ask yourself if this seems like a reasonable answer. Looking at the baseball diamond, the distance from home plate to second base appears to be about 1.5 times the distance from home plate to first base. So, 127.3 feet seems reasonable. You can check the answer exactly by using the Pythagorean theorem.

More Problems

Guided Instruction

Problem 2 Solve for x and y in the figure. Check your answer using the Pythagorean theorem.

The figure is a 30°-60°-90° triangle. Use the relationship of the lengths of the sides of the special triangle.

Step 1 The length of the shorter leg is one half the length of the hypotenuse.

$$x = \frac{1}{2}(12)$$
$$x = 6$$

Step 2 The length of the longer leg is $\sqrt{3}$ times the length of the shorter leg.

$$y = 6\sqrt{3}$$

Step 3 Substitute the lengths of the sides x and y for a and b into the equation representing the Pythagorean theorem to check the answer.

$$a^2 + b^2 = c^2$$
$$6^2 + (6\sqrt{3})^2 = 12^2$$
$$36 + 36 \cdot 3 = 144$$
$$36 + 108 = 144$$
$$144 = 144$$

Solution In the figure, $x = 6$ and $y = 6\sqrt{3}$.

Pythagorean triples are sets of three positive integers a, b, and c that satisfy the Pythagorean theorem. Some common examples include 3-4-5, 5-12-13, 8-15-17, and 7-24-25. If you multiply each number in a Pythagorean triple by the same number, you get another Pythagorean triple.

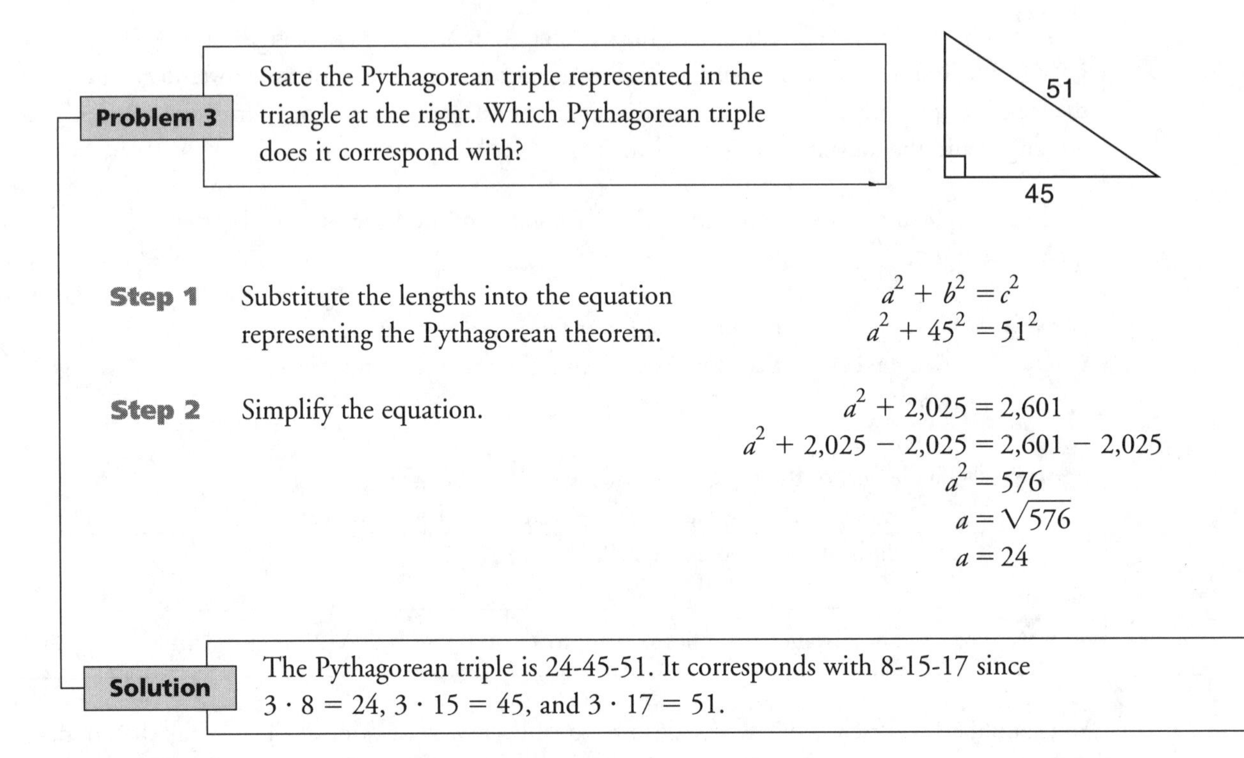

Problem 3 State the Pythagorean triple represented in the triangle at the right. Which Pythagorean triple does it correspond with?

Step 1 Substitute the lengths into the equation representing the Pythagorean theorem.

$$a^2 + b^2 = c^2$$
$$a^2 + 45^2 = 51^2$$

Step 2 Simplify the equation.

$$a^2 + 2{,}025 = 2{,}601$$
$$a^2 + 2{,}025 - 2{,}025 = 2{,}601 - 2{,}025$$
$$a^2 = 576$$
$$a = \sqrt{576}$$
$$a = 24$$

Solution The Pythagorean triple is 24-45-51. It corresponds with 8-15-17 since $3 \cdot 8 = 24$, $3 \cdot 15 = 45$, and $3 \cdot 17 = 51$.

Apply the TEKS Find the missing lengths in each special triangle. Give answers in simplest radical form.

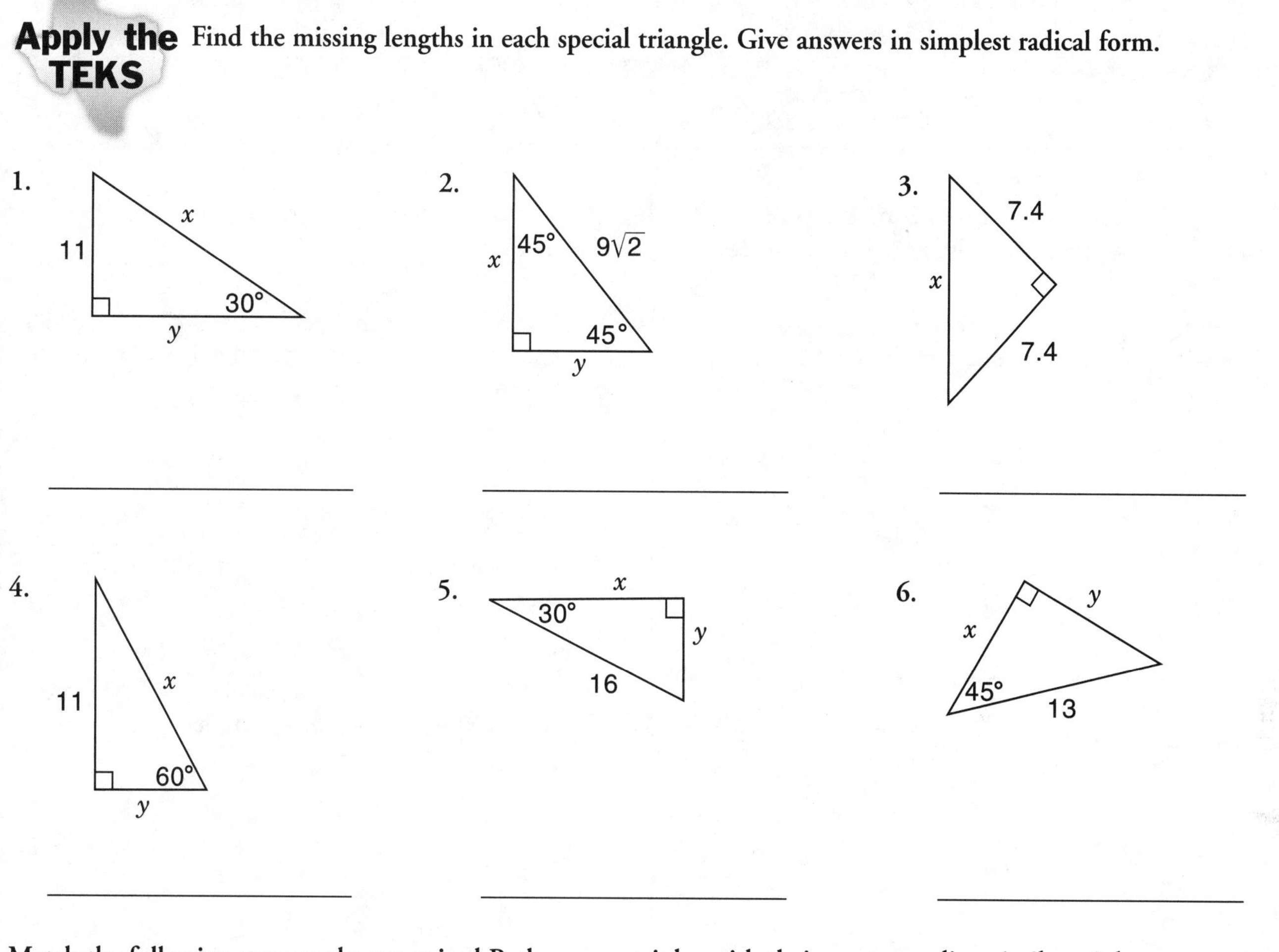

Match the following commonly recognized Pythagorean triples with their corresponding similar triples. Write the letter in the space provided.

7. 24-10-26 ________

8. 6-8-10 ________

9. 48-14-50 ________

10. 16-30-34 ________

a. 3-4-5
b. 5-12-13
c. 8-15-17
d. 7-24-25

Suppose the shorter leg of a 30°-60°-90° triangle is a units long. Fill in the missing steps below to verify that the length of the hypotenuse is $2a$ units long and the longer leg is $a\sqrt{3}$ units long.

Pythagorean theorem: $a^2 + b^2 = c^2$

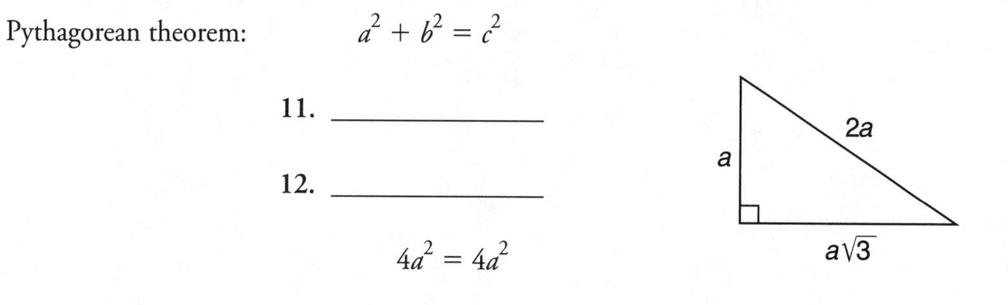

$4a^2 = 4a^2$

TAKS Objective 6 The student will demonstrate an understanding of geometric relationships and spatial reasoning.
TEKS G(c)1C

TAKS Objective 10 The student will demonstrate an understanding of the mathematical processes and tools used in problem solving.
TEKS 8.14A, 8.14B

DIRECTIONS Read each question. Then circle the letter for the correct answer. If a correct answer is not here, circle the letter for "Not Here."

1 A cable for a power transformer forms a 60° angle with the ground as shown in the figure.

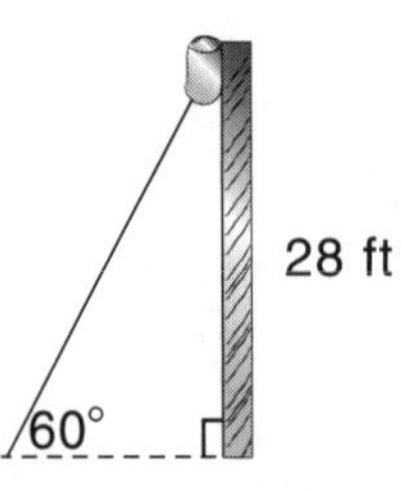

What is the approximate length of the cable?

A 16 ft

B 21 ft

C 32 ft

D 35 ft

2 Which of the following sets of numbers is NOT a Pythagorean triple?

F 9-40-41

G 9-12-15

H 5-12-13

J Not Here

3 If the length of the hypotenuse of a 45°-45°-90° triangle is $18\sqrt{2}$ meters, what is the perimeter of the triangle?

A $36 + 18\sqrt{2}$ m

B 54 m

C $54\sqrt{2}$ m

D Not Here

4 If 18 and 30 are two members of a Pythagorean triple, what is the third member?

F 15

G 24

H 35

J 42

5 What is the value of x in the figure?

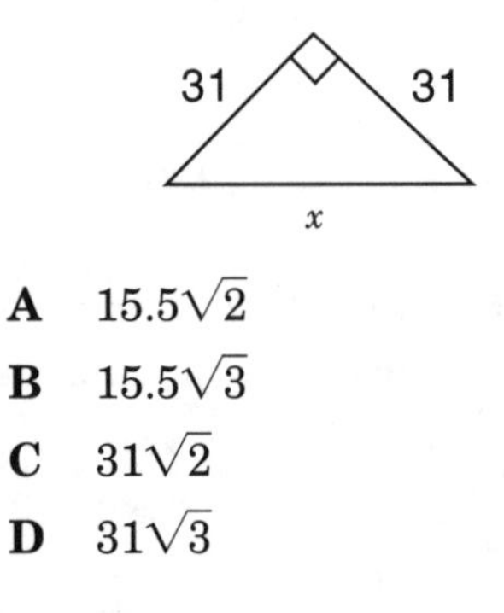

A $15.5\sqrt{2}$

B $15.5\sqrt{3}$

C $31\sqrt{2}$

D $31\sqrt{3}$

Focus on TEKS Lesson 35 Symbolic Representation and Conditional Statements

TEKS G(b)3A Determine if the converse of a conditional statement is true or false.
TEKS G(b)3B Construct and justify statements about geometric figures and their properties.
TEKS G(b)4A Select an appropriate representation in order to solve problems.

Mathematical statements often can be written in a more concise and manageable form using a symbolic representation.

A **conditional statement** is also known as an *if-then* statement. The part that follows *if* is called the hypothesis, and the part that follows *then* is the conclusion.

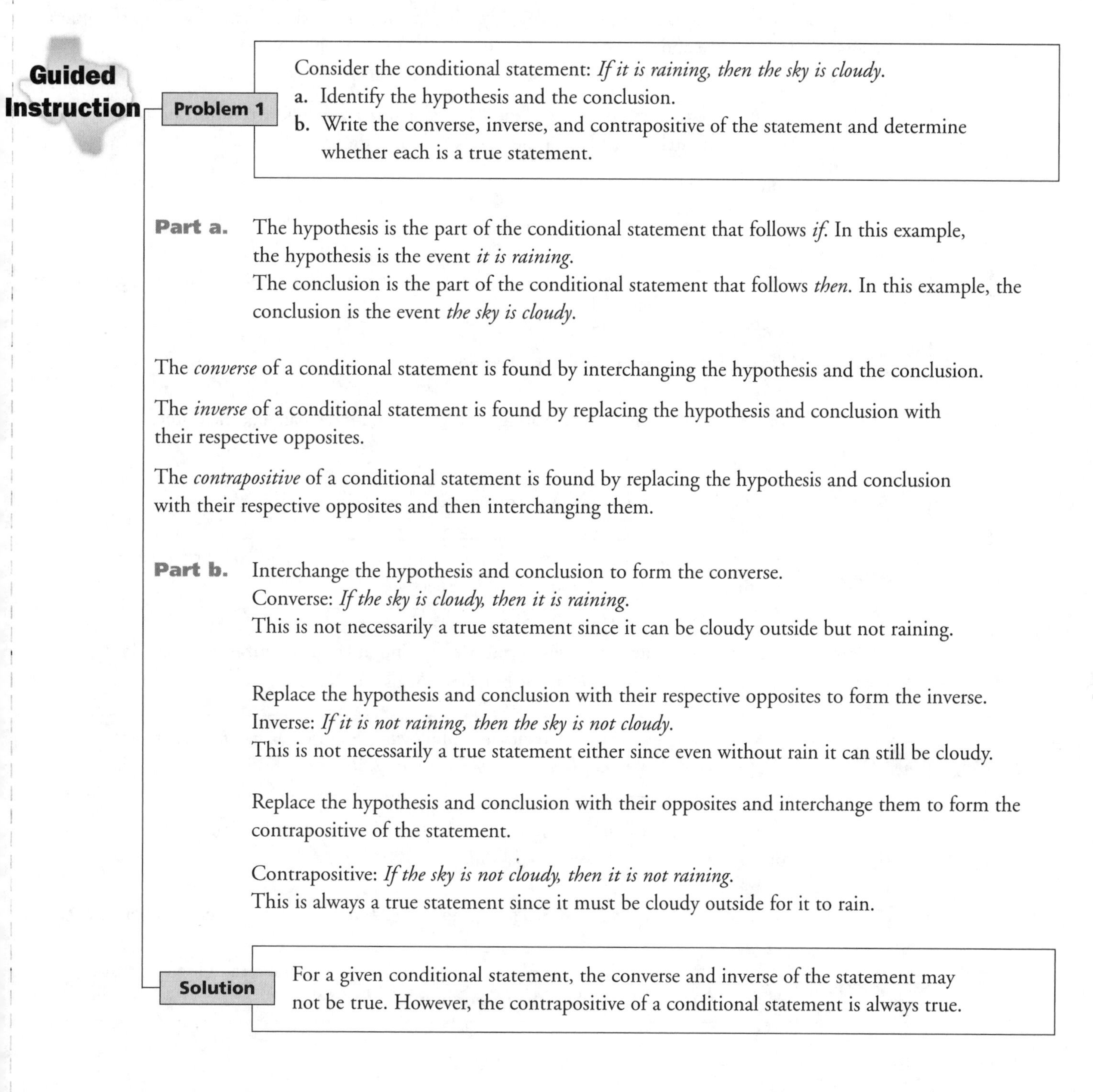

Guided Instruction

Problem 1

Consider the conditional statement: *If it is raining, then the sky is cloudy.*

a. Identify the hypothesis and the conclusion.

b. Write the converse, inverse, and contrapositive of the statement and determine whether each is a true statement.

Part a. The hypothesis is the part of the conditional statement that follows *if.* In this example, the hypothesis is the event *it is raining.*
The conclusion is the part of the conditional statement that follows *then.* In this example, the conclusion is the event *the sky is cloudy.*

The *converse* of a conditional statement is found by interchanging the hypothesis and the conclusion.

The *inverse* of a conditional statement is found by replacing the hypothesis and conclusion with their respective opposites.

The *contrapositive* of a conditional statement is found by replacing the hypothesis and conclusion with their respective opposites and then interchanging them.

Part b. Interchange the hypothesis and conclusion to form the converse.
Converse: *If the sky is cloudy, then it is raining.*
This is not necessarily a true statement since it can be cloudy outside but not raining.

Replace the hypothesis and conclusion with their respective opposites to form the inverse.
Inverse: *If it is not raining, then the sky is not cloudy.*
This is not necessarily a true statement either since even without rain it can still be cloudy.

Replace the hypothesis and conclusion with their opposites and interchange them to form the contrapositive of the statement.

Contrapositive: *If the sky is not cloudy, then it is not raining.*
This is always a true statement since it must be cloudy outside for it to rain.

Solution

For a given conditional statement, the converse and inverse of the statement may not be true. However, the contrapositive of a conditional statement is always true.

More Problems

Guided Instruction

Problem 2

Consider the conditional statement: *If two figures are congruent, then the figures are similar.* Rewrite the statement along with its converse, inverse, and contrapositive using a symbolic representation.

Step 1 Let p represent the hypothesis, *two figures are congruent,* and let q represent the conclusion, *the figures are similar.* Then the conditional statement can be rewritten as the following: $p \Rightarrow q$.

The expression $p \Rightarrow q$ is read "p implies q" or "If p, then q." It is a shorthand way of writing conditional statements. To write the opposite of an event p, the symbol $\neg$ is used. For example, the expression $\neg p$ is read as "not p," and it means the opposite of the event p.

Step 2 To write the converse of the conditional statement $p \Rightarrow q$, follow the same procedure as before. Interchange the hypothesis and the conclusion.

Converse: $q \Rightarrow p$

This statement is read, "If q, then p."

Step 3 The inverse is the negation, or opposite, of both the hypothesis and conclusion. It is written:

Inverse: $\neg p \Rightarrow \neg q$

This statement is read, "If not p, then not q."

Step 4 Form the contrapositive by negating both events and interchanging their order.

Contrapositive: $\neg q \Rightarrow \neg p$

This statement is read, "if not q, then not p."

Solution For the conditional statement $p \Rightarrow q$, the converse, inverse, and contrapositive are written $q \Rightarrow p$, $\neg p \Rightarrow \neg q$, and $\neg q \Rightarrow \neg p$, respectively.

To show that a conditional statement is false, you need to find only one **counterexample**. This is an example for which the hypothesis is true but the conclusion is false.

Problem 3

Give a counterexample to show that the following conditional statement is false: *If the product of two numbers is 24, then both of the numbers are even.*

Step 1 Try to think of two numbers that satisfy the hypothesis but will not satisfy the conclusion of the conditional statement.

Step 2 Consider the numbers 3 and 8. Their product is 24, but 3 is not an even number.

Solution The conditional statement is not true because there is a counterexample that proves it false. A counterexample is the pair of numbers 3 and 8.

Apply the TEKS **For each conditional statement, identify the hypothesis and the conclusion. Then write the converse, inverse, and contrapositive of the statement. Tell if each statement is *true*.**

1. *If a figure is a square, then it is a rectangle.*

   hypothesis: ______________________ conclusion: ______________________

   converse: ____

   inverse: ____

   contrapositive: ____

2. *If a triangle has a right angle, then it is a right triangle.*

   hypothesis: ______________________ conclusion: ______________________

   converse: ____

   inverse: ____

   contrapositive: ____

Consider the statement: *If two angles are complementary, then the sum of their measures is* 90°. Let *A* represent the hypothesis and *B* represent the conclusion. Match each statement with the correct symbolic representation. Write the letter in the space provided.

3. $B \Rightarrow A$ ______

4. $\neg B \Rightarrow \neg A$ ______

5. $\neg A \Rightarrow \neg B$ ______

6. $A \Rightarrow B$ ______

a. Original conditional statement
b. Converse
c. Inverse
d. Contrapositive

State whether each conditional statement is *true* or *false*. If it is false, give a counterexample.

7. If two lines are parallel, then the lines have the same slope.

   ____

8. If the sum of two numbers is zero, then the numbers have the same absolute value.

   ____

9. For two real numbers a and b, if $a < b$, then $a^2 < b^2$.

   ____

TAKS Objective 6 The student will demonstrate an understanding of geometric relationships and spatial reasoning.
TEKS G(b)4A

DIRECTIONS Read each question. Then circle the letter for the correct answer. If a correct answer is <u>not here</u>, circle the letter for "Not Here."

1 Consider the conditional statement: *If two lines are perpendicular, then the lines form four right angles*. Which of the following statements represents the inverse of the converse of this statement?

A If two lines are not perpendicular, then the lines do not form four right angles.

B If two lines form four right angles, then the lines are perpendicular.

C If two lines do not form four right angles, then the lines are not perpendicular.

D Not Here

2 If p represents the hypothesis and q represents the conclusion of a conditional statement, which of the following symbolizes the inverse of the conditional statement?

F $p \Rightarrow q$

G $q \Rightarrow p$

H $\neg p \Rightarrow \neg q$

J $\neg q \Rightarrow \neg p$

3 If a conditional statement is false, which of the following is also false?

A The converse

B The inverse

C The contrapositive

D Not Here

4 If the lengths of the sides of a triangle are three consecutive integers, it is not a right triangle. Which of the following figures serves as a counterexample to prove this is a false statement?

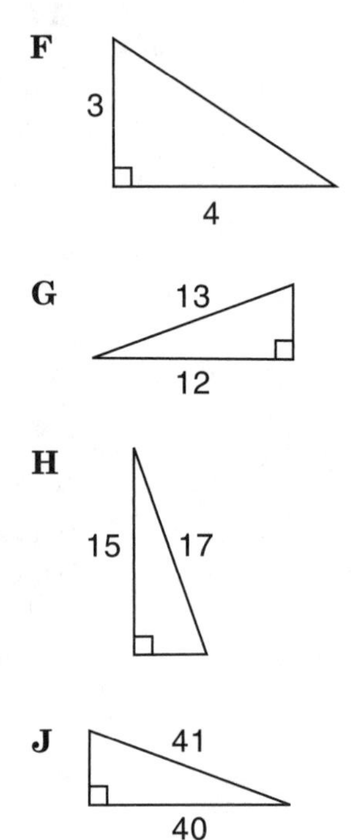

Focus on TEKS

Lesson 36 Proving Mathematics True and Deductive Reasoning

TEKS G(b)3C Demonstrate what it means to prove mathematically that statements are true.
TEKS G(b)3E Use deductive reasoning to prove a statement.

Throughout this chapter, you have made generalized conjectures and statements about certain geometric properties. In this lesson, you will explore how to prove mathematically that a statement is true.

Deductive reasoning is a technique in which you assume that the hypothesis of a statement is true, and then write a series of statements and reasons that lead to the conclusion.
The set of statements and reasons forms a mathematical **proof**.

Guided Instruction

Problem 1

Consider the figure at the right. Prove that if $WY = XZ$, then $WX = YZ$.

W X Y Z

Just by looking at the figure, you might already agree that the conclusion is true but could you justify it mathematically? You could use a ruler to measure the length of each line segment to show that $WX = YZ$. However, that would prove the statement is true only for this particular figure. If points W and Z were moved an equal distance, you would have to measure all of the segments again. A mathematical proof handles every possible case at once by considering the general case.

To justify the statements of a mathematical proof, *postulates*, or assumptions, are often cited. A postulate necessary to complete this proof is the *segment addition postulate*, which states that if point C is between points A and B, then $AC + CB = AB$.

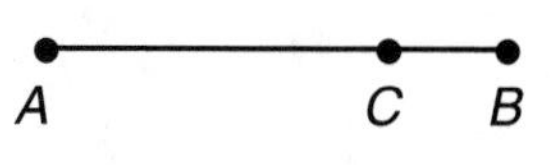

You can use the segment addition postulate along with other mathematical properties to complete the proof in this example.

Step 1 Begin by setting up a table with two columns, *Statements* and *Reasons*. List any given information. Since we are assuming the hypothesis is true, this is given information.

Step 2 Think about the conclusion you are trying to reach. In this case, notice that both $\overline{WY}$ and $\overline{XZ}$ contain $\overline{XY}$. If we could somehow remove this common segment, we would have $WX = YZ$.

Step 3 Fill in the table with statements along with reasons that justify those statements until you reach the desired conclusion.

Statements	Reasons
1. $WY = XZ$	1. Given
2. $WY = WX + XY$ $XZ = XY + YZ$	2. Segment Addition Postulate
3. $WX + XY = XY + YZ$	3. Substitution
4. $WX = YZ$	4. Subtraction Property of Equality

Solution The proof is shown in the table. This form of proof is called a *two-column proof*.

Another Problem

Guided Instruction

Problem 2

Refer to the figure at the right. Construct a paragraph proof to show that if $m\angle LOM = m\angle NOP$, then $m\angle LON = m\angle MOP$.

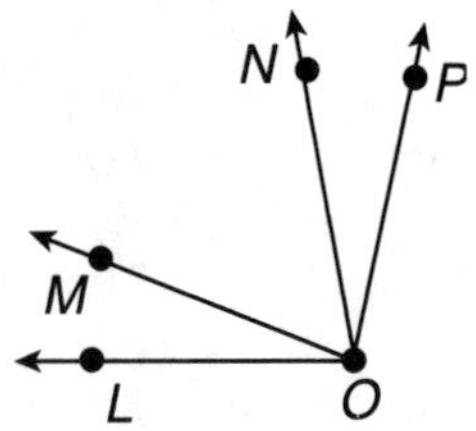

In a *paragraph proof,* the statements and reasons justifying the statements are not presented in two columns. Instead, they appear in the sentences of a paragraph so that the proof reads like a text.

The *angle addition postulate* states that if point C is in the interior of $\angle AOB$, then $m\angle AOC + m\angle COB = m\angle AOB$.

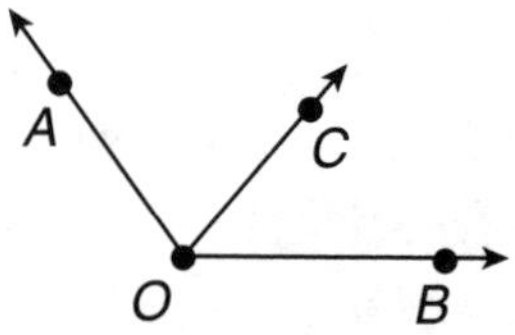

Use the angle addition postulate and other mathematical properties to reach the desired conclusion. Then formulate the proof by listing the statements and reasons in paragraph form.

Step 1 The proof will still begin by listing any given information. Since we are using deductive reasoning, assume that the hypothesis is true and list it as given information.

Step 2 Again, consider what you know from the given information and try to think how you can use it to reach the desired conclusion. Notice that both of the angle measures in the conclusion involve $\angle MON$. If you add the measure of this angle to the measures of the two angles in the hypothesis, you should achieve the desired result.

Step 3 After the given information, list all of the necessary statements and reasons in sentences until you arrive at the conclusion.

It is given that $m\angle LOM = m\angle NOP$. According to the addition property of equality, we can add $m\angle MON$ to both sides of this equation to obtain $m\angle LOM + m\angle MON = m\angle NOP + m\angle MON$. By the angle addition postulate, $m\angle LOM + m\angle MON = m\angle LON$, and $m\angle NOP + m\angle MON = m\angle MOP$. Substituting these expressions into the previous equation will yield $m\angle LON = m\angle MOP$. This gives the desired conclusion and completes the proof.

Solution

The paragraph proof above shows that if $m\angle LOM = m\angle NOP$, then $m\angle LON = m\angle MOP$. If you were asked to construct a two-column proof of this statement, the procedure would be very similar. You would follow the same deductive reasoning process, but the statements and reasons would be listed in the two-column format.

Apply the TEKS When two adjacent angles have opposite rays as their noncommon sides, they are said to form a linear pair. According to the linear pair postulate, if two angles form a linear pair, then they are supplementary. So in the figure, $m\angle ABC + m\angle CBD = 180°$.

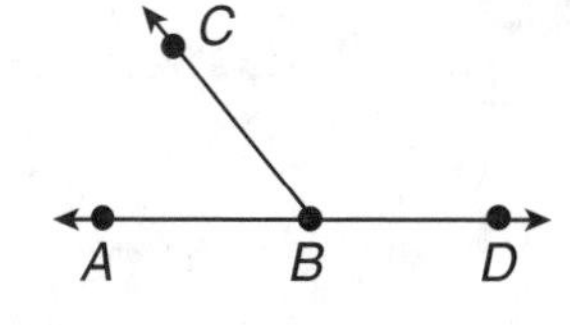

Fill in the blanks to complete the two-column proof. Then answer the questions that follow.

1. Refer to the figure at the right. Prove that if $\overrightarrow{VX}$ and $\overrightarrow{VZ}$ are opposite rays and $\overrightarrow{VW}$ and $\overrightarrow{VY}$ are opposite rays, then $m\angle XVW = m\angle ZVY$.

Statements	Reasons
1. $\overrightarrow{VX}$ and $\overrightarrow{VZ}$ are opposite rays.	1. ______________
2. ______________	2. Given
3. $\angle XVW$ and $\angle WVZ$ form a linear pair.	3. ______________
4. $\angle WVZ$ and $\angle ZVY$ form a linear pair.	4. Definition of a linear pair
5. $m\angle XVW + m\angle WVZ = 180°$	5. ______________
6. ______________	6. Linear Pair Postulate
7. $m\angle XVW + m\angle WVZ = m\angle WVZ + m\angle ZVY$	7. ________ $m\angle WVZ + m\angle ZVY$ for 180°.
8. ______________	8. ________ Property of Equality

2. What is the name for the special kind of angles represented by $\angle XVW$ and $\angle ZVY$?

____

3. What is another way of stating the result of the above two-column proof?

____

4. Describe the steps involved in completing a deductive reasoning proof.

____

____

5. Compare some of the advantages and disadvantages of writing a two-column proof as opposed to a paragraph proof.

____

____

TEKS G(b)3C, G(b)3E

DIRECTIONS Read each question. Then circle the letter for the correct answer. If a correct answer is not here, circle the letter for "Not Here."

1 If a statement is given that ∠1 and ∠2 are supplementary, which fact can you use when proving a geometric relationship true?

A The sum of the angles is 90°.

B The sum of the angles is 180°.

C The angles have the same measurement.

D Not Here

2 To use a property of equality when proving a statement true, which condition must be present?

F An equation

G Addition of two or more values

H A variable

J Only numbers or variables

3 Which type of mathematical proof involves showing the symbolic manipulation in steps with verbal definitions to justify each step?

A Flowproof

B Paragraph proof

C Counterexample

D 2-column proof

4 Which statement is true about general mathematical and geometrical relationships that have been proven true?

F The proof of the true relationship must be included in all proofs that use the relationship.

G The true relationship can be referenced in all proofs that use the relationship.

H When a relationship is proven true, it is valid only for the proof in which it is included.

J Not Here

Focus on TEKS

Lesson 37 Inductive Reasoning

TEKS G(b)3D Use inductive reasoning to formulate a conjecture.

In this lesson, you will explore another method of mathematical reasoning called inductive reasoning.

Inductive reasoning is a process in which you look for patterns among data and figures and use the patterns to make a generalized educated guess about the data or figures.
The educated guess is referred to as a **conjecture**.

Guided Instruction

Problem 1 Refer to the figures at the right.

a. Use inductive reasoning to ketch the next two figures in the pattern.

b. Write a function rule for the number of dots in the nth figure. Use this function to make a conjecture about the number of dots in the twentieth figure.

Part a. Look for a pattern in the progression of figures.

Step 1 Notice that each of the figures is in the shape of a square, so the next two figures also will be in the shape of a square.

Step 2 Look at the dimension of each figure. The first figure could be considered a 1 by 1 square, the second a 2 by 2 square and so on. So the fifth and sixth figures should be 5 by 5 and 6 by 6 squares, respectively.

Part b. Examine the number of dots in each of the first six figures. They contain 1, 4, 9, 16, 25, and 36 dots, respectively. Notice that each of these numbers is a perfect square. If $n = 1, 2, 3, \ldots$, then the function rule that determines the number of dots in the nth figure is $f(n) = n^2$.

To find the number of dots in the twentieth figure, evaluate the function at $n = 20$.

$$f(n) = n^2$$
$$f(20) = 20^2$$
$$f(20) = 400$$

Solution The number of dots in the twentieth figure is 400.

More Problems

Guided Instruction

Problem 2

Refer to the figures below and sketch the next figure of the pattern. How many nonoverlapping regions do you think will be formed inside the circle if 11 lines intersect at a single point?

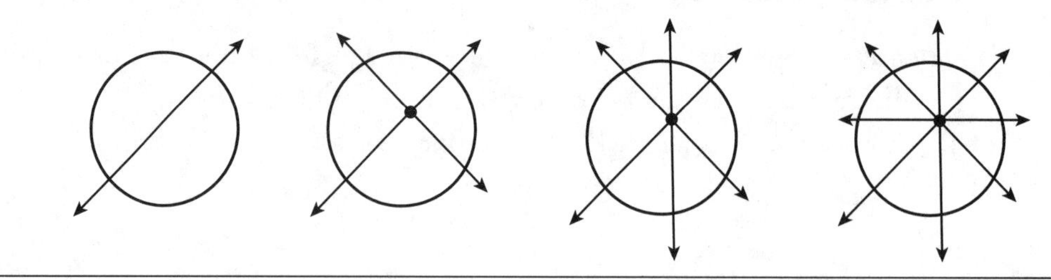

Step 1 Look for a pattern in the figures. At each step a new line is drawn through the common point inside the circle. To draw the next figure, simply draw another line.

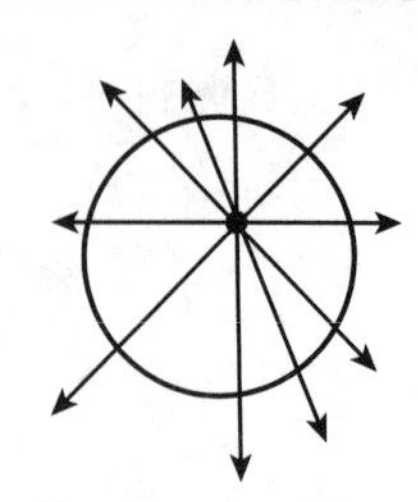

Step 2 To generalize the pattern, count the number of nonoverlapping regions formed inside the circle at each step. Organize the results in a table.

Number of lines	1	2	3	4	5
Number of regions	2	4	6	8	10

Step 3 Notice that for each additional line drawn through the common point two more regions are formed. A function rule that describes the number of regions formed when n lines are drawn through the point is $f(n) = 2n$.

Step 4 Evaluate $f(n)$ at $n = 11$ to make a conjecture about how many regions are formed when 11 lines are drawn.

$$f(n) = 2n$$
$$f(11) = 2(11)$$
$$f(11) = 22$$

Solution There will be 22 nonoverlapping regions formed when 11 lines are drawn.

Problem 3

Mr. Andrews notices that the construction crew across the street has eaten lunch between noon and 1:00 P.M. every day for the past two weeks. He makes a conjecture that at 12:45 P.M. next Monday the crew will be at lunch. Do you agree or disagree with this conjecture? Explain.

Solution Since Mr. Andrews has observed the same behavior for the past two weeks, his conjecture is probably accurate. However, it is certainly possible that the crew will not be eating lunch next Monday at 12:45 P.M. This is an important point about inductive reasoning. A conjecture derived from inductive reasoning might be true, but it is not necessarily true.

Apply the TEKS Refer to each set of figures. Sketch the next figure in the space provided. Then write a function rule that determines the number of points in the *n*th figure.

1.

____

2. Make a conjecture about how many dots will be in the fiftieth figure in Exercise 1. __________

3.

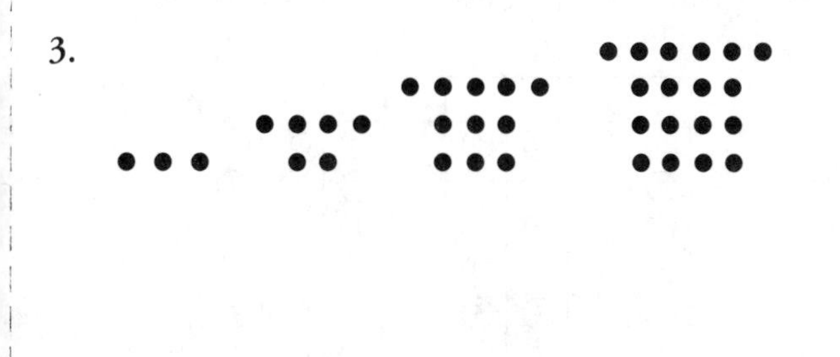

____

4. Make a conjecture about how many dots will be in the twenty-fourth figure in Exercise 3. __________

For each of the following situations, tell whether or not you agree with the conjecture. Explain your reasoning.

5. Monica notices that the outside temperature has been below 30° Fahrenheit on each of the last 12 days. She makes a conjecture that tomorrow's temperature will be below 30° Fahrenheit.

____

6. Eduardo constructed the three figures at the right to determine how many line segments can be drawn through a set of points, no three of which are collinear. He made the conjecture that for 5 points, he could draw 8 line segments.

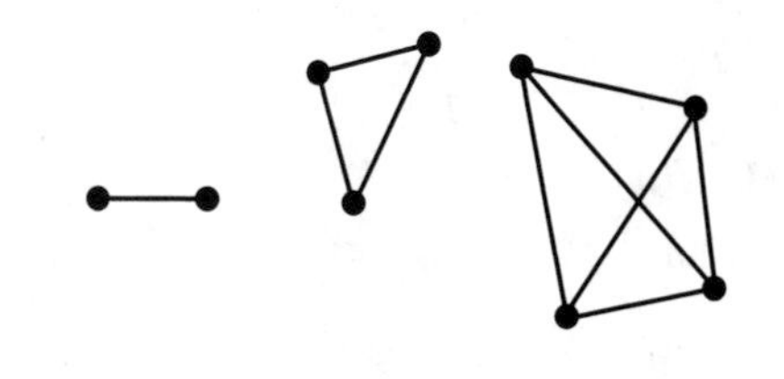

____

7. Sketch the next figure in the pattern from Exercise 6 in the space provided below to determine if Eduardo's conjecture was correct. If not, how many line segments can be drawn through the 5 points?

____

DIRECTIONS Read each question. Then circle the letter for the correct answer. If a correct answer is not here, circle the letter for "Not Here."

1 Consider the pattern of numbers shown below.

1
131
13531
1357531

Use inductive reasoning to determine the next number in the pattern.

A 13579531

B 1357997531

C 135797531

D Not Here

2 The pattern of dots shown below continues infinitely with more dots being added at each step.

Step 1 Step 2 Step 3

Which function rule could be used to determine the number of dots in the nth step?

F $f(n) = 2n(n - 3)$

G $f(n) = n(n + 2) - 1$

H $f(n) = 2n + 3$

J $f(n) = n^2 + n - 1$

3 Lori has determined that the function rule $f(n) = 2n + 7$ gives the total number of points in the nth figure of a pattern. Using this function, how many points would Lori conjecture are contained in the eleventh figure?

Record your answer and fill in the bubbles on the grid below. Be sure to use the correct place value.

4 Refer to the pattern of dots shown below.

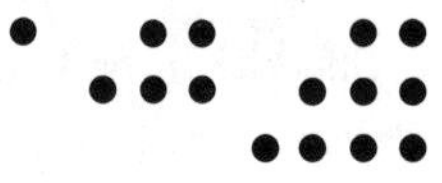

What is the next figure in the pattern?

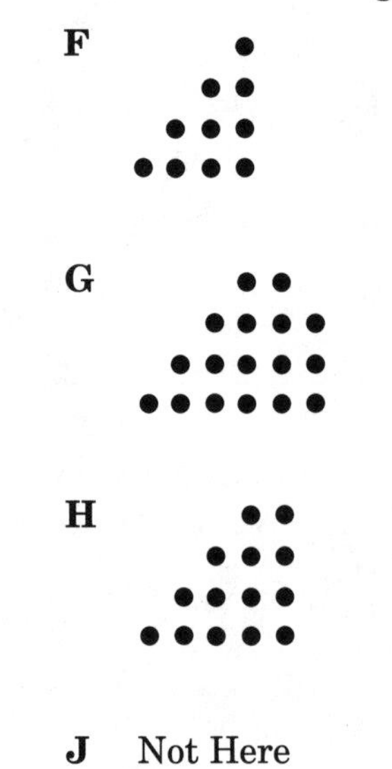

J Not Here

DIRECTIONS Read each question. Then circle the letter for the correct answer. If a correct answer is <u>not</u> <u>here</u>, circle the letter for "Not Here."

1 Refer to the figure below.

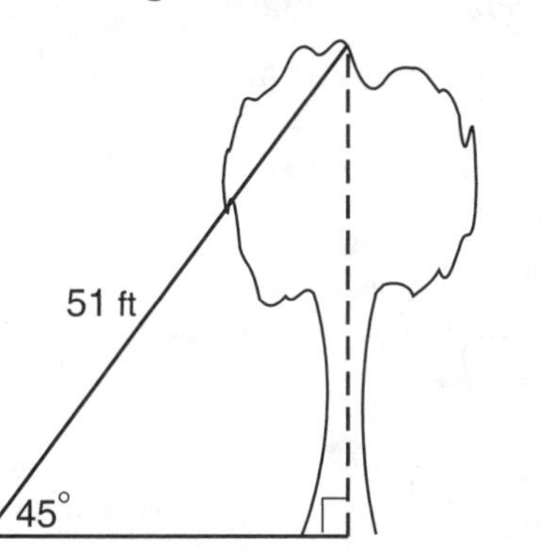

What is the approximate height of the tree? Round your answer to the nearest foot.

A 51 ft

B 36 ft

C 29 ft

D 26 ft

2 Consider the conditional statement: *If two parallel lines are cut by a transversal, then alternate interior angles are congruent.* Which of the following represents the contrapositive of this statement?

F *If alternate interior angles are congruent, then two parallel lines are cut by a transversal.*

G *If two parallel lines are not cut by a transversal, then alternate interior angles are not congruent.*

H *If alternate interior angles are not congruent, then two parallel lines are not cut by a transversal.*

J Not Here

3 If three of the angles of a trapezoid have measures of 72°, 95°, and 81°, what is the measure of the fourth angle?

A 64°

B 98°

C 106°

D 112°

4 Refer to the right triangle shown below.

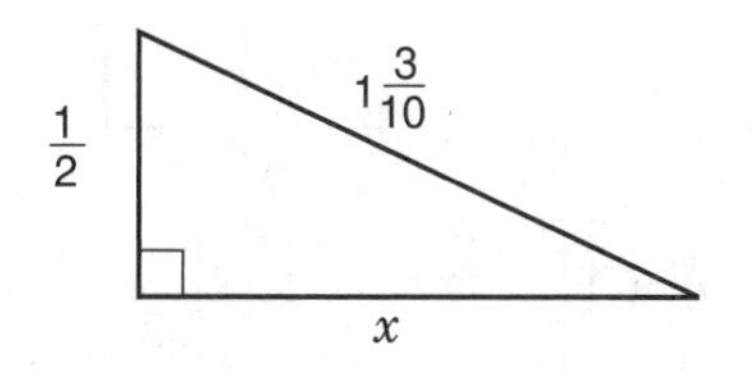

What is the value of x in the figure?

F 1

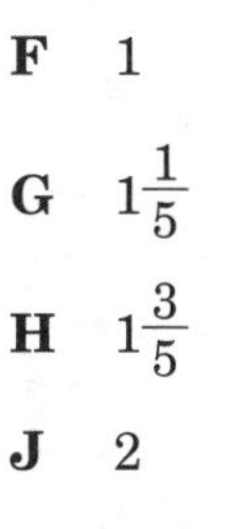

G $1\frac{1}{5}$

H $1\frac{3}{5}$

J 2

5 One of the vertices of a pentagon has the coordinates (5, 5). What are the coordinates of this vertex after being reflected across the x-axis?

A (−5, 5)

B (5, −5)

C (−5, −5)

D Not Here

6 The pattern of dots shown below continues infinitely with more dots being added at each step.

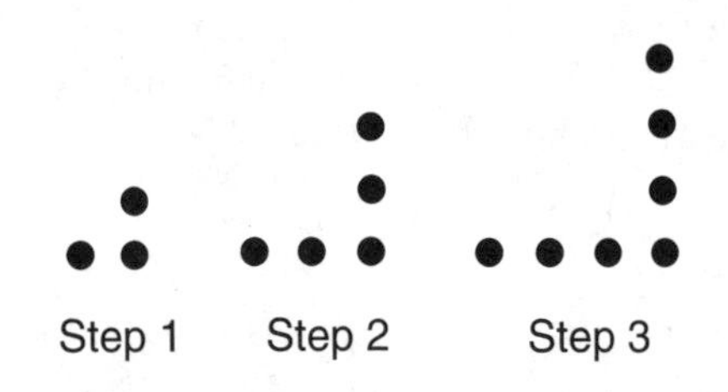

How many dots will be contained in the sixty-first step of the pattern?

Record your answer and fill in the bubbles the grid below. Be sure to use the correct place value.

				.			
0	0	0	0		0	0	0
1	1	1	1		1	1	1
2	2	2	2		2	2	2
3	3	3	3		3	3	3
4	4	4	4		4	4	4
5	5	5	5		5	5	5
6	6	6	6		6	6	6
7	7	7	7		7	7	7
8	8	8	8		8	8	8
9	9	9	9		9	9	9

7 The base of a triangle is contained in the line with the equation $6y - 5x = 24$. The height of the triangle is contained in the line with the equation $y = mx + 9$. What is the value of m in this equation?

A $-1\frac{1}{5}$

B $-\frac{5}{6}$

C $\frac{5}{6}$

D $1\frac{1}{5}$

8 Which of the following pairs of figures could be used to create a tessellation in the plane?

F A regular hexagon and a regular pentagon

G A circle and a square

H A square and a right triangle

J Not Here

9 What is the length of the base of the triangle shown below?

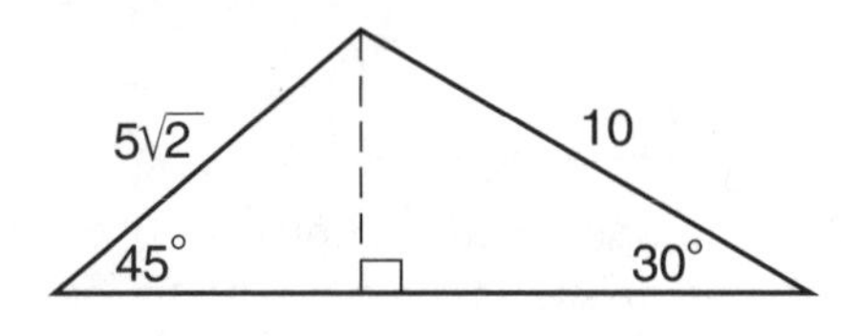

A $10\sqrt{3}$

B $5\sqrt{2} + 5\sqrt{3}$

C $10\sqrt{5}$

D $5 + 5\sqrt{3}$

10 A conditional statement is represented by the symbols $p \Rightarrow q$, and its converse is represented by the symbols $q \Rightarrow p$. If the conditional statement and its converse are both true, which of the following statements is NOT necessarily true?

F $|q \Rightarrow |p$

G $|p \Rightarrow |q$

H $p \Rightarrow q$

J Not Here

11 Which kinds of transformation were most likely used to create the following figure?

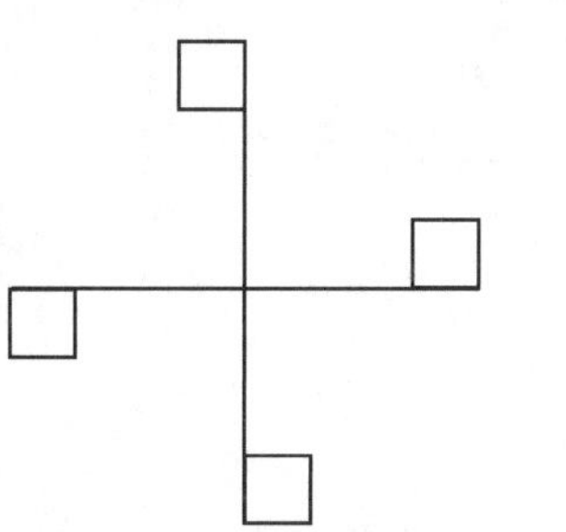

A Rotations and translations

B Rotations only

C Translations and reflections

D Translations only

12 If the length of the longer leg of a 30°-60°-90° triangle is 24 centimeters, what is the length of the hypotenuse of the triangle to the nearest centimeter?

F 42 cm

G 28 cm

H 21 cm

J 12 cm

13 Which of the following sets of ordered pairs represents the vertices of a square?

A (0, −2), (5, 0), (3, 5), (−2, 3)

B (−1, 4), (−2, 6), (4, −1), (7, 9)

C (0, 0), (1, 7), (7, −1), (7, 8)

D Not Here

14 In the figure shown below, line ℓ_1 is parallel to line ℓ_2.

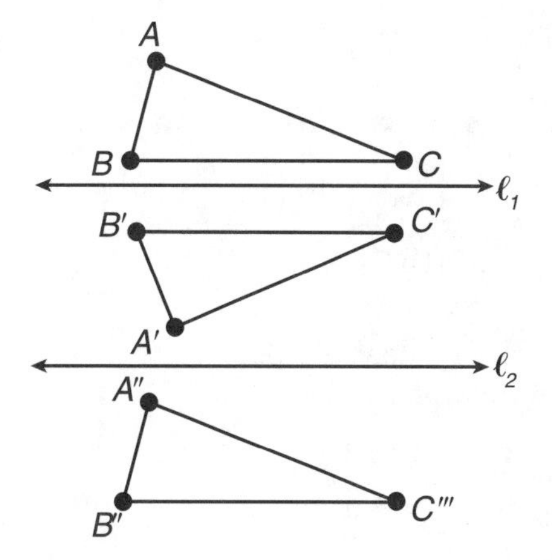

Which of the following conjectures is demonstrated by this figure?

F If line ℓ_1 is parallel to line ℓ_2, then a reflection over line ℓ_1 followed by a reflection over line ℓ_2 is a rotation.

G Two reflections across two parallel lines is a technique used to tessellate a plane.

H If line ℓ_1 is parallel to line ℓ_2, then a reflection over line ℓ_1 followed by a reflection over line ℓ_2 is a translation.

J Not Here

15 Find the measures of the angles in the figure.

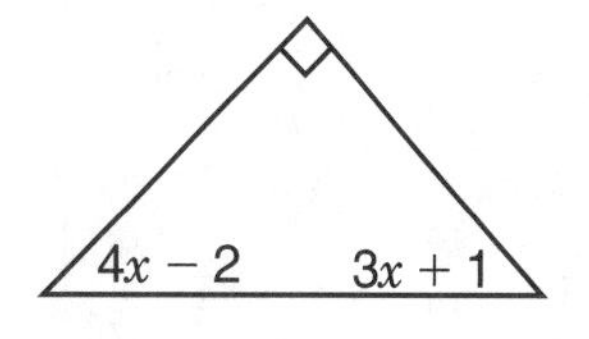

A 20°, 70°, 90°

B 13°, 77°, 90°

C 30°, 60°, 90°

D 40°, 50°, 90°

16 The pattern of dots shown below continues infinitely with more dots being added at each step.

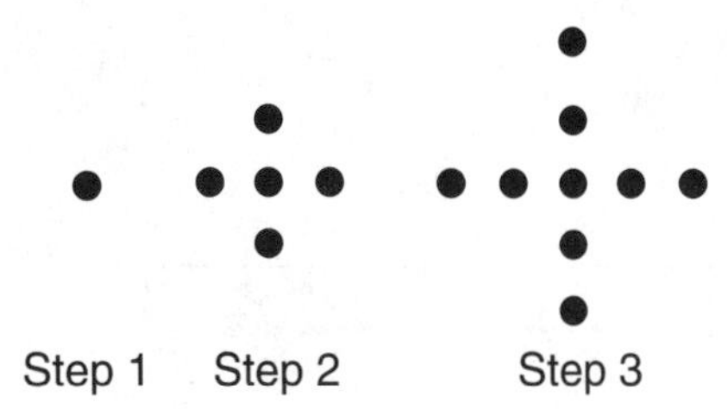

Which function rule could be used to determine the number of dots in the nth step?

F $f(n) = 2(n + 2) - 1$

G $f(n) = 4(n - 1) + 1$

H $f(n) = 4n + 1$

J Not Here

17 Refer to the 30°-60°-90° triangle shown below.

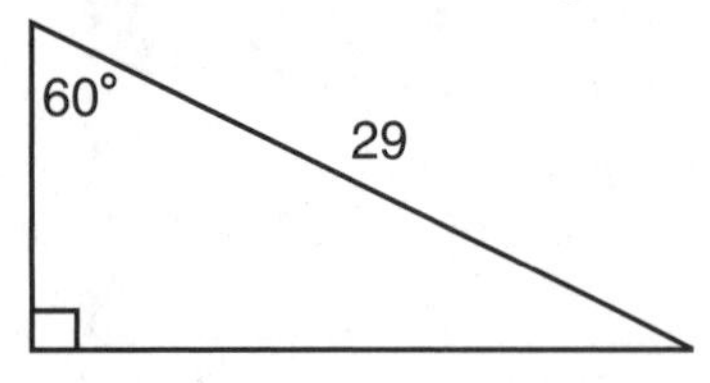

What is the length of the longer leg of the triangle rounded to the nearest whole number?

Record your answer and fill in the bubbles on the grid below. Be sure to use the correct place value.

				.			
0	0	0	0		0	0	0
1	1	1	1		1	1	1
2	2	2	2		2	2	2
3	3	3	3		3	3	3
4	4	4	4		4	4	4
5	5	5	5		5	5	5
6	6	6	6		6	6	6
7	7	7	7		7	7	7
8	8	8	8		8	8	8
9	9	9	9		9	9	9

18 Which of the following sets of measurements could be the lengths of the sides of an obtuse triangle?

F 8 ft, 17 ft, 15 ft

G 1.4 cm, 1.7 cm, 2.1 cm

H 7 m, 11 m, 13 m

J 2 mi, 3 mi, 4 mi

19 Which of the following figures could NOT be used as a basic unit to create a tessellation?

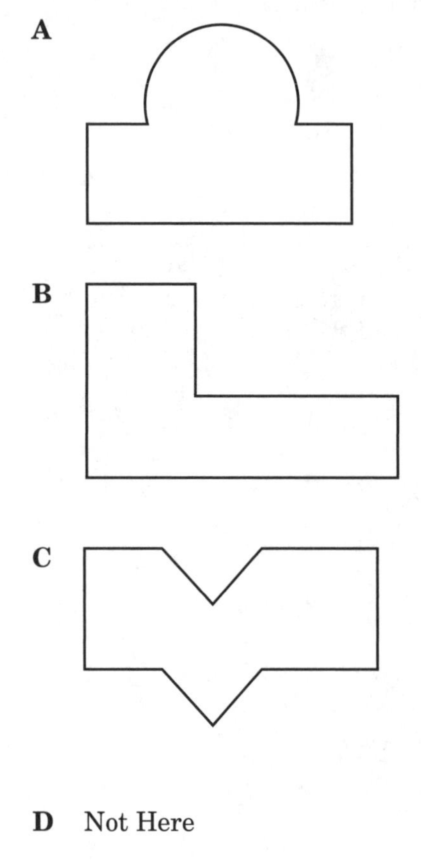

D Not Here

20 Which of the following sets of numbers is not a Pythagorean triple?

F 6, 8, 10

G 7, 24, 25

H 14, 9, 18

J 40, 104, 96

Lesson 38 Characteristics of Three-Dimensional Figures

TEKS G(e)2D Analyze the characteristics of three-dimensional figures and their component parts.

Plane figures have two dimensions. Solids have three dimensions. Solids can be classified either as polyhedrons or as solids with curved surfaces.

A **polyhedron** is a solid formed by polygons. Each polygon is a **face** of the polyhedron. All of the faces of a regular polyhedron are congruent regular polygons. An **edge** is the line where two faces intersect. A **vertex** is the point where three or more edges intersect. Most polyhedrons are named by their number of faces.

Prisms and pyramids are named by the shapes of their bases. A **prism** is a polyhedron with two parallel, congruent bases and lateral faces that are all parallelograms. A **pyramid** is a polyhedron with one base and lateral faces that are all triangles intersecting at a vertex.

Some solids have curved surfaces and cannot be classified as polyhedrons. A **cone** has one circular base and one vertex. A **cylinder** has two circular bases. A **sphere** has no bases or vertices and is the set of all points in space at a constant radius from its center. Solids can be either *oblique* or *right*.

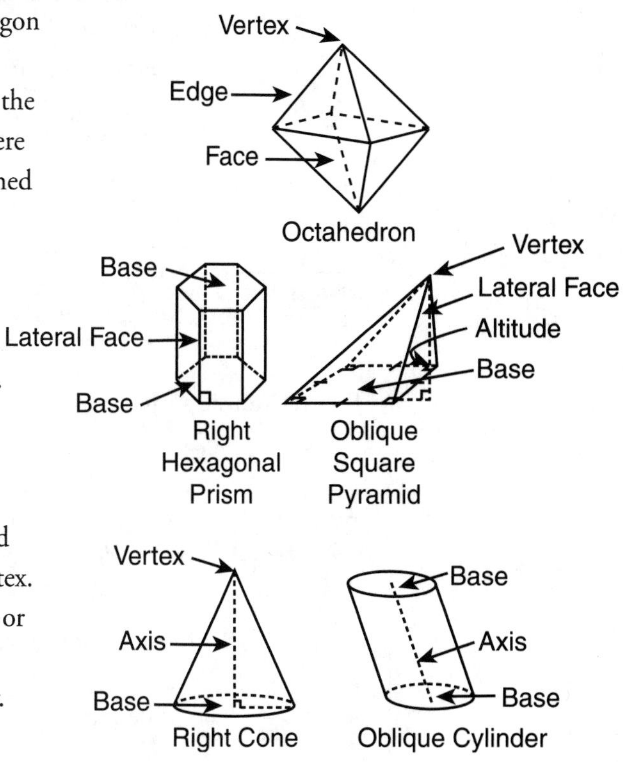

Guided Instruction

Problem 1

A Platonic solid is a regular polyhedron. These solids all have faces that are either equilateral triangles, squares, or regular pentagons. Draw a four-sided Platonic solid. How many faces, edges, and vertices does it have?

60°
60°
60°

Each face is an equilateral triangle.
All faces are congruent.

This Platonic solid is called a *regular tetrahedron*.

Solution

A tetrahedron has 4 faces, 6 edges, and 4 vertices.

More Problems

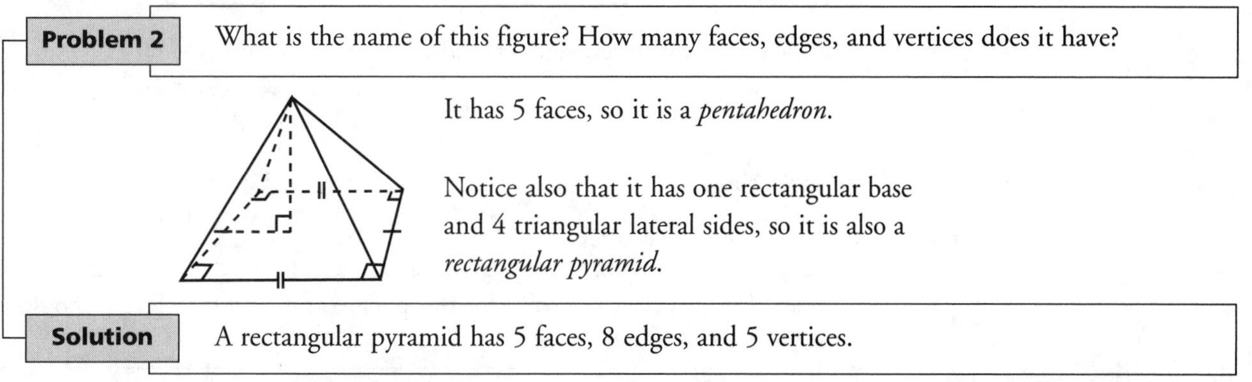

Problem 2

What is the name of this figure? How many faces, edges, and vertices does it have?

It has 5 faces, so it is a *pentahedron*.

Notice also that it has one rectangular base and 4 triangular lateral sides, so it is also a *rectangular pyramid*.

Solution

A rectangular pyramid has 5 faces, 8 edges, and 5 vertices.

Guided Instruction

Problem 3

Complete the table below. Describe a relationship, if one exists, between the number of faces, edges, and vertices of polyhedron?

Polyhedron	Faces	Vertices	Edges
Tetrahedron	4	4	6
Rectangular Pyramid	5	5	8
Hexahedron	6		
Hexagonal Prism	8		
Regular Octahedron	8 (triangles)		
Nonahedron	9		
Dodecahedron	12		

Solution

Yes. The sum of the number of faces and the number of vertices is 2 more than the number of edges.

This relationship can be represented algebraically by **Euler's formula**:
$F + V - E = 2$, where F, V, and E represent the number of faces, vertices, and edges.

Problem 4

A *regular icosahedron* is a 20-sided Platonic solid. It has 12 vertices. How many edges does it have?

Step 1 Write Euler's formula. $F + V - E = 2$

Step 2 Substitute known quantities. $20 + 12 - E = 2$

Step 3 Solve for the unknown variable. $E = 30$

Solution

A regular icosahedron has 30 edges.

If any two points of a solid can be connected by a line segment so that some of the points on the line segment are not points of the solid, then the solid is **concave**. If no such line is possible, then the solid is **convex**. So far, all of the solids discussed in this lesson have been convex polyhedrons.

Problem 5

The letter T shown is an example of a concave polyhedron. Does Euler's formula work for this polyhedron? What can you conclude about the relationship between Euler's formula and concave polyhedrons?

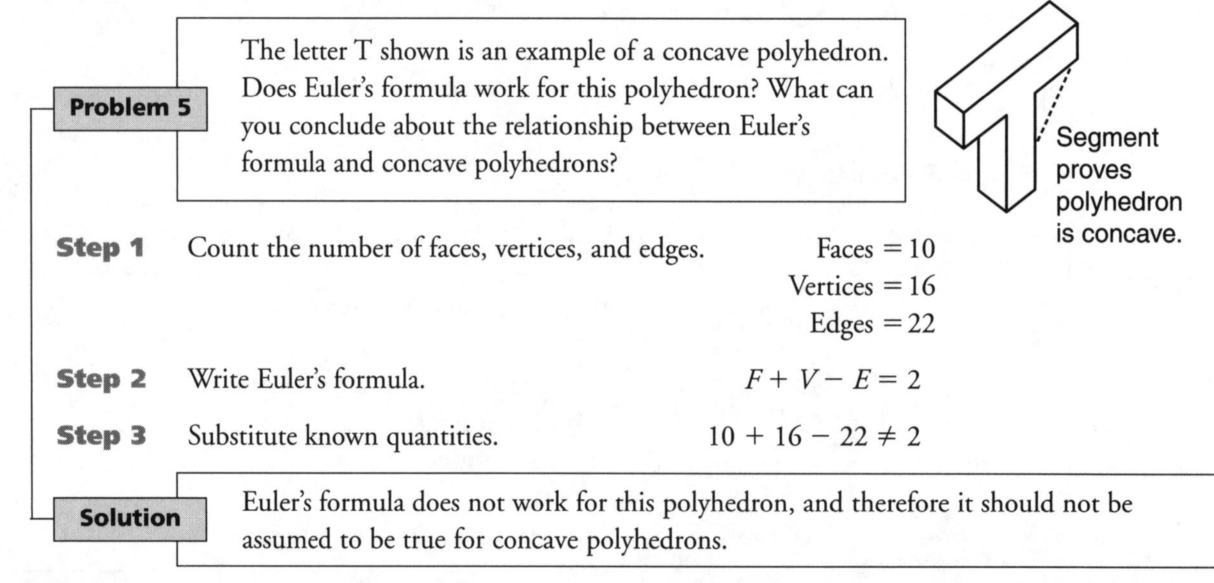

Step 1 Count the number of faces, vertices, and edges.

Faces = 10
Vertices = 16
Edges = 22

Step 2 Write Euler's formula. $F + V - E = 2$

Step 3 Substitute known quantities. $10 + 16 - 22 \neq 2$

Solution

Euler's formula does not work for this polyhedron, and therefore it should not be assumed to be true for concave polyhedrons.

Apply the TEKS Identify each solid with as many names as you can.

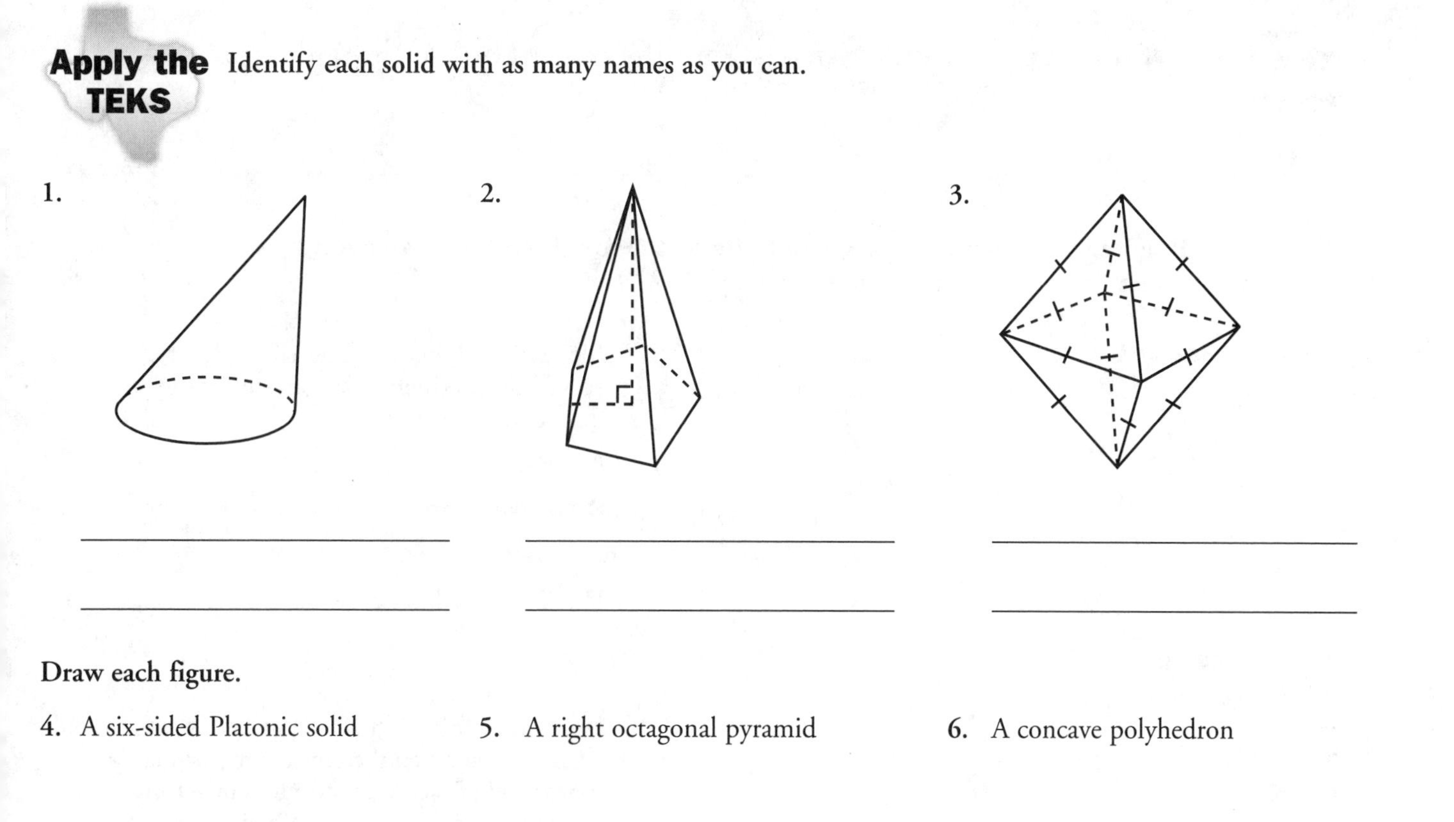

Draw each figure.

4. A six-sided Platonic solid

5. A right octagonal pyramid

6. A concave polyhedron

Find the missing information for each convex polyhedron. Use Euler's formula.

7. Faces: 7
   Vertices: 7
   Edges: ___________

8. Faces: 12
   Vertices: ___________
   Edges: 30

9. Faces: ___________
   Vertices: 12
   Edges: 18

For Exercises 10–14, refer to the pyramid and prism.

10. Name two parallel, congruent faces. ___________

11. What is the name of the line segment perpendicular to the plane defined by the points *H, I,* and *J* and passing through point *K*? ___________

12. What is the height of the pyramid? ___________

13. Is the pyramid oblique or right? ___________

14. Explain how you can determine the number of edges in the prism without counting them. ___________

TAKS Objective 7 The student will demonstrate an understanding of two- and three-dimensional representations of geometric relationships and shapes.
TEKS G(e)2D

DIRECTIONS Read each question. Then circle the letter for the correct answer. If a correct answer is not here, circle the letter for "Not Here."

1 Identify the solid.

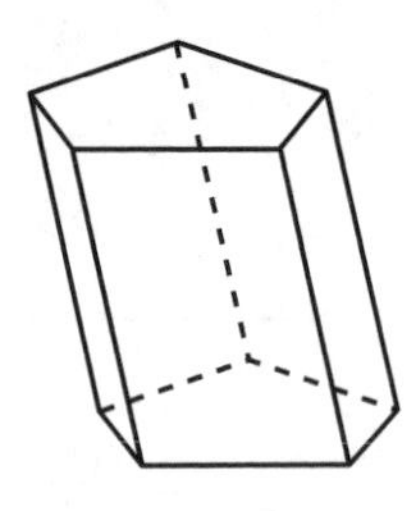

A Tetrahedron

B Pentahedron

C Pentagonal pyramid

D Not Here

2 A convex polyhedron has 7 faces and 12 edges. How many vertices does it have?

Record your answer and fill in the bubbles on the grid below. Be sure to use the correct place value.

				.			
0	0	0	0		0	0	0
1	1	1	1		1	1	1
2	2	2	2		2	2	2
3	3	3	3		3	3	3
4	4	4	4		4	4	4
5	5	5	5		5	5	5
6	6	6	6		6	6	6
7	7	7	7		7	7	7
8	8	8	8		8	8	8
9	9	9	9		9	9	9

3 A convex polyhedron has 15 edges and 10 vertices. Which of these best describes the polyhedron?

A Pentagonal pyramid

B Hexahedron

C Heptahedron

D Octagonal prism

4 Ernie is a stained glass artist. He wants to make a three-dimensional convex work, which is comprised of pieces of stained glass that are all the same shape and size. Which of these shapes would you recommend that Ernie NOT try?

F

G

H

J

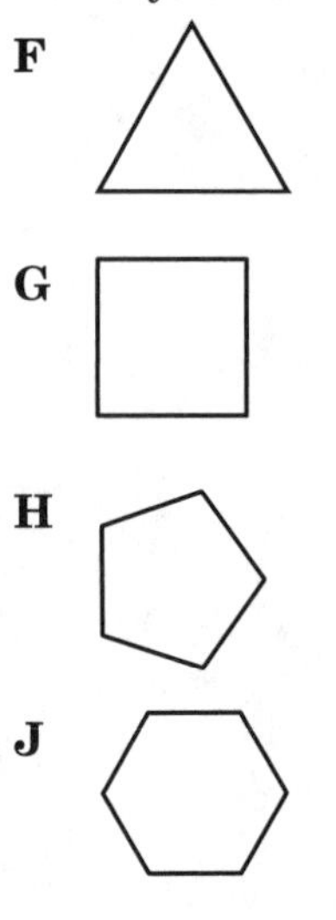

5 Which of these is NOT true about a spherical soccer ball made of pentagonal and hexagonal leather patches?

A The ball is not a polyhedron.

B The ball is not a solid.

C The ball is not a Platonic solid.

D Not Here

Lesson 39 Cross Sections of Three-Dimensional Objects

TEKS G(d)1A Describe and draw cross sections of three-dimensional objects.

A **cross section** of a solid is the intersection of a solid and a plane. When a plane intersects a three-dimensional object, the cross section is either a point, line, polygon, or curved plane figure.

Guided Instruction

Problem 1 Describe the cross section of the cube.

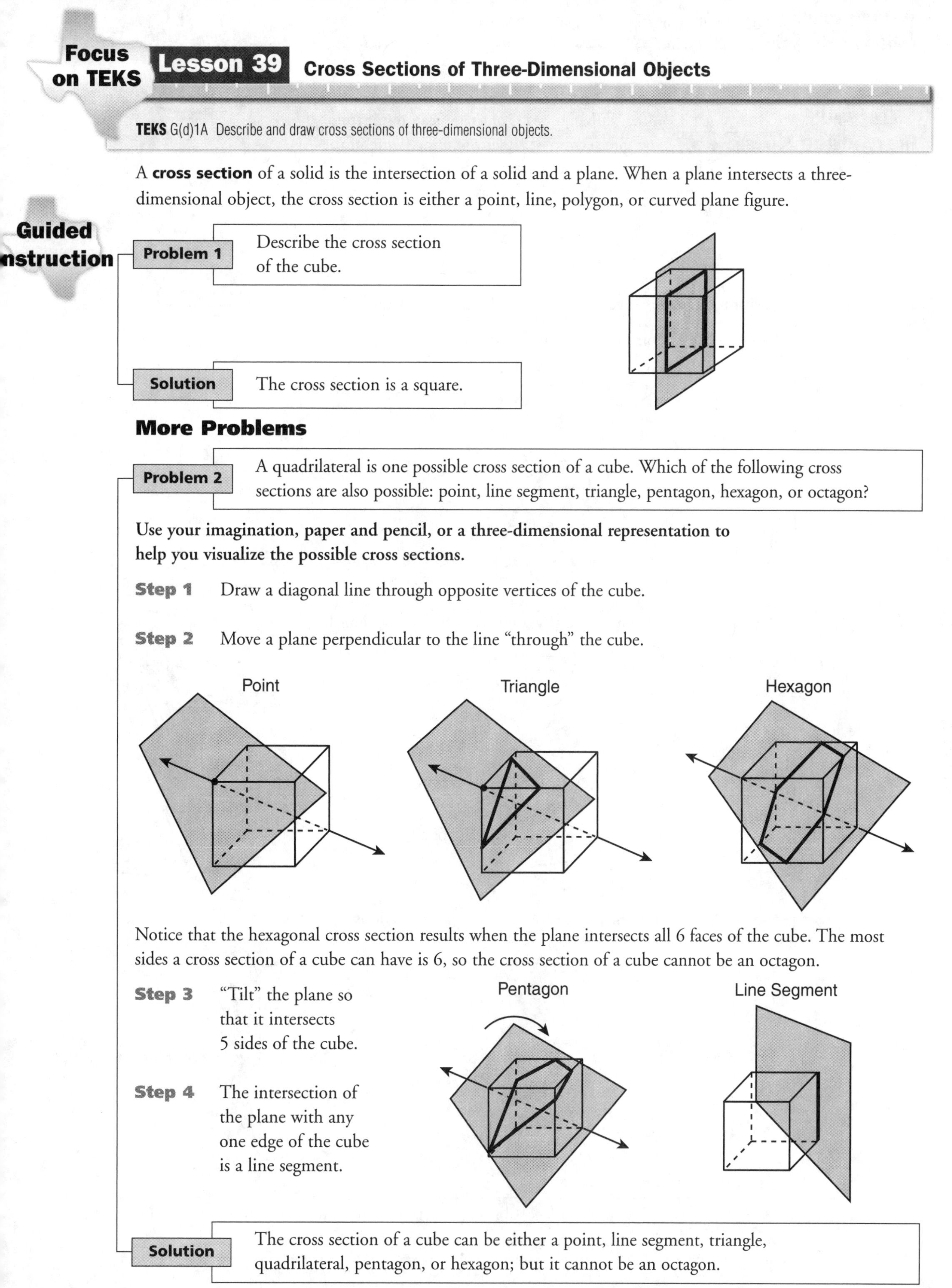

Solution The cross section is a square.

More Problems

Problem 2 A quadrilateral is one possible cross section of a cube. Which of the following cross sections are also possible: point, line segment, triangle, pentagon, hexagon, or octagon?

Use your imagination, paper and pencil, or a three-dimensional representation to help you visualize the possible cross sections.

Step 1 Draw a diagonal line through opposite vertices of the cube.

Step 2 Move a plane perpendicular to the line "through" the cube.

Notice that the hexagonal cross section results when the plane intersects all 6 faces of the cube. The most sides a cross section of a cube can have is 6, so the cross section of a cube cannot be an octagon.

Step 3 "Tilt" the plane so that it intersects 5 sides of the cube.

Step 4 The intersection of the plane with any one edge of the cube is a line segment.

Solution The cross section of a cube can be either a point, line segment, triangle, quadrilateral, pentagon, or hexagon; but it cannot be an octagon.

Problem 3

What different kinds of shapes can result from the intersection of a plane and the figure of the two right cones pictured?

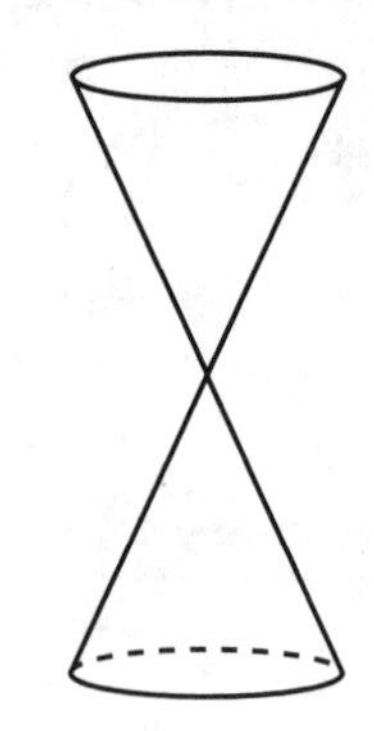

Position the plane at various angles and at various heights.

Step 1 Position the plane horizontally at various heights.

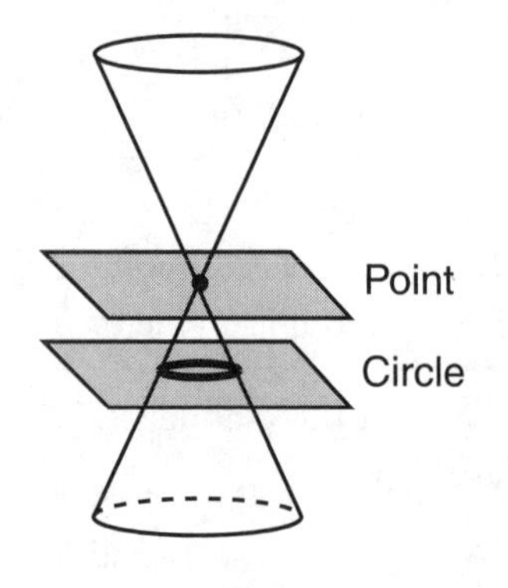

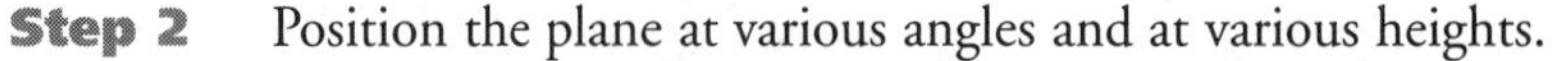

Step 2 Position the plane at various angles and at various heights.

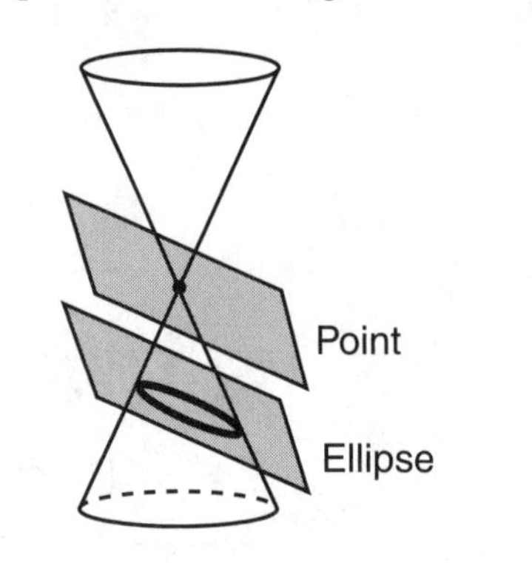

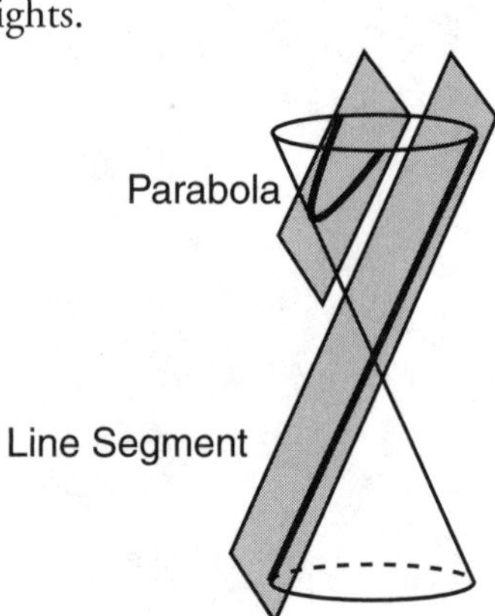

Step 3 Position the plane vertically at various locations.

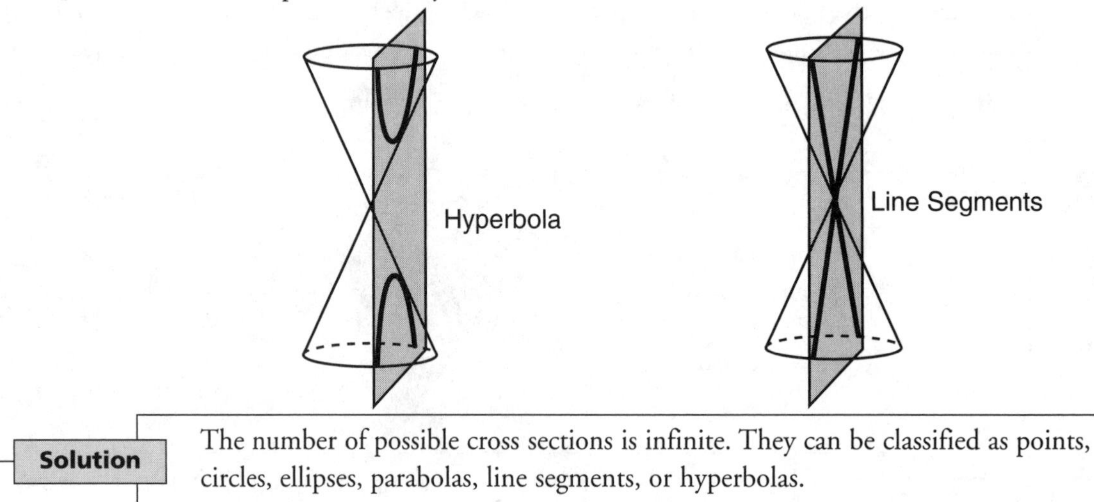

Solution

The number of possible cross sections is infinite. They can be classified as points, circles, ellipses, parabolas, line segments, or hyperbolas.

Apply the TEKS Match each object with all possible cross sections from the list.

1. Tennis ball: ______________________________

2. Egg: ______________________________

3. Brick: ______________________________

4. Can of frozen orange juice: ______________________________

5. Conical paper cup: ______________________________

point	hexagon
line	octagon
triangle	concave polyhedron
quadrilateral	circle
rectangle	ellipse
square	parabola
pentagon	hyperbola

Describe each cross section.

6. 7. 8.

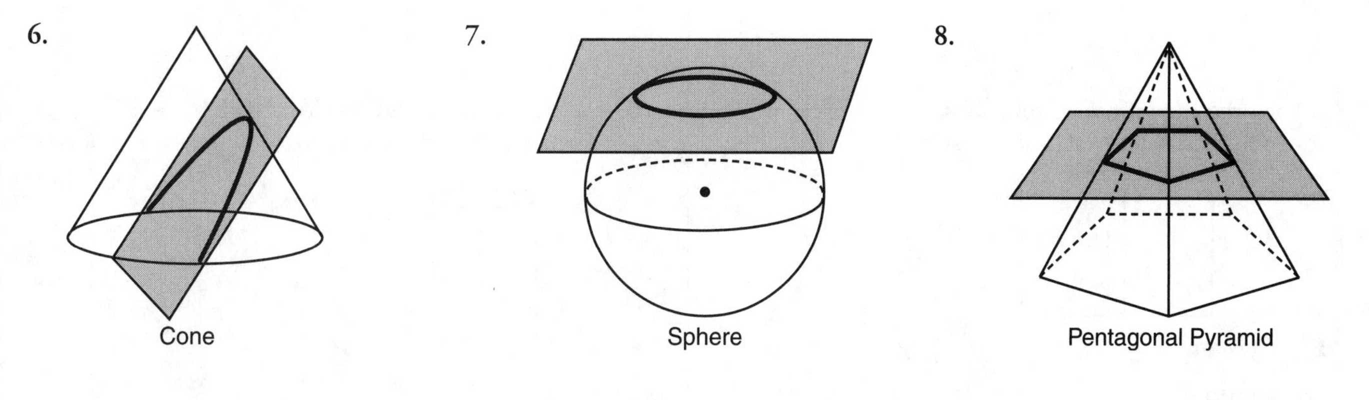

______________ ______________ ______________

Draw and classify the cross section of the solid shown when it is cut by the following planes.

9. A plane defined by the points *D*, *C*, and *B*

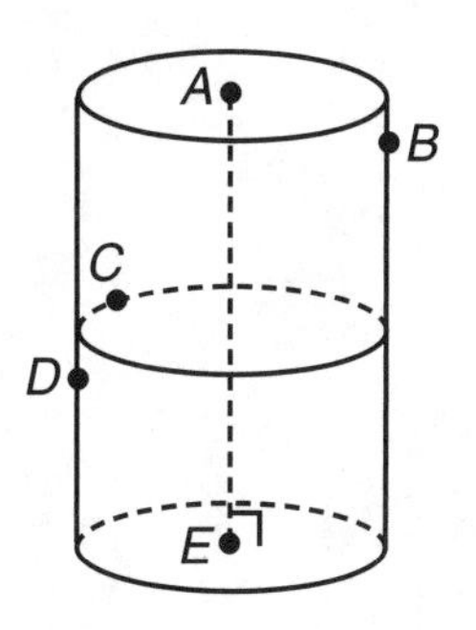

10. A plane through *C* and parallel to $\overline{AE}$

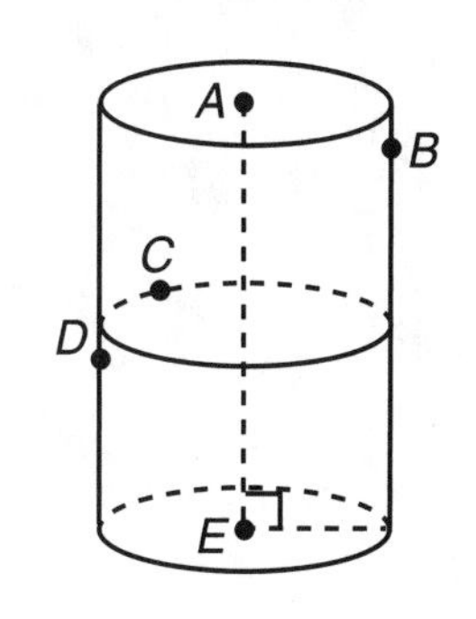

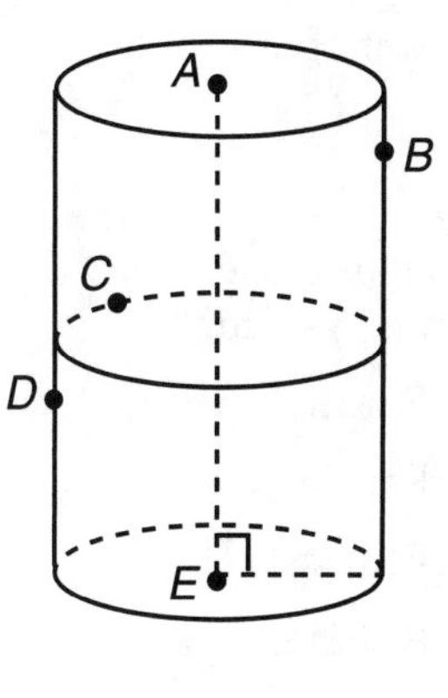

______________ ______________

Answer the question.

11. Explain how the cross section of a cube can be an equilateral triangle.

____

DIRECTIONS Read each question. Then circle the letter for the correct answer. If a correct answer is not here, circle the letter for "Not Here."

1 Which of these is NOT a possible cross section of a cube?

A Point

B Triangle

C Hexagon

D Not Here

2 If the cross section of a solid is shown, which of these is a characteristic of the solid?

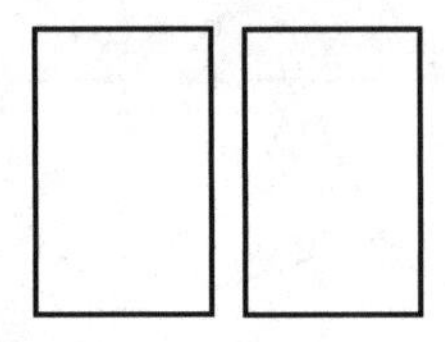

F Convex

G Concave

H Quadrilateral

J Not Here

3 Which of these is NOT a possible cross section of an empty cup?

A Parallelogram

B Parabola

C Ellipse

D Not Here

4 What is the most number of sides that a cross section of a tetrahedron can have?

F 2

G 3

H 4

J Not Here

5 Which of these solids CANNOT have a rectangular cross section?

A

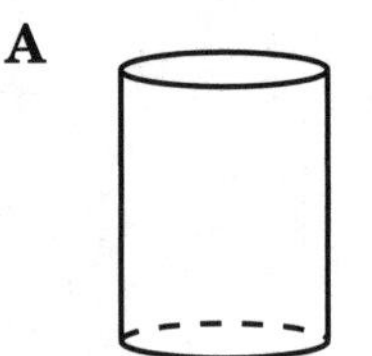

B

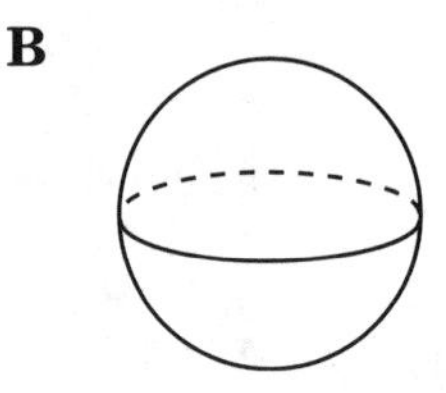

C

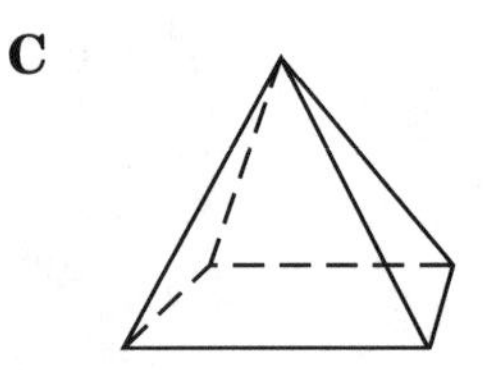

D

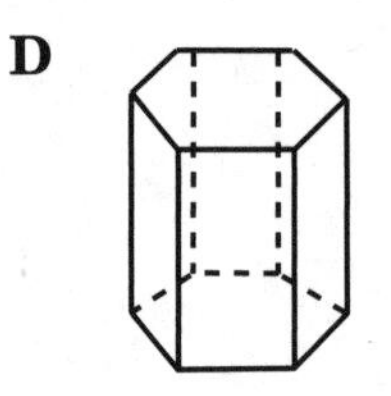

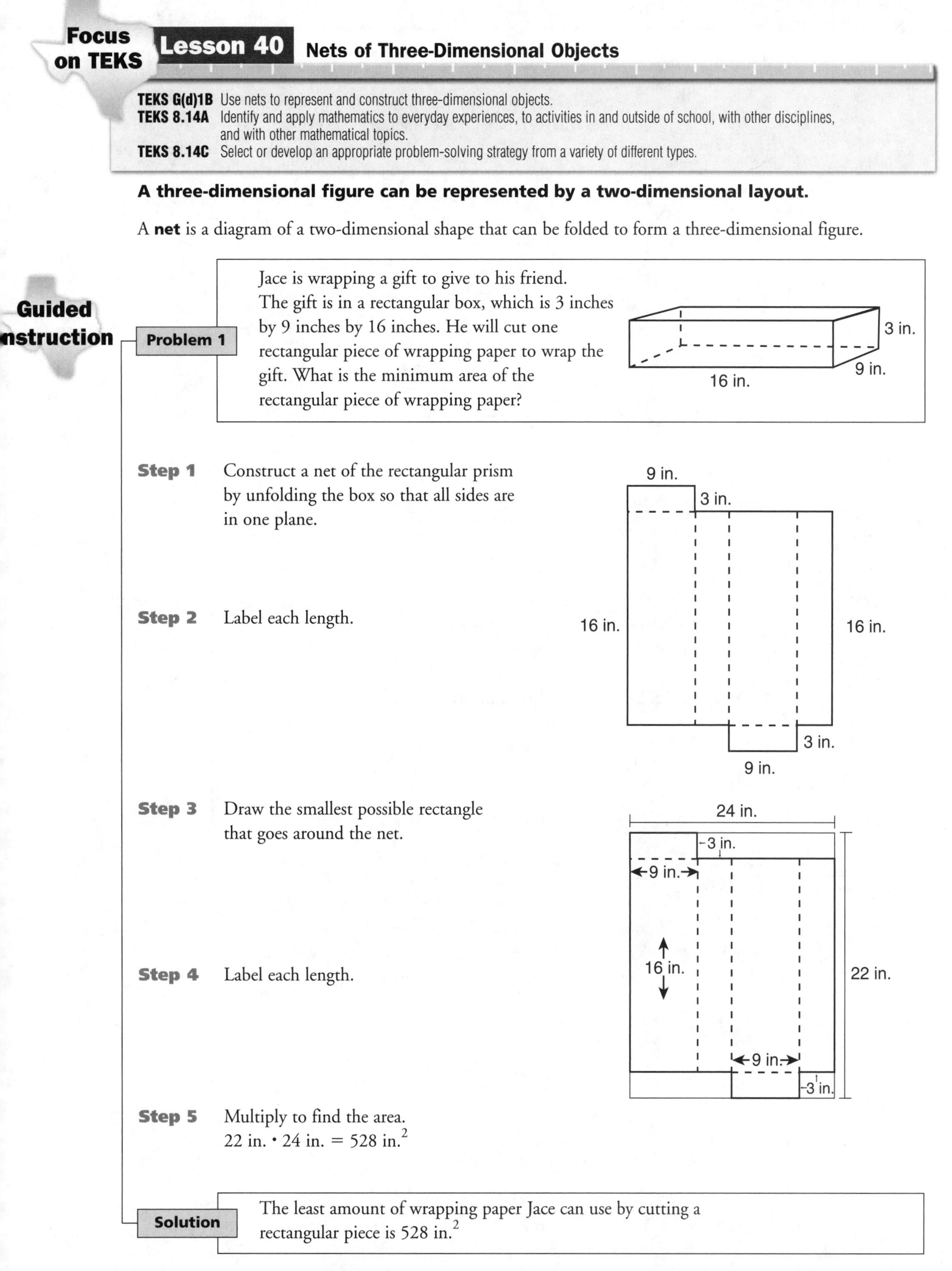

Focus on TEKS

Lesson 40 Nets of Three-Dimensional Objects

TEKS G(d)1B Use nets to represent and construct three-dimensional objects.
TEKS 8.14A Identify and apply mathematics to everyday experiences, to activities in and outside of school, with other disciplines, and with other mathematical topics.
TEKS 8.14C Select or develop an appropriate problem-solving strategy from a variety of different types.

A three-dimensional figure can be represented by a two-dimensional layout.

A **net** is a diagram of a two-dimensional shape that can be folded to form a three-dimensional figure.

Guided Instruction

Problem 1

Jace is wrapping a gift to give to his friend. The gift is in a rectangular box, which is 3 inches by 9 inches by 16 inches. He will cut one rectangular piece of wrapping paper to wrap the gift. What is the minimum area of the rectangular piece of wrapping paper?

Step 1 Construct a net of the rectangular prism by unfolding the box so that all sides are in one plane.

Step 2 Label each length.

Step 3 Draw the smallest possible rectangle that goes around the net.

Step 4 Label each length.

Step 5 Multiply to find the area.
$22 \text{ in.} \cdot 24 \text{ in.} = 528 \text{ in.}^2$

Solution The least amount of wrapping paper Jace can use by cutting a rectangular piece is 528 in.^2

More Problems

Guided Instruction

Problem 2 Two business associates are staying in a large hotel for a convention. The hotel is 80 stories tall. It is in the shape of a rectangular prism, and the rooms are arranged on the perimeter of the building around a huge open area in the middle. A net of the hotel is shown, with points representing the location of four available rooms. If the two business associates want to reserve the two closest rooms, which two rooms should they reserve?

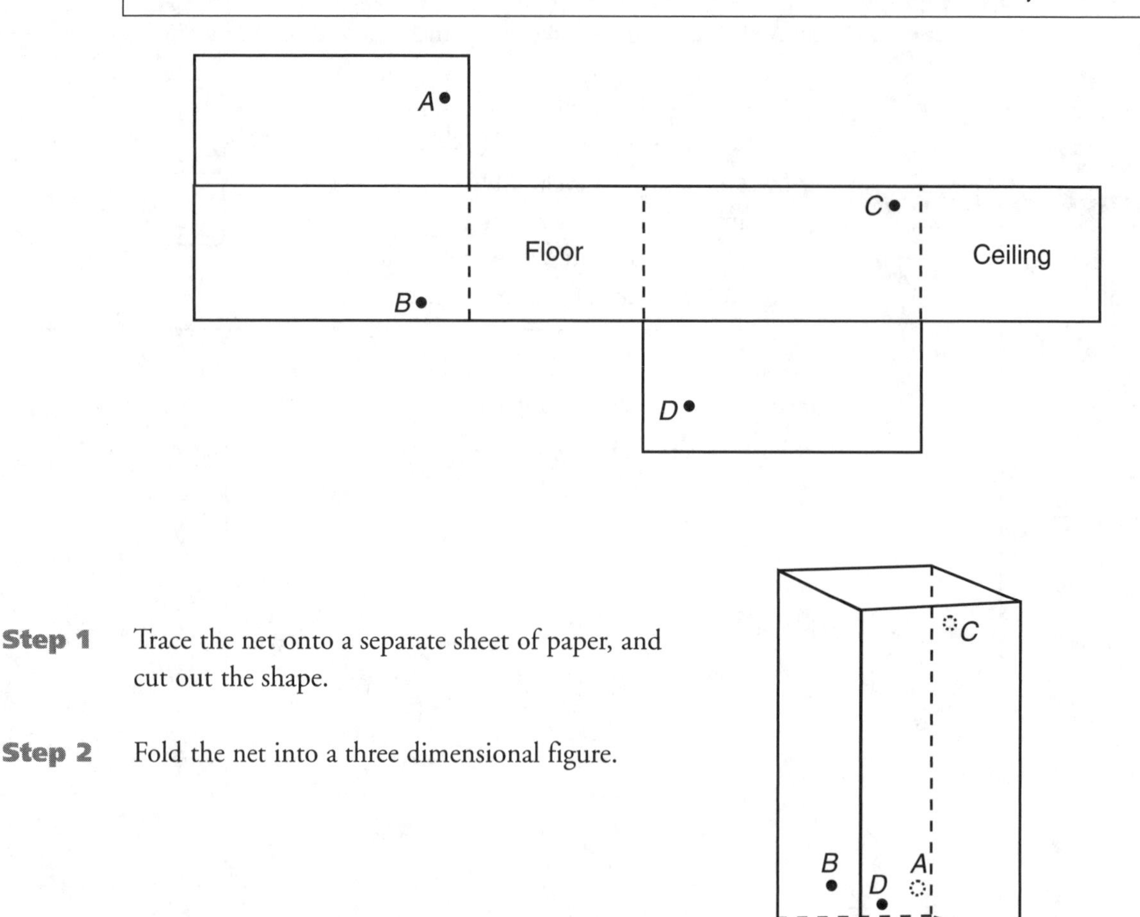

Step 1 Trace the net onto a separate sheet of paper, and cut out the shape.

Step 2 Fold the net into a three dimensional figure.

Solution They should reserve the rooms represented by points *B* and *D*.

Problem 3 What three-dimensional figure is represented by the net?

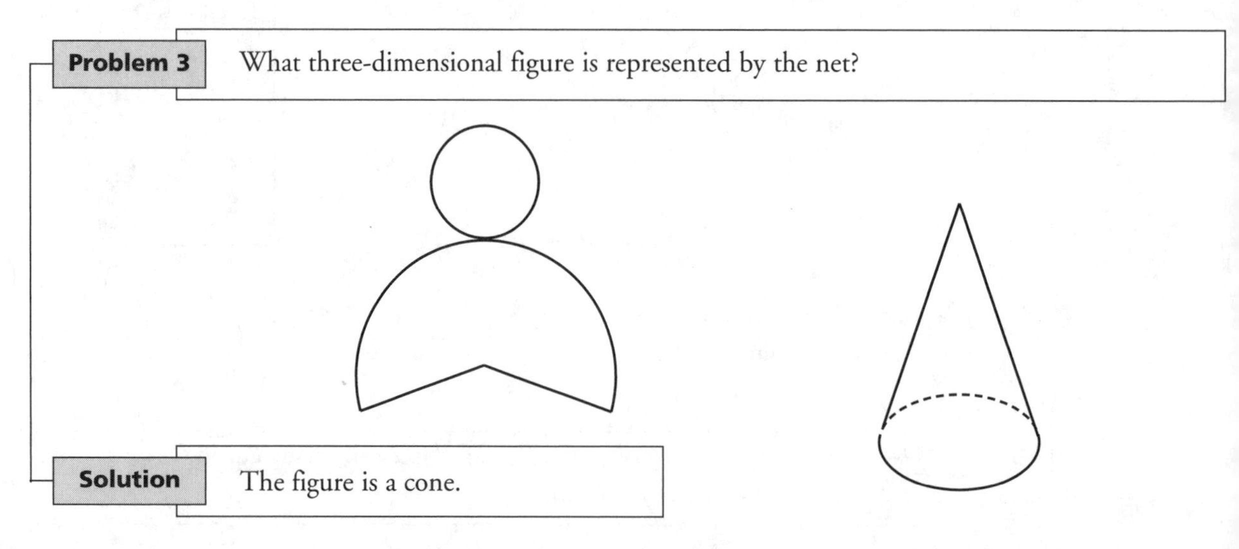

Solution The figure is a cone.

Apply the TEKS Name the three-dimensional figure represented by the net.

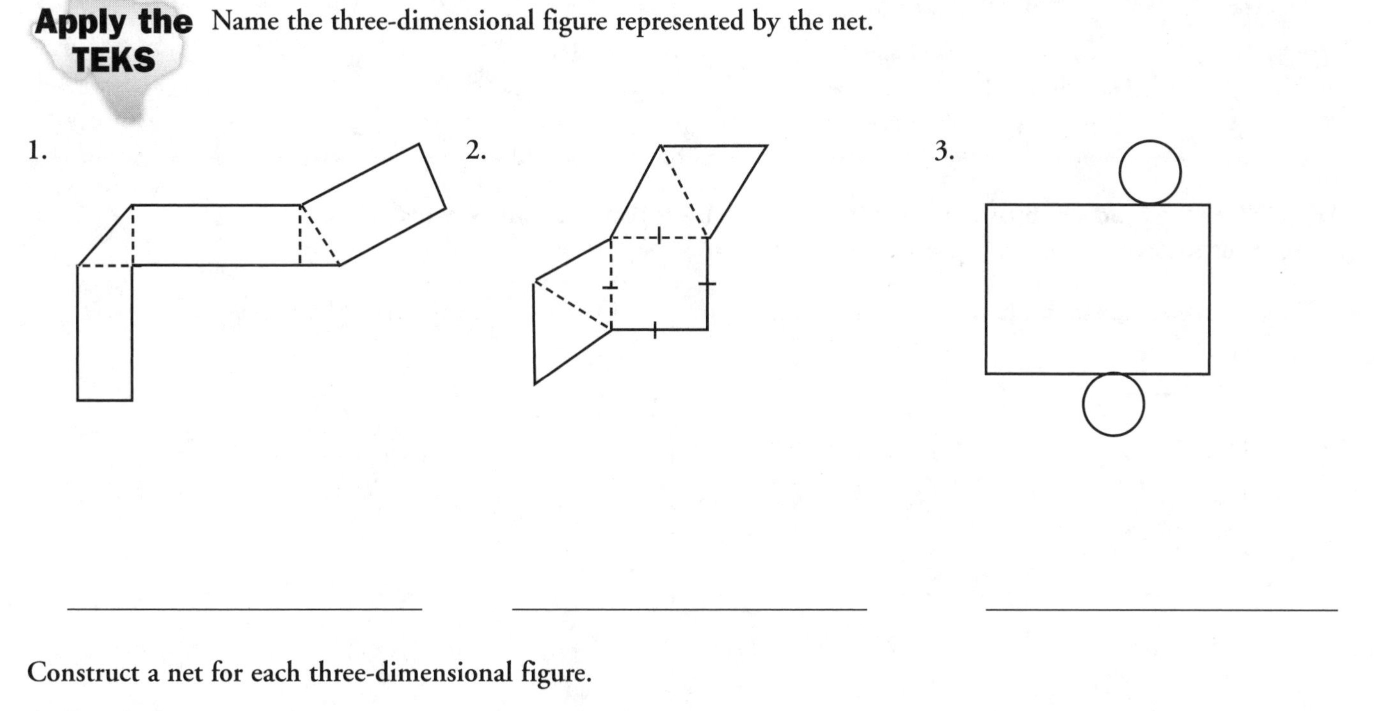

Construct a net for each three-dimensional figure.

4. Tetrahedron
5. Hexagonal prism
6. Cone

Construct the three-dimensional figure represented by the net.

7.

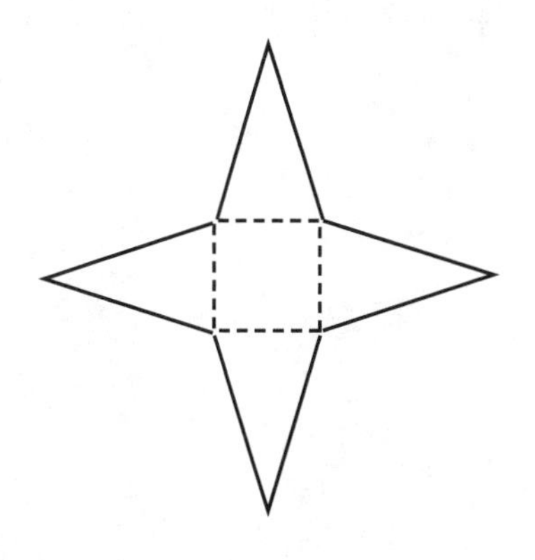

8. Explain one way nets are useful.

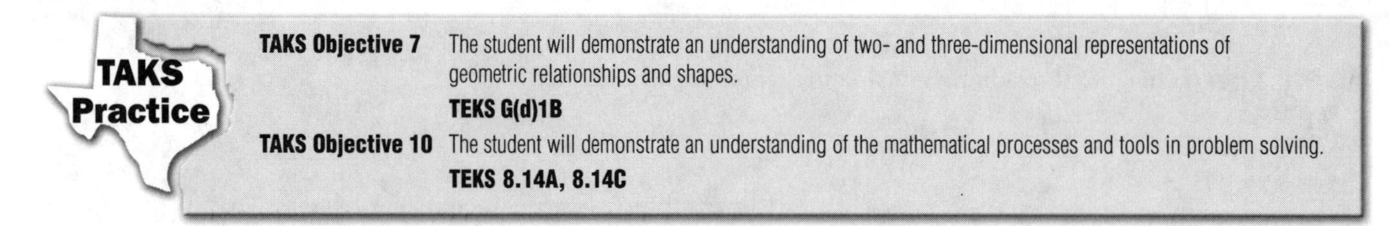

DIRECTIONS Read each question. Then circle the letter for the correct answer. If a correct answer is <u>not</u> <u>here</u>, circle the letter for "Not Here."

1 What three-dimensional figure is represented by this net?

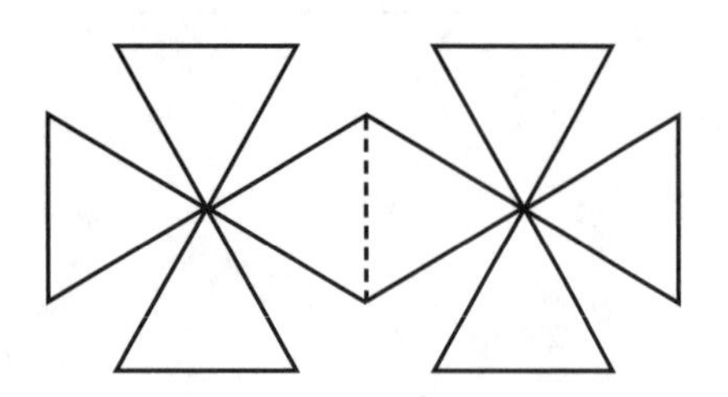

A Regular octahedron

B Regular tetrahedron

C Double pyramid

D Triangular prism

2 Dwayne and Rashona are building a new two-story house in the shape of a rectangular prism. They want the two kids' rooms to be as far away from one another as possible. A net of the house is shown, with points representing the location of four possible rooms.

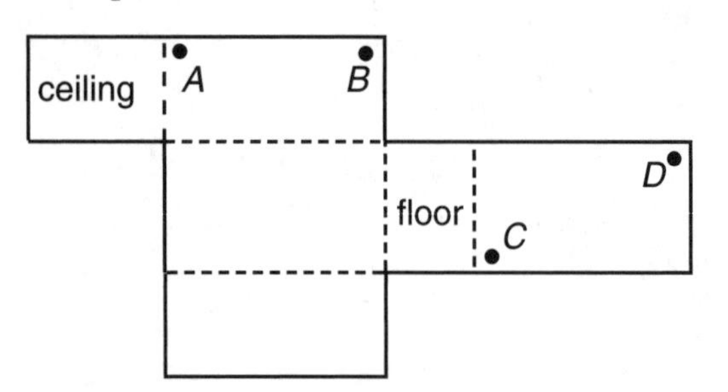

Which two locations should they choose for the kids' rooms?

F *A* and *B*

G *A* and *C*

H *A* and *D*

J *B* and *C*

3 Which of these is NOT a net?

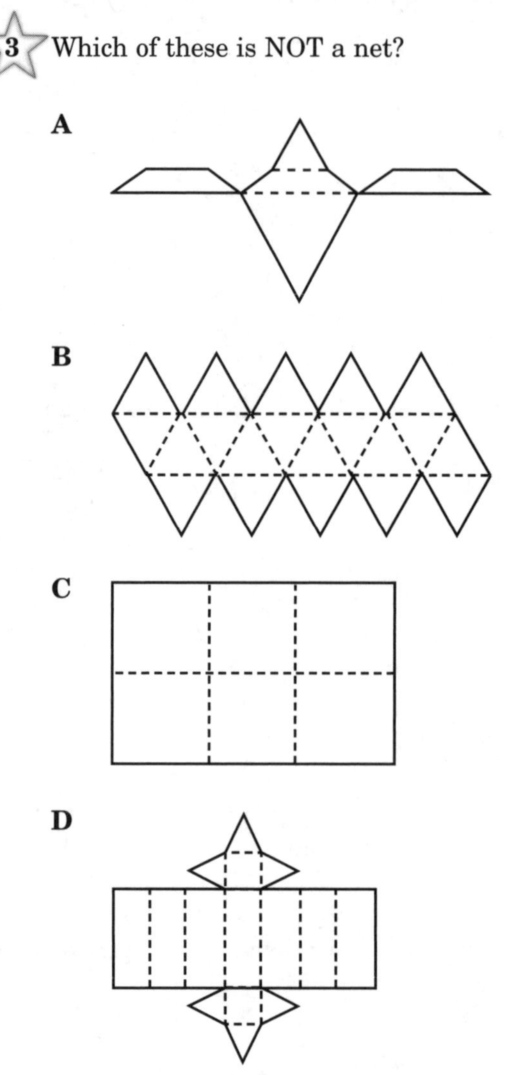

Focus on TEKS

Lesson 41 Views of Three-Dimensional Objects

TEKS G(d)1C Use top, front, side, and corner views of three-dimensional objects to create accurate and complete representations and solve problems.

Three-dimensional objects can be viewed straight on or at an angle.

When viewed at an angle, an object appears three-dimensional. An **isometric drawing** shows a corner view of an object, in which the shape of the object is preserved.

When viewed straight on, an object appears two-dimensional because only one face of the object is seen. An **orthographic drawing** shows a straight-on view of an object.

Guided Instruction

Problem 1 Draw a three-dimensional letter T to show one corner view.

Solution

Use isometric graph paper to draw a corner view.

Step 1 Start with the near corner.

Step 2 Work toward the far corner.

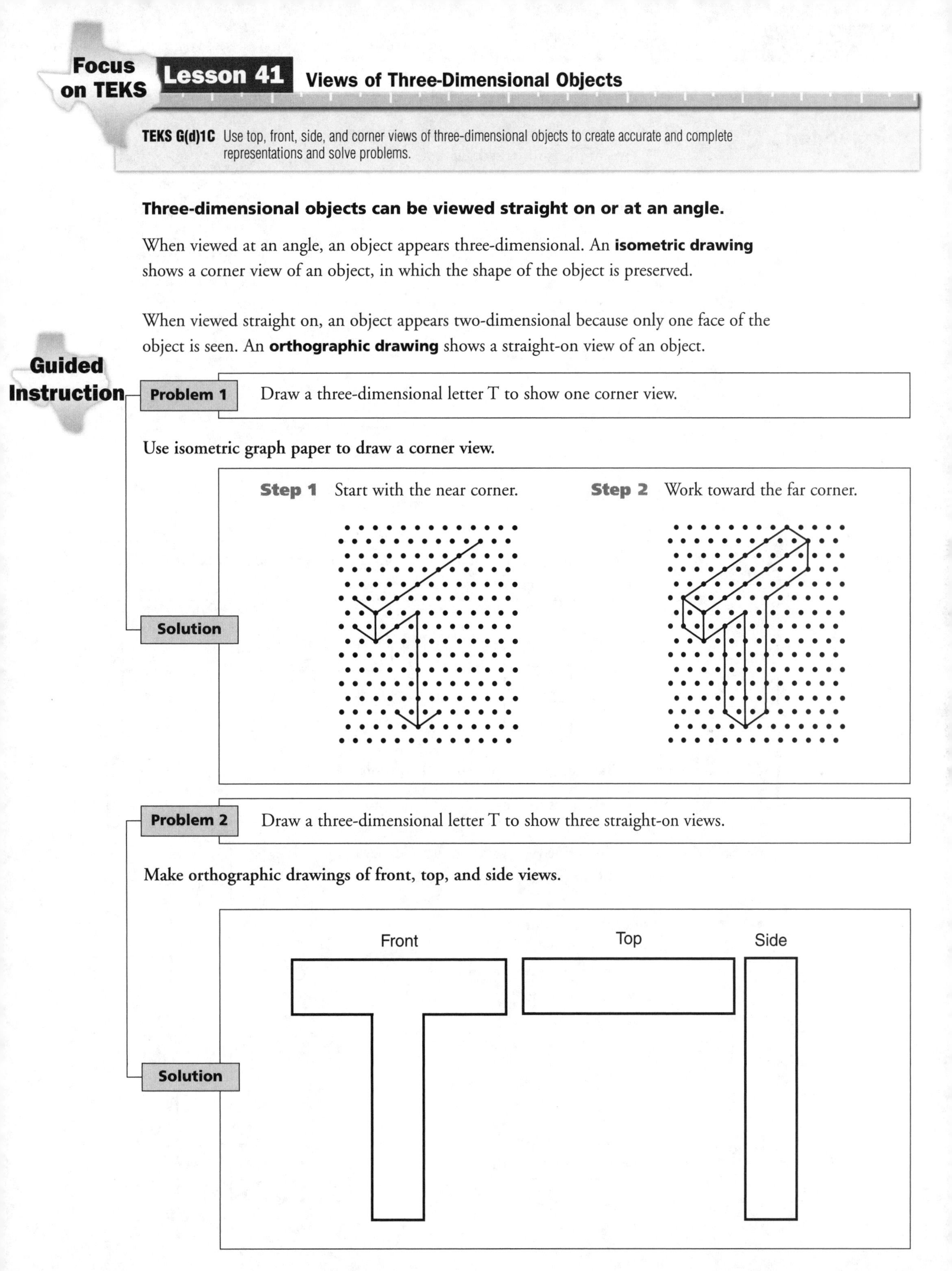

Problem 2 Draw a three-dimensional letter T to show three straight-on views.

Solution

Make orthographic drawings of front, top, and side views.

Guided Instruction

More Problems

Problem 3 Create front, top, and right-side orthographic views of the isometric drawing.

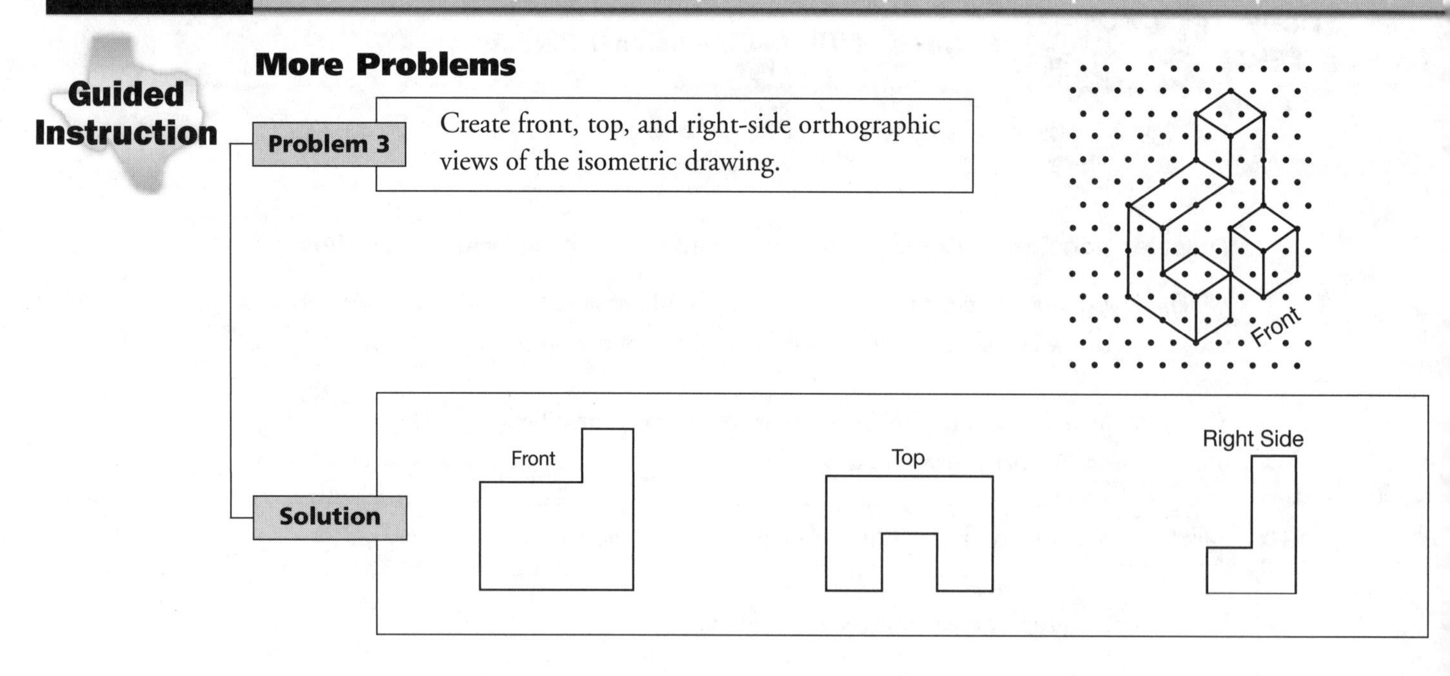

Solution

A foundation drawing is a diagram of the foundation showing the height of each part.

Problem 4 An object is composed of 12 cubes. Create an isometric drawing of the object represented by the orthographic drawings.

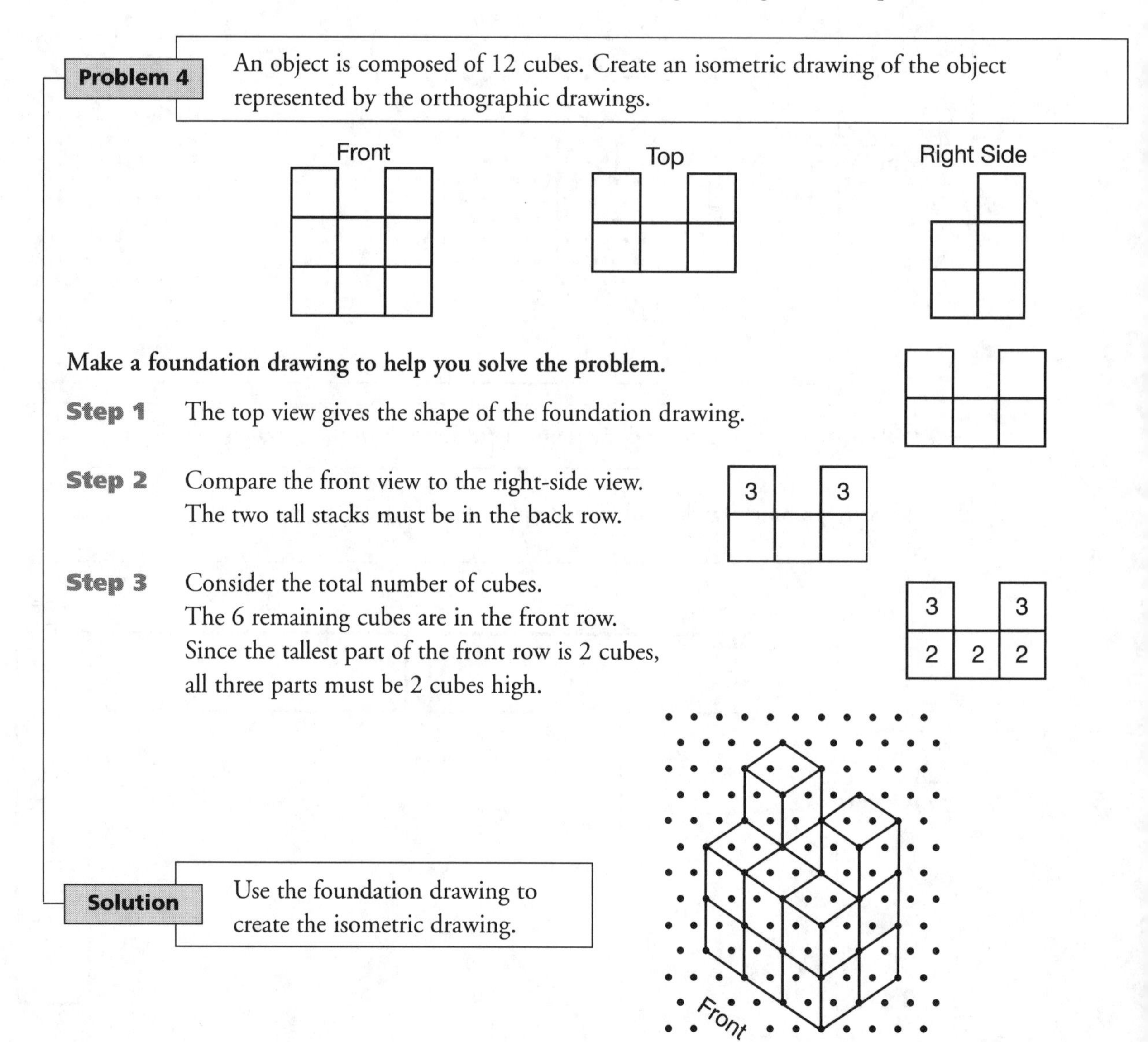

Make a foundation drawing to help you solve the problem.

Step 1 The top view gives the shape of the foundation drawing.

Step 2 Compare the front view to the right-side view. The two tall stacks must be in the back row.

Step 3 Consider the total number of cubes. The 6 remaining cubes are in the front row. Since the tallest part of the front row is 2 cubes, all three parts must be 2 cubes high.

Solution Use the foundation drawing to create the isometric drawing.

Apply the TEKS Create an isometric drawing for each object.

1. The letter F

2. Rectangular prism

3. An object composed of 15 cubes

Create front, top, and right-side orthographic views from each isometric drawing. Make each top view a foundation drawing.

4.

5.

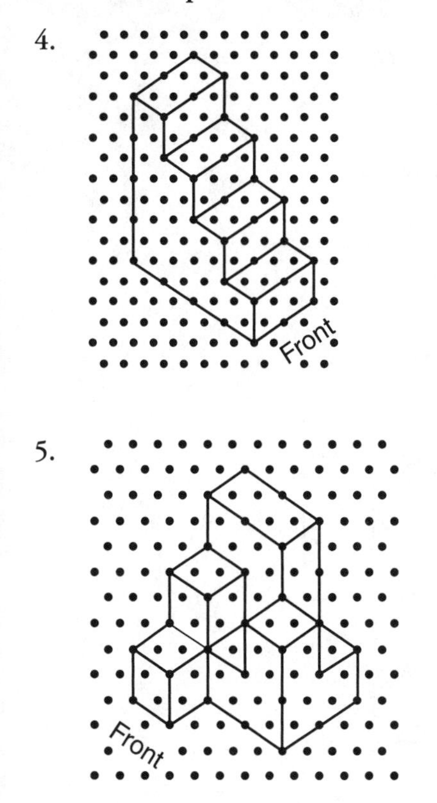

Create an isometric drawing from the orthogonal views.

6.

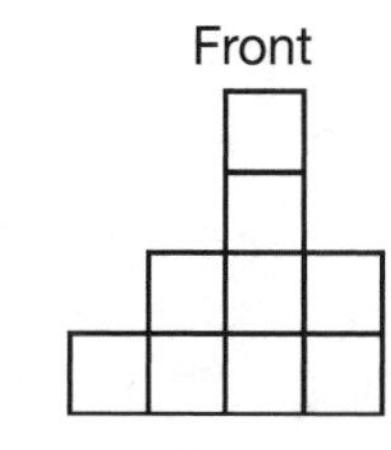

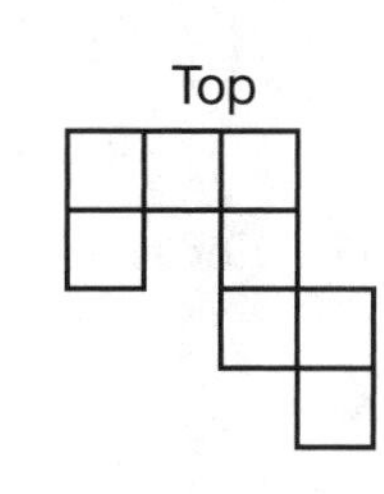

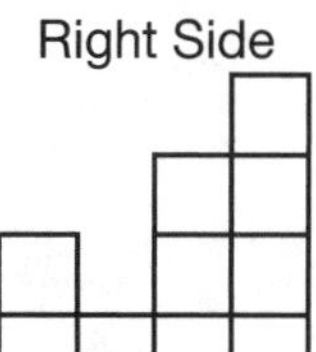

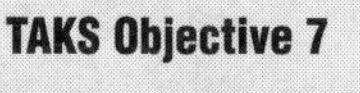

TAKS Objective 7 The students will demonstrate an understanding of two- and three-dimensional representations of geometric relationships and shapes.
TEKS G(d)1C

DIRECTIONS Read each question. Then circle the letter for the correct answer. If a correct answer is not here, circle the letter for "Not Here."

1 Shown below are the front, top, and right-side views of an object composed of cubes.

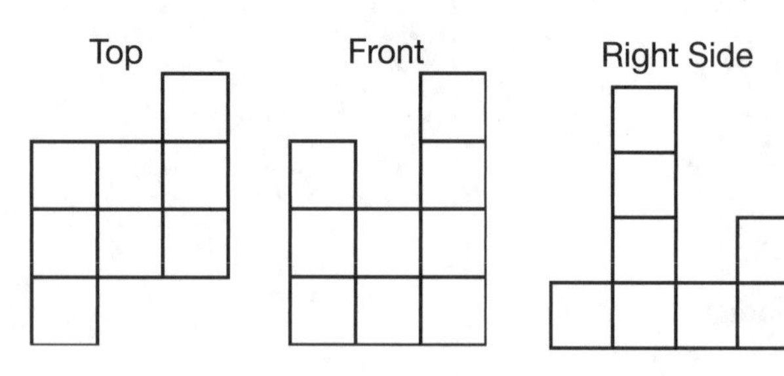

How many cubes is the object composed of?

A 8

B 15

C 18

D 25

2 Shown below are an isometric and an orthogonal view of an object.

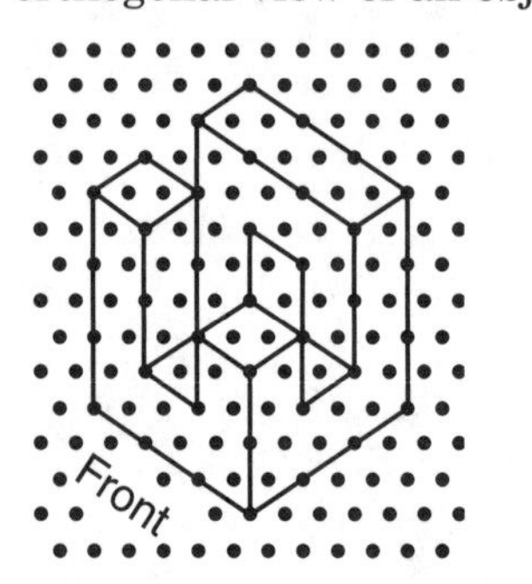

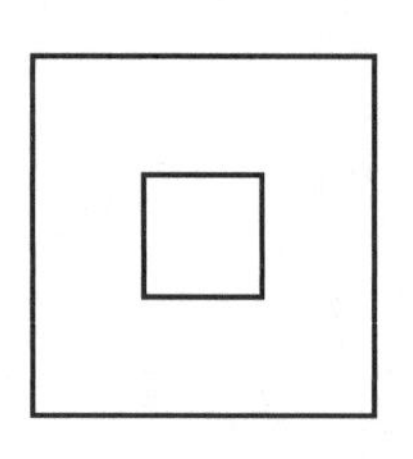

Which orthogonal view is shown?

F Front

G Top

H Right side

J Left side

3 Shown below is the foundation drawing of an object.

2	2	3
3	2	2
2	1	2

Which of the following is a possible orthographic view of the object?

A

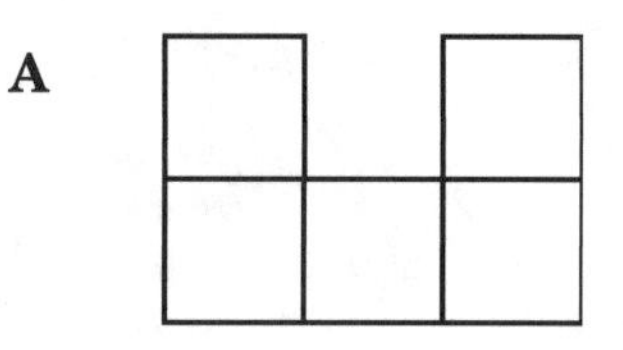

B

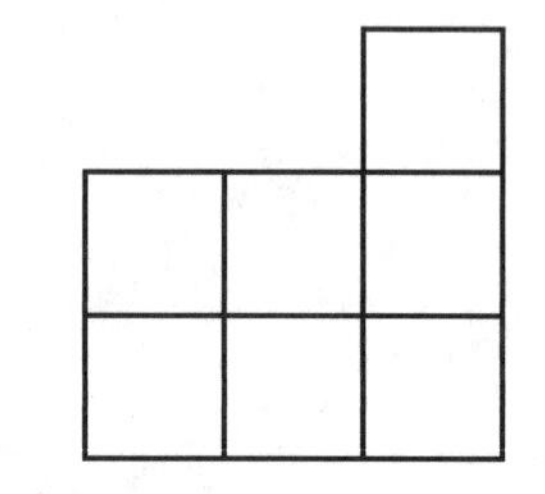

C

D Not Here

Focus on TEKS

Lesson 42 Representing Geometric Figures on the Coordinate System

TEKS G(d)2A Use one- and two-dimensional coordinate systems to represent points, lines, line segments, and figures.
TEKS G(d)2B Use slope and equations of lines to investigate geometric relationships, including parallel lines, perpendicular lines, and special segments of triangles and other polygons.
TEKS G(e)2A Based on explorations and using concrete models, formulate and test conjectures about the properties of parallel and perpendicular lines.

Many two-dimensional figures, especially quadrilaterals, can be represented and identified on a coordinate grid by using properties of parallel and perpendicular lines.

A **quadrilateral** is a four-sided polygon.
A **parallelogram** is a quadrilateral with two pairs of parallel sides.
A **rectangle** is a parallelogram with four right angles.
A **square** is a rectangle with four congruent sides.
A **rhombus** is a quadrilateral with two pairs of parallel, congruent sides.
A **trapezoid** is a quadrilateral with exactly one pair of parallel sides.

Guided Instruction

Problem 1 A quadrilateral is defined by the graphs of l_1: $y = -\frac{2}{3}x + 7$; l_2: $y = \frac{3}{2}x + 2$; l_3: $2x + 3y = -7$; and l_4: $y = \frac{3}{2}x - 5$. Graph the quadrilateral and identify a more precise name.

Step 1 Write each equation in slope-intercept form.
The only equation not in slope-intercept form is l_3.

$$2x + 3y = -7$$
$$2x - 2x + 3y = -2x - 7$$
$$\frac{3y}{3} = \frac{-2x - 7}{3}$$
$$y = -\frac{2}{3}x - \frac{7}{3}$$

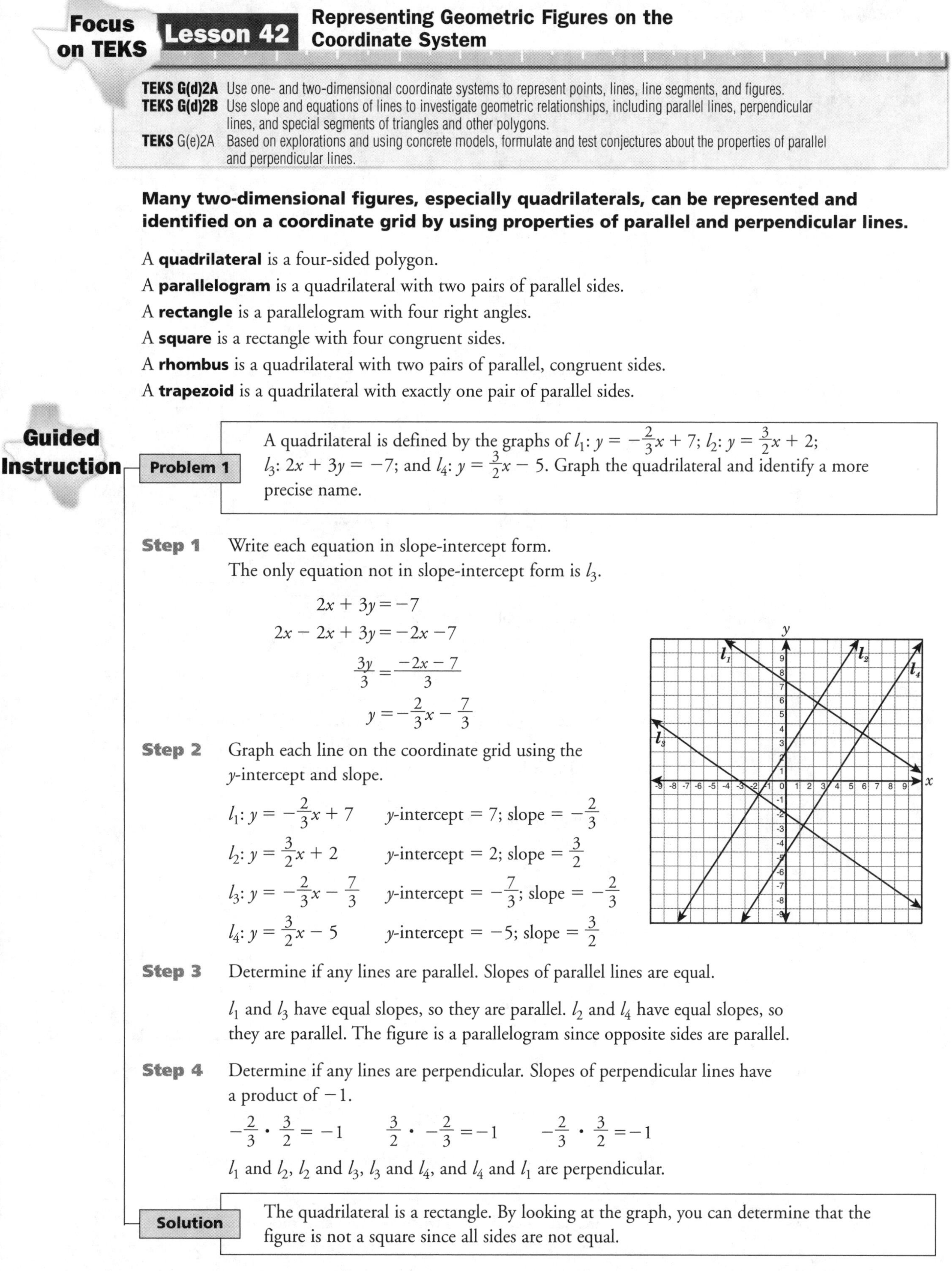

Step 2 Graph each line on the coordinate grid using the y-intercept and slope.

l_1: $y = -\frac{2}{3}x + 7$ y-intercept = 7; slope = $-\frac{2}{3}$
l_2: $y = \frac{3}{2}x + 2$ y-intercept = 2; slope = $\frac{3}{2}$
l_3: $y = -\frac{2}{3}x - \frac{7}{3}$ y-intercept = $-\frac{7}{3}$; slope = $-\frac{2}{3}$
l_4: $y = \frac{3}{2}x - 5$ y-intercept = -5; slope = $\frac{3}{2}$

Step 3 Determine if any lines are parallel. Slopes of parallel lines are equal.

l_1 and l_3 have equal slopes, so they are parallel. l_2 and l_4 have equal slopes, so they are parallel. The figure is a parallelogram since opposite sides are parallel.

Step 4 Determine if any lines are perpendicular. Slopes of perpendicular lines have a product of -1.

$-\frac{2}{3} \cdot \frac{3}{2} = -1$ $\frac{3}{2} \cdot -\frac{2}{3} = -1$ $-\frac{2}{3} \cdot \frac{3}{2} = -1$

l_1 and l_2, l_2 and l_3, l_3 and l_4, and l_4 and l_1 are perpendicular.

Solution The quadrilateral is a rectangle. By looking at the graph, you can determine that the figure is not a square since all sides are not equal.

Guided Instruction

More Problems

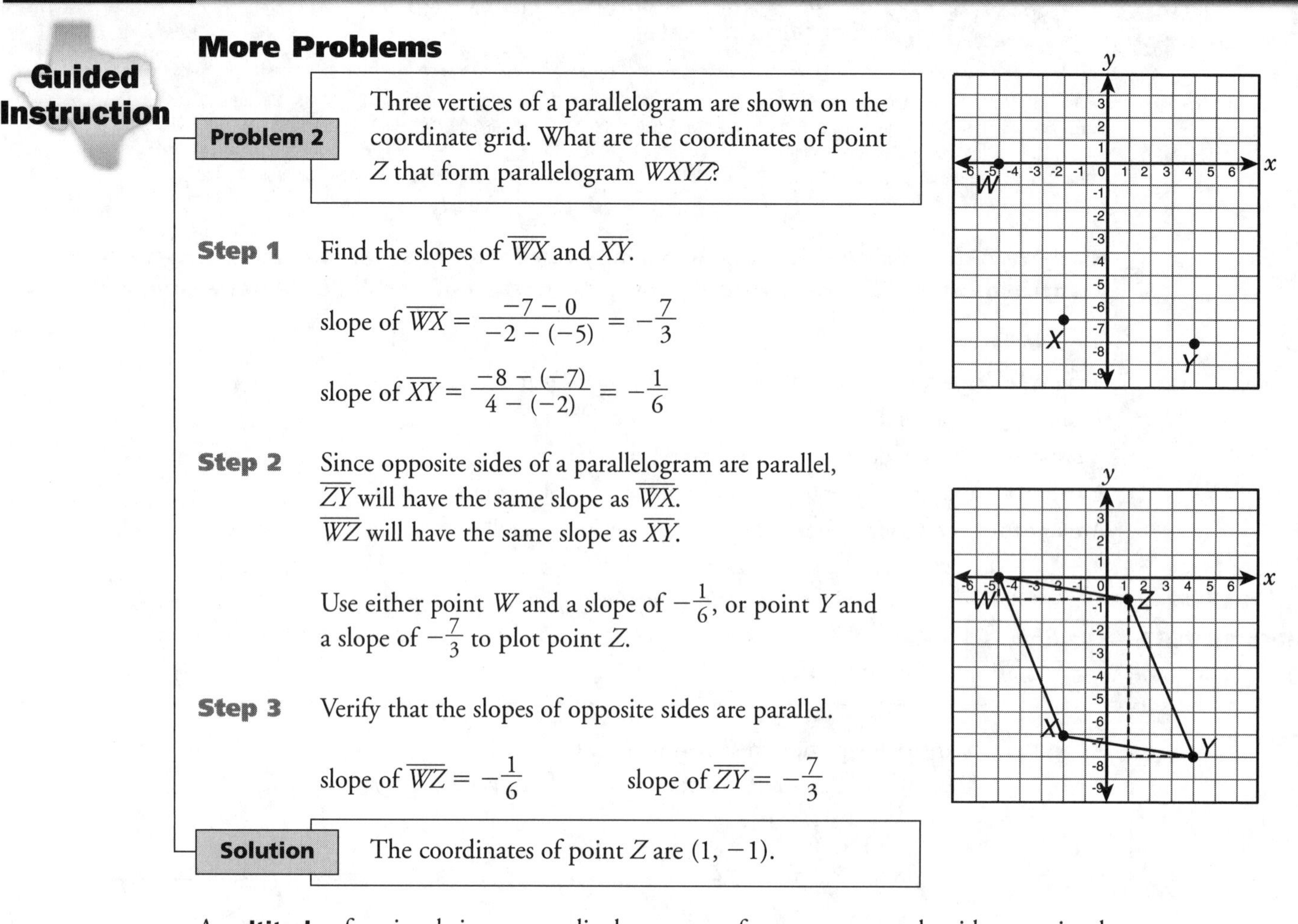

Problem 2

Three vertices of a parallelogram are shown on the coordinate grid. What are the coordinates of point Z that form parallelogram $WXYZ$?

Step 1 Find the slopes of $\overline{WX}$ and $\overline{XY}$.

$$\text{slope of } \overline{WX} = \frac{-7-0}{-2-(-5)} = -\frac{7}{3}$$

$$\text{slope of } \overline{XY} = \frac{-8-(-7)}{4-(-2)} = -\frac{1}{6}$$

Step 2 Since opposite sides of a parallelogram are parallel,
$\overline{ZY}$ will have the same slope as $\overline{WX}$.
$\overline{WZ}$ will have the same slope as $\overline{XY}$.

Use either point W and a slope of $-\frac{1}{6}$, or point Y and a slope of $-\frac{7}{3}$ to plot point Z.

Step 3 Verify that the slopes of opposite sides are parallel.

slope of $\overline{WZ} = -\frac{1}{6}$ slope of $\overline{ZY} = -\frac{7}{3}$

Solution The coordinates of point Z are $(1, -1)$.

An **altitude** of a triangle is a perpendicular segment from a vertex to the side opposite that vertex.

Problem 3

On a coordinate grid, graph $\triangle ABC$ with vertices A (3, 7), B (5, −2), and C (−4, 4). Then draw the three altitudes of the triangle to make a conjecture about the relationship among a triangle's altitudes.

Step 1 Graph $\triangle ABC$ on a coordinate grid.

Step 2 Find the slope of each segment.

slope of $\overline{AB} = -\frac{9}{2}$

slope of $\overline{BC} = -\frac{2}{3}$

slope of $\overline{AC} = \frac{3}{7}$

Step 3 Since point A is opposite $\overline{BC}$, find the slope of the altitude from point A to $\overline{BC}$.

$m \cdot (-\frac{2}{3}) = -1$ Think: What number times $-\frac{2}{3}$ equals -1? $m = \frac{3}{2}$

Using point A and a slope of $\frac{3}{2}$, draw the altitude from point A to $\overline{BC}$.

Step 4 Repeat Step 3 to draw the other two altitudes. The altitudes of $\triangle ABC$ intersect at one point.

Solution Conjecture: The altitudes of a triangle intersect at one point.

Apply the TEKS Graph each quadrilateral defined by the given equations. Then identify the most precise name for each quadrilateral.

1. $y = -\frac{3}{4}x + 5,\ y = \frac{1}{4}x + 1,\ y = -\frac{3}{4}x - 3,\ y = \frac{1}{4}x - 3$

2. $x + y = 7,\ y = \frac{1}{3}x + 3,\ y = -4x - 2,\ y = \frac{1}{3}x - 4$

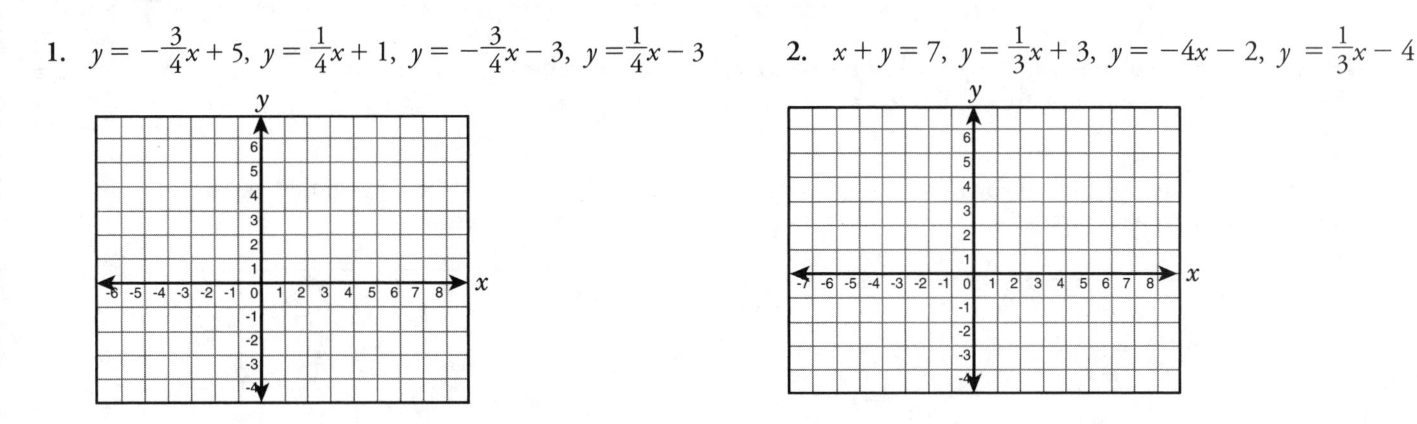

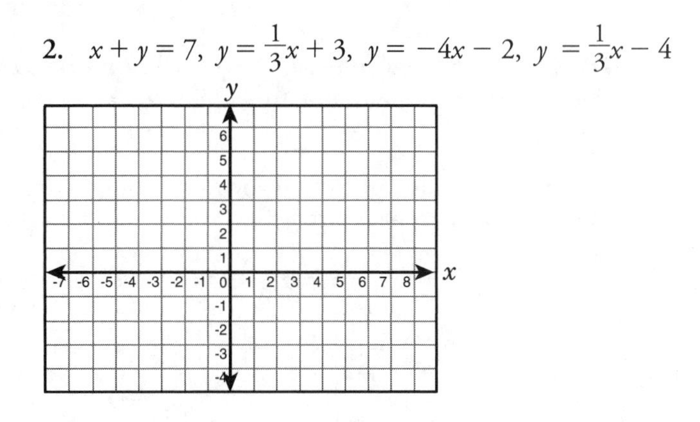

______________________ ______________________

Three vertices of parallelogram are shown on the coordinate grid.

3. Find the coordinates of point Q that form parallelogram $MNPQ$.

____

4. Find the coordinates of point R that form parallelogram $MNRP$.

____

Explore the conjecture from Problem 3 by graphing each triangle and drawing the triangle's altitudes. Then complete Exercises 5–6.

5. $\triangle JKL$ with vertices $J\,(0, 5)$, $K\,(6, -1)$, and $L\,(-6, -4)$

6. $\triangle WXY$ with vertices $W\,(1, 7)$, $X\,(7, -2)$, and $Y\,(-2, -5)$

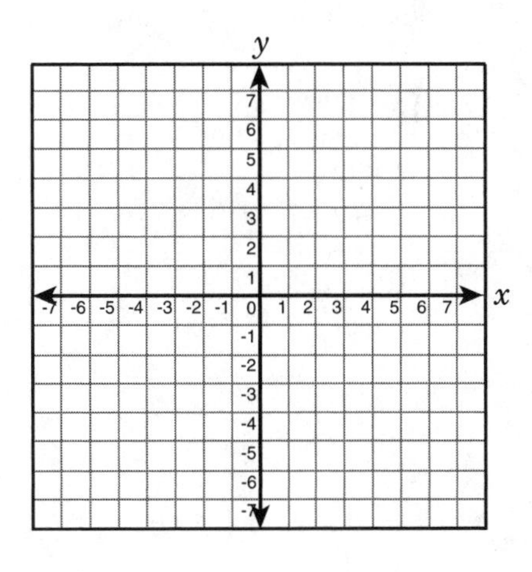

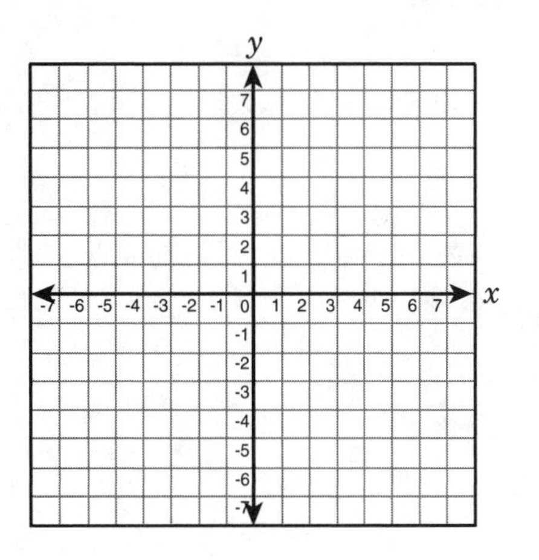

7. Explain whether or not you think the conjecture in Problem 3 is true.

____

TAKS Objective 7 The student will demonstrate an understanding of two- and three-dimensional representations of geometric relationships and shapes.
TEKS G(d)2A, G(d)2B, G(e)2A

DIRECTIONS Read each question. Then circle the letter for the correct answer. If a correct answer is not here, circle the letter for "Not Here."

1 Three of the four lines that form a rectangle are shown on the coordinate grid.

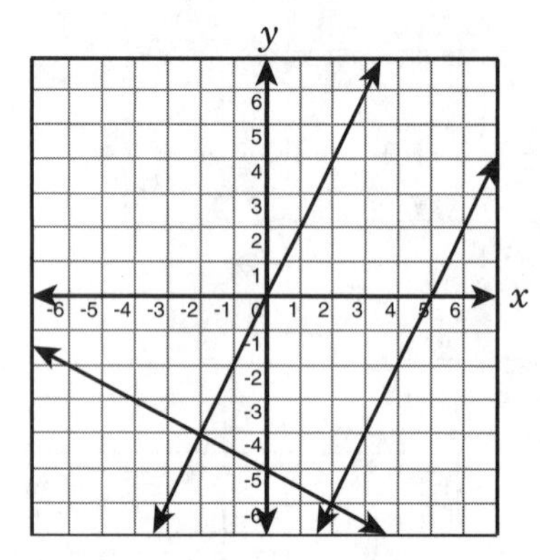

Which of the following equations could represent the fourth line?

A $y = -2x + 3$

B $y = \frac{1}{2}x + 1$

C $y = 2x + 5$

D Not Here

2 Which of the following sets of equations will form a right triangle?

F $y = \frac{1}{3}x + 2,\ x = 3,\ y = -x - 2$

G $y = -\frac{3}{2}x - 3,\ y = -\frac{1}{4}x - 1,\ 2x - 3y = 22$

H $y = 3x + 2,\ y = -x + 5,\ y = \frac{1}{3}x - 2$

J Not Here

3 Rhombus *DEFG* is graphed on the coordinate grid.

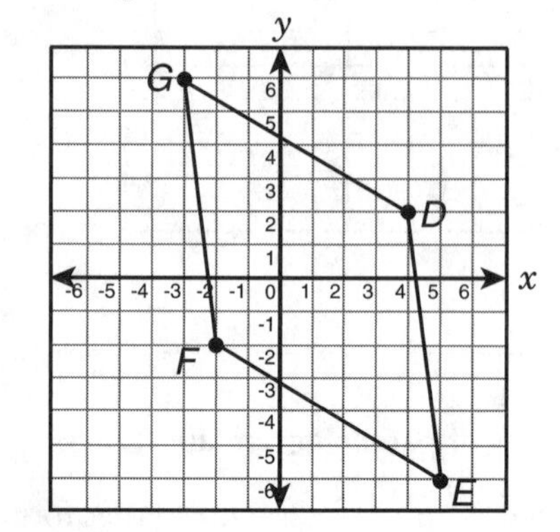

Which is NOT a conjecture about the diagonals of a rhombus?

A The slopes of the diagonals have a product of – 1.

B The diagonals form 90° angles at their intersection.

C The diagonals are perpendicular.

D Not Here

4 What are the coordinates of point *C* that make *ABCD* a parallelogram?

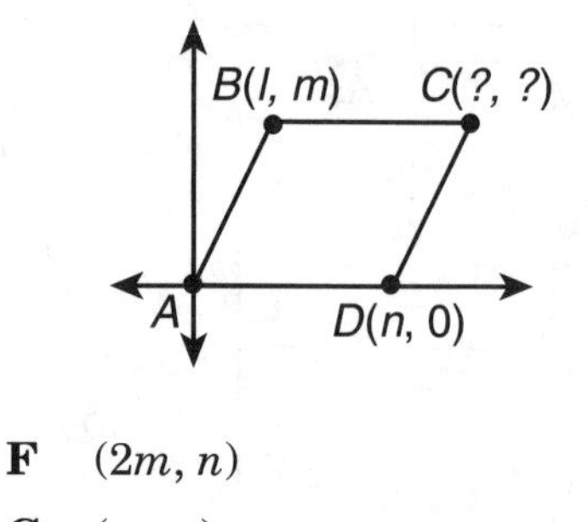

F $(2m, n)$

G (n, m)

H $(n + l, m)$

J $(2 + n, m)$

Focus on TEKS

Lesson 43 Distance and Midpoint Formulas

TEKS G(d)2C Develop and use formulas including distance and midpoint.

You can apply what you have learned about the coordinate system to calculate distances and find the midpoints of line segments.

The **distance** between two points is the length of the line segment connecting the points. The **midpoint** of a line segment is the point that is halfway between the endpoints of the segment.

Guided Instruction

Problem 1

A line segment has endpoints $A(2, 3)$ and $B(12, 9)$. Verify that point $M(7, 6)$ is the midpoint of the segment.

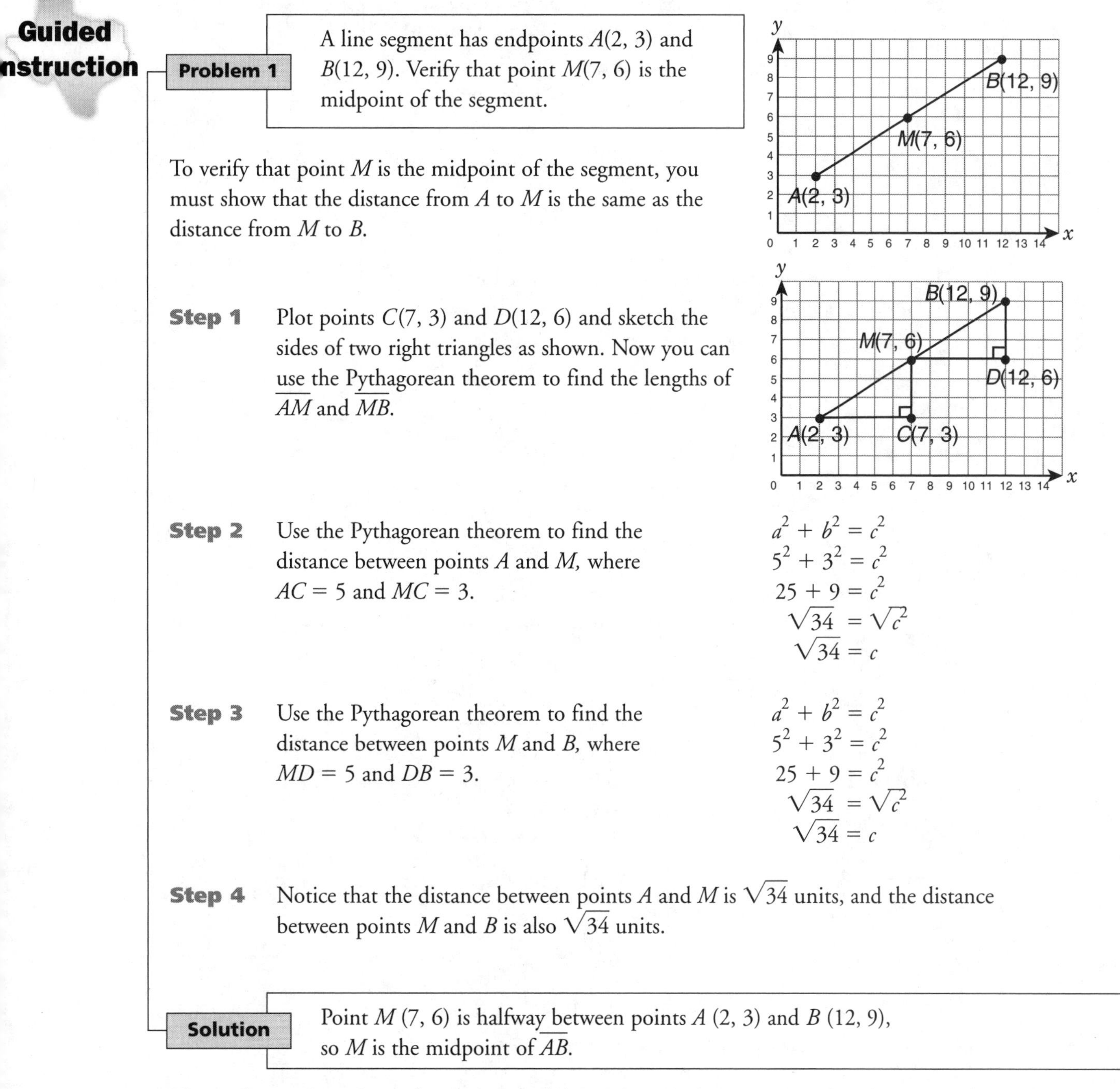

To verify that point M is the midpoint of the segment, you must show that the distance from A to M is the same as the distance from M to B.

Step 1 Plot points $C(7, 3)$ and $D(12, 6)$ and sketch the sides of two right triangles as shown. Now you can use the Pythagorean theorem to find the lengths of $\overline{AM}$ and $\overline{MB}$.

Step 2 Use the Pythagorean theorem to find the distance between points A and M, where $AC = 5$ and $MC = 3$.

$$a^2 + b^2 = c^2$$
$$5^2 + 3^2 = c^2$$
$$25 + 9 = c^2$$
$$\sqrt{34} = \sqrt{c^2}$$
$$\sqrt{34} = c$$

Step 3 Use the Pythagorean theorem to find the distance between points M and B, where $MD = 5$ and $DB = 3$.

$$a^2 + b^2 = c^2$$
$$5^2 + 3^2 = c^2$$
$$25 + 9 = c^2$$
$$\sqrt{34} = \sqrt{c^2}$$
$$\sqrt{34} = c$$

Step 4 Notice that the distance between points A and M is $\sqrt{34}$ units, and the distance between points M and B is also $\sqrt{34}$ units.

Solution

Point M (7, 6) is halfway between points A (2, 3) and B (12, 9), so M is the midpoint of $\overline{AB}$.

The midpoint formula can be used to find the midpoint of a segment with endpoints (x_1, y_1) and (x_2, y_2). The midpoint of the segment will have the following coordinates:

$$\left(\frac{x_1 + x_2}{2}, \frac{y_1 + y_2}{2}\right)$$

This will give the same coordinates for point M as you found in Problem 1.

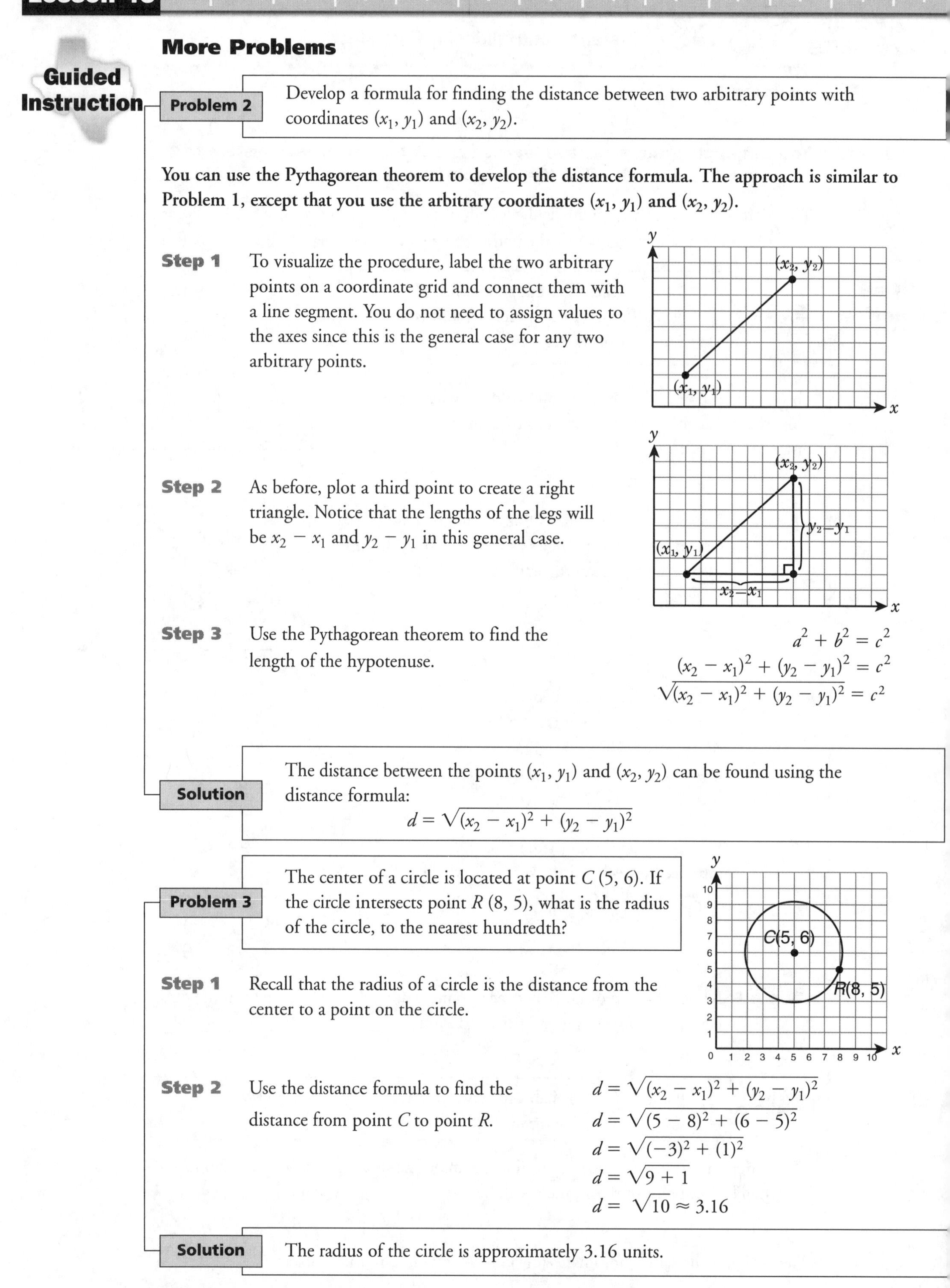

More Problems

Guided Instruction

Problem 2 Develop a formula for finding the distance between two arbitrary points with coordinates (x_1, y_1) and (x_2, y_2).

You can use the Pythagorean theorem to develop the distance formula. The approach is similar to Problem 1, except that you use the arbitrary coordinates (x_1, y_1) and (x_2, y_2).

Step 1 To visualize the procedure, label the two arbitrary points on a coordinate grid and connect them with a line segment. You do not need to assign values to the axes since this is the general case for any two arbitrary points.

Step 2 As before, plot a third point to create a right triangle. Notice that the lengths of the legs will be $x_2 - x_1$ and $y_2 - y_1$ in this general case.

Step 3 Use the Pythagorean theorem to find the length of the hypotenuse.

$$a^2 + b^2 = c^2$$
$$(x_2 - x_1)^2 + (y_2 - y_1)^2 = c^2$$
$$\sqrt{(x_2 - x_1)^2 + (y_2 - y_1)^2} = c^2$$

Solution The distance between the points (x_1, y_1) and (x_2, y_2) can be found using the distance formula:

$$d = \sqrt{(x_2 - x_1)^2 + (y_2 - y_1)^2}$$

Problem 3 The center of a circle is located at point C (5, 6). If the circle intersects point R (8, 5), what is the radius of the circle, to the nearest hundredth?

Step 1 Recall that the radius of a circle is the distance from the center to a point on the circle.

Step 2 Use the distance formula to find the distance from point C to point R.

$$d = \sqrt{(x_2 - x_1)^2 + (y_2 - y_1)^2}$$
$$d = \sqrt{(5 - 8)^2 + (6 - 5)^2}$$
$$d = \sqrt{(-3)^2 + (1)^2}$$
$$d = \sqrt{9 + 1}$$
$$d = \sqrt{10} \approx 3.16$$

Solution The radius of the circle is approximately 3.16 units.

Apply the TEKS Use the distance formula to find the distance between each pair of points. Round your answers to the nearest hundredth.

1. (4, 1) and (8, 10) __________

2. (−3, 6) and (9, −1) __________

3. (0, 0) and (5, 5) __________

4. (−7, 4) and (−7, 10) __________

5. (6, −9) and (3, 0) __________

6. (5, −4) and (5, −4) __________

Use the midpoint formula to match each pair of coordinates to its midpoint. Write the appropriate letter in the space provided.

7. A (2, 1), B (10, 7) ______

8. A (−4, 7), B (0, −1) ______

9. A (0, 5), B (1, 2) ______

10. A(−1, −1), B (11, 6) ______

A. M (−2, 3)

B. M (5, 2.5)

C. M (0.5, 3.5)

D. M (6, 4)

Refer to the figure to answer the following questions.

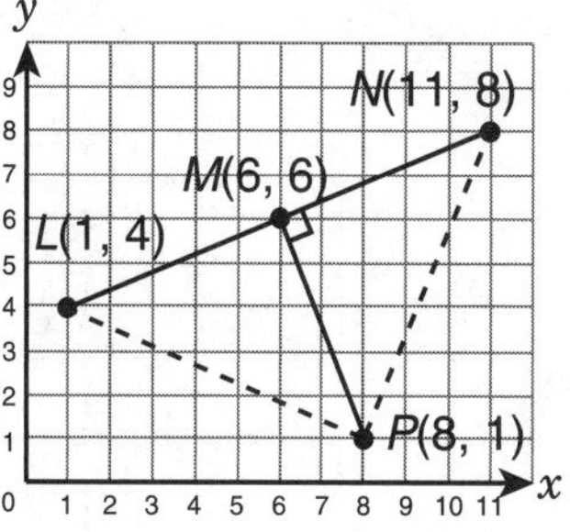

11. What is the slope of $\overline{LN}$? __________

12. What is the slope of $\overline{MP}$? __________

13. What are the coordinates of the midpoint of $\overline{LN}$? __________

14. How would you describe the relationship between $\overline{LN}$ and $\overline{MP}$?

____

15. A segment that is perpendicular to another segment at its midpoint is called a **perpendicular bisector.** According to the Perpendicular Bisector Theorem, if a point lies on the perpendicular bisector of a segment, then the point is equidistant from the endpoints of the segment. Find the distance from L to P and from N to P to verify the Perpendicular Bisector Theorem for this example.

____

TAKS Objective 7 The student will demonstrate an understanding of two- and three-dimensional representations of geometric relationships and shapes.

TEKS G(d)2C

DIRECTIONS Read each question. Then circle the letter for the correct answer. If a correct answer is not here, circle the letter for "Not Here."

1 The endpoints of a line segment are given by the coordinates $Y(-4, 7)$ and $Z(6, 3)$. What are the coordinates of the midpoint of $\overline{YZ}$?

A $M(5, 1)$

B $M(-2, 4)$

C $M(1, 5)$

D Not Here

2 The center of a circle is located at point $C(-2, 9)$. The circle intersects point $P(4, 5)$. What is the diameter of the circle, rounded to the nearest tenth?

F 7.2

G 14.4

H 16.4

J Not Here

3 What is the length of the shortest side of the triangle, rounded to the nearest tenth?

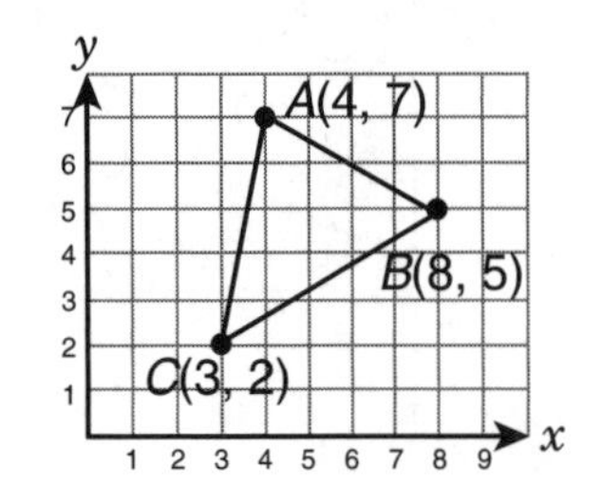

A 6.1

B 5.2

C 4.5

D 3.9

4 If point M is the midpoint of $\overline{AB}$, what are the coordinates of point B?

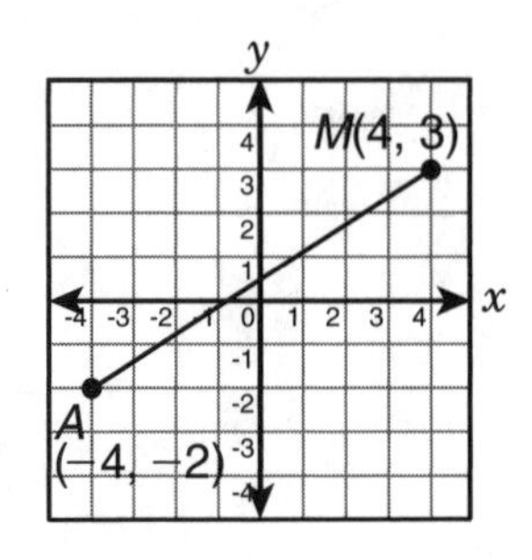

F $B(14, 9)$

G $B(12, 8)$

H $B(10, 7)$

J Not Here

5 A trapezoid has vertices $Q(-1, 3)$, $R(4, 3)$, $S(6, -2)$, and $T(-2, -2)$. What is the perimeter of the trapezoid, to the nearest tenth?

Record your answer and fill in the bubbles on the grid below. Be sure to use the correct place value.

				.			
0	0	0	0		0	0	0
1	1	1	1		1	1	1
2	2	2	2		2	2	2
3	3	3	3		3	3	3
4	4	4	4		4	4	4
5	5	5	5		5	5	5
6	6	6	6		6	6	6
7	7	7	7		7	7	7
8	8	8	8		8	8	8
9	9	9	9		9	9	9

Building Stamina™

DIRECTIONS Read each question. Then circle the letter for the correct answer. If a correct answer is not here, circle the letter for "Not Here."

1 A soup company is designing a new can for its product. Which of the following could be used as a net to model the surface area of the can?

A

B

C

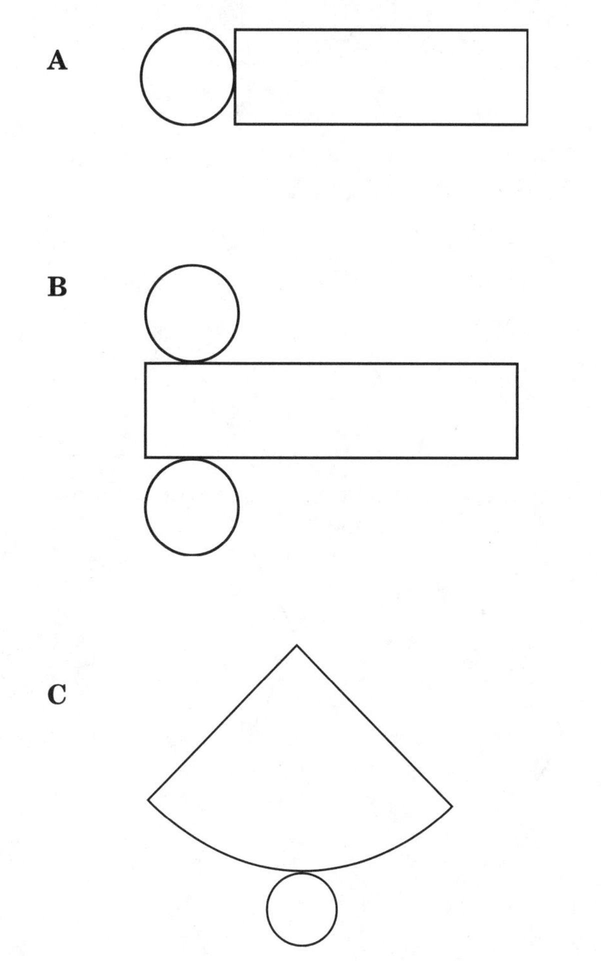

D Not Here

2 The endpoints of a segment are A (4, 1) and B (−2, 9). Which equation represents the perpendicular bisector of $\overline{AB}$?

F $y = \frac{3}{4}x + \frac{17}{4}$

G $y = \frac{1}{3}x + \frac{9}{2}$

H $y = -\frac{4}{3}x + \frac{19}{3}$

J $y = \frac{3}{4}x + 4$

3 Two parallel lines with the equations $y = \frac{2}{3}x + 19$ and $y = mx + 5$ contain opposite sides of a parallelogram. What is the value of m in the second linear equation?

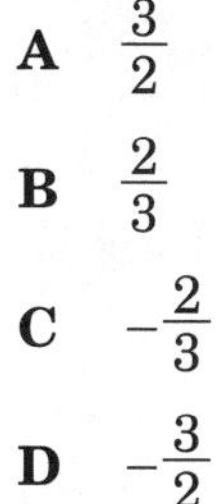

A $\frac{3}{2}$

B $\frac{2}{3}$

C $-\frac{2}{3}$

D $-\frac{3}{2}$

4 The vertices of $\triangle PQR$ are P (2, 1), Q (10, 2), and R (3, −5). List the sides of $\triangle PQR$ in order of length from least to greatest.

F $\overline{PQ}$, $\overline{PR}$, $\overline{RQ}$

G $\overline{RQ}$, $\overline{PQ}$, $\overline{PR}$

H $\overline{PR}$, $\overline{PQ}$, $\overline{RQ}$

J $\overline{PR}$, $\overline{RQ}$, $\overline{PQ}$

5 Point B (1, −4) lies on segment $\overline{AC}$. Point A is at (−5, −7) and the length of $\overline{AB}$ is $\frac{3}{8}$ the length of $\overline{AC}$. What is the distance from A to C? Round your answer to the nearest hundredth.

Record your answer and fill in the bubbles on the grid below. Be sure to use the correct place value.

				.			
0	0	0	0		0	0	0
1	1	1	1		1	1	1
2	2	2	2		2	2	2
3	3	3	3		3	3	3
4	4	4	4		4	4	4
5	5	5	5		5	5	5
6	6	6	6		6	6	6
7	7	7	7		7	7	7
8	8	8	8		8	8	8
9	9	9	9		9	9	9

6 What is the precise name for quadrilateral $WXYZ$ with vertices $W(9, 1)$, $X(4, -4)$, $Y(-2, -1)$, and $Z(-3, 7)$?

F Square

G Rhombus

H Parallelogram

J Trapezoid

7 The top, side, and front views of an object built with cubes are shown below.

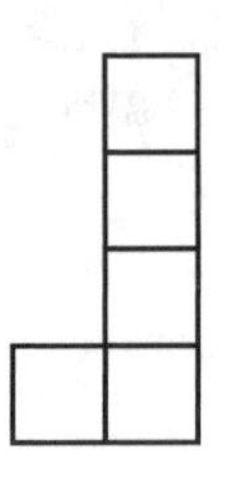

Top View

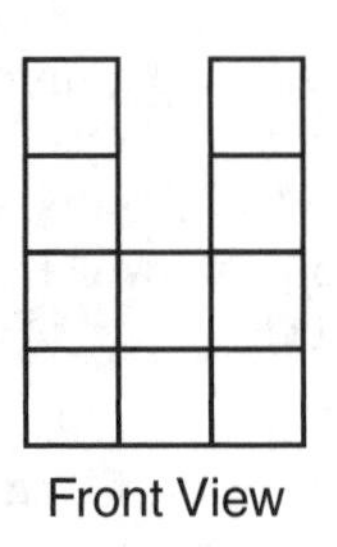

Side View

Front View

How many cubes were used to create the figure?

A 10

B 12

C 14

D 16

8 The base of an isosceles triangle is represented by $\overline{XY}$.

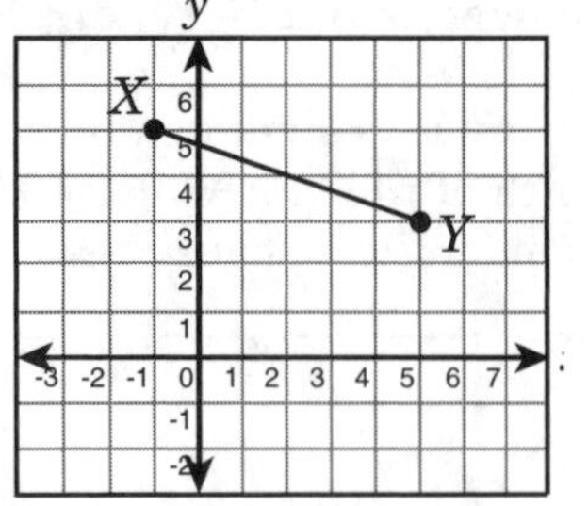

Which coordinate pair could represent point Z, the third vertex of $\triangle XYZ$?

F (2, 2)

G (3, 7)

H (4, 0)

J (23, 0)

9 Which Platonic solid is formed when the net shown below is folded?

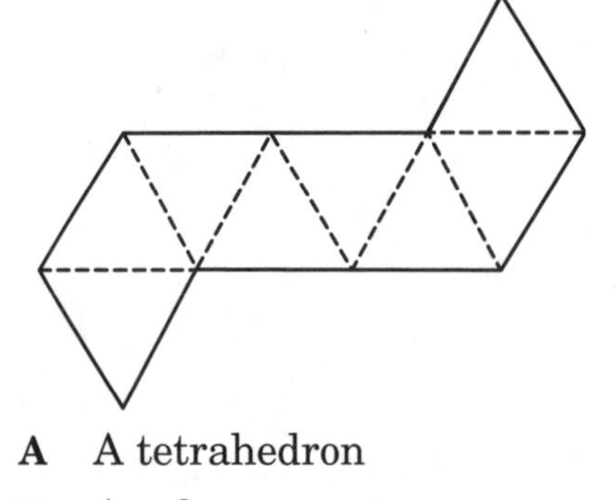

A A tetrahedron

B A cube

C An octahedron

D Not Here

10 Which of the following sets of equations form a square?

F $x = 4, x = -2, y = -3, y = 2$

G $y = -\frac{1}{2}x + 3, y = 2x + 3, y = -\frac{1}{2}x - 2, y = 2x - 7$

H $y = x + 1, y = -x + 1, y = x - 6, y = -x - 4$

J $y = -\frac{3}{2}x + 7, y = \frac{1}{3}x + 3, y = -\frac{3}{2}x - 3, y = \frac{1}{3}x - 3$

11 Which of the following sets of coordinates represents the vertices of a right triangle in the coordinate plane?

A $A\ (1, -9), B\ (5, 3), C\ (11, 12)$

B $A\ (6, 2), B\ (13, 8), C\ (9, 7)$

C $A\ (-8, -5), B\ (1, 3), C\ (6, 15)$

D $A\ (-4, -3), B\ (-1, 2), C\ (9, -4)$

12 Consider the isometric drawing.

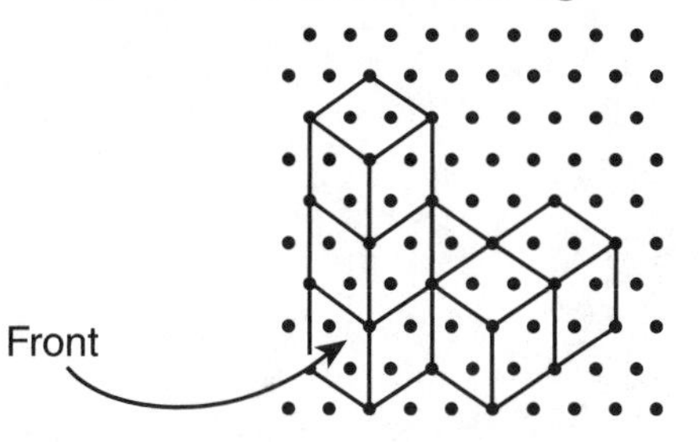

Which of the following figures shows the top view of the isometric drawing?

F

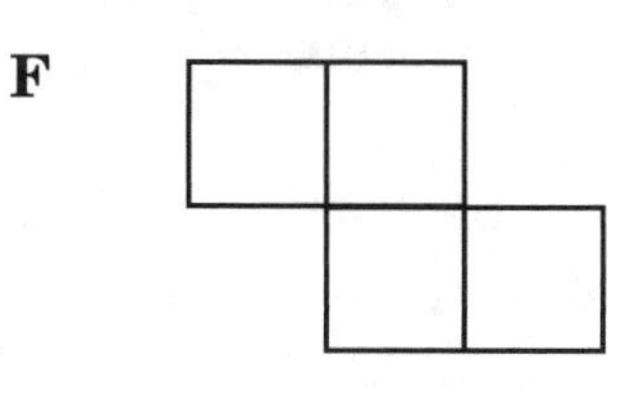

G

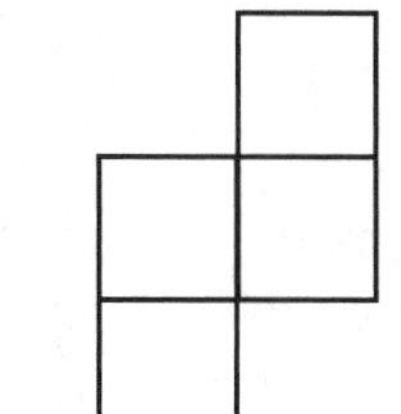

H

J Not Here

13 A quadrilateral has vertices $A\ (5, 1)$, $B\ (3, -6)$, $C\ (-4, -4)$, and $D\ (-2, 3)$. What is the perimeter of the quadrilateral, to the nearest hundredth?

Record your answer and fill in the bubbles on the grid below. Be sure to use the correct place value.

				.			
0	0	0	0		0	0	0
1	1	1	1		1	1	1
2	2	2	2		2	2	2
3	3	3	3		3	3	3
4	4	4	4		4	4	4
5	5	5	5		5	5	5
6	6	6	6		6	6	6
7	7	7	7		7	7	7
8	8	8	8		8	8	8
9	9	9	9		9	9	9

14 Maria is wrapping a birthday gift in the rectangular box shown below.

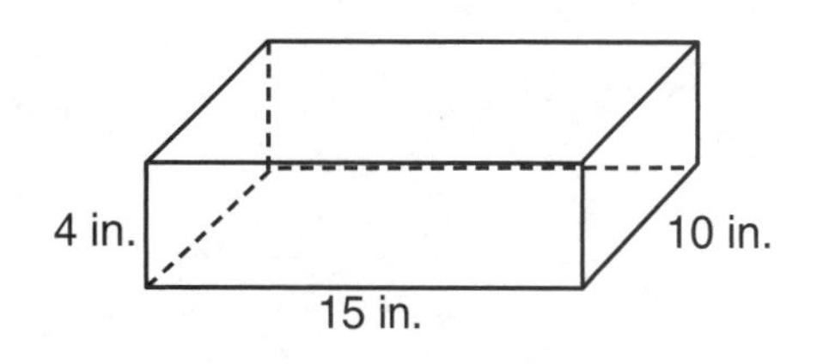

She wants to cut just one rectangular piece of wrapping paper to wrap the gift. What are the dimensions of the smallest piece of wrapping paper that Maria can use to completely cover the box?

F 23 in. × 28 in.

G 28 in. × 35 in.

H 20 in. × 26 in.

J 25 in. × 30 in.

15 Point D is the midpoint of $\overline{AB}$, and point E is the midpoint of $\overline{AC}$.

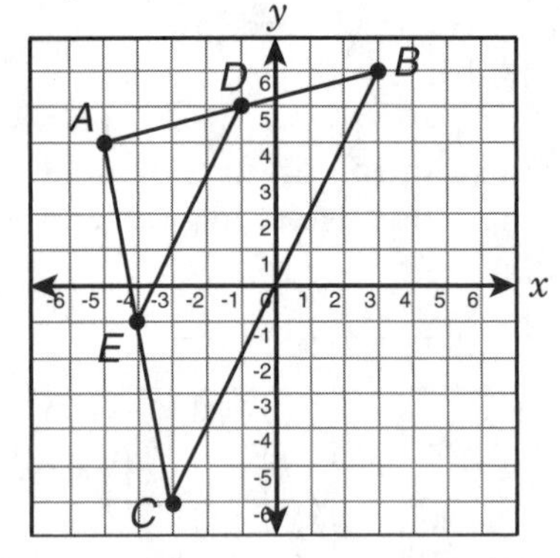

Which of the following statements is true?

A $\overline{DE}$ is parallel to $\overline{BC}$.

B $\overline{DE}$ is perpendicular to $\overline{CB}$.

C $DE = 2(AC)$

D $\overline{DE}$ is perpendicular to $\overline{AB}$.

16 What kind of three-dimensional figure will be formed when the net below is folded?

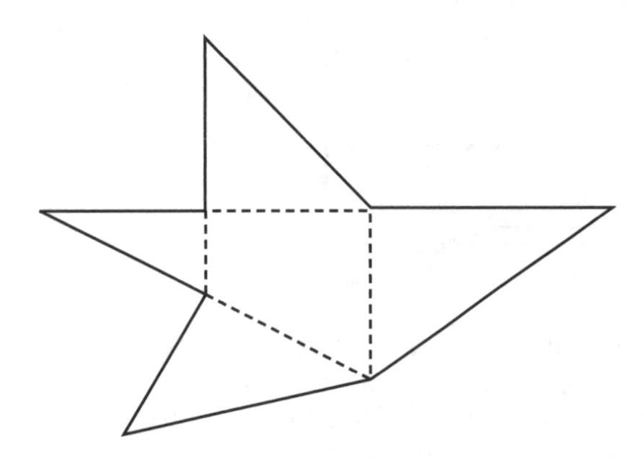

F A rectangular prism

G An oblique pyramid

H A right pyramid

J A hexagonal prism

17 If point M is the midpoint of $\overline{AB}$, what are the coordinates of point A?

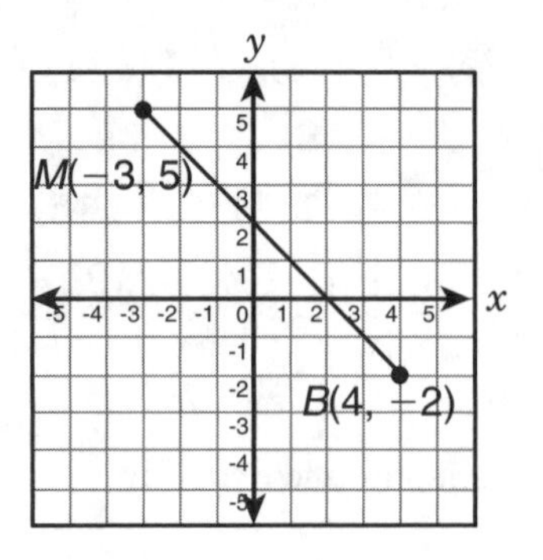

A $A(-10, 12)$

B $A(-8, 12)$

C $A(-12, 11)$

D $A(-9, 14)$

18 Which of the following sets of faces, edges, and vertices could NOT represent a convex polyhedron?

F 8 faces, 12 edges, 6 vertices

G 10 faces, 18 edges, 12 vertices

H 4 faces, 6 edges, 4 vertices

J Not Here

19 On a coordinate grid, Carl created a map of the path he takes to get from his house to school. He begins at the origin and travels to A (3, 7) and then to B (5, 4). From point B, the school is located at C (7, 8). If each unit on the coordinate grid represents 20 feet, about how long is Carl's path from home to school?

A 80 ft

B 190 ft

C 350 ft

D 650 ft

Focus on TEKS

Lesson 44 Perimeter and Area of Polygons

TEKS G(c)1A Use numeric and geometric patterns to make generalizations about geometric properties, including properties of polygons, ratios in similar figures and solids, and angle relationships in polygons and circles.
TEKS G(e)1A Find area of polygons and composite figures.
TEKS G(e)2B Based on explorations and using concrete models, formulate and test conjectures about the properties and attributes of polygons and their component parts.
TEKS G(f)1D Describe the effect on perimeter, area, and volume when length, width, or height of a three-dimensional solid is changed and apply this idea in solving problems.

Perimeter and area are often used in real-world situations, such as construction and interior design.

A **polygon** is a closed plane figure formed by three or more line segments. One way to classify a polygon is by its number of sides. The table at right shows this classification.

Number of Sides	Polygon
3	Triangle
4	Quadrilateral
5	Pentagon
6	Hexagon
7	Heptagon
8	Octagon
9	Nonagon
10	Decagon
12	Dodecagon
n	*N*-gon

The **perimeter** of a polygon is the distance around the polygon. Perimeter is found by adding the lengths of all the sides.

The **area** of a polygon is the number of square units in the interior of the polygon.

Guided Instruction

Problem 1

Mrs. Jansen is going to paint the walls of her dining room and then put a wallpaper border around the top of the walls. The dining room is 12 feet by 10.5 feet with 9-foot ceilings. There is also a window that is 5 feet by 4.25 feet and a door that is 3 feet by 7 feet. A gallon of paint costs $19.25, and one coat covers approximately 400 square feet. The wallpaper border costs $33.75 per roll, and each roll is 15 feet long. How much will it cost Mrs. Jansen to apply two coats of paint and put up a wallpaper border in her dining room?

Step 1 Find the perimeter of the dining room. $P = 12 + 12 + 10.5 + 10.5 = 45$ ft

Step 2 Determine the number of rolls of wallpaper border she will need. $\frac{45}{15} = 3$

Step 3 Find the cost of the wallpaper border. $\$33.75 \cdot 3 = \$101.25$

Step 4 Find the area of the walls that will be painted. Two walls are 12 feet by 9 feet and two walls are 10.5 feet by 9 feet. Subtract the area of the window and door, since they will not be painted.

Area of a rectangle = base • height $2(12 \cdot 9) = 216 \text{ ft}^2$ $2(10.5 \cdot 9) = 189 \text{ ft}^2$

Total area of walls to be painted $= 216 + 189 - (5 \cdot 4.25) - (3 \cdot 7) = 362.75 \text{ ft}^2$

Step 5 Determine the number of gallons of paint she will need. Since she will paint two coats, $362.75 \cdot 2$, or 725.5 ft^2 will need to be painted. $\frac{725.5}{400} \approx 1.8$

Step 6 Mrs. Jansen will need 2 gallons of paint. Find the cost of the paint. $\$19.25 \cdot 2 = \$38.50$

Step 7 Find the total cost of the paint and wallpaper border. $\$101.25 + \$38.50 = \$139.75$

Solution The total cost of the paint and wallpaper border will be $139.75.

Guided Instruction

There are several special quadrilaterals with different formulas for area.

Quadrilateral	Properties	Area formula
Parallelogram	two pairs of parallel sides	$A = bh$, where b is the base and h is the height
Rhombus	four congruent sides	$A = \frac{1}{2}d_1d_2$, where d_1 and d_2 are the diagonals
Rectangle	four right angles	$A = bh$, where b is the base and h is the height
Square	four right angles and four congruent sides	$A = s^2$, where s is a side
Trapezoid	exactly one pair of parallel sides	$A = \frac{1}{2}h(b_1 + b_2)$ where h is the height and b_1 and b_2 are the bases

More Problems

Problem 2

Identify each quadrilateral and find its area.

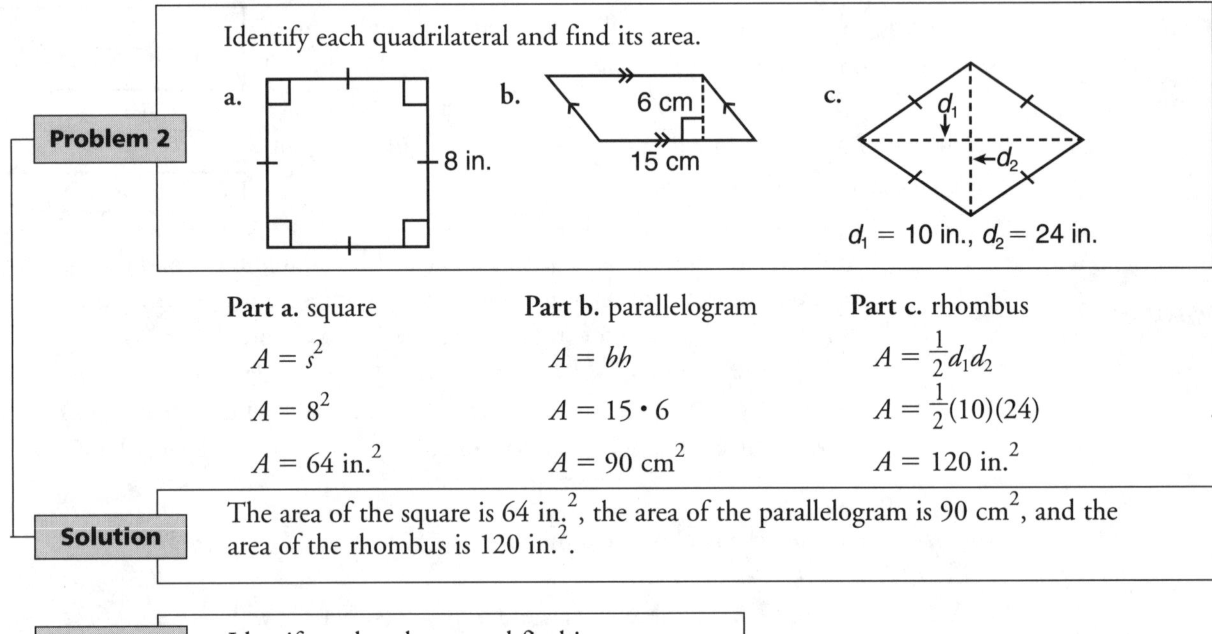

Part a. square

$A = s^2$

$A = 8^2$

$A = 64 \text{ in.}^2$

Part b. parallelogram

$A = bh$

$A = 15 \cdot 6$

$A = 90 \text{ cm}^2$

Part c. rhombus

$A = \frac{1}{2}d_1d_2$

$A = \frac{1}{2}(10)(24)$

$A = 120 \text{ in.}^2$

Solution

The area of the square is 64 in.^{2}, the area of the parallelogram is 90 cm^2, and the area of the rhombus is 120 in.^{2}.

Problem 3

Identify each polygon and find its area.

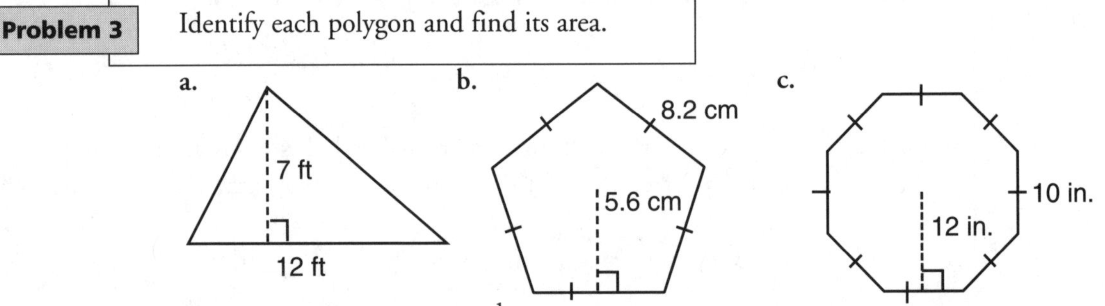

The formula for the area of a triangle is $A = \frac{1}{2}bh$, where b is the base and h is the height. The formula for the area of a regular polygon is $A = \frac{1}{2}ap$, where a is the apothem and p is the perimeter of the polygon. The *apothem* is the perpendicular distance from the center to a side.

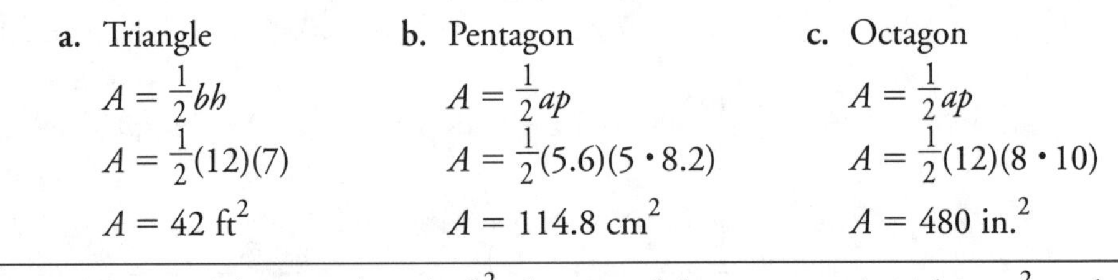

a. Triangle

$A = \frac{1}{2}bh$

$A = \frac{1}{2}(12)(7)$

$A = 42 \text{ ft}^2$

b. Pentagon

$A = \frac{1}{2}ap$

$A = \frac{1}{2}(5.6)(5 \cdot 8.2)$

$A = 114.8 \text{ cm}^2$

c. Octagon

$A = \frac{1}{2}ap$

$A = \frac{1}{2}(12)(8 \cdot 10)$

$A = 480 \text{ in.}^2$

Solution

The area of the triangle is 42 ft^2, the area of the pentagon is 114.8 cm^2, and the area of the octagon is 480 in.^{2}.

Apply the TEKS Identify each polygon in as many ways as possible.

Find the perimeter and area of each figure.

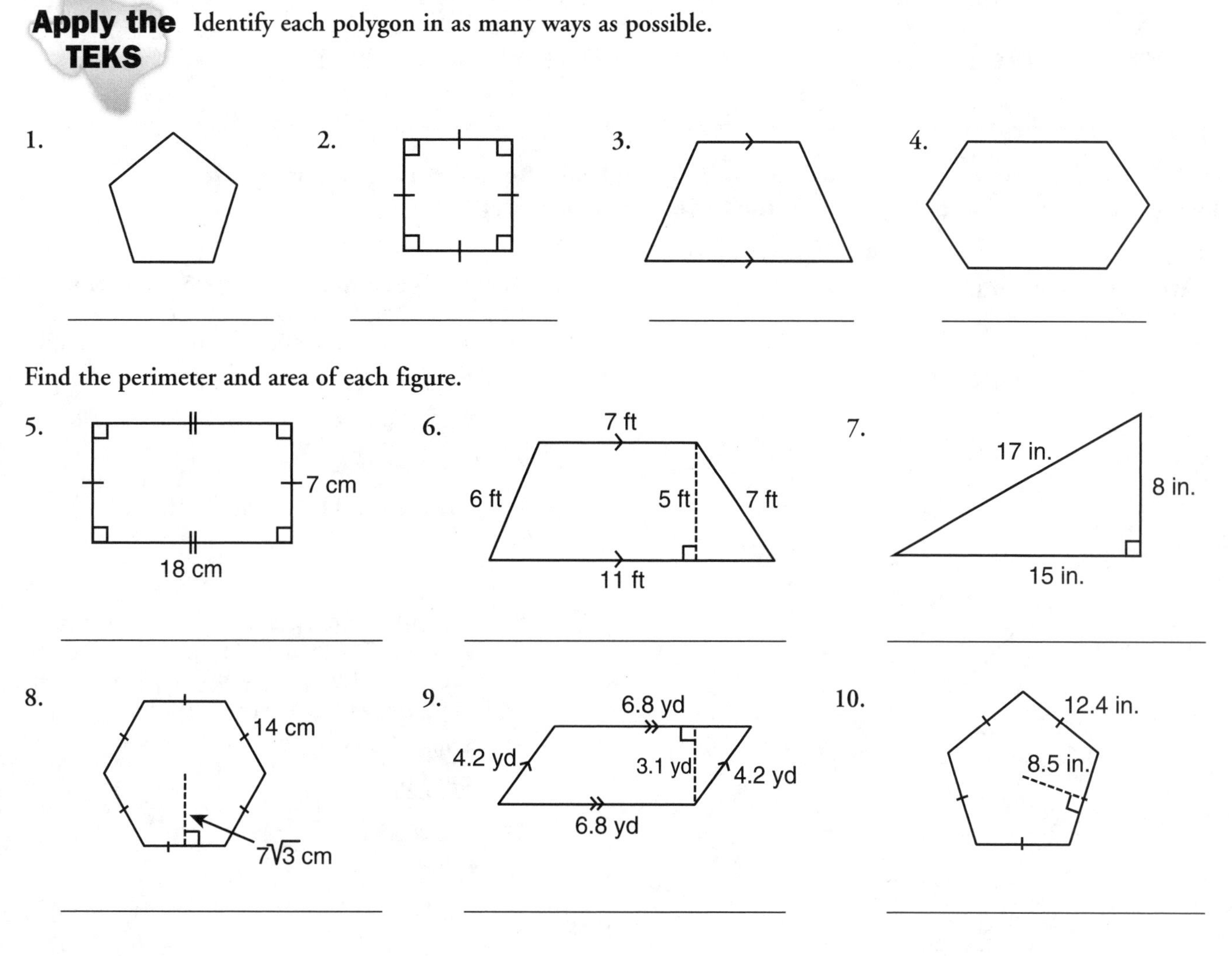

Solve each problem.

11. A rectangle has an area of 48 cm^2. What are the dimensions of the rectangle if its perimeter is 28 cm? ______

12. If all the dimensions of the triangle in Exercise 7 are halved, how does that affect the perimeter and area of the triangle?

______

13. A rectangle is 15 ft by 6 ft. If the dimensions are doubled, how does this affect the perimeter and area of the rectangle?

______

Find the perimeter and area of each composite figure.

TAKS Practice

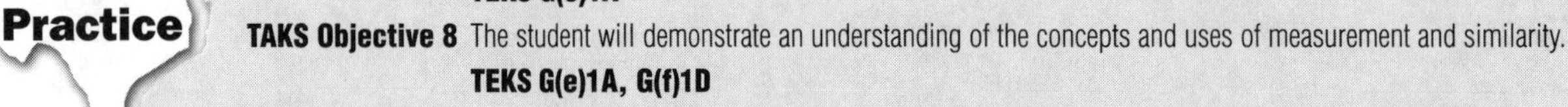

TAKS Objective 6 The student will demonstrate an understanding of geometric relationships and spatial reasoning.
TEKS G(c)1A

TAKS Objective 8 The student will demonstrate an understanding of the concepts and uses of measurement and similarity.
TEKS G(e)1A, G(f)1D

DIRECTIONS Read each question. Then circle the letter for the correct answer. If a correct answer is not here, circle the letter for "Not Here."

1 Which of the following triangles does NOT have an area of 18 cm^2?

A

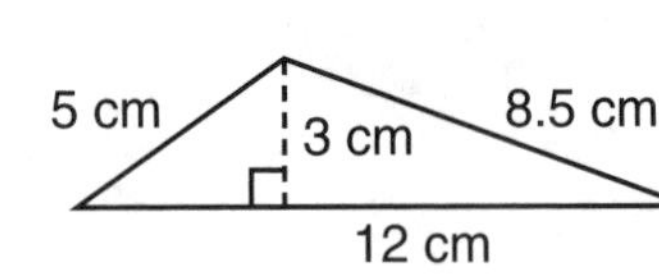

B

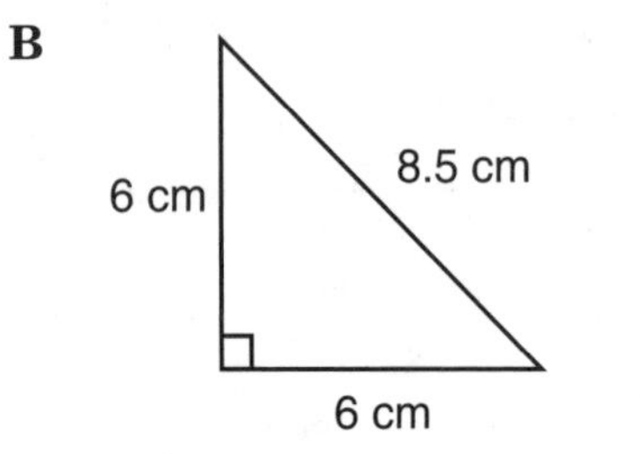

C

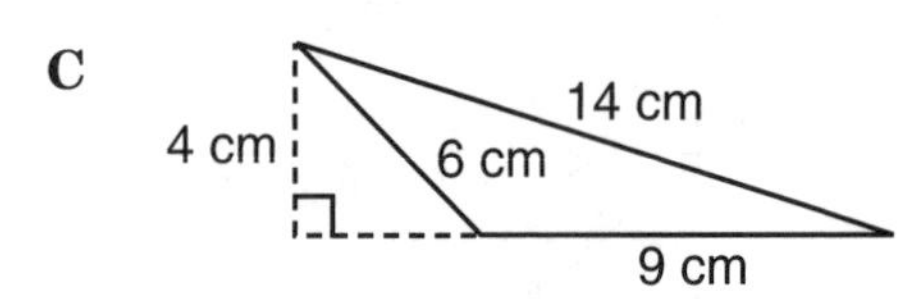

D Not Here

2 The base of a rectangle is 6 cm longer than its height. The area of the rectangle is 91 cm^2. What is the perimeter of the rectangle?

F 13 cm

G 20 cm

H 38.2 cm

J 40 cm

3 The base of parallelogram is 25 ft and the height is 17 ft. What is the effect on the area of the parallelogram if the dimensions are tripled?

A The area remains the same.

B The area is 3 times greater.

C The area is 6 times greater.

D The area is 9 times greater.

4 The Parkers are putting new carpet in their family room. The room is 21 feet by 27 feet. If carpet costs $11.25 per square yard, how much will the Parkers pay for the carpet?

F $708.75

G $740.25

H $2,126.25

J $6,378.75

5 What is the total area of the 5-foot walkway surrounding the swimming pool?

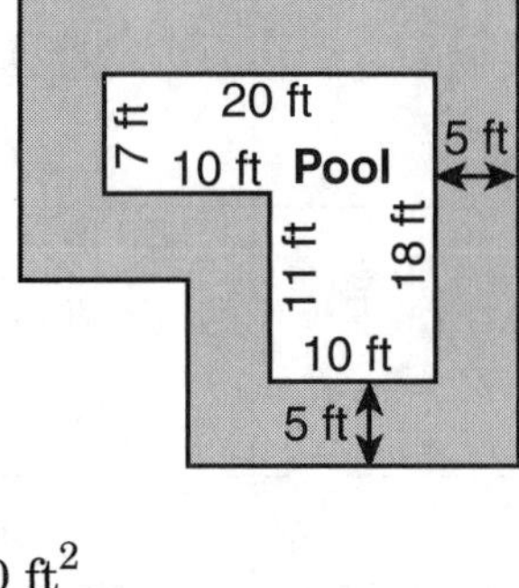

A 250 ft^2

B 350 ft^2

C 480 ft^2

D 530 ft^2

Focus on TEKS

Lesson 45 Circles, Sectors, and Arc Lengths

TEKS G(b)2B Make and verify conjectures about angles, lines, polygons, circles, and three-dimensional figures, choosing from a variety of approaches such as coordinate, transformational, or axiomatic.

TEKS G(e)1B Find area of sectors and arc lengths of circles using proportional reasoning.

Some properties and attributes of circles are applied in conjunction with the circumference ($C = \pi d$ or $C = 2\pi r$) and area ($A = \pi r^2$) formulas of circles to solve problems.

An **arc** of a circle is a section of the circumference between two distinct points on the circle. **Arc length** is part of, or a fraction of, the circumference. The length of the arc is the product of the fraction of the circumference the arc represents and the circumference of the circle.

$$\text{Length of } \widehat{AB} = \frac{m\widehat{AB}}{360} \cdot 2\pi r$$

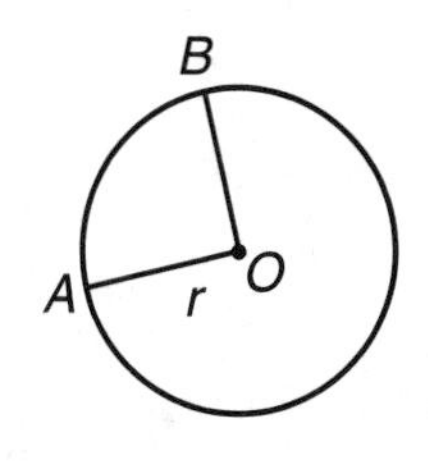

A **sector** of a circle is a region bounded by two radii of the circle and their intercepted arc. The area of a sector is the product of the fraction of the circumference the arc represents and the area of the circle.

$$\text{Area of sector } AOB = \frac{m\widehat{AB}}{360} \cdot \pi r^2$$

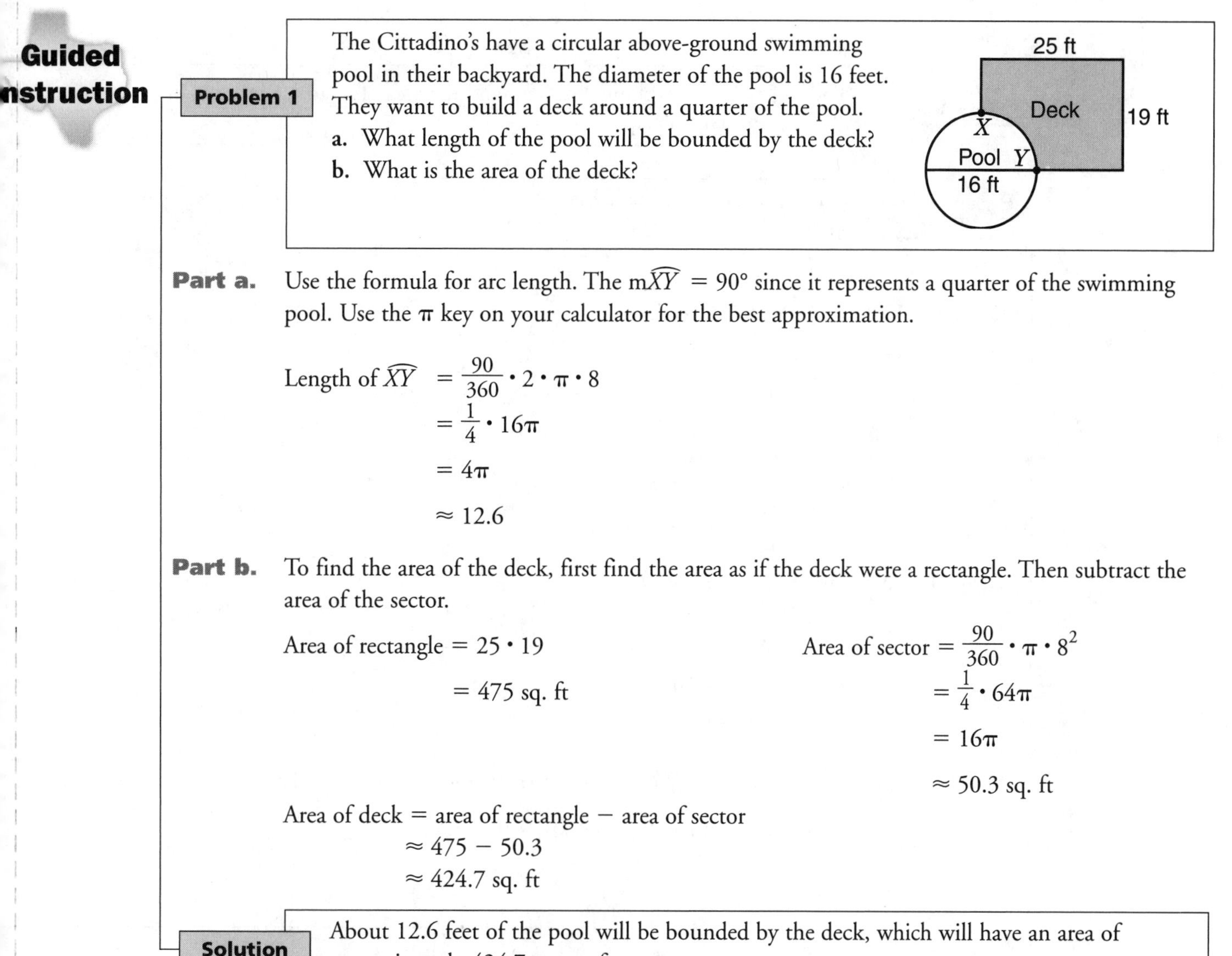

Guided Instruction

Problem 1

The Cittadino's have a circular above-ground swimming pool in their backyard. The diameter of the pool is 16 feet. They want to build a deck around a quarter of the pool.

a. What length of the pool will be bounded by the deck?

b. What is the area of the deck?

Part a. Use the formula for arc length. The $m\widehat{XY} = 90°$ since it represents a quarter of the swimming pool. Use the π key on your calculator for the best approximation.

$$\begin{aligned}\text{Length of } \widehat{XY} &= \frac{90}{360} \cdot 2 \cdot \pi \cdot 8 \\ &= \frac{1}{4} \cdot 16\pi \\ &= 4\pi \\ &\approx 12.6\end{aligned}$$

Part b. To find the area of the deck, first find the area as if the deck were a rectangle. Then subtract the area of the sector.

$$\begin{aligned}\text{Area of rectangle} &= 25 \cdot 19 \\ &= 475 \text{ sq. ft}\end{aligned}$$

$$\begin{aligned}\text{Area of sector} &= \frac{90}{360} \cdot \pi \cdot 8^2 \\ &= \frac{1}{4} \cdot 64\pi \\ &= 16\pi \\ &\approx 50.3 \text{ sq. ft}\end{aligned}$$

$$\begin{aligned}\text{Area of deck} &= \text{area of rectangle} - \text{area of sector} \\ &\approx 475 - 50.3 \\ &\approx 424.7 \text{ sq. ft}\end{aligned}$$

Solution About 12.6 feet of the pool will be bounded by the deck, which will have an area of approximately 424.7 square feet.

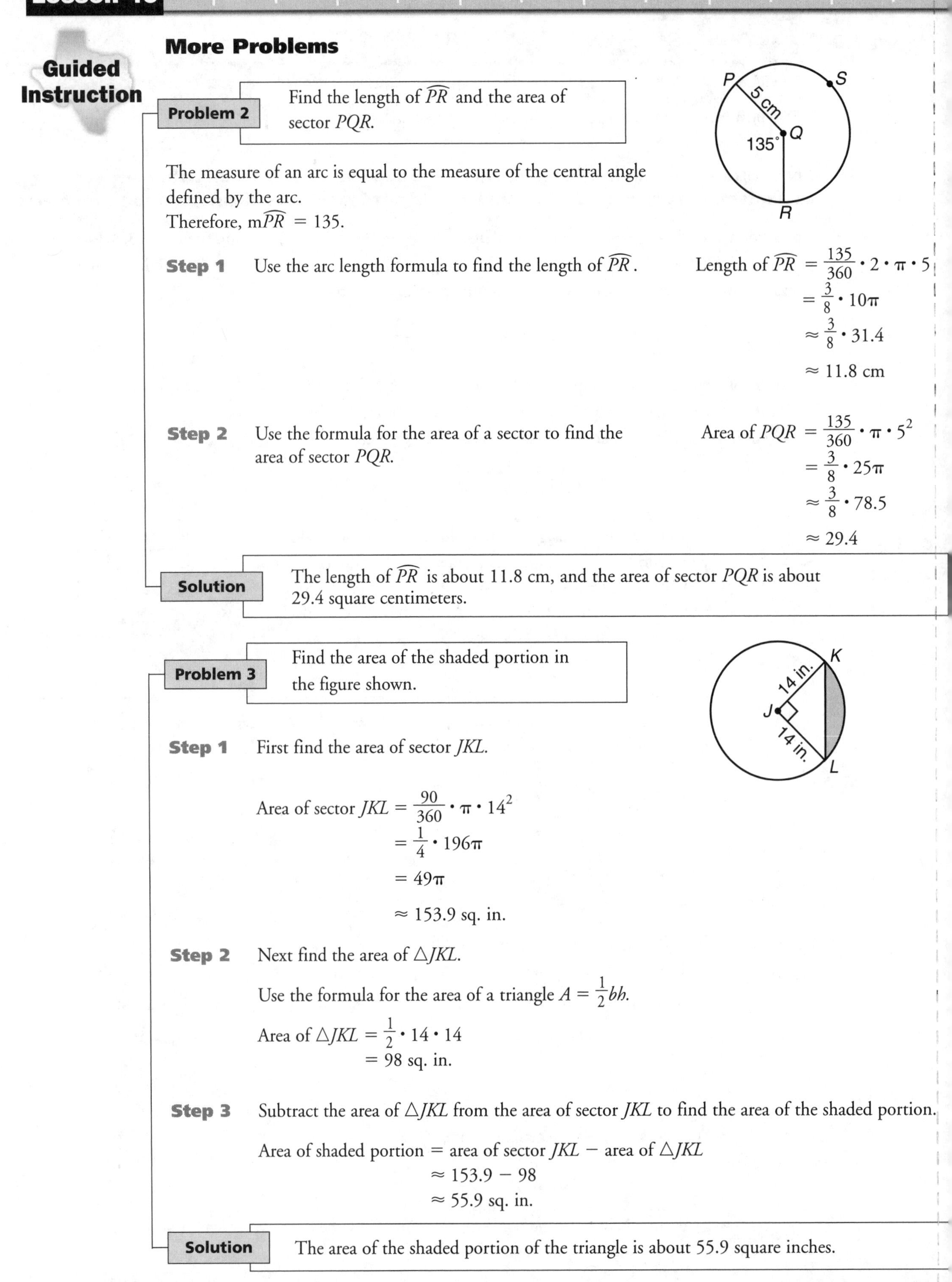

Guided Instruction

More Problems

Problem 2 Find the length of $\widehat{PR}$ and the area of sector PQR.

The measure of an arc is equal to the measure of the central angle defined by the arc.
Therefore, $m\widehat{PR} = 135$.

Step 1 Use the arc length formula to find the length of $\widehat{PR}$.

$$\begin{aligned}\text{Length of } \widehat{PR} &= \frac{135}{360} \cdot 2 \cdot \pi \cdot 5\\ &= \frac{3}{8} \cdot 10\pi\\ &\approx \frac{3}{8} \cdot 31.4\\ &\approx 11.8 \text{ cm}\end{aligned}$$

Step 2 Use the formula for the area of a sector to find the area of sector PQR.

$$\begin{aligned}\text{Area of } PQR &= \frac{135}{360} \cdot \pi \cdot 5^2\\ &= \frac{3}{8} \cdot 25\pi\\ &\approx \frac{3}{8} \cdot 78.5\\ &\approx 29.4\end{aligned}$$

Solution The length of $\widehat{PR}$ is about 11.8 cm, and the area of sector PQR is about 29.4 square centimeters.

Problem 3 Find the area of the shaded portion in the figure shown.

Step 1 First find the area of sector JKL.

$$\begin{aligned}\text{Area of sector } JKL &= \frac{90}{360} \cdot \pi \cdot 14^2\\ &= \frac{1}{4} \cdot 196\pi\\ &= 49\pi\\ &\approx 153.9 \text{ sq. in.}\end{aligned}$$

Step 2 Next find the area of $\triangle JKL$.

Use the formula for the area of a triangle $A = \frac{1}{2}bh$.

$$\begin{aligned}\text{Area of } \triangle JKL &= \frac{1}{2} \cdot 14 \cdot 14\\ &= 98 \text{ sq. in.}\end{aligned}$$

Step 3 Subtract the area of $\triangle JKL$ from the area of sector JKL to find the area of the shaded portion.

$$\begin{aligned}\text{Area of shaded portion} &= \text{area of sector } JKL - \text{area of } \triangle JKL\\ &\approx 153.9 - 98\\ &\approx 55.9 \text{ sq. in.}\end{aligned}$$

Solution The area of the shaded portion of the triangle is about 55.9 square inches.

Apply the TEKS Find the circumference and area of each circle. Round your answers to the nearest tenth.

1. radius = 9 ft

circumference: ______________

area: ______________

2. diameter = 21 cm

circumference: ______________

area: ______________

3. radius = $12\frac{1}{2}$ in.

circumference: ______________

area: ______________

Find the length of $\overset{\frown}{XY}$ in each circle. Round your answers to the nearest tenth.

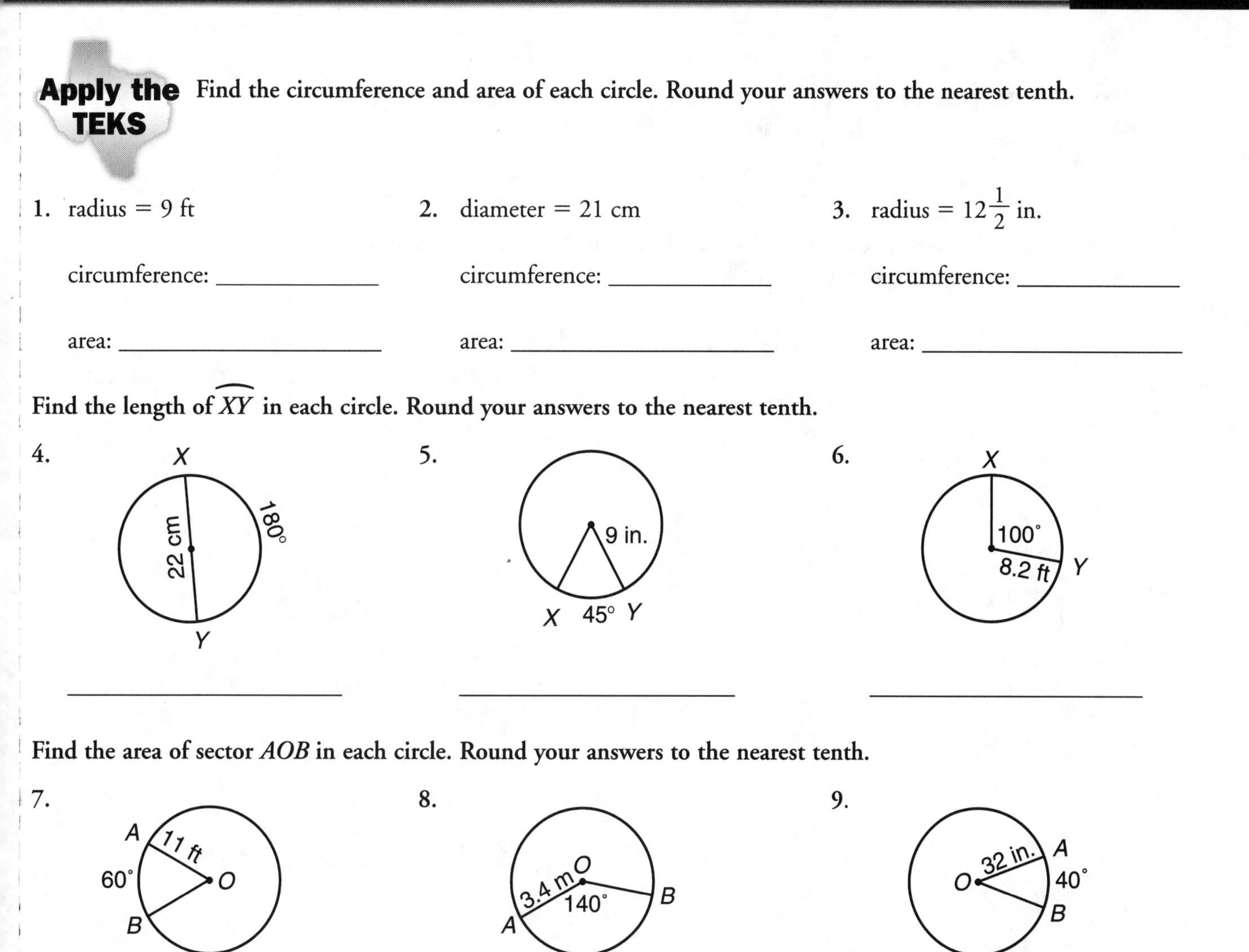

______________ ______________ ______________

Find the area of sector *AOB* in each circle. Round your answers to the nearest tenth.

7.

A 11 ft 60° O B

8.

3.4 m O 140° A B

9.

O 32 in. A 40° B

______________ ______________ ______________

Find the area of the shaded portion in each circle. Round your answers to the nearest tenth.

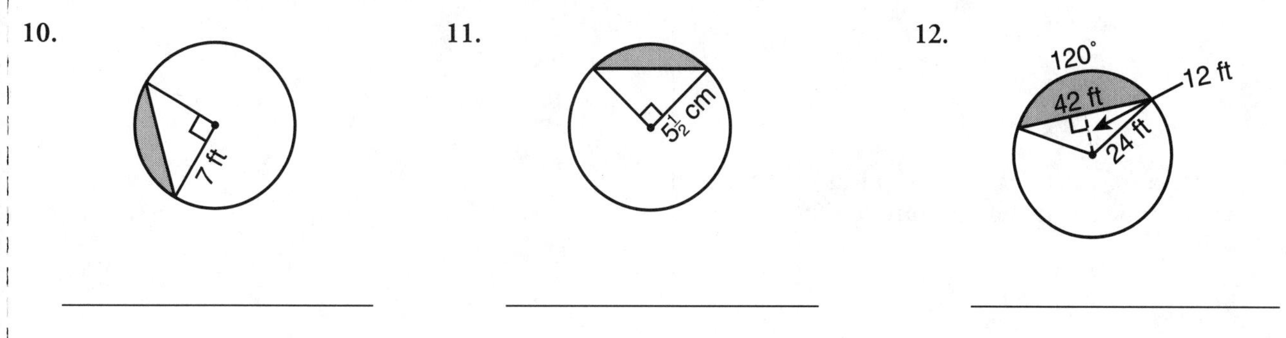

______________ ______________ ______________

13. The radius of a dartboard is 10 inches. The dartboard is divided into 20 equal sectors. What is the area of one sector of the dartboard to the nearest tenth? ______________

TAKS Objective 8 The student will demonstrate an understanding of the concepts and uses of measurement and similarity.
TEKS G(e)1B

DIRECTIONS Read each question. Then circle the letter for the correct answer. If a correct answer is not here, circle the letter for "Not Here."

1 Which shaded portion has the greatest area?

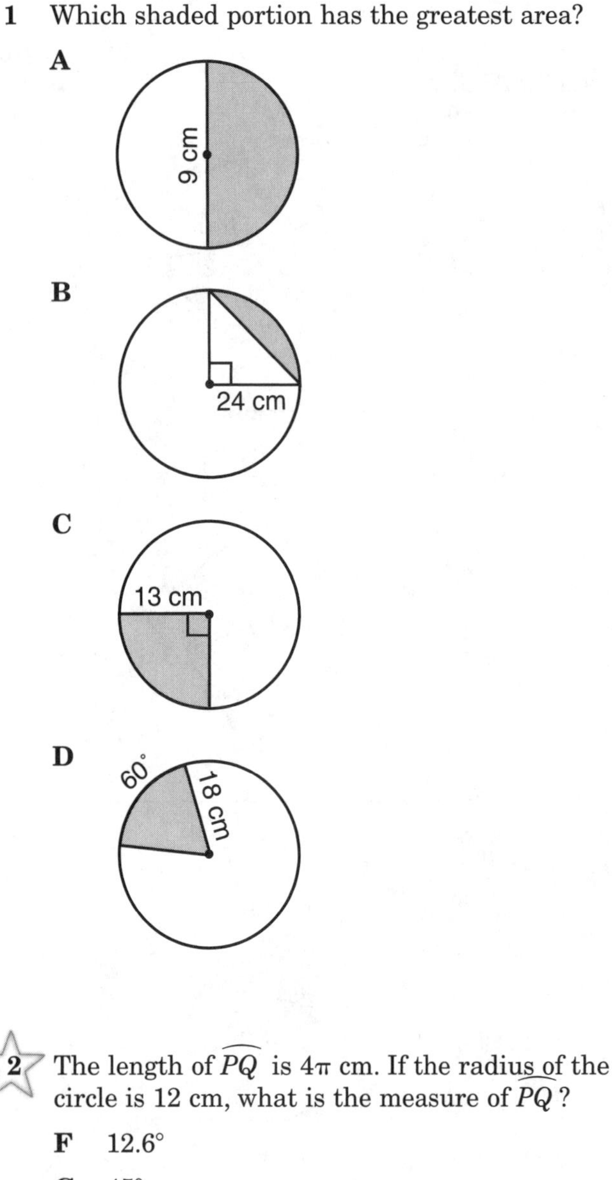

2 The length of $\overset{\frown}{PQ}$ is 4π cm. If the radius of the circle is 12 cm, what is the measure of $\overset{\frown}{PQ}$?

F 12.6°

G 45°

H 60°

J 90°

3 A windshield wiper is 20.5 inches long and rotates 85°. The shaded portion of the figure represents the area cleared by the windshield wiper.

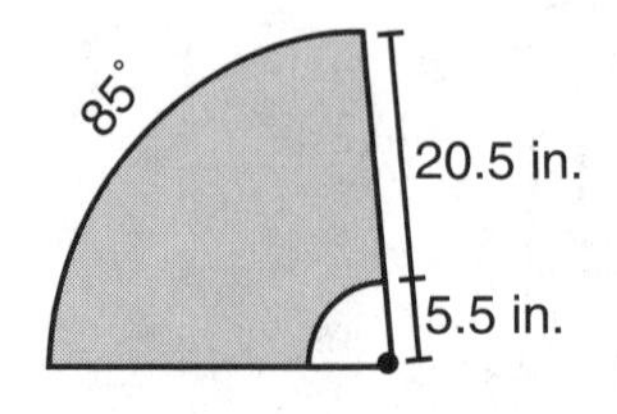

What is the area that the windshield wiper clears to the nearest tenth?

A 501.4 in.^{2}

B 479.0 in.^{2}

C 289.3 in.^{2}

D 22.4 in.^{2}

4 A large pizza from Papa's Pizzeria has a diameter of 18 inches. If each large pizza is cut into 10 equal slices, what is the approximate area of 3 slices of pizza?

F 21 in.^{2}

G 25 in.^{2}

H 76 in.^{2}

J Not Here

Focus on TEKS

Lesson 46 Tangents, Secants, and Chords

TEKS G(b)2B Make and verify conjectures about angles, lines, polygons, circles, and three-dimensional figures, choosing from a variety of approaches such as coordinate, transformational, or axiomatic.
TEKS G(c)1A Use numeric and geometric patterns to make generalizations about geometric properties, including angle relationships in circles.
TEKS G(e)2C Based on explorations and using concrete models, formulate and test conjectures about the properties and attributes of circles and the lines that intersect them.

When lines and circles intersect, the angles formed have interesting properties.

A **tangent** is a line that intersects a circle at exactly one point. This point is called the **point of tangency**. The radius that contains the point of tangency is perpendicular to the tangent line.

A **secant** is a line that intersects a circle at two points.

A **chord** is a segment with endpoints on a circle. In Problem 1, $\overline{BC}$ and $\overline{DE}$ are chords of circle A.

Guided Instruction

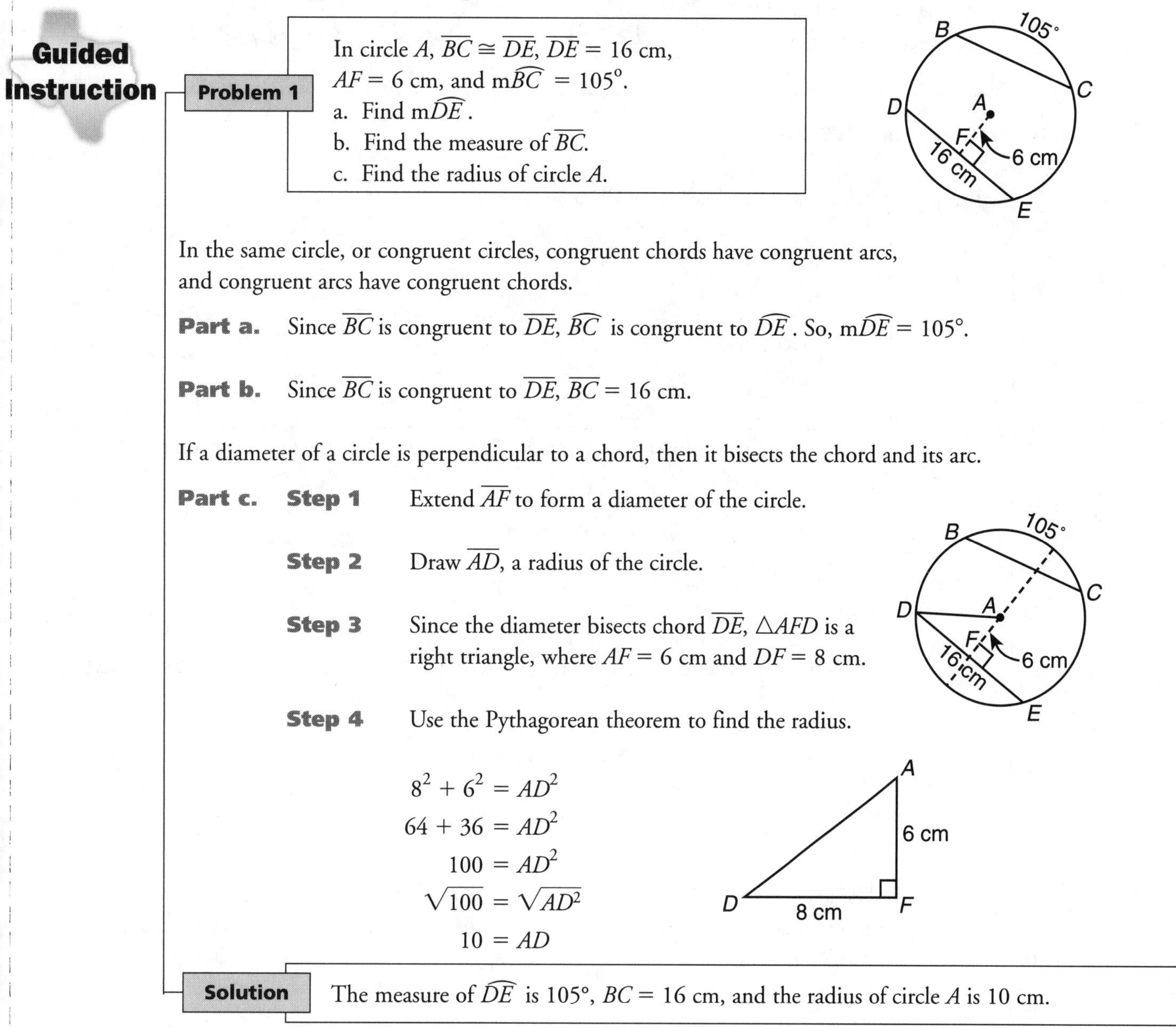

Problem 1

In circle A, $\overline{BC} \cong \overline{DE}$, $DE = 16$ cm, $AF = 6$ cm, and $m\widehat{BC} = 105°$.

a. Find $m\widehat{DE}$.

b. Find the measure of $\overline{BC}$.

c. Find the radius of circle A.

In the same circle, or congruent circles, congruent chords have congruent arcs, and congruent arcs have congruent chords.

Part a. Since $\overline{BC}$ is congruent to $\overline{DE}$, $\widehat{BC}$ is congruent to $\widehat{DE}$. So, $m\widehat{DE} = 105°$.

Part b. Since $\overline{BC}$ is congruent to $\overline{DE}$, $BC = 16$ cm.

If a diameter of a circle is perpendicular to a chord, then it bisects the chord and its arc.

Part c. **Step 1** Extend $\overline{AF}$ to form a diameter of the circle.

Step 2 Draw $\overline{AD}$, a radius of the circle.

Step 3 Since the diameter bisects chord $\overline{DE}$, $\triangle AFD$ is a right triangle, where $AF = 6$ cm and $DF = 8$ cm.

Step 4 Use the Pythagorean theorem to find the radius.

$$8^2 + 6^2 = AD^2$$
$$64 + 36 = AD^2$$
$$100 = AD^2$$
$$\sqrt{100} = \sqrt{AD^2}$$
$$10 = AD$$

Solution The measure of $\widehat{DE}$ is 105°, $BC = 16$ cm, and the radius of circle A is 10 cm.

Guided Instruction

Tangents, secants, and chords form many different angles.

Angle formed by:	Illustration	Formula
two chords with the vertex on the circle (called an inscribed angle), or a chord and a tangent		$m\angle 1 = \frac{1}{2}x$
intersection of two chords		$m\angle 1 = \frac{1}{2}(x + y)$
two secants, two tangents, or a secant and a tangent		$m\angle 1 = \frac{1}{2}(x - y)$

Another Problem

Problem 2 Find the value of the variable in each figure.

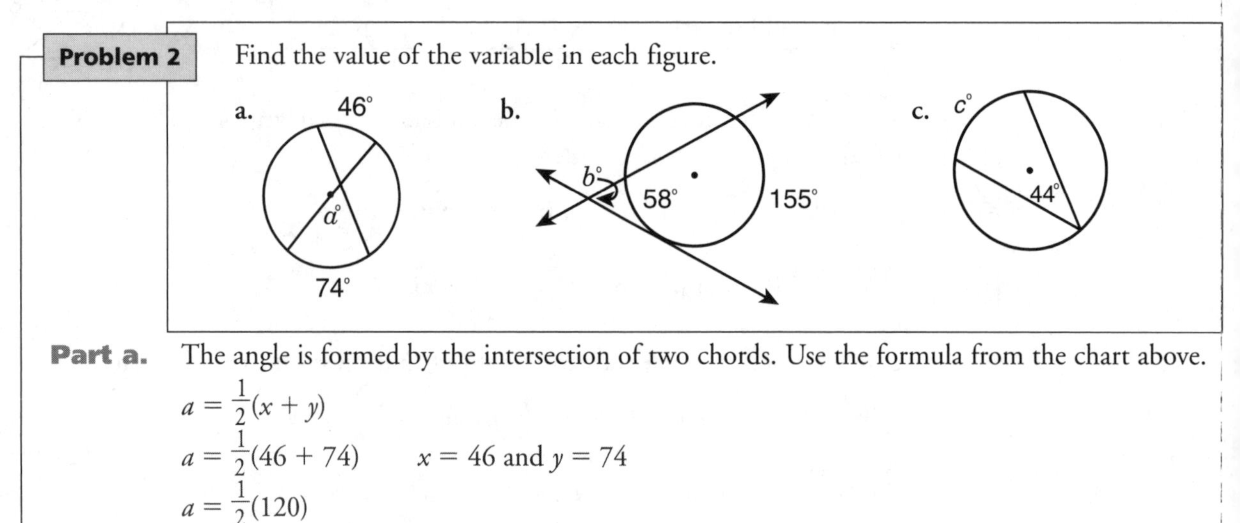

Part a. The angle is formed by the intersection of two chords. Use the formula from the chart above.

$a = \frac{1}{2}(x + y)$

$a = \frac{1}{2}(46 + 74)$ $\quad x = 46$ and $y = 74$

$a = \frac{1}{2}(120)$

$a = 60$

Part b. The angle is formed by a secant and a tangent. Use the formula from the chart above.

$b = \frac{1}{2}(x - y)$

$b = \frac{1}{2}(155 - 58)$ $\quad x = 155$ and $y = 58$

$b = \frac{1}{2}(97)$

$b = 48.5$

Part c. The angle is an inscribed angle formed by two chords whose vertex is on the circle. Notice in the chart above, the formula is for the inscribed angle. However, in this case, c is the measure of the intercepted arc.

$44 = \frac{1}{2}c$

$2(44) = (\frac{1}{2}c) \cdot 2$

$88 = c$

Solution In the figures above, $a = 60$, $b = 48.5$, and $c = 88$.

Apply the TEKS **Refer to circle A and the given information for Exercises 1–8.**

Given: $\overline{BG} \cong \overline{CE}$; $m\widehat{CDE} = 106°$; $CE = 22$

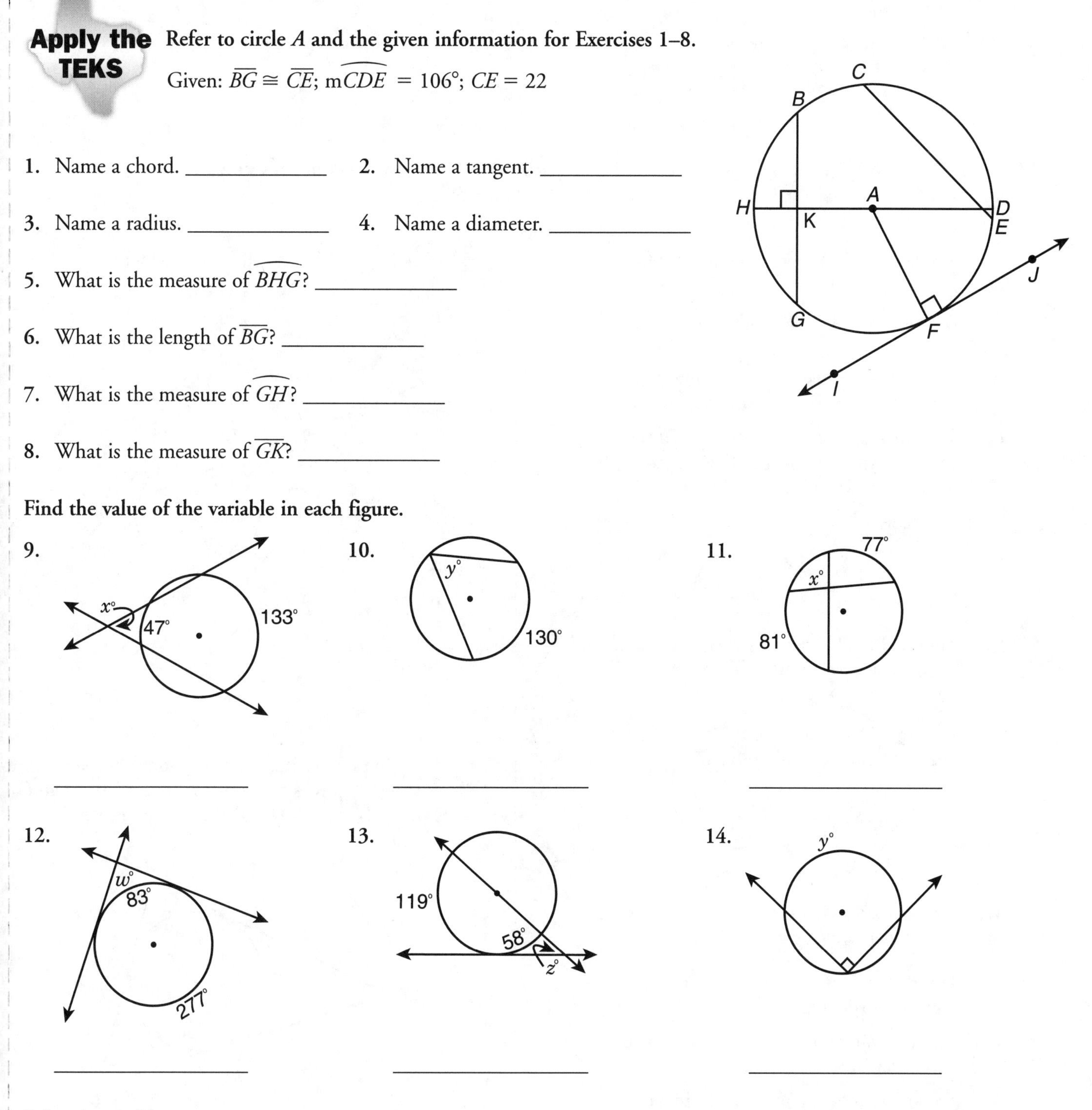

1. Name a chord. ____________
2. Name a tangent. ____________
3. Name a radius. ____________
4. Name a diameter. ____________
5. What is the measure of $\widehat{BHG}$? ____________
6. What is the length of $\overline{BG}$? ____________
7. What is the measure of $\widehat{GH}$? ____________
8. What is the measure of $\overline{GK}$? ____________

Find the value of the variable in each figure.

9. ____________

10. ____________

11. ____________

12. ____________

13. ____________

14. ____________

Solve the problem.

15. A circle is *circumscribed* about a polygon if all vertices of the polygon are on the circle. The polygon is said to be *inscribed* in the circle. $\triangle PQR$ is inscribed in circle N. Find the measures of each angle of $\triangle PQR$.

____

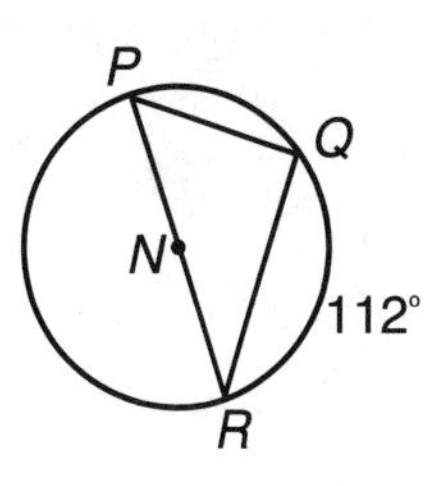

TAKS Objective 6 The student will demonstrate an understanding of geometric relationships and spatial reasoning.
TEKS G(b)2B, **G(c)1A**, G(e)2C

DIRECTIONS Read each question. Then circle the letter for the correct answer. If a correct answer is <u>not here</u>, circle the letter for "Not Here."

1 Which of the following statements is NOT true about a tangent?

A A tangent line intersects a circle at one point.

B A tangent line is perpendicular to a radius of the circle at the point of tangency.

C The measure of the angle formed by two tangent lines is half the difference of the measures of the intercepted arcs.

D Not Here

2 Quadrilateral *DEFG* is inscribed in circle *A* and quadrilateral *PQRS* is inscribed in circle *B*.

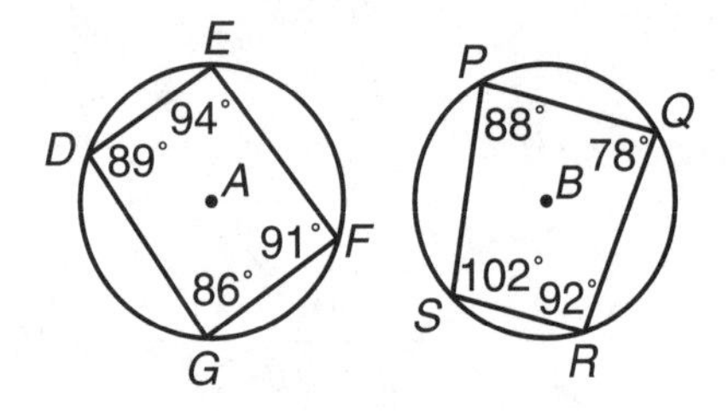

Which of the following conjectures can be made based on these two figures?

F Quadrilaterals that are inscribed in a circle are rectangles.

G The diagonals of a quadrilateral inscribed in a circle are congruent.

H Opposite angles of a quadrilateral inscribed in a circle are supplementary.

J The sum of the angle measures of a quadrilateral inscribed in a circle is less than 360°.

3 Which variable has the greatest value in circle *P*?

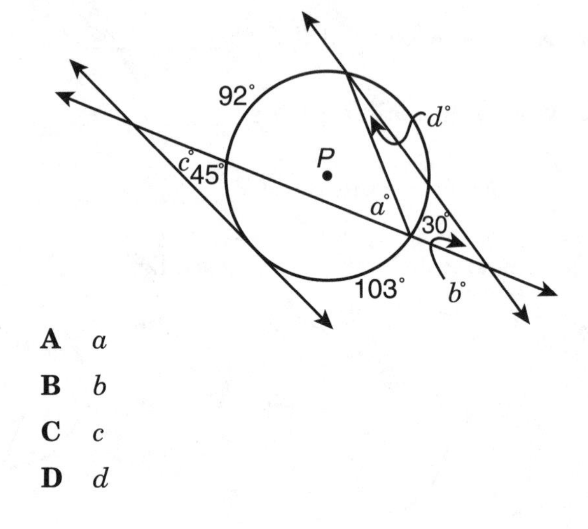

A a

B b

C c

D d

4 A circle is inscribed in a polygon when each side of the polygon is tangent to the circle. Circle F is inscribed in $\triangle ABC$. What is the measure of $\angle B$?

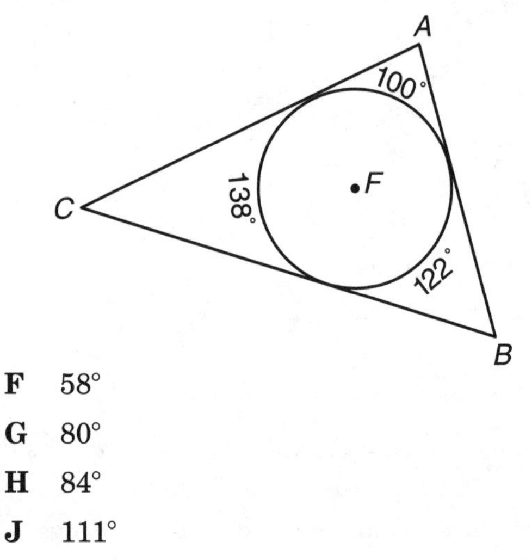

F 58°

G 80°

H 84°

J 111°

Focus on TEKS

Lesson 47 Volume and Surface Area of Prisms and Pyramids

TEKS G(e)1D Find surface area and volumes of prisms and pyramids in problem situations.

Volume and surface area of prisms and pyramids can be used to solve problems in many real-world situations.

Surface area is the sum of the areas of all the faces and bases of a three-dimensional object.

Volume is the number of cubic units needed to fill a three-dimensional object.

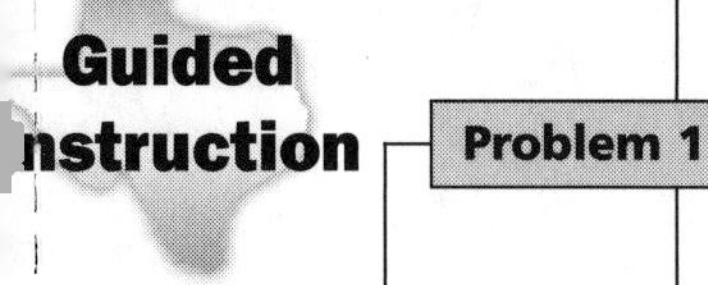

Guided Instruction

Problem 1

The marketing department of a food company must decide between two different packages for a new cracker. The package is a rectangular prism. Box A is 8.5 inches by 10 inches by 3.25 inches. Box B is 9 inches by 11.75 inches by 2.5 inches. To appeal to customers, they want the box with the largest surface area. To keep the price low, they also need the box with the smallest volume. Which box should they choose?

Box A: 10 in., 8.5 in., 3.25 in.

Box B: 11.75 in., 9 in., 2.5 in.

The formula for the surface area of a prism is SA = $ph + 2B$, where p is the perimeter of the base, h is the height of the prism, and B is the area of one base.

Step 1 Find the surface area of each box.

Box A

$SA = ph + 2B$
$SA = [2(8.5) + 2(3.25)]10 + 2(8.5 \cdot 3.25)$
$SA = (23.5)10 + 2(27.625)$
$SA = 235 + 55.25$
$SA = 290.25 \text{ in.}^2$

Box B

$SA = ph + 2B$
$SA = [2(9) + 2(2.5)]11.75 + 2(9 \cdot 2.5)$
$SA = (23)11.75 + 2(22.5)$
$SA = 270.25 + 45$
$SA = 315.25 \text{ in.}^2$

The formula for the volume of a prism is $V = Bh$, where B is the area of one base, and h is the height of the prism.

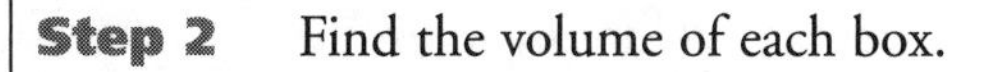

Step 2 Find the volume of each box.

Box A

$V = Bh$
$V = (8.5 \cdot 3.25)10$
$V = (27.625)10$
$V = 276.25 \text{ in.}^3$

Box B

$V = Bh$
$V = (9 \cdot 2.5)11.75$
$V = (22.5)11.75$
$V = 264.375 \text{ in.}^3$

Step 3 Compare the surface area and volume of the boxes. Box A has a surface area of 290.25 in.^2, and Box B has a surface area of 315.25 in.^2
Box A has a volume of 276.25 in.^3, and Box B has a volume of 264.375 in.^3

Solution

The marketing department should choose Box B since it has a larger surface area and a smaller volume.

Guided Instruction

More Problems

Problem 2

Melinda is an artist who creates objects out of clear plastic. She is making an hourglass with two identical regular square pyramids.

a. How much clear plastic does Melinda need for one hourglass?

b. How much sand will she need to completely fill one of the pyramids?

13 cm

12 cm

10 cm

The formula for the surface area of a pyramid is $SA = \frac{1}{2}pl + B$, where p is the perimeter of the base, l is the slant height of the pyramid, and B is the area of the base.

Part a. First find the surface area of one pyramid.

$SA = \frac{1}{2}pl + B$

$SA = \frac{1}{2}(4 \cdot 10)(13) + (10 \cdot 10)$

$SA = \frac{1}{2}(40)(13) + 100$

$SA = 260 + 100$

$SA = 360 \text{ cm}^2$

Double the surface area of one pyramid to find the surface area of both pyramids.
$SA = 2 \cdot 360 = 720 \text{ cm}^2$

The formula for the volume of a pyramid is $V = \frac{1}{3}Bh$, where B is the area of the base, and h is the height of the pyramid.

Part b. Find the volume of one pyramid.

$V = \frac{1}{3}Bh$

$V = \frac{1}{3}(10 \cdot 10)(12)$

$V = \frac{1}{3}(100)(12)$

$V = 400 \text{ cm}^3$

Solution Melinda will need 720 cm^2 of clear plastic for one hourglass, and she will need 400 cm^3 of sand to fill one pyramid.

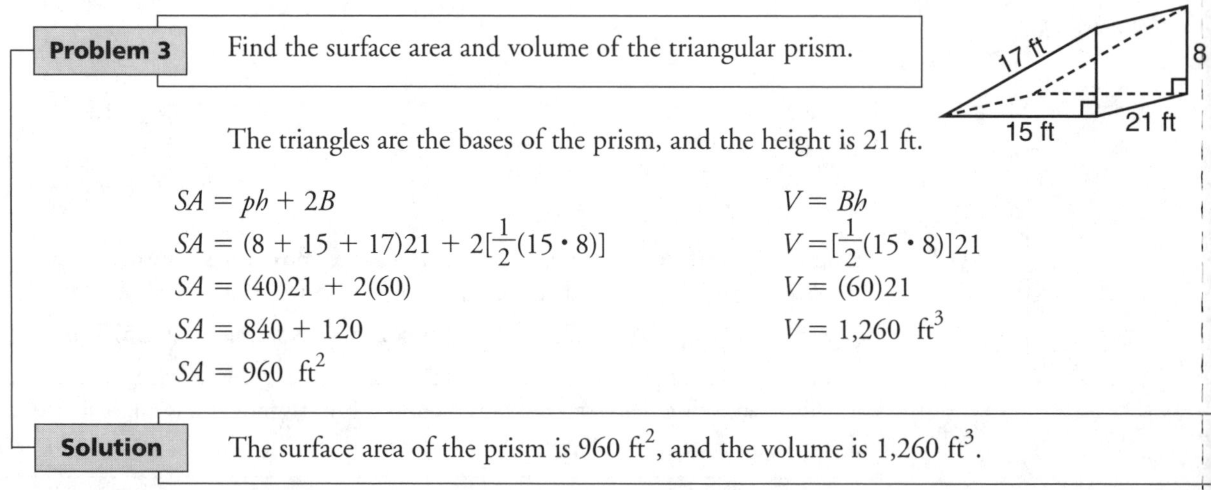

Problem 3 Find the surface area and volume of the triangular prism.

The triangles are the bases of the prism, and the height is 21 ft.

$SA = ph + 2B$

$SA = (8 + 15 + 17)21 + 2[\frac{1}{2}(15 \cdot 8)]$

$SA = (40)21 + 2(60)$

$SA = 840 + 120$

$SA = 960 \text{ ft}^2$

$V = Bh$

$V = [\frac{1}{2}(15 \cdot 8)]21$

$V = (60)21$

$V = 1{,}260 \text{ ft}^3$

Solution The surface area of the prism is 960 ft^2, and the volume is $1{,}260 \text{ ft}^3$.

Apply the TEKS **Find the surface area and volume of each figure. Assume all pyramids are regular.**

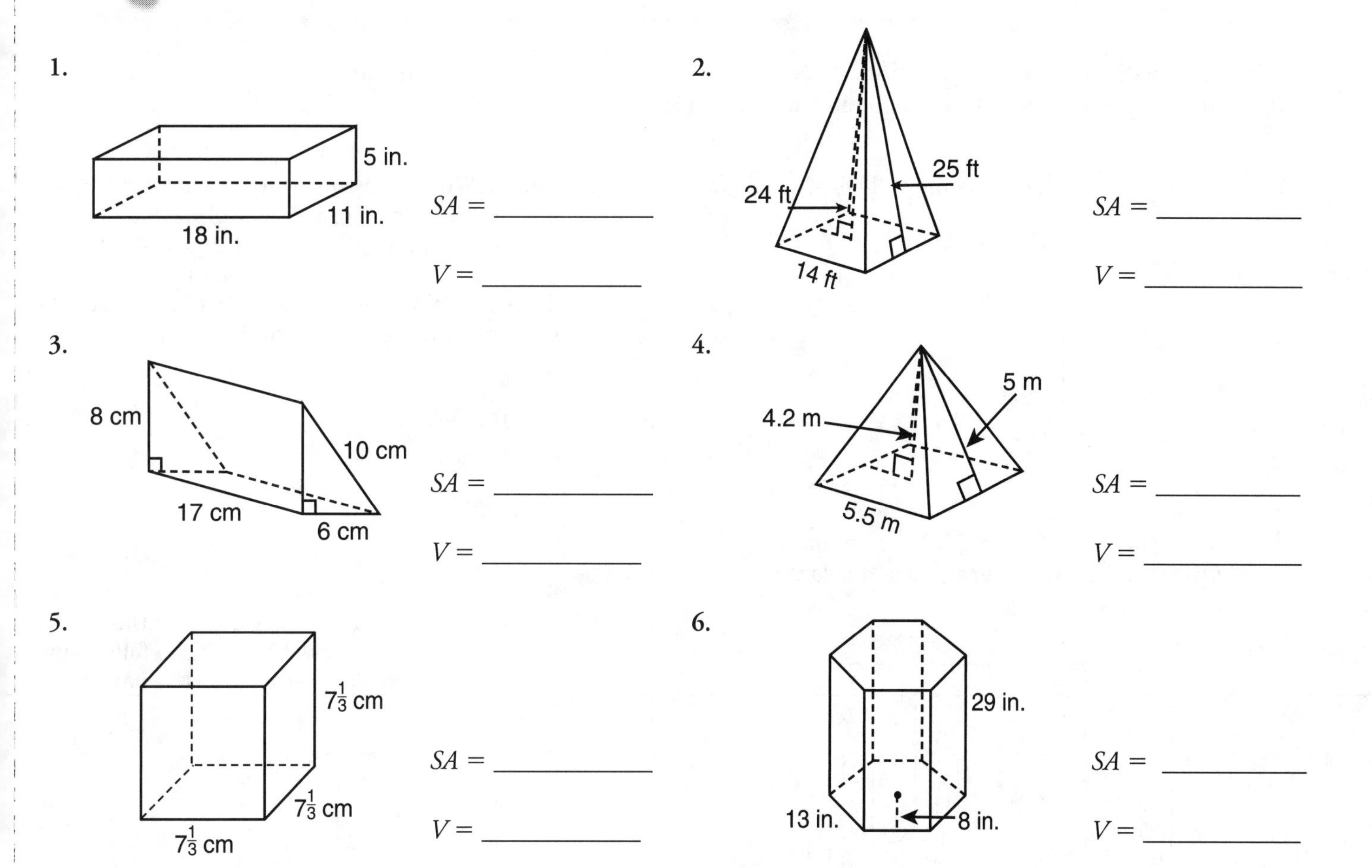

Solve each problem.

7. The Great Pyramid of Giza has a square base with each side about 756 feet long. The slant height of the pyramid is about 612 feet. What is the approximate surface area of the Great Pyramid of Giza? (Hint: Do not include the base.) ____________

8. Find the volume and surface area of each rectangular prism.

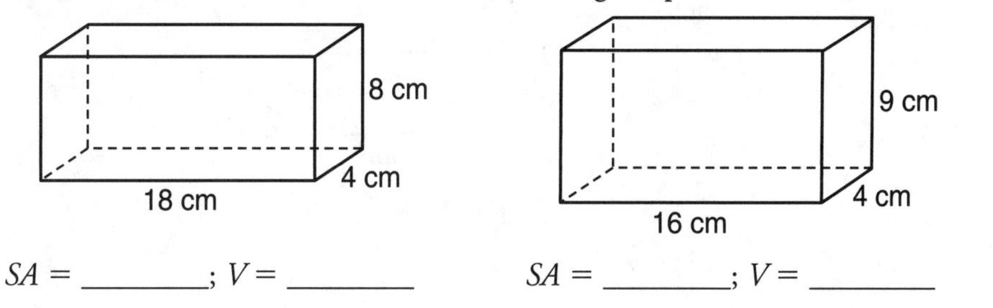

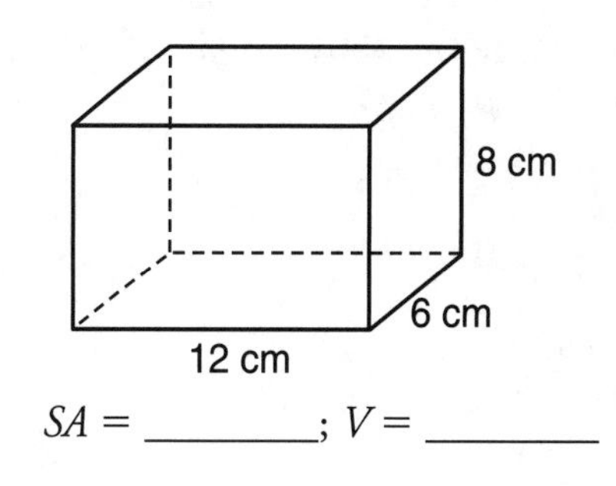

$SA =$ ________; $V =$ ________ $SA =$ ________; $V =$ ________ $SA =$ ________; $V =$ ________

9. What do you observe about your calculations in Exercise 8?

____

TAKS Objective 8 The student will demonstrate an understanding of the concepts and uses of measurement and similarity.
TEKS G(e)1D

DIRECTIONS Read each question. Then circle the letter for the correct answer. If a correct answer is not here, circle the letter for "Not Here."

1 What is the volume of the figure below?

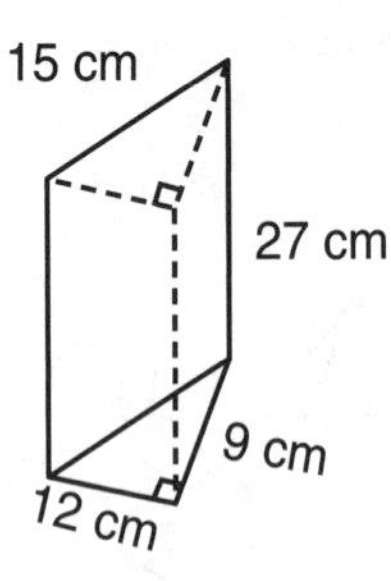

Record your answer and fill in the bubbles on the grid below. Be sure to use the correct place value.

				.			
0	0	0	0		0	0	0
1	1	1	1		1	1	1
2	2	2	2		2	2	2
3	3	3	3		3	3	3
4	4	4	4		4	4	4
5	5	5	5		5	5	5
6	6	6	6		6	6	6
7	7	7	7		7	7	7
8	8	8	8		8	8	8
9	9	9	9		9	9	9

2 The surface area of a regular square pyramid with a 13-inch base is 663 square inches. What is the slant height of the pyramid?

F 11.8 in.

G 17 in.

H 19 in.

J 32 in.

3 The McWilliams have a rectangular swimming pool in their backyard. The pool is 18 feet by 11 feet, with a depth of 4 feet in the shallow end, which gradually increases to 8 feet in the deep end. Which of the following is a reasonable amount of water needed to fill the pool?

A 800 ft^3

B 1,200 ft^3

C 1,500 ft^3

D 1,900 ft^3

4 Pedro has a piece of wrapping paper that is 36 inches by 48 inches. Which of the following boxes can Pedro NOT wrap with the paper he has?

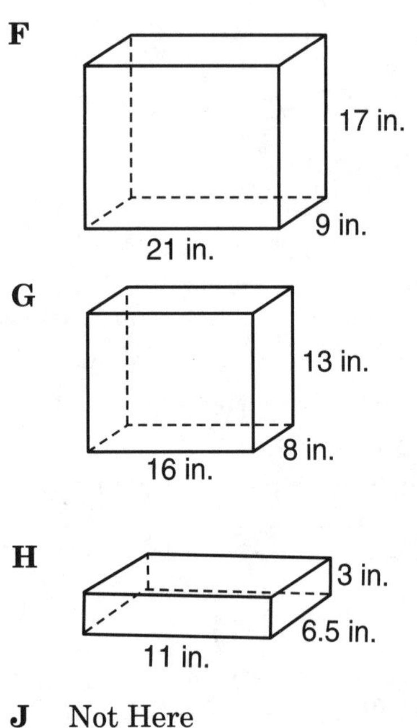

J Not Here

Focus on TEKS

Lesson 48 Volume and Surface Area of Spheres, Cones, and Cylinders

TEKS G(e)1D Find surface area and volume of spheres, cones, and cylinders in problem situations.

Volume and surface area of spheres, cones, and cylinders can be used to solve problems in many real-world situations.

Lateral area is the surface area of a cone, cylinder, prism or pyramid excluding the bases.

Guided Instruction

Problem 1

A mechanic uses a funnel to pour substances, such as oil, into compartments of a car's engine. What is the approximate surface area and volume of the funnel at the right?

Step 1 Consider two separate figures, a cone and a cylinder.

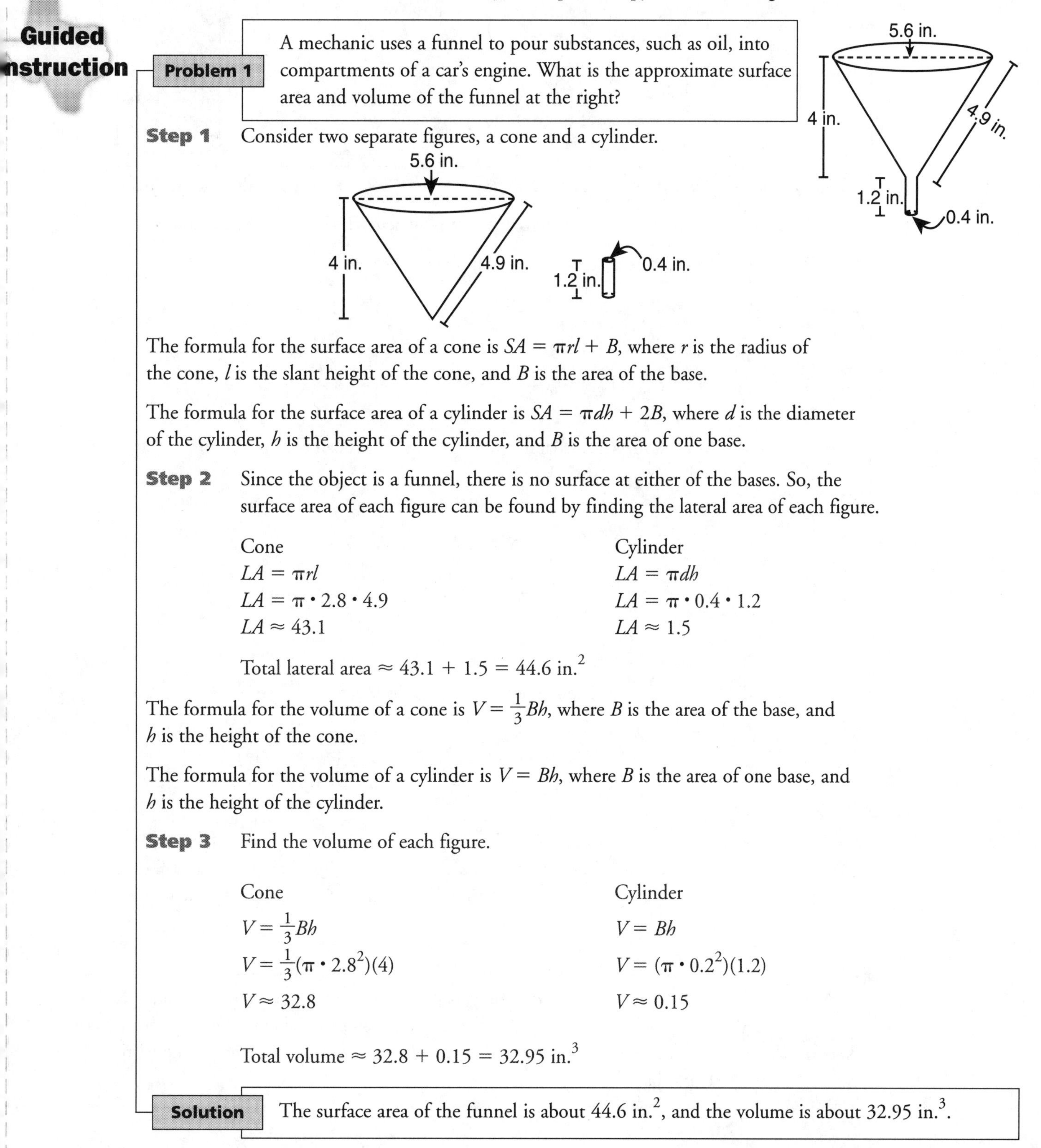

The formula for the surface area of a cone is $SA = \pi rl + B$, where r is the radius of the cone, l is the slant height of the cone, and B is the area of the base.

The formula for the surface area of a cylinder is $SA = \pi dh + 2B$, where d is the diameter of the cylinder, h is the height of the cylinder, and B is the area of one base.

Step 2 Since the object is a funnel, there is no surface at either of the bases. So, the surface area of each figure can be found by finding the lateral area of each figure.

Cone	Cylinder
$LA = \pi rl$	$LA = \pi dh$
$LA = \pi \cdot 2.8 \cdot 4.9$	$LA = \pi \cdot 0.4 \cdot 1.2$
$LA \approx 43.1$	$LA \approx 1.5$

Total lateral area $\approx 43.1 + 1.5 = 44.6$ in.^{2}

The formula for the volume of a cone is $V = \frac{1}{3}Bh$, where B is the area of the base, and h is the height of the cone.

The formula for the volume of a cylinder is $V = Bh$, where B is the area of one base, and h is the height of the cylinder.

Step 3 Find the volume of each figure.

Cone	Cylinder
$V = \frac{1}{3}Bh$	$V = Bh$
$V = \frac{1}{3}(\pi \cdot 2.8^2)(4)$	$V = (\pi \cdot 0.2^2)(1.2)$
$V \approx 32.8$	$V \approx 0.15$

Total volume $\approx 32.8 + 0.15 = 32.95$ in.^{3}

Solution The surface area of the funnel is about 44.6 in.^{2}, and the volume is about 32.95 in.^{3}.

Guided Instruction

Another Problem

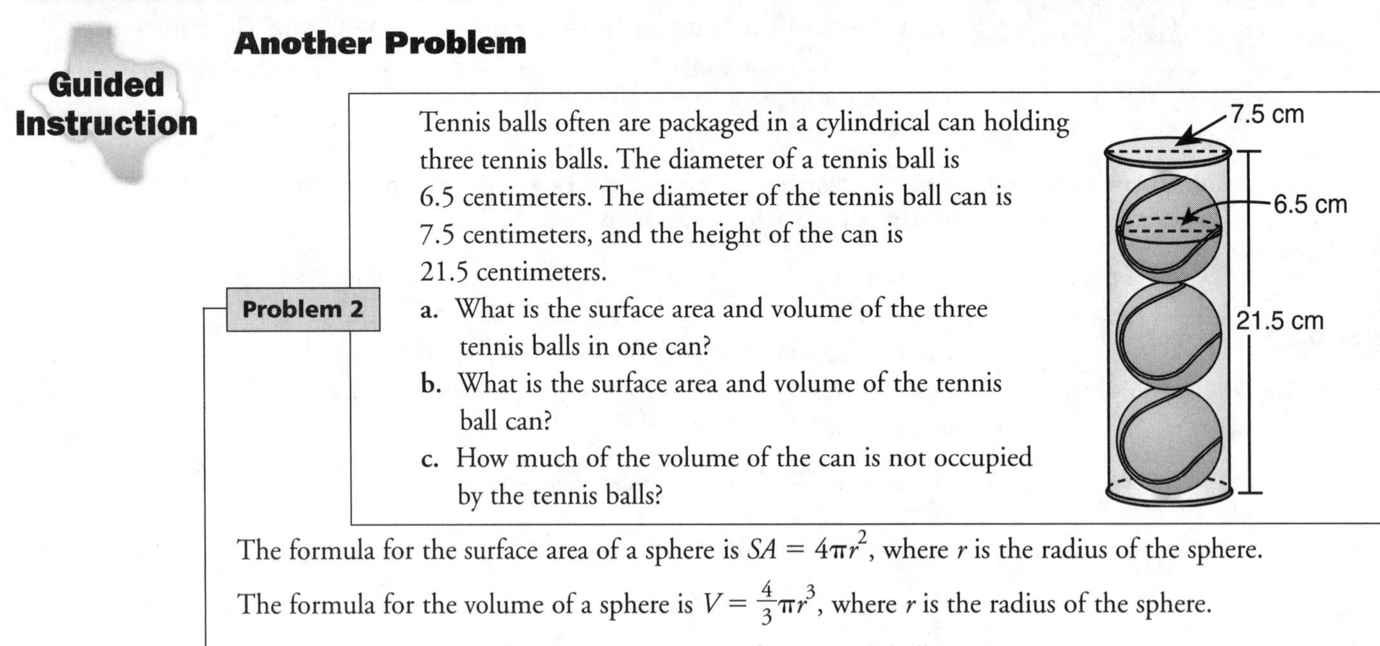

Problem 2

Tennis balls often are packaged in a cylindrical can holding three tennis balls. The diameter of a tennis ball is 6.5 centimeters. The diameter of the tennis ball can is 7.5 centimeters, and the height of the can is 21.5 centimeters.

a. What is the surface area and volume of the three tennis balls in one can?

b. What is the surface area and volume of the tennis ball can?

c. How much of the volume of the can is not occupied by the tennis balls?

The formula for the surface area of a sphere is $SA = 4\pi r^2$, where r is the radius of the sphere.

The formula for the volume of a sphere is $V = \frac{4}{3}\pi r^3$, where r is the radius of the sphere.

Part a. Find the surface area and volume of one tennis ball.

$SA = 4\pi r^2$

$SA = 4 \cdot \pi \cdot 3.25^2$

$SA \approx 132.7 \text{ cm}^2$

$V = \frac{4}{3}\pi r^3$

$V = \frac{4}{3} \cdot \pi \cdot 3.25^3$

$V \approx 143.8 \text{ cm}^3$

Multiply the surface area and volume of one tennis ball by 3 to find the surface area and volume of three balls.

Total surface area $\approx 3 \cdot 132.7$
$\approx 398.1 \text{ cm}^2$

Total volume $\approx 3 \cdot 143.8$
$\approx 431.4 \text{ cm}^3$

Part b. Find the surface area and volume of the tennis ball can.

$SA = \pi dh + 2B$

$SA = (\pi \cdot 7.5 \cdot 21.5) + 2(\pi \cdot 3.75^2)$

$SA \approx 506.6 + 88.4$

$SA \approx 595 \text{ cm}^2$

$V = Bh$

$V = (\pi \cdot 3.75^2)21.5$

$V \approx 949.8 \text{ cm}^3$

Part c. Subtract the volume of three tennis balls from the volume of the tennis ball can to determine how much of the volume of the can is not occupied by the tennis balls.

$949.8 - 431.4 \approx 518.4 \text{ cm}^3$

Solution

The surface area of three tennis balls is about 398.1 cm^2, and the volume is about 431.4 cm^3. The surface area of the tennis ball can is about 595 cm^2, and the volume is about 949.8 cm^3. About 518.4 cm^3 of a tennis ball can are not occupied by the three tennis balls.

Apply the TEKS Find the surface area and volume of each figure. Round your answers to the nearest tenth.

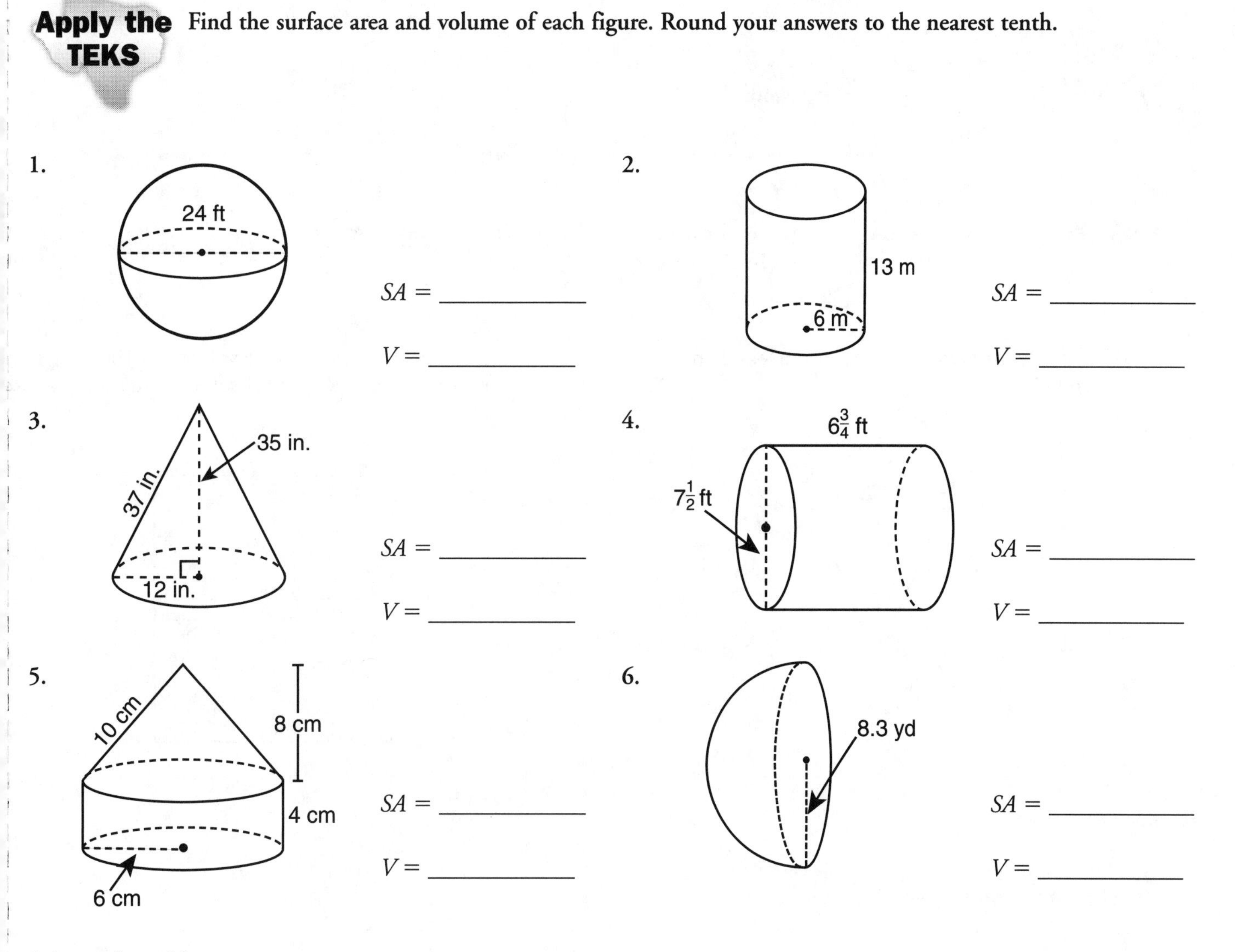

Solve each problem.

7. The diameter of a volleyball is 21.9 centimeters. What is the surface area and volume of a volleyball to the nearest tenth?

____

8. A can of soup has a diameter of a $2\frac{5}{8}$ inches and a height of $3\frac{7}{8}$ inches. What is the surface area and volume of the soup can to the nearest tenth?

____

9. How are the formulas for the volume of a cylinder and a cone similar?

____

10. If the volume of a cylinder is 219 ft^3, what would be the volume of a cone with the same base and height as the cylinder?

____

TAKS Objective 8 The student will demonstrate an understanding of the concepts and uses of measurement and similarity.
TEKS G(e)1D

DIRECTIONS Read each question. Then circle the letter for the correct answer. If a correct answer is not here, circle the letter for "Not Here."

1 What is the approximate surface area of the figure below?

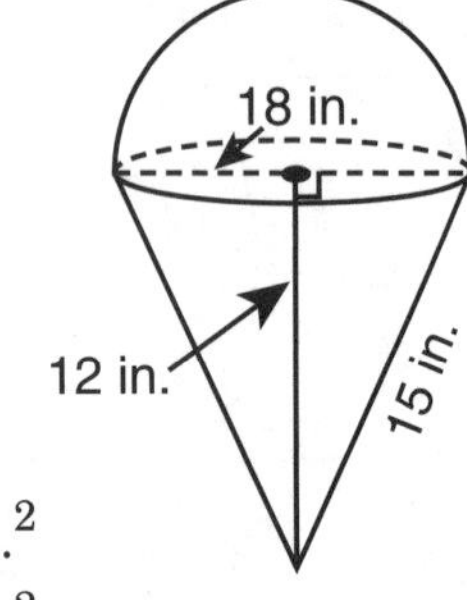

A 2,545 in.^{2}

B 1,188 in.^{2}

C 933 in.^{2}

D 848 in.^{2}

2 The volume of a sphere is $85\frac{1}{3}\pi$ centimeters^3. What is the diameter of the sphere?

F 4 cm

G 8 cm

H 9.2 cm

J 16 cm

3 A company is designing a label for a new product, which will be packaged in a cylindrical can. Which of the following dimensions of the can will have the greatest lateral area for the label?

A Diameter = 3.5 in., height = 4 in.

B Diameter = 2.75 in., height = 4.8 in.

C Diameter = 3 in., height = 4.25 in.

D Diameter = 2.6 in., height = 5 in.

4 What is the approximate volume of the figure created when $\triangle ABC$ is rotated about the y-axis?

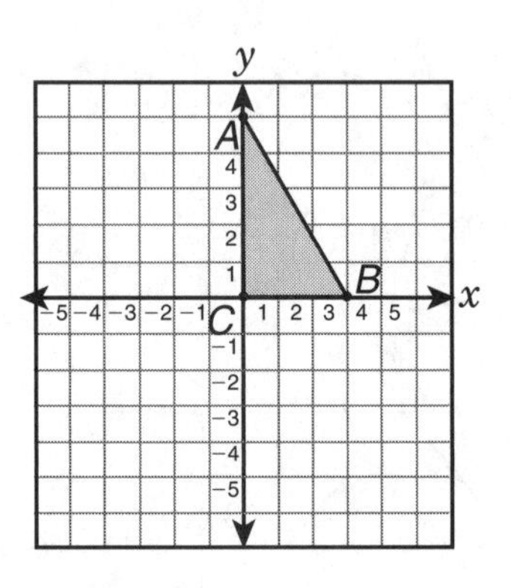

F 55.0 units^3

G 75.4 units^3

H 78.5 units^3

J Not Here

5 A steel bearing is used to reduce friction between two surfaces. The bearing below is used to reduce friction on the hinges of a door.

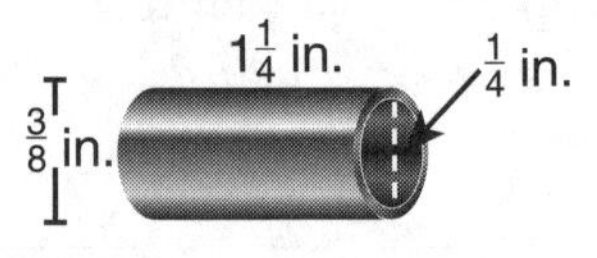

What is the volume of the steel bearing?

A 0.0614 in.^{3}

B 0.0767 in.^{3}

C 0.3068 in.^{3}

D 0.4909 in.^{3}

Focus on TEKS

Lesson 49 Effects on Area and Volume of Changing the Length, Width, and Height

TEKS G(f)1D Describe the effect on perimeter, area, and volume when length, width, or height of a three-dimensional solid is changed and apply this idea in solving problems.

Certain patterns can be discovered and explored when the dimensions of three-dimensional figures are changed.

Guided Instruction

Problem 1

Jen is wrapping gifts for her mom. She has two identical small boxes and one large box. The gifts are too big to fit in one small box, so she will need to use either both small boxes or the large box. The small boxes are 9 inches by 6.5 inches by 1.75 inches. The large box dimensions are exactly double the small box dimensions.

a. Which option will require less wrapping paper?

b. Describe the effect in the surface area of the two different box sizes.

c. Make and verify a conjecture about the surface area of a rectangular prism when the dimensions are doubled.

Part a. Step 1 Find the amount of wrapping paper required if she uses the two smaller boxes by finding the surface area of the smaller box and doubling it.

$SA = ph + 2B$

$SA = [2(9) + 2(6.5)]1.75 + 2(9 \cdot 6.5)$

$SA = (31)1.75 + 2(58.5)$

$SA = 171.25$

SA of 2 small boxes $= 2 \cdot 171.25 = 342.5$ in.^{2}

Step 2 Find the dimensions of the large box and then find its surface area.

$9 \cdot 2 = 18$ $\quad$ $6.5 \cdot 2 = 13$ $\quad$ $1.75 \cdot 2 = 3.5$

$SA = [2(18) + 2(13)]3.5 + 2(18 \cdot 13)$

$SA = (62)3.5 + 2(234)$

$SA = 685$ in.^{2}

Step 3 Compare the surface areas. The two small boxes will require 342.5 in.^{2} of wrapping paper, and the large box will require 685 in.^{2} of wrapping paper.

Part b. Compare the surface area of the large box with the surface area of one small box. $\frac{685}{171.25} = 4$

The surface area of the large box is four times the surface area of the small box.

Part c. Make a conjecture. When the dimensions of a rectangular prism are doubled, the surface area is quadrupled.

Verify the conjecture. Consider a prism that is a units by b units by c units. Doubling the dimensions, the prism will be $2a$ units by $2b$ units by $2c$ units. Calculate the surface area of each.

$SA = (2a + 2b)c + 2(ab)$

$SA = 2ac + 2bc + 2ab$

$SA = [2(2a) + 2(2b)]2c + 2(2a \cdot 2b)$

$SA = (4a + 4b)2c + 2(4ab)$

$SA = 8ac + 8bc + 8ab$

Multiply by 4.

$SA = 4(2ac + 2bc + 2ab) = 8ac + 8bc + 8ab$

Solution

Using two small boxes will require less wrapping paper. As shown in Part c, when the dimensions of a rectangular prism are doubled, the surface area is quadrupled.

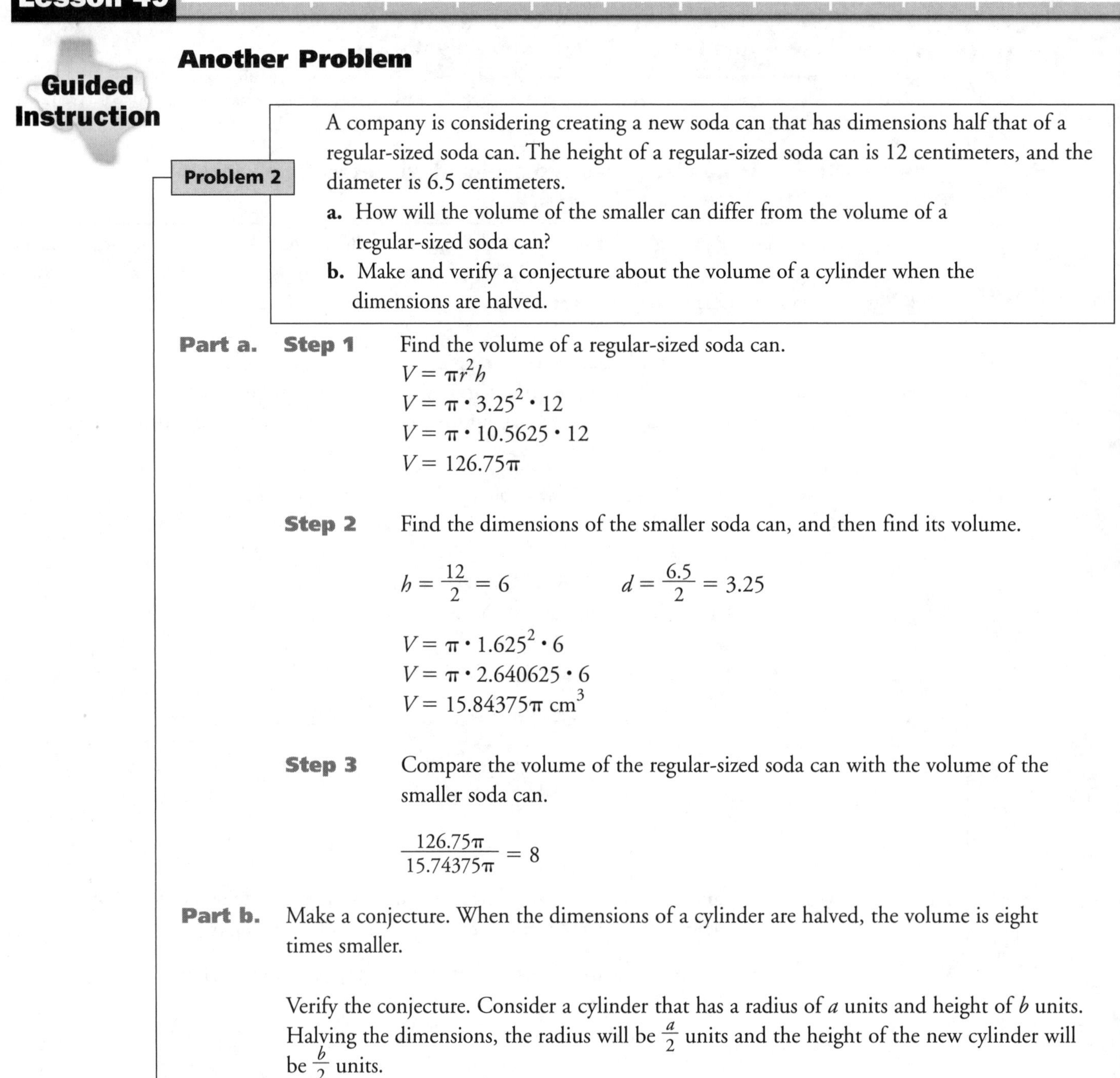

Another Problem

Guided Instruction

Problem 2

A company is considering creating a new soda can that has dimensions half that of a regular-sized soda can. The height of a regular-sized soda can is 12 centimeters, and the diameter is 6.5 centimeters.

a. How will the volume of the smaller can differ from the volume of a regular-sized soda can?

b. Make and verify a conjecture about the volume of a cylinder when the dimensions are halved.

Part a. **Step 1** Find the volume of a regular-sized soda can.

$V = \pi r^2 h$

$V = \pi \cdot 3.25^2 \cdot 12$

$V = \pi \cdot 10.5625 \cdot 12$

$V = 126.75\pi$

Step 2 Find the dimensions of the smaller soda can, and then find its volume.

$h = \frac{12}{2} = 6$ $\quad d = \frac{6.5}{2} = 3.25$

$V = \pi \cdot 1.625^2 \cdot 6$

$V = \pi \cdot 2.640625 \cdot 6$

$V = 15.84375\pi \text{ cm}^3$

Step 3 Compare the volume of the regular-sized soda can with the volume of the smaller soda can.

$\frac{126.75\pi}{15.74375\pi} = 8$

Part b. Make a conjecture. When the dimensions of a cylinder are halved, the volume is eight times smaller.

Verify the conjecture. Consider a cylinder that has a radius of a units and height of b units. Halving the dimensions, the radius will be $\frac{a}{2}$ units and the height of the new cylinder will be $\frac{b}{2}$ units.

$V = \pi a^2 b$

$V = \pi(\frac{a}{2})^2(\frac{b}{2})$

$V = \pi(\frac{a^2}{4})(\frac{b}{2})$

$V = \frac{\pi a^2 b}{8}$

Divide by 8.

$V = \frac{\pi a^2 b}{8}$

Solution

The volume of the smaller soda can will be eight times smaller than the volume of the regular-sized soda can. As shown in Part b, when the dimensions of a cylinder are halved, the volume is eight times smaller.

Apply the TEKS **Describe the effect on surface area and volume when the dimensions of each three-dimensional figure are changed as described below.**

1.

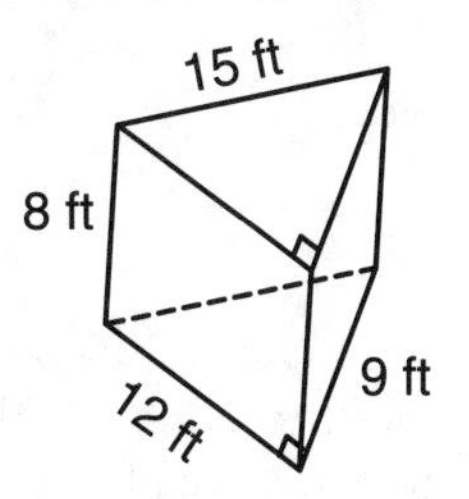

Change: height is changed from 8 ft to 16 ft

____

____

2.

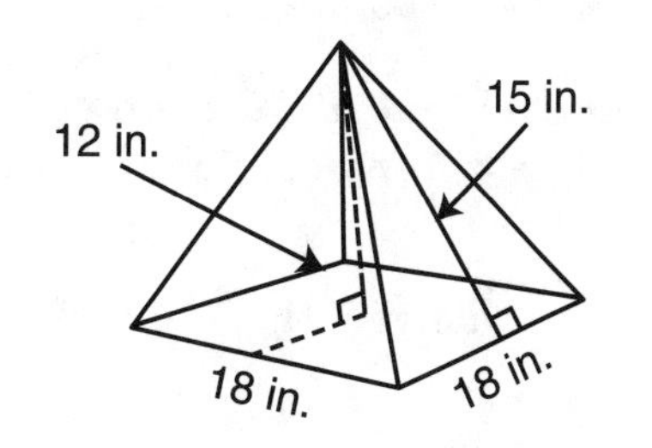

Change: all dimensions are halved

____

____

3.

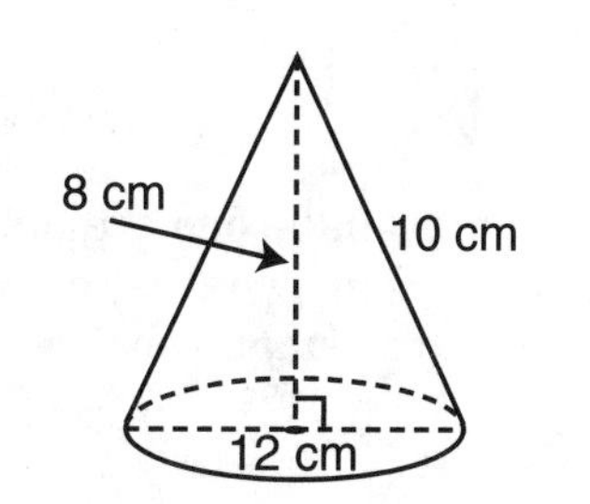

Change: all dimensions are tripled

____

____

4.

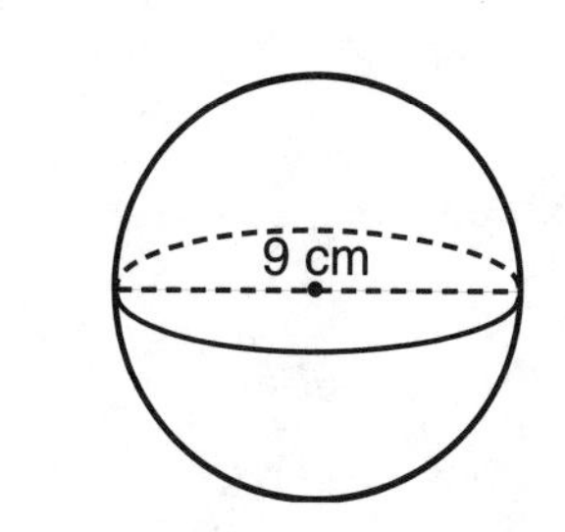

Change: diameter is changed from 9 cm to 3 cm

____

____

Answer each problem.

5. Make and verify a conjecture about how the volume of a rectangular prism changes when the height is doubled.

____

____

6. Make and verify a conjecture about how the surface area of a cone changes when the dimensions are halved.

____

____

7. The diameter of a croquet ball is 8.6 centimeters. The diameter of a golf ball is half the diameter of a croquet ball. How does the surface area and volume of a golf ball differ from the surface area and volume of a croquet ball?

____

TAKS Objective 8 The student will demonstrate an understanding of the concepts and uses of measurement and similarity.
TEKS G(f)1D

DIRECTIONS Read each question. Then circle the letter for the correct answer. If a correct answer is <u>not here</u>, circle the letter for "Not Here."

1 How does the volume change if the height of the cylinder is tripled?

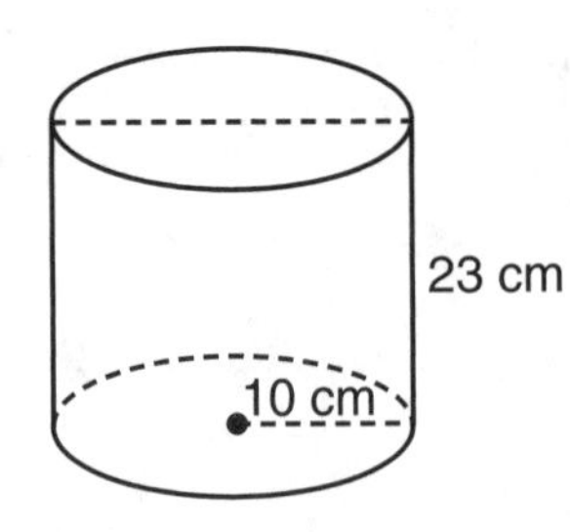

A The volume is doubled.

B The volume is tripled.

C The volume is 9 times larger.

D The volume is 27 times larger.

2 If the volumes of two similar pyramids are 96 square units and 2,592 square units, how are the pyramids related?

F The dimensions of one pyramid are double the dimensions of the other pyramid.

G The dimensions of one pyramid are 3 times the dimensions of the other pyramid.

H The dimensions of one pyramid are 6 times the dimensions of the other pyramid.

J The dimensions of one pyramid are 9 times the dimensions of the other pyramid.

3 An ice-cream parlor offers three different sizes of sugar cones: large, medium, and small. The dimensions of the large cone are shown below.

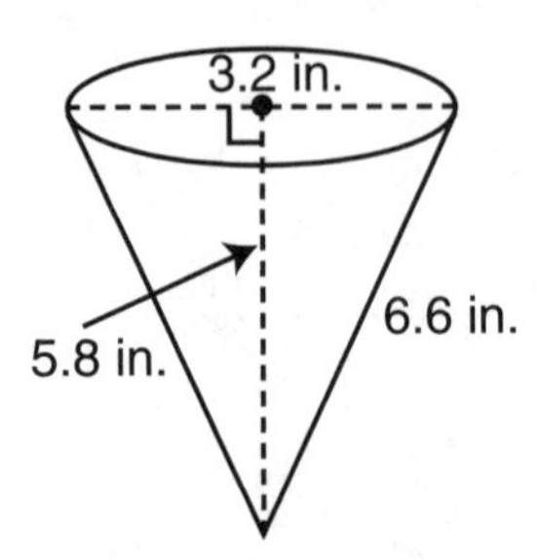

If the dimensions of the small cone are half the dimensions of the large cone, what is the approximate volume of the small cone?

A 1.9 in.^{3}

B 2.2 in.^{3}

C 8.7 in.^{3}

D Not Here

4 The surface area of a rectangular prism is 298 square units. If the dimensions are tripled, what is the surface area of the figure in square units?

Record your answer and fill in the bubbles on the grid below. Be sure to use the correct place value.

				•			
0	0	0	0		0	0	0
1	1	1	1		1	1	1
2	2	2	2		2	2	2
3	3	3	3		3	3	3
4	4	4	4		4	4	4
5	5	5	5		5	5	5
6	6	6	6		6	6	6
7	7	7	7		7	7	7
8	8	8	8		8	8	8
9	9	9	9		9	9	9

Focus on TEKS

Lesson 50 Triangles and Congruence

TEKS G(e)3B Justify and apply triangle congruence relationships.

Triangles can be proven congruent using several different congruence statements.

If three sides of one triangle are congruent to three sides of another triangle, the triangles are congruent by the **Side-Side-Side (SSS) Congruence Postulate.**

If two sides and the included angle of one triangle are congruent to two sides and the included angle of another triangle, the triangles are congruent by the **Side-Angle-Side (SAS) Congruence Postulate.**

If two angles and the included side of one triangle are congruent to two angles and the included side of another triangle, the triangles are congruent by the **Angle-Side-Angle (ASA) Congruence Postulate.**

If two angles and a nonincluded side of one triangle are congruent to two angles and a nonincluded side of another triangle, the triangles are congruent by the **Angle-Angle-Side (AAS) Congruence Postulate.**

If the hypotenuse and leg of one right triangle are congruent to the hypotenuse and corresponding leg of another right triangle, the triangles are congruent by the **Hypotenuse-Leg (HL) Postulate.**

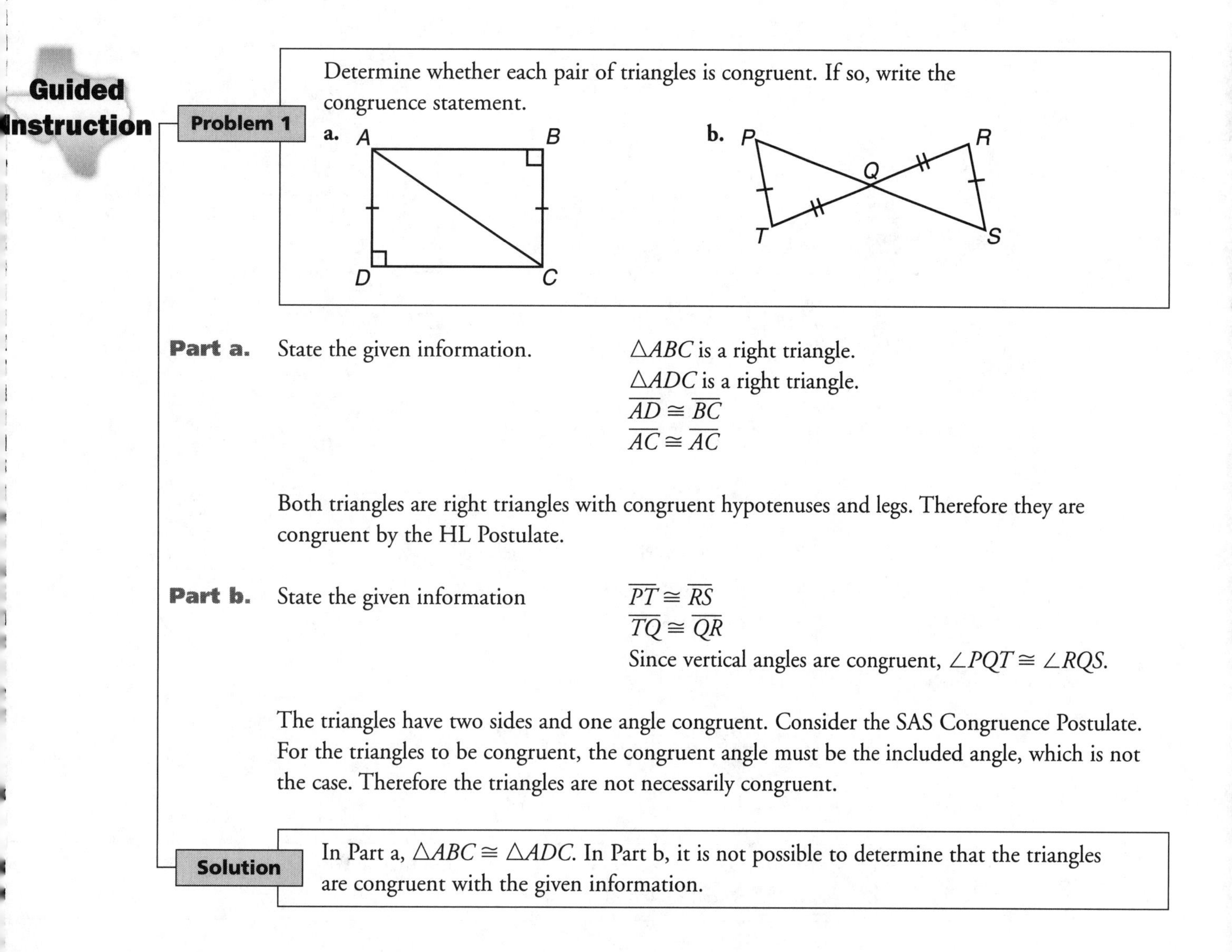

Guided Instruction

Problem 1

Determine whether each pair of triangles is congruent. If so, write the congruence statement.

a.

b.

Part a. State the given information.

$\triangle ABC$ is a right triangle.
$\triangle ADC$ is a right triangle.
$\overline{AD} \cong \overline{BC}$
$\overline{AC} \cong \overline{AC}$

Both triangles are right triangles with congruent hypotenuses and legs. Therefore they are congruent by the HL Postulate.

Part b. State the given information

$\overline{PT} \cong \overline{RS}$
$\overline{TQ} \cong \overline{QR}$
Since vertical angles are congruent, $\angle PQT \cong \angle RQS$.

The triangles have two sides and one angle congruent. Consider the SAS Congruence Postulate. For the triangles to be congruent, the congruent angle must be the included angle, which is not the case. Therefore the triangles are not necessarily congruent.

Solution

In Part a, $\triangle ABC \cong \triangle ADC$. In Part b, it is not possible to determine that the triangles are congruent with the given information.

Guided Instruction

When two triangles are congruent, their corresponding parts are congruent. This is often stated with the abbreviation CPCTC, which stands for *corresponding parts of congruent triangles are congruent.*

More Problems

Problem 2

Determine if the triangles are congruent. If so, state the congruent parts of the two triangles.

A
D
C
B
F
E

Step 1 First determine if the triangles are congruent by stating the given information.

$\angle C \cong \angle F$; $\overline{CB} \cong \overline{FE}$; $\angle B \cong \angle E$

The triangles have two angles and one side congruent. Consider the ASA and the AAS Congruence Postulates. Since the congruent side is the included side of the two congruent angles, the triangles are congruent by the ASA Congruence Postulate.

Step 2 Use CPCTC to state the congruent parts.

$\angle A \cong \angle D$	$\overline{AB} \cong \overline{DE}$
$\angle B \cong \angle E$	$\overline{CB} \cong \overline{FE}$
$\angle C \cong \angle F$	$\overline{AC} \cong \overline{DF}$

Solution $\triangle ABC \cong \triangle DEF$ by the ASA Congruence Postulate, and all pairs of corresponding sides and corresponding angles are congruent by CPCTC.

Problem 3

Justify that $\overline{XW} \cong \overline{XY}$ and $\angle XWZ \cong \angle XYZ$ in the triangles at the right.

X
W
Y
Z

Step 1 Determine if the triangles are congruent.

$\overline{WZ} \cong \overline{YZ}$; $\angle WZX \cong \angle XZY$; $\overline{XZ} \cong \overline{XZ}$

The triangles have two sides and the included angle congruent. Therefore the triangles are congruent by the SAS Congruence Postulate.

Step 2 Use CPCTC to state the congruent parts.

$\angle XWZ \cong \angle XYZ$	$\overline{XW} \cong \overline{XY}$
$\angle WZX \cong \angle YZX$	$\overline{WZ} \cong \overline{YZ}$
$\angle WXZ \cong \angle YXZ$	$\overline{XZ} \cong \overline{XZ}$

Solution Solution $\triangle WXZ \cong \triangle YXZ$ by the SAS Congruence Postulate, and $\overline{XW} \cong \overline{XY}$ and $\angle XWZ \cong \angle XYZ$ by CPCTC.

Apply the TEKS Determine whether each pair of triangles is able to be proved congruent. If so, write the congruence statement and state the postulate or theorem used to prove the triangles congruent. If not, write *not possible.*

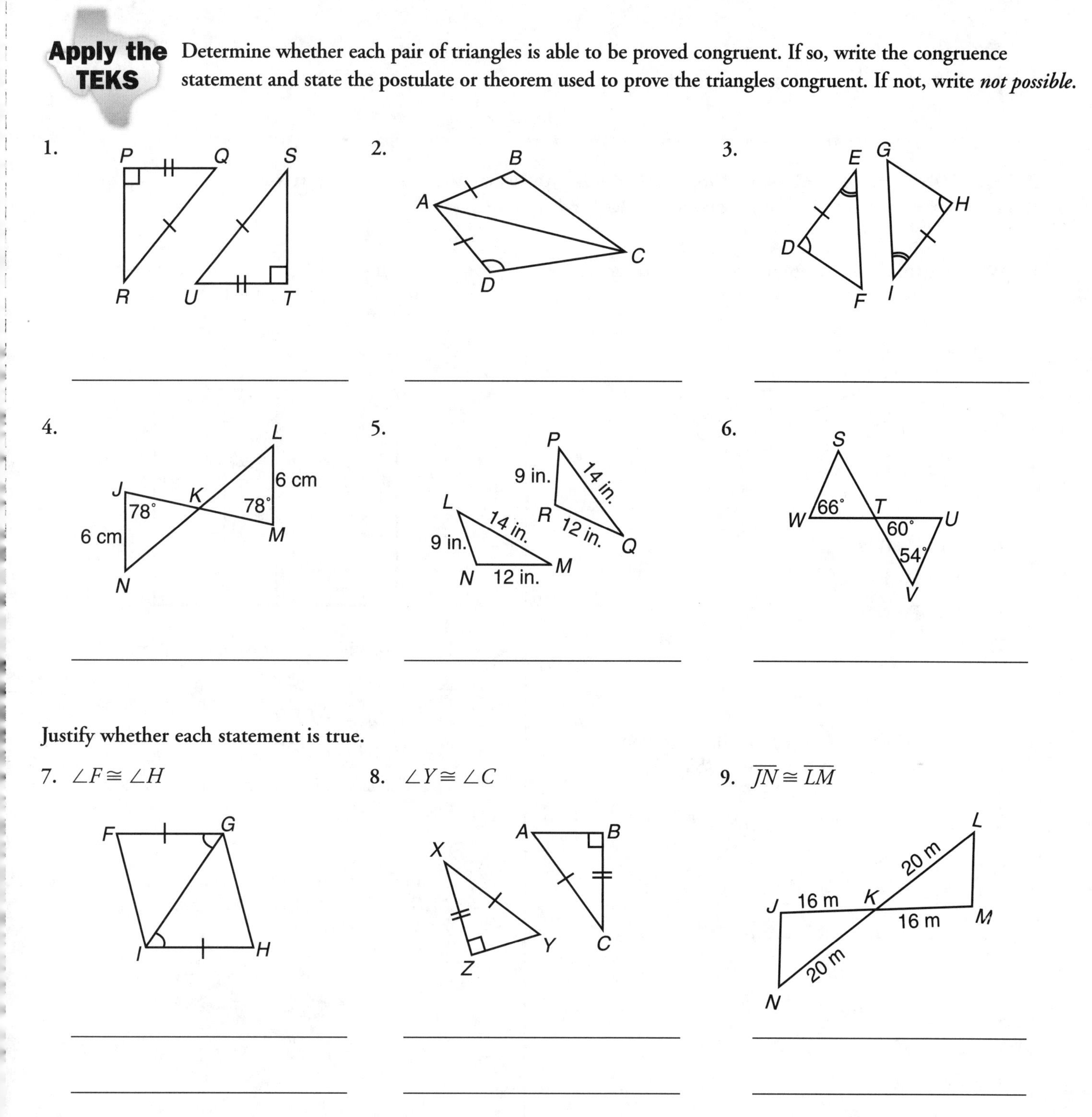

1. ______

2. ______

3. ______

4. ______

5. ______

6. ______

Justify whether each statement is true.

7. $\angle F \cong \angle H$

8. $\angle Y \cong \angle C$

9. $\overline{JN} \cong \overline{LM}$

Answer the question.

10. Explain why two triangles cannot be proven congruent by an Angle-Angle-Angle Congruence Postulate. Provide an example.

DIRECTIONS Read each question. Then circle the letter for the correct answer. If a correct answer is not here, circle the letter for "Not Here."

1 What postulate or theorem can you use to prove $\triangle JLK \cong \triangle ONM$?

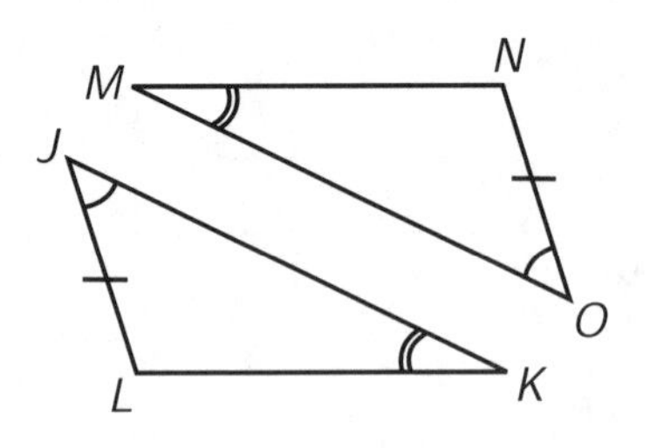

A SAS Postulate

B ASA Postulate

C AAS Postulate

D Not Here

2 What additional information will allow you to use the HL Theorem to prove $\triangle QST \cong \triangle SQR$?

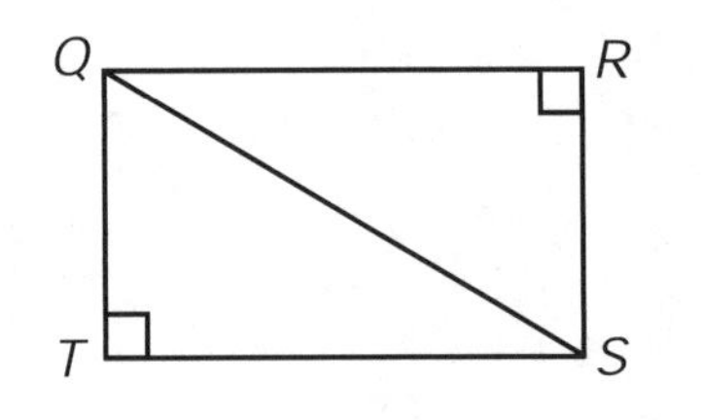

F $\angle TQS \cong \angle RSQ$

G $\overline{QT} \cong \overline{SR}$

H $\overline{QS} \cong \overline{QS}$

J $\angle QST \cong \angle SQR$

3 Determine whether the two triangles on the coordinate grid are congruent.

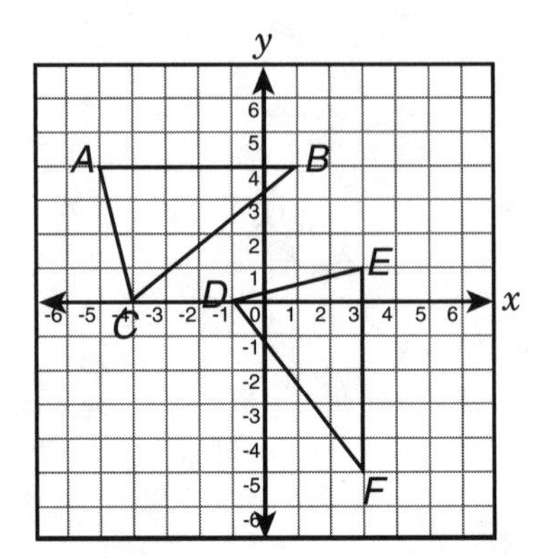

If so, what is the congruence statement?

A $\triangle ABC \cong \triangle DEF$

B $\triangle ABC \cong \triangle EFD$

C $\triangle CAB \cong \triangle DFE$

D The triangles are not congruent.

4 Jamaal created the kite shown below, in which $\triangle AGC \cong \triangle EGC$, $\overline{CG} \perp \overline{AE}$, and $\angle BFA \cong \angle DFE$.

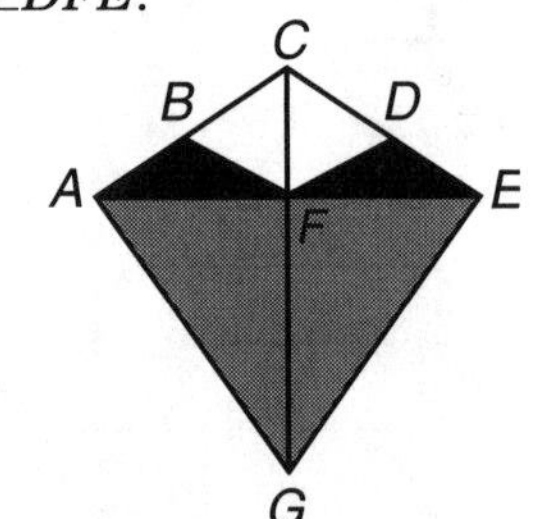

Which of the following congruence statements is NOT true?

F $\triangle AFG \cong \triangle EFG$

G $\triangle BFA \cong \triangle DFE$

H $\triangle ACF \cong \triangle ECF$

J Not Here

Focus on TEKS

Lesson 51 Similar Figures and Their Properties

TEKS G(c)1A Use numeric and geometric patterns to make generalizations about geometric properties, including ratios in similar figures and solids.
TEKS G(f)1A Use similarity properties and transformations to explore and justify conjectures about geometric figures.
TEKS G(f)1B Use ratios to solve problems involving similar figures.

Generalizations about the perimeters, areas, and volumes of similar polygons and similar solids can be made by observing patterns.

Similar polygons have congruent corresponding angles and proportional corresponding sides.

The **scale factor** is the ratio of corresponding sides.

Guided Instruction

Problem 1

The Bender's old family room was 12 feet by 16 feet. They put an addition on their house to expand the size of the family room to 21 feet by 28 feet.

a. Is the new family room similar to the old family room? If so, what is the scale factor?
b. What are the perimeters of the old and new family rooms?
c. What are the areas of the old and new family rooms?
d. Make a conjecture about the relationship between the perimeters and areas of similar polygons.

Part a. Step 1 Set up a proportion to determine if the old and new family rooms are similar. If they are similar, the cross-products will be equal.

$$\frac{\text{old width}}{\text{new width}} \rightarrow \frac{12\text{ ft}}{21\text{ ft}} = \frac{16\text{ ft}}{28\text{ ft}} \leftarrow \frac{\text{old length}}{\text{new length}}$$

Cross products: $12\text{ ft} \cdot 28\text{ ft} = 21\text{ ft} \cdot 16\text{ ft}$
$336\text{ ft}^2 = 336\text{ ft}^2$

Step 2 Find the scale factor. $\frac{12}{21} = \frac{12 \div 3}{21 \div 3} = \frac{4}{7}$

Part b. Find the perimeter of the old and new family rooms.

Old family room: $P = 2(12) + 2(16) = 56$ ft New family room: $P = 2(21) + 2(28) = 98$ ft

Part c. Find the area of the old and new family rooms.

Old family room: $A = 12 \cdot 16 = 192\text{ ft}^2$ New family room: $A = 21 \cdot 28 = 588\text{ ft}^2$

Part d. Examine the ratio of the old and new perimeters. $\frac{56}{98} = \frac{56 \div 14}{98 \div 14} = \frac{4}{7}$

Examine the ratio of the old and new areas. $\frac{192}{588} = \frac{192 \div 12}{588 \div 12} = \frac{16}{49} = \frac{4^2}{7^2}$

Conjecture: If the scale factor of similar polygons is $a : b$, then the ratio of perimeters of the polygons is $a : b$ and the ratio of the areas of the polygons is $a^2 : b^2$.
This conjecture is indeed true.

Solution

The old and new family room are similar with a scale factor of 4 : 7. The ratio of the perimeters is 4 : 7, and the ratio of the areas is $4^2 : 7^2$, or 16 : 49.

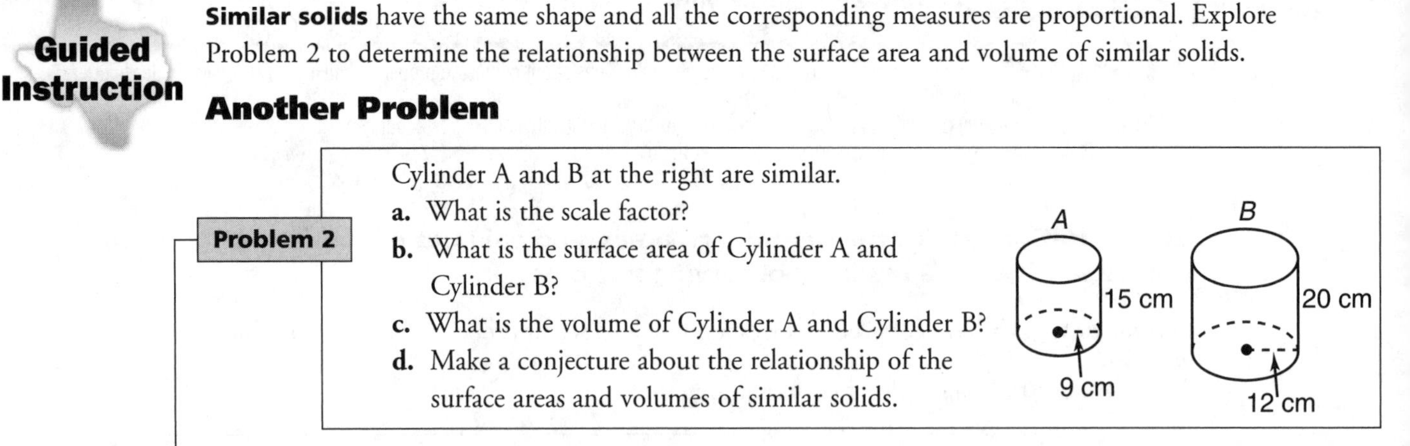

Guided Instruction

Similar solids have the same shape and all the corresponding measures are proportional. Explore Problem 2 to determine the relationship between the surface area and volume of similar solids.

Another Problem

Problem 2

Cylinder A and B at the right are similar.

a. What is the scale factor?

b. What is the surface area of Cylinder A and Cylinder B?

c. What is the volume of Cylinder A and Cylinder B?

d. Make a conjecture about the relationship of the surface areas and volumes of similar solids.

Part a. Find the scale factor.

$\frac{9}{12} = \frac{3}{4}$ or $\frac{15}{20} = \frac{3}{4}$

Part b. Find the surface areas of Cylinder A and Cylinder B.

Cylinder A

$SA = \pi dh + 2B$
$SA = (\pi \cdot 18 \cdot 15) + 2(\pi \cdot 9^2)$
$SA = 270\pi + 162\pi$
$SA = 432\pi \text{ cm}^2$

Cylinder B

$SA = \pi dh + 2B$
$SA = (\pi \cdot 24 \cdot 20) + 2(\pi \cdot 12^2)$
$SA = 480\pi + 288\pi$
$SA = 768\pi \text{ cm}^2$

Part c. Find the volumes of Cylinder A and Cylinder B.

Cylinder A

$V = \pi r^2 h$
$V = \pi \cdot 9^2 \cdot 15$
$V = 1{,}215\pi \text{ cm}^3$

Cylinder B

$V = \pi r^2 h$
$V = \pi \cdot 12^2 \cdot 20$
$V = 2{,}880\pi \text{ cm}^3$

Part d. Examine the ratio of the cylinders' surface areas.

$$\frac{432\pi}{768\pi} = \frac{432}{768} = \frac{432 \div 48}{768 \div 48} = \frac{9}{16}$$

Examine the ratio of the cylinders' volumes.

$$\frac{1{,}215\pi}{2{,}880\pi} = \frac{1{,}215}{2{,}880} = \frac{1{,}215 \div 45}{2{,}880 \div 45} = \frac{27}{64}$$

Conjecture: If the scale factor of similar solids is $a : b$, then the ratio of surface areas of the solids is $a^2 : b^2$ and the ratio of the volumes of the solids is $a^3 : b^3$.
This conjecture is indeed true.

Solution

The scale factor of Cylinder A and Cylinder B is 3 : 4. The ratio of the surface areas is $3^2 : 4^2$, or 9 : 16. The ratio of the volumes is $3^3 : 4^3$, or 27 : 64.

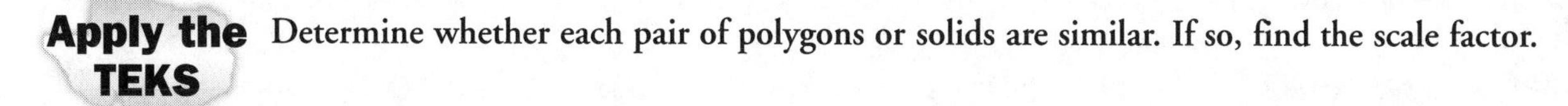

Apply the TEKS **Determine whether each pair of polygons or solids are similar. If so, find the scale factor.**

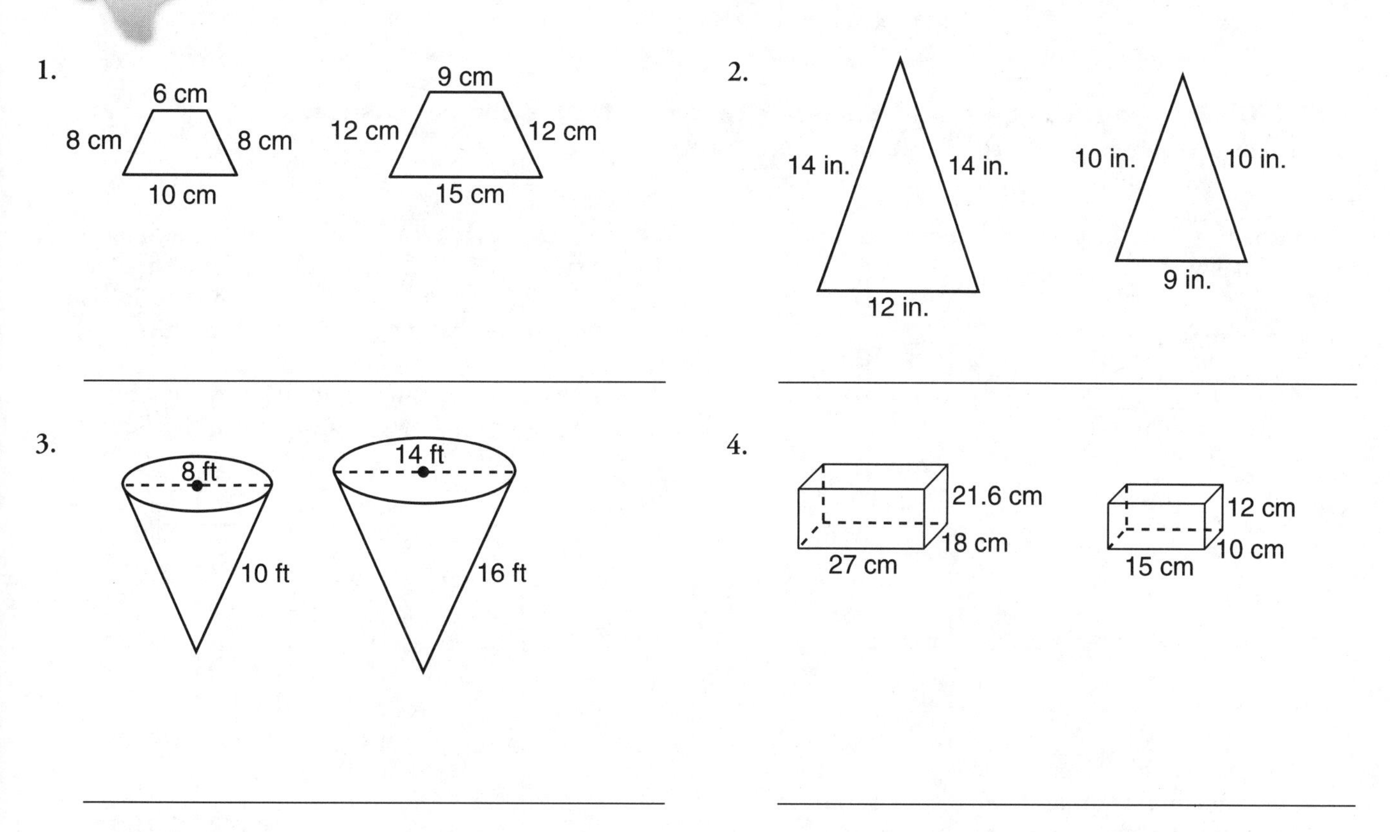

Complete the tables.

5. The table refers to the ratios of similar polygons.

Scale factor	2 : 3			5 : 11
Ratio of perimeters		6 : 7		
Ratio of areas			25 : 64	

6. The table refers to the ratios of similar solids.

Scale factor			8 : 9	
Ratio of surface areas	9 : 49			
Ratio of volumes		64 : 729		343 : 1331

Solve the problems.

7. A company packages cereal in two different sized boxes, which are similar by a scale factor of 4 : 5. The smaller cereal box has a volume of 136 cubic inches. What is the volume of the larger cereal box?

TAKS Objective 6 The student will demonstrate an understanding of geometric relationships and spatial reasoning.
TEKS G(c)1A

TAKS Objective 8 The student will demonstrate an understanding of the concepts and uses of measurement and similarity.
TEKS G(f)1A, G(f)1B

DIRECTIONS Read each question. Then circle the letter for the correct answer. If a correct answer is not here, circle the letter for "Not Here."

1 What is the scale factor of the parallelograms shown below?

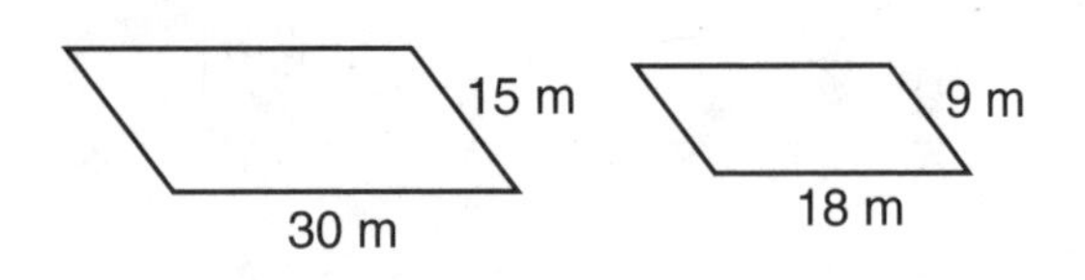

A 5 : 3

B 4 : 3

C 5 : 7

D The parallelograms are not similar.

2 If the ratio of similar polygons is 3 : 5 and the larger polygon has an area of 85 square units, which equation can be used to find the area of the smaller polygon?

F $\frac{3}{5} = \frac{x}{85}$

G $\frac{9}{25} = \frac{x}{85}$

H $\frac{9}{25} = \frac{85}{x}$

J $\frac{27}{125} = \frac{85}{x}$

3 The ratio of volumes of two similar solids is 512 : 2,197. What is the ratio of the surface areas of the solids?

A 128 : 338

B 81 : 196

C 64 : 169

D 8 : 13

4 The scale factor of two similar triangular prisms is 5 : 7. If the volume of the smaller triangular prism is 280 cubic units, what is the volume of the larger triangular prism?

Record your answer and fill in the bubbles on the grid below. Be sure to use the correct place value.

				.			
0	0	0	0		0	0	0
1	1	1	1		1	1	1
2	2	2	2		2	2	2
3	3	3	3		3	3	3
4	4	4	4		4	4	4
5	5	5	5		5	5	5
6	6	6	6		6	6	6
7	7	7	7		7	7	7
8	8	8	8		8	8	8
9	9	9	9		9	9	9

5 An architect is drawing a blueprint, or a scale drawing, of a new house she is designing. The area of the master bedroom on the blueprint is 42 square inches. If the scale factor of the drawing is 1 inch : 3 feet, what will be the actual area of the master bedroom?

A 126 ft^2

B 378 ft^2

C 1,134 ft^2

D Not Here

Focus on TEKS

Lesson 52 Triangle Similarity Relationships

TEKS G(f)1C In a variety of ways, develop, apply, and justify triangle similarity relationships, such as right triangle ratios, trigonometric ratios, and Pythagorean triples.

For two triangles to be similar, angle measures of one triangle must be congruent to the angle measures of the other triangle, and the corresponding sides must be proportional.

If two angles of one triangle are congruent to two angles of another triangle, the triangles are similar by the **Angle-Angle (AA) similarity postulate**.

If the corresponding sides of two triangles are proportional, the triangles are similar by the **Side-Side-Side (SSS) similarity theorem**.

If an angle of one triangle is congruent to an angle of another triangle and the sides including those angles are proportional, then the triangles are similar by the **Side-Angle-Side (SAS) similarity theorem**.

Guided Instruction

Problem 1 Use an example to justify the AA similarity postulate.

Step 1 Draw two triangles that have two congruent angles. Name them $\triangle ABC$ and $\triangle DEF$.

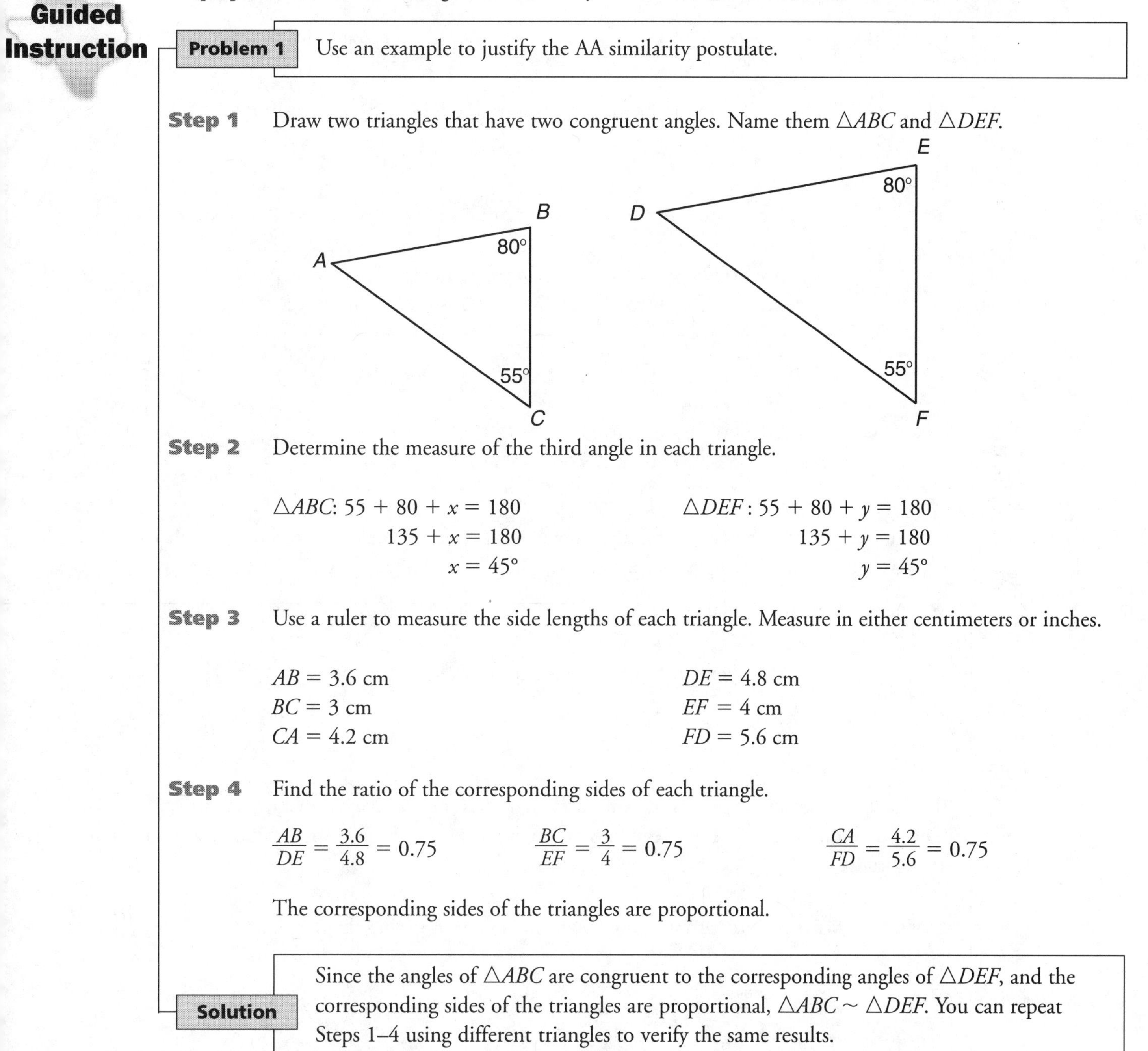

Step 2 Determine the measure of the third angle in each triangle.

$\triangle ABC$: $55 + 80 + x = 180$
$135 + x = 180$
$x = 45°$

$\triangle DEF$: $55 + 80 + y = 180$
$135 + y = 180$
$y = 45°$

Step 3 Use a ruler to measure the side lengths of each triangle. Measure in either centimeters or inches.

$AB = 3.6$ cm
$BC = 3$ cm
$CA = 4.2$ cm

$DE = 4.8$ cm
$EF = 4$ cm
$FD = 5.6$ cm

Step 4 Find the ratio of the corresponding sides of each triangle.

$\frac{AB}{DE} = \frac{3.6}{4.8} = 0.75$ $\frac{BC}{EF} = \frac{3}{4} = 0.75$ $\frac{CA}{FD} = \frac{4.2}{5.6} = 0.75$

The corresponding sides of the triangles are proportional.

Solution Since the angles of $\triangle ABC$ are congruent to the corresponding angles of $\triangle DEF$, and the corresponding sides of the triangles are proportional, $\triangle ABC \sim \triangle DEF$. You can repeat Steps 1–4 using different triangles to verify the same results.

Guided Instruction

More Problems

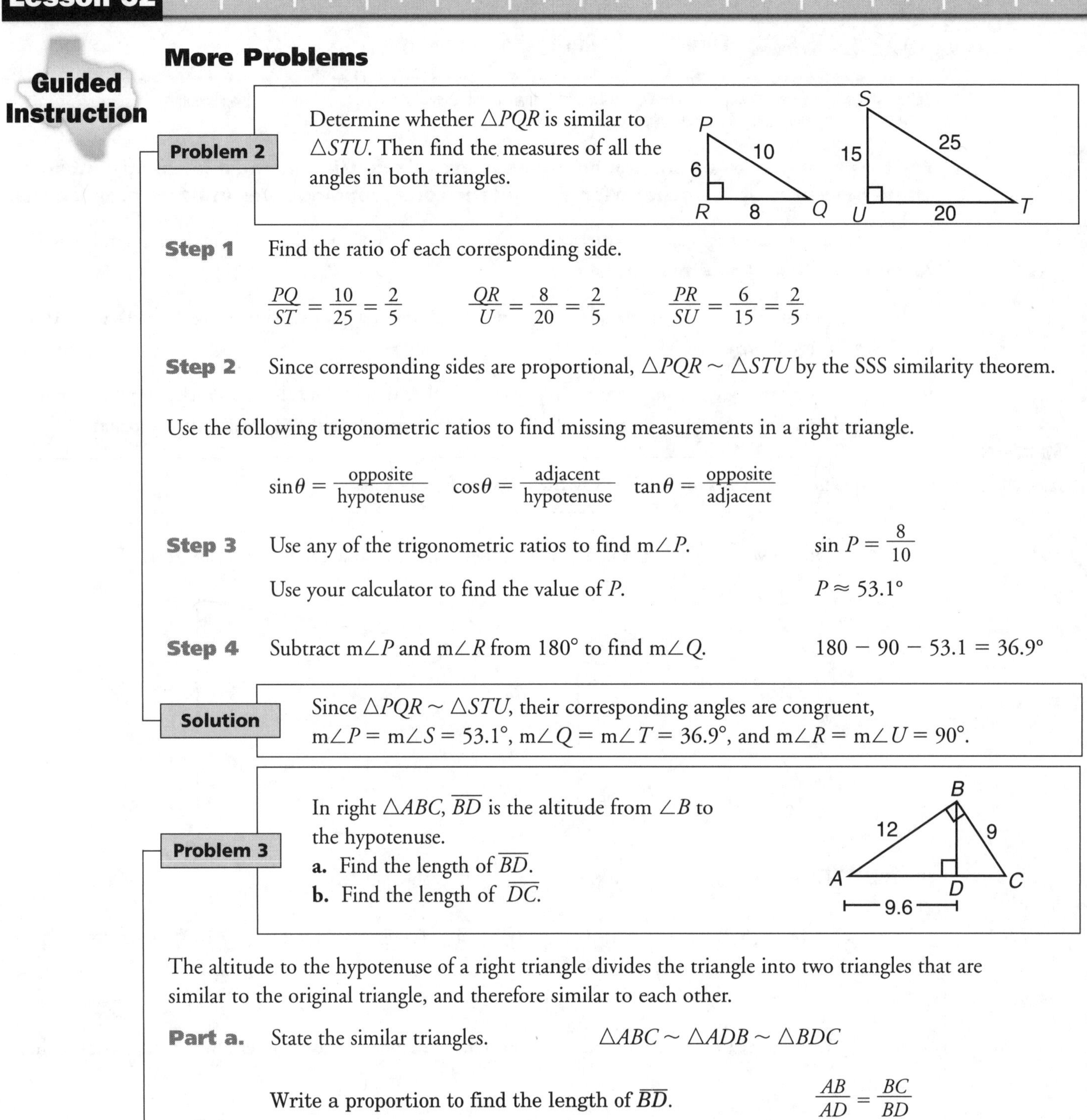

Problem 2

Determine whether $\triangle PQR$ is similar to $\triangle STU$. Then find the measures of all the angles in both triangles.

Step 1 Find the ratio of each corresponding side.

$$\frac{PQ}{ST} = \frac{10}{25} = \frac{2}{5} \qquad \frac{QR}{U} = \frac{8}{20} = \frac{2}{5} \qquad \frac{PR}{SU} = \frac{6}{15} = \frac{2}{5}$$

Step 2 Since corresponding sides are proportional, $\triangle PQR \sim \triangle STU$ by the SSS similarity theorem.

Use the following trigonometric ratios to find missing measurements in a right triangle.

$$\sin\theta = \frac{\text{opposite}}{\text{hypotenuse}} \qquad \cos\theta = \frac{\text{adjacent}}{\text{hypotenuse}} \qquad \tan\theta = \frac{\text{opposite}}{\text{adjacent}}$$

Step 3 Use any of the trigonometric ratios to find $m\angle P$. $\sin P = \frac{8}{10}$

Use your calculator to find the value of P. $P \approx 53.1°$

Step 4 Subtract $m\angle P$ and $m\angle R$ from 180° to find $m\angle Q$. $180 - 90 - 53.1 = 36.9°$

Solution

Since $\triangle PQR \sim \triangle STU$, their corresponding angles are congruent, $m\angle P = m\angle S = 53.1°$, $m\angle Q = m\angle T = 36.9°$, and $m\angle R = m\angle U = 90°$.

Problem 3

In right $\triangle ABC$, $\overline{BD}$ is the altitude from $\angle B$ to the hypotenuse.

a. Find the length of $\overline{BD}$.

b. Find the length of $\overline{DC}$.

The altitude to the hypotenuse of a right triangle divides the triangle into two triangles that are similar to the original triangle, and therefore similar to each other.

Part a. State the similar triangles. $\triangle ABC \sim \triangle ADB \sim \triangle BDC$

Write a proportion to find the length of $\overline{BD}$.

$$\frac{AB}{AD} = \frac{BC}{BD}$$
$$\frac{12}{9.6} = \frac{9}{BD}$$
$$BD = 7.2$$

The geometric mean of two positive numbers a and b is the positive number x, such that $\frac{a}{x} = \frac{x}{b}$. The geometric mean of the two segments of the hypotenuse defined by the altitude is the length of the altitude.

Part b. Write the proportion using the geometric mean to find the length of $\overline{DC}$.

$$\frac{AD}{BD} = \frac{BD}{DC}$$
$$\frac{9.6}{7.2} = \frac{7.2}{DC}$$
$$DC = 5.4$$

Solution

In the figure above, $BD = 7.2$ and $DC = 5.4$.

Determine whether each pair of triangles is similar. If so, write the similarity statement and state the postulate or theorem used to prove the triangles similar.

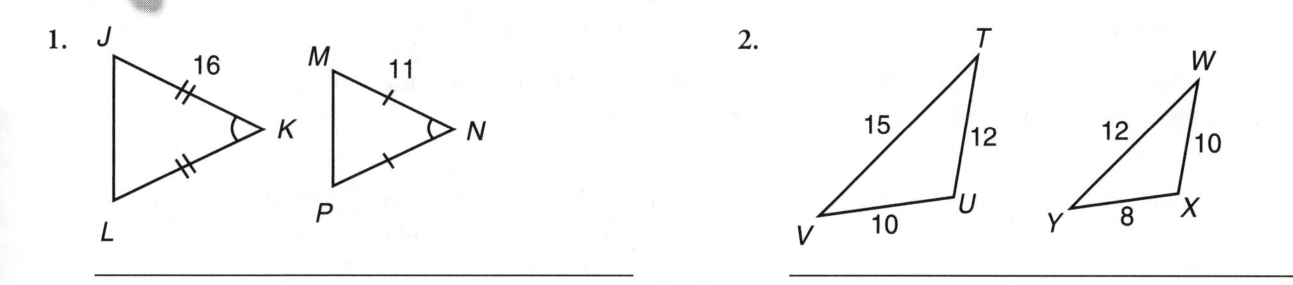

Find the value of x in each figure or pair of figures. If necessary, round to the nearest tenth.

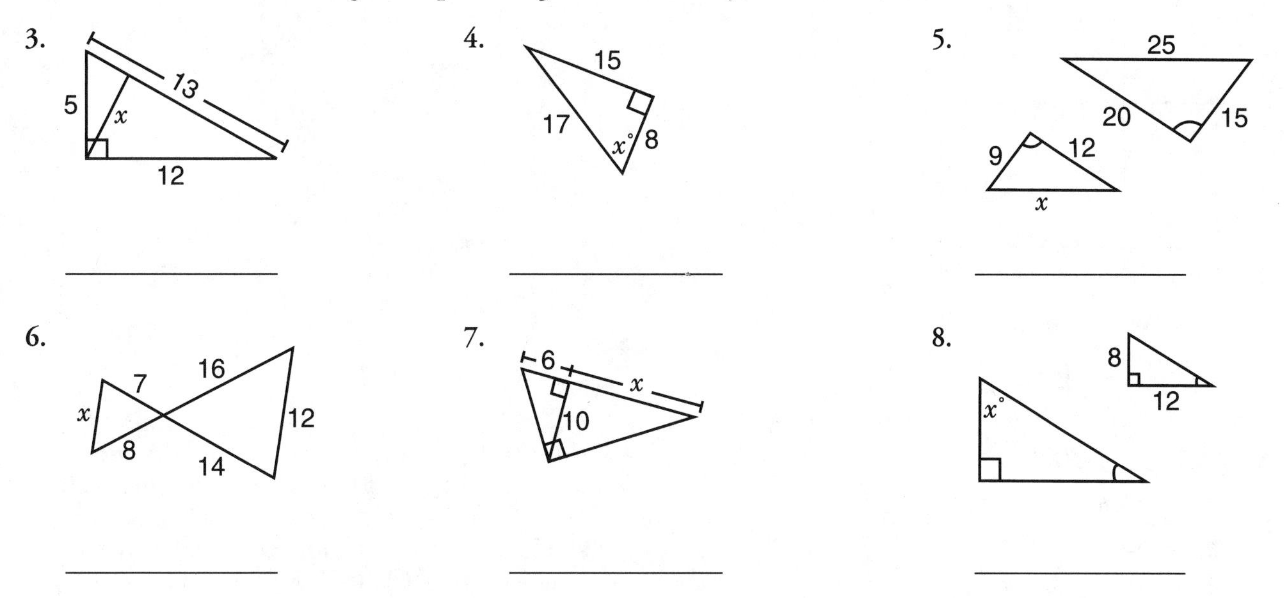

Using indirect measurements, find the height of each object being measured to the nearest foot.

Indirect measurement is a way of taking and using one measurement to find other measurements. The mirror method is a form of indirect measurement used to find the height of an object. The mirror is placed on the ground between a person and the object being measured. The mirror should be placed so that the person can see the top of the object in the mirror. Similar triangles are created and therefore can be used to find the height of the object.

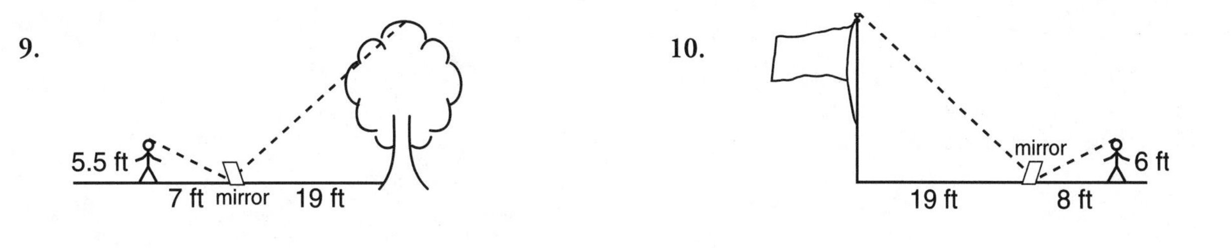

Answer the question.

11. Are all triangles formed by Pythagorean triples similar? Explain.

TAKS Objective 8 The student will demonstrate an understanding of the concepts and uses of measurement and similarity.
TEKS G(f)1C

DIRECTIONS Read each question. Then circle the letter for the correct answer. If a correct answer is not here, circle the letter for "Not Here."

1 Are the triangles on the coordinate grid similar?

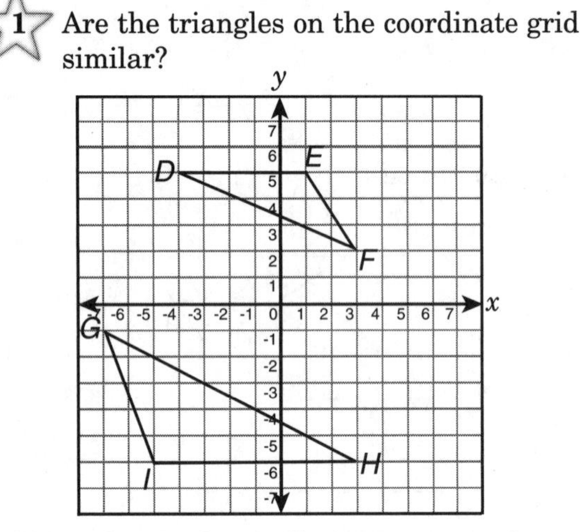

If so, what is the similarity statement?

A Yes; $\triangle DEF \sim \triangle GHI$

B Yes; $\triangle DEF \sim \triangle HGI$

C Yes; $\triangle EFD \sim \triangle IGH$

D No, the triangles are not similar.

2 In the figure below, $QR = 5$.

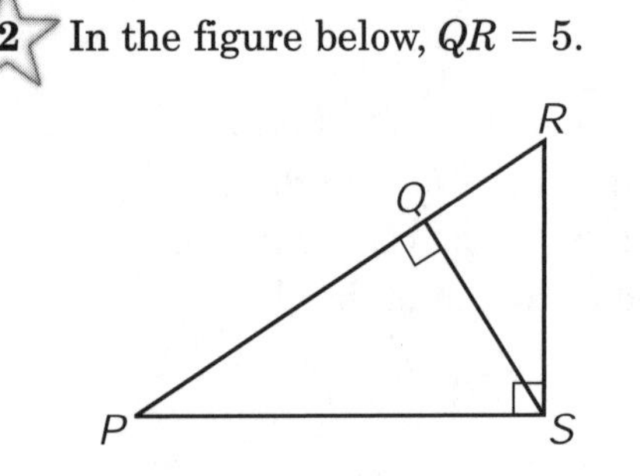

Which additional information will NOT allow you to find the length of the altitude?

F $PR = 21$

G $PS = 20$

H $PQ = 16$

J $RS = 13$

3 Which of the following is NOT a correct trigonometric equation using the triangle below?

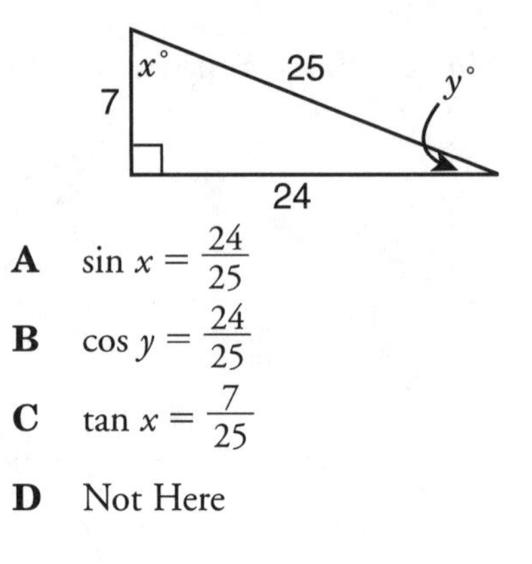

A $\sin x = \frac{24}{25}$

B $\cos y = \frac{24}{25}$

C $\tan x = \frac{7}{25}$

D Not Here

4 Myesha is standing in her front yard and measures the length of the shadow she casts, as well as the shadow, cast by her house. Her shadow is 8 feet long and the shadow of the house is 60 feet long. If Myesha is 5 feet 2 inches tall, how tall is her house to the nearest foot?

F 39 ft

G 41 ft

H 59 ft

J 93 ft

Building Stamina™

DIRECTIONS Read each question. Then circle the letter for the correct answer. If a correct answer is not here, circle the letter for "Not Here."

1 A net for a regular square pyramid is shown below.

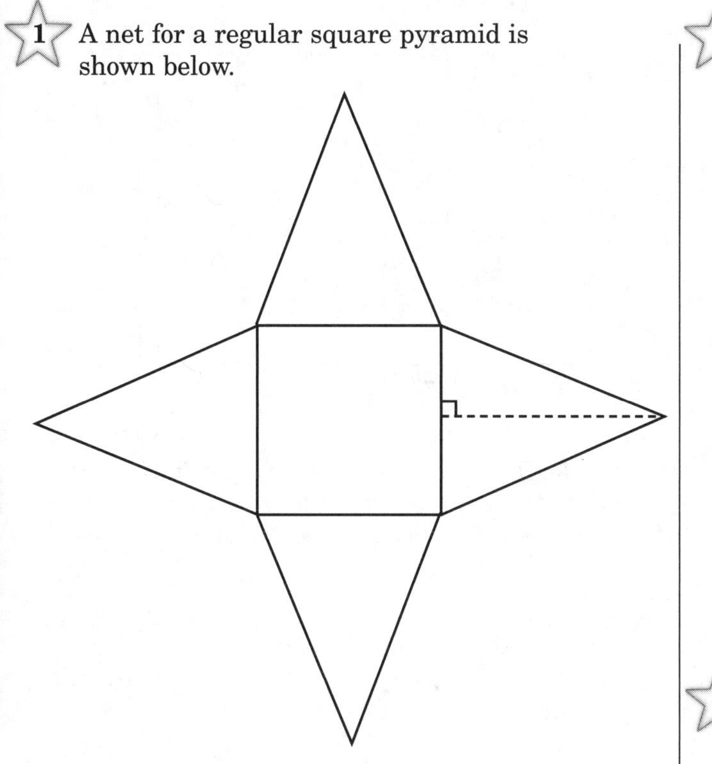

Use the ruler on the Measurement Chart to measure the dimensions to the nearest tenth of a centimeter. What is the surface area of the pyramid to the nearest square centimeter?

A 16 cm^2

B 19 cm^2

C 21 cm^2

D 35 cm^2

2 What is the ratio of the volumes of the spheres?

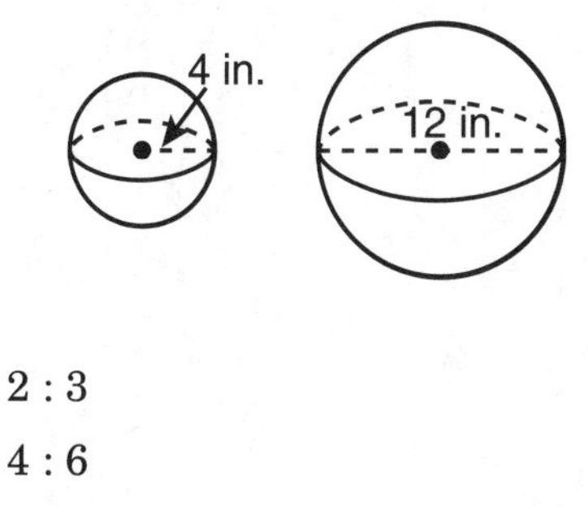

F 2 : 3

G 4 : 6

H 8 : 27

J 85 : 288

3 The figure below is a circle inscribed in a square.

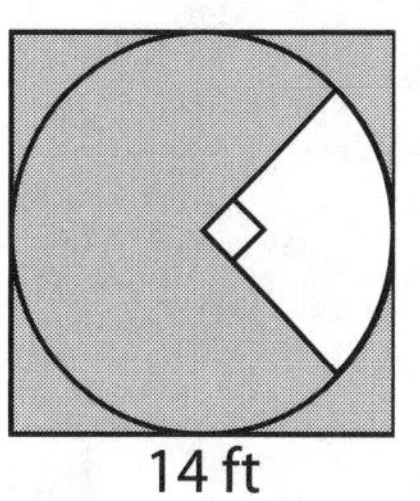

What is the area of the shaded portion to the nearest tenth?

A 147.0 ft^2

B 157.5 ft^2

C 185.0 ft^2

D Not Here

4 Determine whether the polygons are similar.

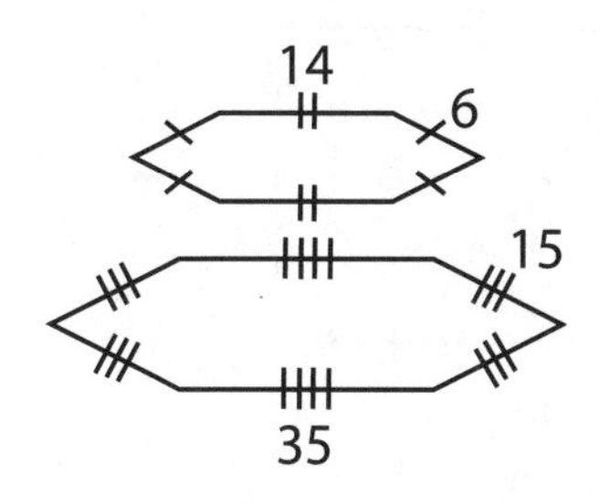

If so, what is the ratio of their perimeters?

F 2 : 5

G 4 : 25

H 8 : 125

J The polygons are not similar.

5 The sides of one right triangle are 6, 8, and 10. The sides of another right triangle are 10, 24, and 26. Determine if the triangles are similar. If so, what is the ratio of corresponding sides?

A 3 : 5

B 1 : 3

C 5 : 13

D The triangles are not similar.

6 The ratio of the volumes of two similar pyramids is 343 : 729. What is the ratio of their surface areas?

F 81 : 196

G 49 : 81

H $114\frac{1}{3} : 276\frac{2}{3}$

J Not Here

7 Which of the following figures has the greatest area?

A

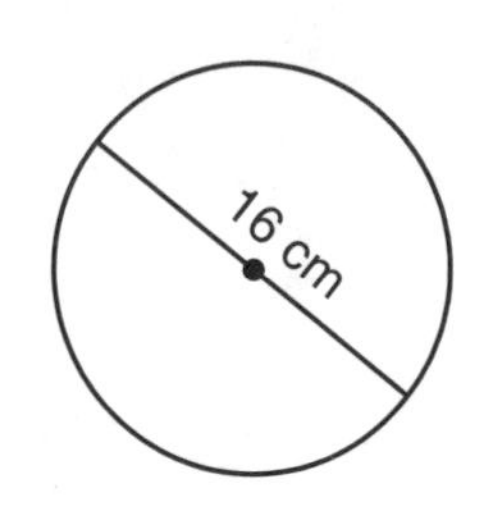

B

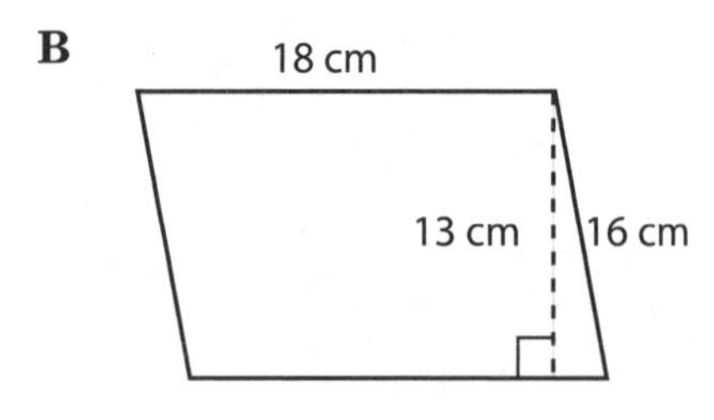

C

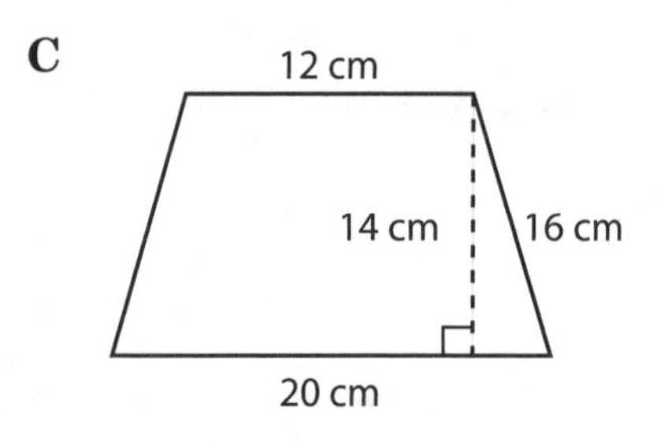

D

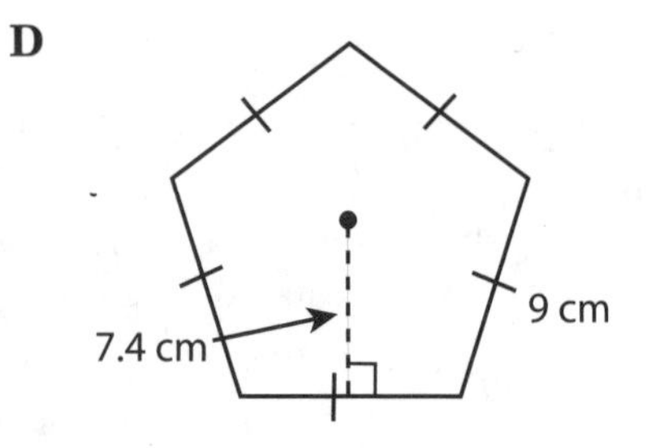

Use the floor plan for the Maxiells' house shown below for Questions 8–9.

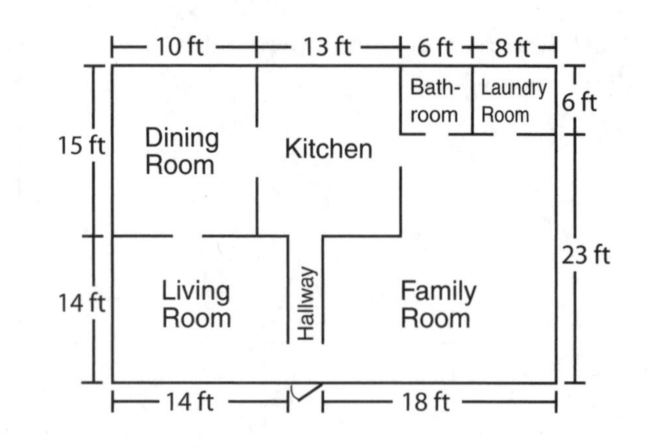

8 The Maxiells are putting new carpet in the living room and family room. How many square feet of carpet will they need?

F 610 ft^2

G 574 ft^2

H 437 ft^2

J 378 ft^2

9 The Maxiells have a rectangular area rug on the hardwood floors in the dining room. The rug is 6.5 feet by 11.5 feet. How many square feet of the hardwood floors is NOT covered by the rug?

Record your answer and fill in the bubbles on the grid below. Be sure to use the correct place value.

				.			
0	0	0	0		0	0	0
1	1	1	1		1	1	1
2	2	2	2		2	2	2
3	3	3	3		3	3	3
4	4	4	4		4	4	4
5	5	5	5		5	5	5
6	6	6	6		6	6	6
7	7	7	7		7	7	7
8	8	8	8		8	8	8
9	9	9	9		9	9	9

10 If the length and width of the figure below are doubled, how will it affect the volume of the figure?

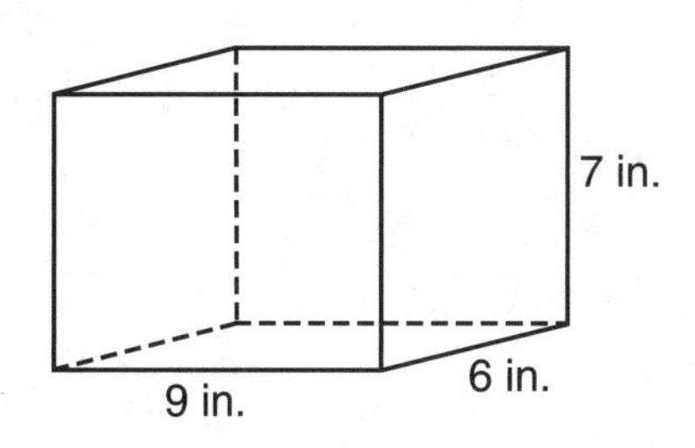

F The volume will be doubled.

G The volume will be quadrupled.

H The volume will be 8 times greater.

J The volume will be 14 times greater.

11 Tina made a 9-inch diameter apple pie, which she cut into 8 slices. Tina and two of her friends each ate a piece of the pie. What is the approximate area of the remaining pie?

A 18 in.^{2}

B 24 in.^{2}

C 40 in.^{2}

D 159 in.^{2}

12 Which of the following statements is NOT true regarding the figure below?

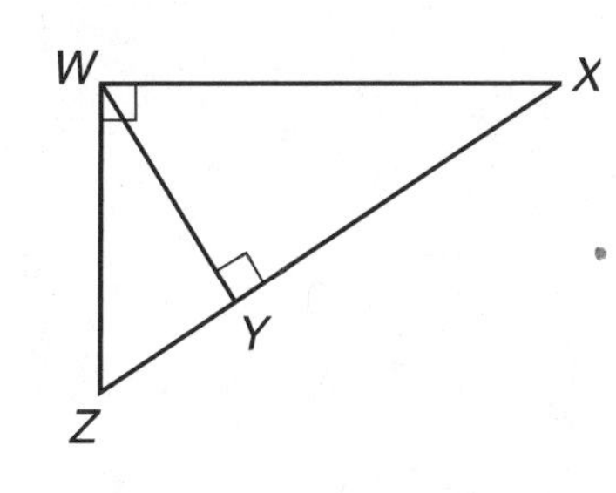

F $\triangle WXZ \sim \triangle YXW$

G $\triangle ZXW \sim \triangle ZWY$

H $\triangle WYZ \sim \triangle XYW$

J Not Here

13 A corollary to a theorem states the following: If the altitude is drawn to the hypotenuse of a right triangle, then each leg of the right triangle is the geometric mean of the length of the hypotenuse and the length of the segment of the hypotenuse that is adjacent to the leg. Use this corollary to find the value of a.

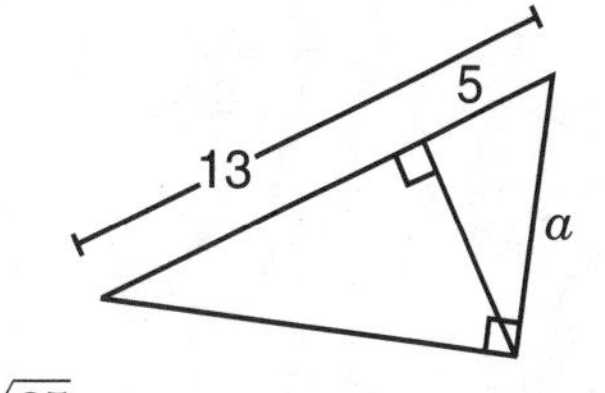

A $\sqrt{65}$

B 12

C $5\sqrt{3}$

D Not Here

14 The marketing department of a company is considering making a key chain with a miniature replica of their top-selling dishwasher detergent. The dimensions of the dishwasher detergent box are 9 inches by 7.5 inches by 2.25 inches. If the replica will be $\frac{1}{5}$ the size of the regular box, what will be the surface area of the miniature replica?

F 1.215 in.^{2}

G 8.37 in.^{2}

H 30.375 in.^{2}

J 41.85 in.^{2}

15 Determine if the triangles are similar. If so, what proves the two triangles are similar?

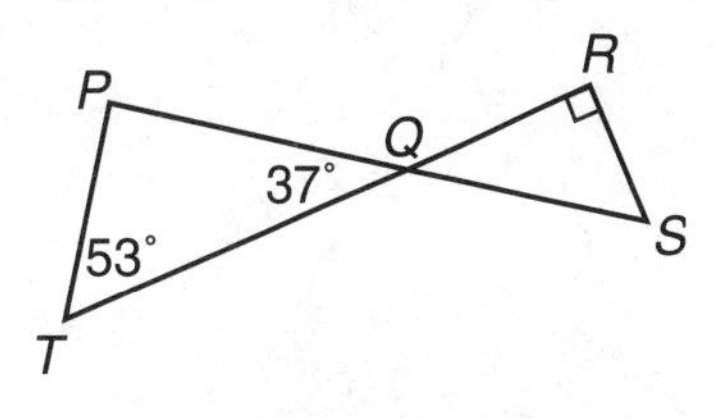

A SSS similarity theorem

B ASA similarity theorem

C AA similarity postulate

D The triangles are not similar.

16 Patrick bought the tent shown below for a camping trip. Before he goes on the camping trip he wants to spray the outside of the tent with a bug repellent. What is the total surface area of the tent that Patrick will need to spray?

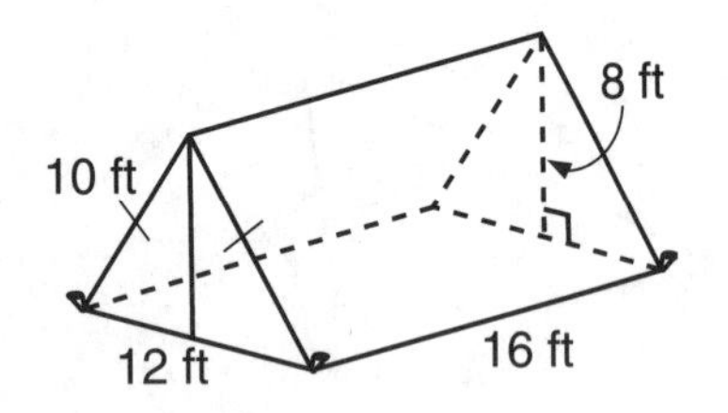

Record your answer and fill in the bubbles on the grid below. Be sure to use the correct place value.

				.			
0	0	0	0		0	0	0
1	1	1	1		1	1	1
2	2	2	2		2	2	2
3	3	3	3		3	3	3
4	4	4	4		4	4	4
5	5	5	5		5	5	5
6	6	6	6		6	6	6
7	7	7	7		7	7	7
8	8	8	8		8	8	8
9	9	9	9		9	9	9

17 What is the area of $\triangle JKL$ to the nearest yard?

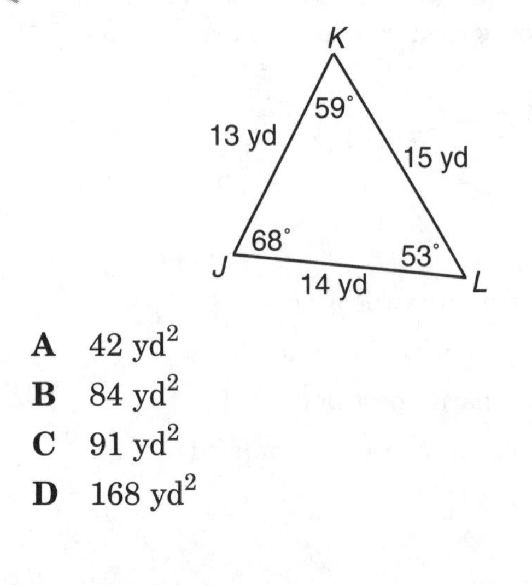

A 42 yd^2

B 84 yd^2

C 91 yd^2

D 168 yd^2

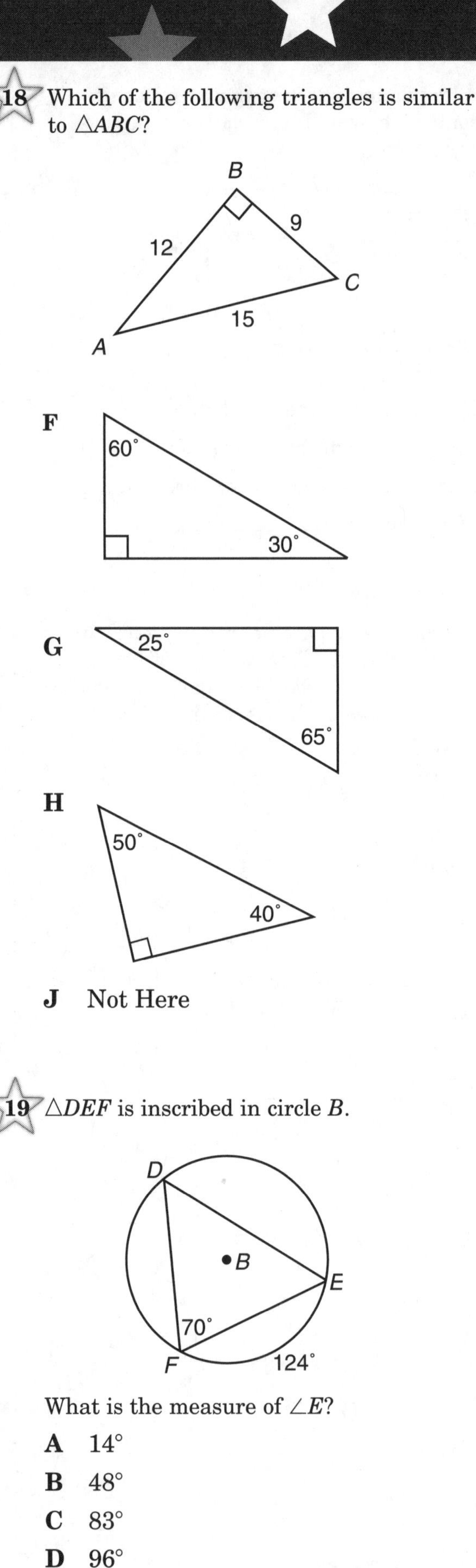

18 Which of the following triangles is similar to $\triangle ABC$?

F

G

H

J Not Here

19 $\triangle DEF$ is inscribed in circle B.

What is the measure of $\angle E$?

A 14°

B 48°

C 83°

D 96°

Focus on TEKS

Lesson 53 Proportional and Nonproportional Relationships

TEKS 8.3A Compare and contrast proportional and nonproportional relationships.
TEKS 8.3B Find solutions to application problems involving proportional relationships such as similarity.

You can apply what you have learned about ratios to solve problems involving proportional relationships.

Recall that a **ratio** is a comparison of two numbers.
A **proportion** is an equation which states that two ratios are equivalent. The two ratios are said to be *proportional* or *in proportion.*

Guided Instruction

Problem 1

The following table shows the cost of renting a jet ski based on 30-minute increments.

Rental Time (min)	Cost
30	\$21.50
60	\$43.00
90	\$64.50
Each Additional $\frac{1}{2}$ Hour	\$21.50

a. Determine whether the data in the table represent a proportional or a nonproportional relationship.

b. How much would it cost to rent a jet ski for 3 hours?

Part a. To determine if the data are in proportion or not, compare each cost term with its associated amount of time to see if there is a common ratio.

It does not matter which term is used in the numerator and which term is used in the denominator, as long as it is consistent.

$$\frac{\text{Cost}}{\frac{1}{2}\text{ hour increments}}$$

$$\frac{\$21.50}{1} = \$21.50$$

$$\frac{\$43}{2} = \$21.50$$

$$\frac{\$64.50}{3} = \$21.50$$

Notice that in each case, there is a common ratio of \$21.50. Since each additional half-hour increment will cost \$21.50, the data are proportional.

Part b. You can use the common ratio of \$21.50 per half-hour increment to calculate the total cost of renting a jet ski for 3 hours.

There are six half-hour increments in a 3-hour period.

$$\frac{\text{Cost}}{6\text{ half-hours}} = \frac{\$21.50}{1}$$

Multiply 6 by \$21.50 to find the total cost.

$$\text{Cost} = \$129.00$$

Solution The data in the table are in proportion, and it costs \$129 to rent a jet ski for 3 hours.

More Problems

Guided Instruction

Problem 2 Determine whether the ratios $\frac{14}{49}$ and $\frac{3}{7}$ are proportional.

One way to tell whether two ratios are proportional is to simplify both fractions to lowest terms and see if the reduced fractions are equivalent. Or, show that the cross products are equal. If $\frac{a}{b}$ and $\frac{c}{d}$ are proportional, then $\frac{a}{b} = \frac{c}{d}$. The cross product then says that $ad = bc$.

Step 1 Notice that the ratio $\frac{3}{7}$ is already in lowest terms. To write $\frac{14}{49}$ in lowest terms, divide both the numerator and denominator by the common factor 7. Since $\frac{3}{7} \neq \frac{2}{7}$, the ratios are not proportional.

$$\frac{14}{49} = \frac{14 \div 7}{49 \div 7} = \frac{2}{7}$$

Step 2 As a check, verify that the cross products are not equal.

$$\frac{14}{49} \stackrel{?}{=} \frac{3}{7}$$

$$14 \cdot 7 \stackrel{?}{=} 49 \cdot 3$$

$$98 \neq 147$$

Solution The ratios $\frac{14}{49}$ and $\frac{3}{7}$ do not reduce to the same fraction, so they are not proportional. You also know this, since their cross products are not equal.

Problem 3 A tree casts a 32.5-foot-long shadow at the same time an 24-foot flagpole casts a 15-foot-long shadow. Set up and solve a proportion to find the height of the tree.

24 ft
32.5 ft
15 ft

Step 1 Let h represent the height of the tree. Since the shadows are being cast at the same time of day, the two triangles shown are similar. Recall that when two figures are similar, the ratios of corresponding sides are the same.

Step 2 Set up a proportion of the two ratios. Make sure you are consistent when comparing corresponding sides. Here we are comparing the ratio of the heights with the ratio of the shadow lengths.

$$\frac{h}{24} = \frac{32.5}{15}$$

Step 3 Solve the proportion by setting the two cross products equal to each other and solving for h.

$$\frac{h}{24} = \frac{32.5}{15}$$

$$15h = 24 \cdot 32.5$$

$$15h = 780$$

$$\frac{15h}{15} = \frac{780}{15}$$

$$h = 52$$

Solution The height of the tree is 52 feet.

Determine whether the data in each table represent a proportional or a nonproportional relationship. If it is proportional, state the common ratio.

1.

Weight (oz)	Postage
1	$0.34
2	$0.57
3	$0.80
4	$1.03

2.

Pancake Mix (cups)	Pancakes
$\frac{1}{2}$	2
1	4
$1\frac{1}{2}$	6
2	8

______________________ ______________________

Tell whether each pair of ratios is proportional. Write *yes* or *no*. Show all of your work.

3. $\frac{7}{14}$ and $\frac{15}{30}$

4. $\frac{55}{65}$ and $\frac{33}{44}$

5. $\frac{9}{13}$ and $\frac{450}{640}$

________ ________ ________

Solve for x in each proportion. Show all of your work.

6. $\frac{x}{6} = -\frac{22}{33}$

7. $\frac{x}{22} = \frac{x+4}{30}$

8. $\frac{3}{x-1} = \frac{12}{3x+1}$

________ ________ ________

9. Mrs. Hanley's geometry class is trying to approximate the height of the Washington Monument. They notice that the monument casts a 333-foot-long shadow at the same time that a 5-foot-tall student casts a 3-foot-long shadow. Approximate the height of the Washington Monument by setting up and solving a proportion. Round your answer to the nearest foot.

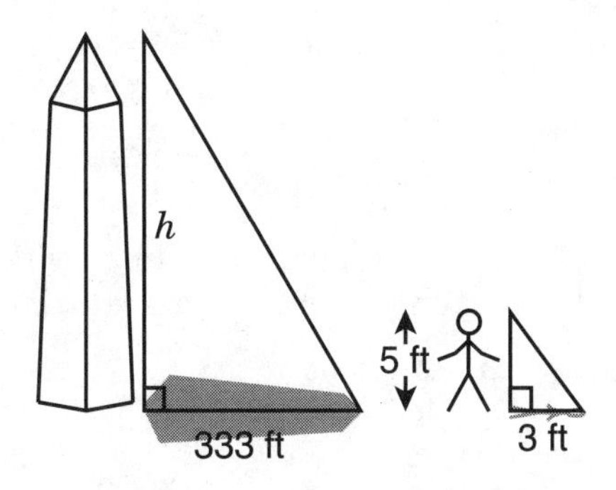

____

Answer the question.

10. Suppose you measure the length of a trees' shadow at 2:00 P.M. and again at 6:00 P.M. Would you expect the ratios of the height of the tree to the lengths of the shadows to be in proportion? Explain.

____

TAKS Objective 9 The student will demonstrate an understanding of percents, proportional relationships, probability, and statistics in application problems.
TEKS 8.3B

DIRECTIONS Read each question. Then circle the letter for the correct answer. If a correct answer is not here, circle the letter for "Not Here."

1 Which of the following ratios is proportional to $\frac{6}{13}$?

A $\frac{30}{52}$

B $\frac{14}{25}$

C $\frac{42}{91}$

D $\frac{27}{65}$

2 What is the value of x in the following proportion?

$$\frac{x+1}{5} = \frac{2x-3}{9}$$

Record your answer and fill in the bubbles on the grid below. Be sure to use the correct place value.

				.			
0	0	0	0		0	0	0
1	1	1	1		1	1	1
2	2	2	2		2	2	2
3	3	3	3		3	3	3
4	4	4	4		4	4	4
5	5	5	5		5	5	5
6	6	6	6		6	6	6
7	7	7	7		7	7	7
8	8	8	8		8	8	8
9	9	9	9		9	9	9

3 If $\frac{a}{b}$ is proportional to $\frac{c}{d}$, which of the following equations is NOT necessarily true?

A $ad = bc$

B $\frac{a}{c} = \frac{b}{d}$

C $ab = cd$

D Not Here

4 In the figure below, $\triangle ABC$ is similar to $\triangle DEF$.

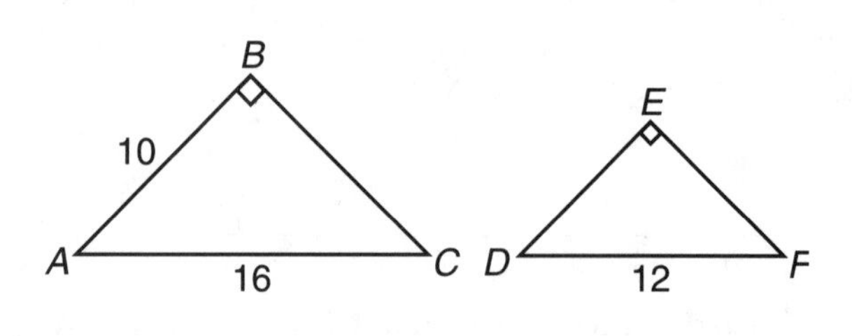

Find the length of $\overline{DE}$.

F 6.5

G 7.5

H 8

J 9

5 A 10-foot-high basketball hoop casts a 12.5-foot-long shadow at the same time a mailbox casts a 5-foot-long shadow. What is the height of the mailbox?

A 3.5 ft

B 4 ft

C 4.5 ft

D 6 ft

Focus on TEKS

Lesson 54 Problems Involving Percents

TEKS 8.3B Estimate and find solutions to application problems involving percents such as rates.

You can use your knowledge of ratios and proportions to solve problems involving percents.

A **percent** is a ratio that compares a number to 100.

Guided Instruction

Problem 1 A stereo system that usually sells for $514 is being discounted 20% during a weekend sale. Estimate the sale price of the stereo system, and compare your estimate to the actual sale price.

Step 1 You can use mental math to estimate the sale price of the stereo system. First, mentally replace $514 with $500 to approximate the amount discounted. This number is close to the actual price of $514. Since it is a round number, it will be easier to manipulate.

Step 2 The stereo system is being discounted 20%. This means that $20 out of every $100 is being discounted. Since there are five $100 increments in our estimated regular price of $500, the discount will be about $5 \cdot \$20 = \$100$.

Step 3 Mentally subtract $100 from the actual regular price of $514. The estimated sale price of the stereo system is $\$514 - \$100 = \$414$.

A proportion can be used to solve for the exact sale price of the stereo system. When proportions are used to solve percent problems, the ratio that compares the percent with 100 is the *rate*. The other ratio compares the percentage and the base, which is equivalent to the rate. These proportions are shown below.

$$\frac{\text{Percentage}}{\text{Base}} = \frac{r}{100} \qquad \frac{\text{Percentage}}{\text{Base}} = \text{Rate}$$

Step 4 Set up a proportion to solve for the sale discount. You want to find what number is 20% of $514. So, the base is $514, the percentage is unknown, and the rate is $\frac{20}{100}$.

$$\frac{x}{514} = \frac{20}{100}$$

Step 5 Solve the proportion for x. Since x represents the amount of discount, the actual sale price can be found by subtracting x from $514.

$$\frac{x}{514} = \frac{20}{100}$$

$$100x = 514 \cdot 20$$

$$100x = 10{,}280$$

$$\frac{100x}{100} = \frac{10{,}280}{100}$$

$$x = 102.80$$

Sale Price: $\$514 - \$102.80 = \$411.20$

Solution The estimated sale price, which was found using mental math, was $414, whereas the actual sale price is $411.20. This was a good estimate.

Guided Instruction

More Problems

Problem 2 What percent of 240 is 62.4?

Step 1 Set up a proportion to find the percent. Let x represent the percent.

$$\frac{62.4}{240} = \frac{x}{100}$$

Step 2 Solve the proportion for x.

$$\frac{62.4}{240} = \frac{x}{100}$$
$$62.4 \cdot 100 = 240x$$
$$6{,}240 = 240x$$
$$\frac{6{,}240}{240} = \frac{240x}{240}$$
$$x = 26$$

Solution The number 62.4 is 26% of 240.

Problem 3 What number is 35% of 220?

Step 1 Set up a proportion to find the number. Let x represent the percentage of 220.

$$\frac{x}{220} = \frac{35}{100}$$

Step 2 Solve the proportion for x.

$$\frac{x}{220} = \frac{35}{100}$$
$$100x = 220 \cdot 35$$
$$100x = 7{,}700$$
$$\frac{100x}{100} = \frac{7{,}700}{100}$$
$$x = 77$$

Solution The number 77 is 35% of 220.

Problem 4 How much simple interest is earned if $750 is invested at 6.5% annual interest for a period of 2 years?

Interest is an amount paid or earned for the use of money. For example, you may have to pay interest for borrowing money, or a savings account may pay you interest for using your money. The formula to calculate simple interest is $I = prt$, where I is the interest, p is the principal or initial amount, r is the interest rate, and t is the time in years.

Step 1 Rewrite 6.5% as a decimal.

$$6.5\% = \frac{6.5}{100} = 0.065$$

Step 2 Substitute the appropriate values into the simple interest formula and simplify.

$$I = prt$$
$$I = 750(0.065)(2)$$
$$I = 750(0.13)$$
$$I = 97.50$$

Solution An investment of $750 at 6.5% annual interest over 2 years would earn $97.50 in simple interest.

Apply the TEKS Use a proportion to find each number or percent. Show all of your work.

1. What number is 50% of 122?

____

2. What percent of 172 is 43?

____

3. What percent of 25.8 is 8.6?

____

4. The number 45 is 22.5% of what number?

____

5. What number is 80% of 18.75?

____

6. What percent of 98 is 44.1?

____

Solve each problem.

7. A car that costs $14,985 requires a 10% down payment. Use mental math to estimate the amount of the down payment, and then use a proportion to calculate the actual down payment. How does your estimate compare to the actual amount?

____

8. A blouse that regularly sells for $29 is reduced by 30% during a sidewalk sale. Julie estimates the sale price of the blouse to be about $20. Do you think this a good estimate? Explain why or why not.

____

Use the simple interest formula to solve the following problems.

9. For how many years was $1,000 invested if it earned $125 interest at a rate of 5% per year?

____

10. Michelle borrowed a principal amount of $5,600 to remodel her kitchen. At the end of a 3-year period, she had repaid a total amount of $6,986. How much simple interest did she pay for using the bank's money? What was the annual interest rate of the loan?

____

TAKS Objective 9 The student will demonstrate an understanding of percents, proportional relationships, probability, and statistics in application problems.
TEKS 8.3B

DIRECTIONS Read each question. Then circle the letter for the correct answer. If a correct answer is not here, circle the letter for "Not Here."

1 A refrigerator was originally priced at $689. During a clearance sale, the price of the refrigerator was reduced by 20%. About how much was the price of the refrigerator during the sale?

A $499

B $535

C $549

D $585

2 Robert paid a total of $58.29 for a new pair of shoes. Of that amount, $3.30 was sales tax. What is the sales tax rate in Robert's town?

F 7%

G 6.5%

H 6%

J 5.5%

3 How much simple interest is earned on a principal investment of $500 at 6.25% annual interest over a period of 18 months?

A $562.50

B $93.75

C $46.88

D $45

4 Elizabeth purchased 2 printer cartridges for $31.99 each in a state with a 5.5% sales tax rate. What was the total amount of her bill?

F $71.20

G $67.50

H $35.51

J $33.75

5 Maurice saved $146.25 by purchasing a computer during a clearance sale. If the original price of the computer was $975, what was the percent of the discount that Maurice received?

A 30%

B 25%

C 15%

D 10%

6 Suzanne borrowed $2,250 from her bank at an annual rate of 7%. At the end of the loan term she owed $393.75 in simple interest. How long was the term of the loan?

F 18 months

G 2 years

H 30 months

J 3 years

Lesson 55 Theoretical and Experimental Probabilities

TEKS 8.11B Use theoretical probabilities and experimental results to make predictions and decisions.
TEKS 8.11C Select and use different models to simulate an event.

Ratios and proportional relationships can be used to solve problems involving theoretical and experimental probabilities.

The **probability** of an event is a numerical value between 0 and 1 measuring the likelihood that the event will occur. The closer a probability is to 1, the more likely the event will occur.
The **sample space** of an event is the set of all possible outcomes of the event.

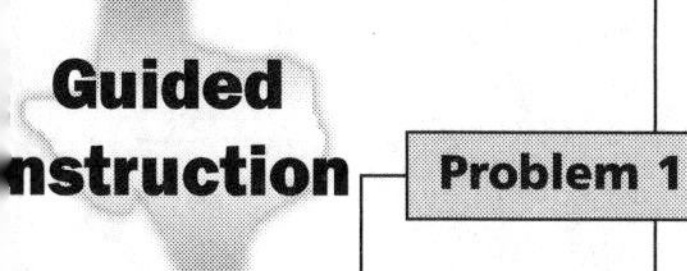

Problem 1

An experiment consists of rolling 2 number cubes, each labeled with the numbers 1 through 6, and recording the result. Orlando rolled the number cubes 50 times. He observed that both number cubes showed an odd number a total of 12 times. Compare the experimental and theoretical probabilities of the experiment.

The mathematical probability, or theoretical probability, of an event is the ratio of the number of favorable outcomes to the number of possible outcomes. This formula for the probability of event E is shown below.

$$P(E) = \frac{\text{number of favorable outcomes}}{\text{number of possible outcomes}}$$

When performing an experiment, the experimental probability of an event is the ratio of the number of favorable outcomes observed to the number of times the experiment is performed.

Step 1 Orlando observed 2 odd numbers on 12 of the 50 rolls. So, the experimental probability is $\frac{12}{50}$, or 0.24.

$$P_{exp}(\text{2 odd numbers}) = \frac{12}{50} = 0.24$$

Step 2 To find the theoretical probability of rolling 2 odd numbers, list all of the elements of the sample space. For example, if one of the cubes shows a 1, the other cube could show a 1, 2, 3, 4, 5, or 6. Use a table to organize all of the possible outcomes.

First Cube \ Second Cube	1	2	3	4	5	6
1	1,1	1,2	1,3	1,4	1,5	1,6
2	2,1	2,2	2,3	2,4	2,5	2,6
3	3,1	3,2	3,3	3,4	3,5	3,6
4	4,1	4,2	4,3	4,4	4,5	4,6
5	5,1	5,2	5,3	5,4	5,5	5,6
6	6,1	6,2	6,3	6,4	6,5	6,6

Step 3 Notice that there are a total of 36 possible outcomes in the sample space. Of these, both number cubes are odd in 9 of the outcomes. Use the probability formula to calculate the theoretical probability.

$$P(\text{2 odd numbers}) = \frac{9}{36} = 0.25$$

Solution

Orlando observed in his experiment that the probability of rolling 2 odd numbers was 0.24. The theoretical probability of rolling 2 odd numbers with 2 number cubes is 0.25. Orlando's experiment seems to be consistent with the mathematical expectation.

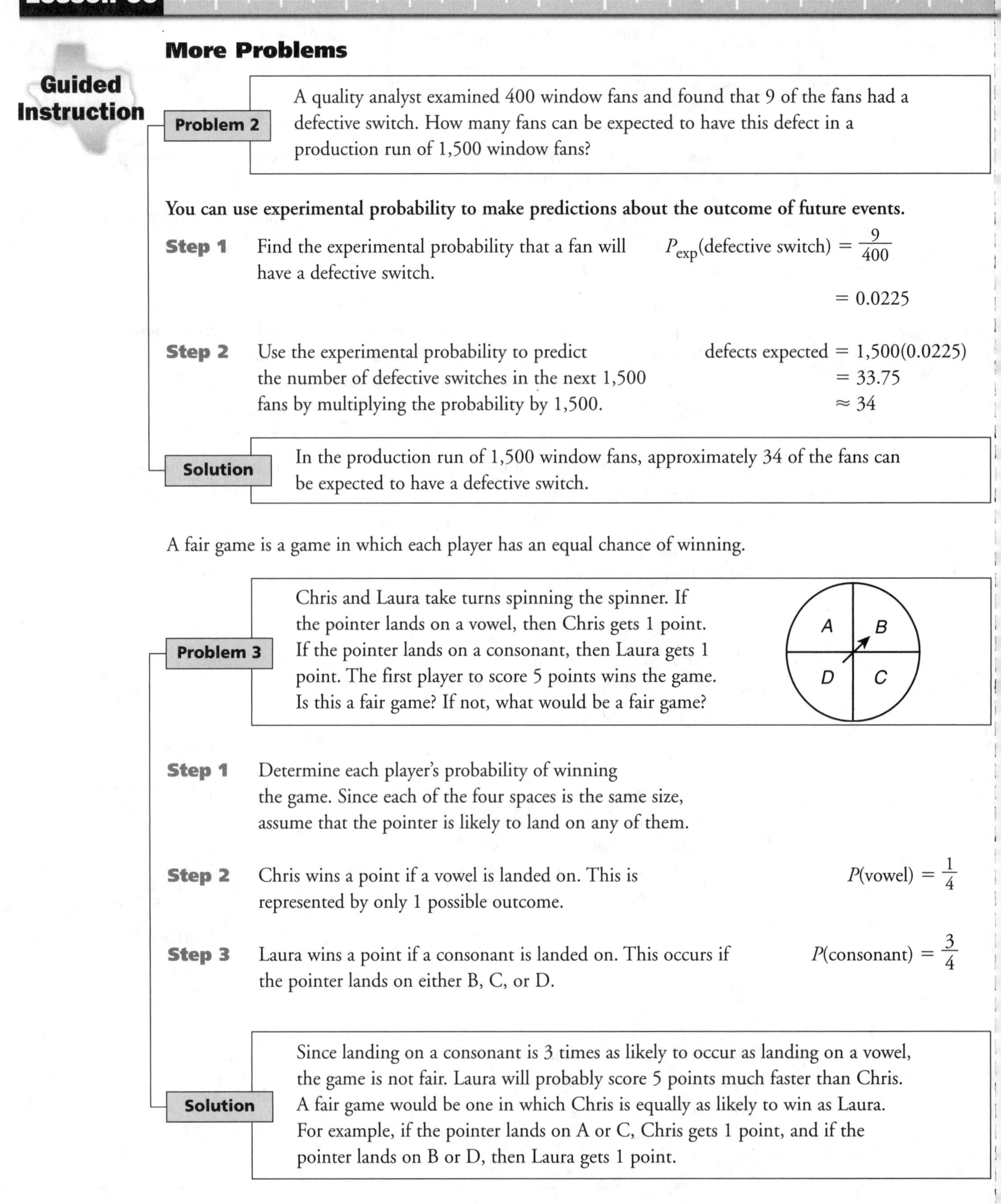

More Problems

Guided Instruction

Problem 2

A quality analyst examined 400 window fans and found that 9 of the fans had a defective switch. How many fans can be expected to have this defect in a production run of 1,500 window fans?

You can use experimental probability to make predictions about the outcome of future events.

Step 1 Find the experimental probability that a fan will have a defective switch.

$$P_{exp}(\text{defective switch}) = \frac{9}{400} = 0.0225$$

Step 2 Use the experimental probability to predict the number of defective switches in the next 1,500 fans by multiplying the probability by 1,500.

$$\text{defects expected} = 1{,}500(0.0225) = 33.75 \approx 34$$

Solution

In the production run of 1,500 window fans, approximately 34 of the fans can be expected to have a defective switch.

A fair game is a game in which each player has an equal chance of winning.

Problem 3

Chris and Laura take turns spinning the spinner. If the pointer lands on a vowel, then Chris gets 1 point. If the pointer lands on a consonant, then Laura gets 1 point. The first player to score 5 points wins the game. Is this a fair game? If not, what would be a fair game?

Step 1 Determine each player's probability of winning the game. Since each of the four spaces is the same size, assume that the pointer is likely to land on any of them.

Step 2 Chris wins a point if a vowel is landed on. This is represented by only 1 possible outcome.

$$P(\text{vowel}) = \frac{1}{4}$$

Step 3 Laura wins a point if a consonant is landed on. This occurs if the pointer lands on either B, C, or D.

$$P(\text{consonant}) = \frac{3}{4}$$

Solution

Since landing on a consonant is 3 times as likely to occur as landing on a vowel, the game is not fair. Laura will probably score 5 points much faster than Chris. A fair game would be one in which Chris is equally as likely to win as Laura. For example, if the pointer lands on A or C, Chris gets 1 point, and if the pointer lands on B or D, then Laura gets 1 point.

Apply the TEKS An experiment consists of spinning the spinner shown at the right and recording the result. If each space is equally likely to be landed on, find each theoretical probability.

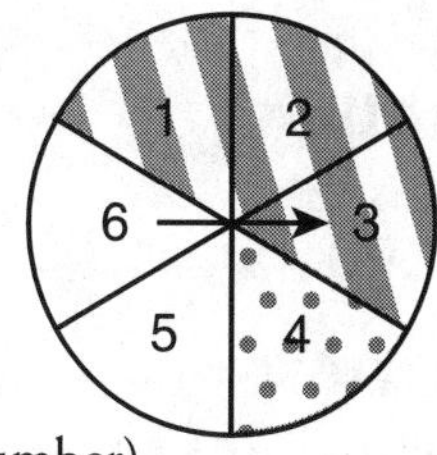

1. $P(4)$ ________

2. $P(\text{stripe})$ ________

3. $P(\text{even number})$ ________

4. $P(\text{solid or } 1)$ ________

5. $P(7)$ ________

6. $P(\text{no dots})$ ________

7. If the spinner is spun 250 times and each result is recorded, how many times would you expect the pointer to land on a dotted space?

____

A deli offers three choices of bread: wheat, rye, or white; two choices of meat: turkey or salami; and two choices of toppings: mayo or mustard. Using this information, answer the following.

8. Suppose a sandwich can consist of one choice of bread, one choice of meat, and one choice of topping. List the sample space of possible sandwiches.

____

9. If a sandwich is chosen at random, what is the probability that it will be turkey with mayo on wheat?

____

Answer each question.

10. It is expected that 0.75% of all portable CD players coming off an assembly line will be defective. In a production run of 5,000 CD players, how many are expected to be defective?

____

11. Do you think it is possible for an event to have a probability greater than 1? Explain why or why not.

____

____

TAKS Objective 9 The student will demonstrate an understanding of percents, proportional relationships, probability, and statistics in application problems.
TEKS 8.11B

DIRECTIONS Read each question. Then circle the letter for the correct answer. If a correct answer is not here, circle the letter for "Not Here."

1 A bag contains 3 red marbles, 7 blue marbles, and 4 white marbles. If a marble is selected from the bag at random, what is the probability of selecting a white marble?

A $\frac{7}{14}$

B $\frac{3}{7}$

C $\frac{5}{14}$

D $\frac{2}{7}$

2 A quality control specialist examined 225 tires at a factory and found that 3 of the tires had defective valve stems. In a production run of 5,000 tires, about how many would you expect to have defective valve stems?

F 22

G 34

H 67

J 81

3 In Clarence's last 180 at-bats, he has struck out 27 times and gotten 53 hits. About how many hits would you expect Clarence to get in his next 40 at-bats?

A 21

B 17

C 16

D 12

4 Tom and Mike are using the spinner shown below to create a probability game.

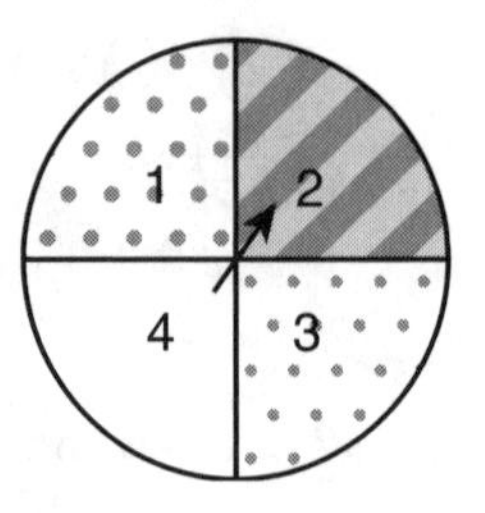

Which of the following scenarios describes a fair game?

F Tom gets a point for stripes, Mike gets a point for dots.

G Tom gets a point for an odd number, Mike gets a point for stripes or solids.

H Tom gets a point for a prime number, Mike gets a point for solids.

J Not Here

5 Which of the following could NOT represent the probability of an event occurring?

A 1.1

B 0.999

C 10^{-6}

D Not Here

Focus on TEKS

Lesson 56 Probabilities of Compound Events

TEKS 8.11A Find the probabilities of compound events (dependent and independent).

In this lesson, you will expand your ability to find probabilities by studying more complex events.

A **compound event** is comprised of two or more simple events.
Events are called **independent events** when the outcome of one event has no effect on the outcome of another event.
Events are called **dependent events** when the outcome of one event does affect the outcome of another event.

Guided Instruction

Problem 1

A bag contains 7 purple chips, 6 white chips, 5 blue chips, and 3 red chips. Tonya selects one chip from the bag, records its color, and then replaces it in the bag. She then selects a second chip from the bag and records its color. What is the probability that Tonya will select a purple chip first and a white chip second?

This scenario represents a compound event. It is comprised of the simple events: *select a purple chip* and *select a white chip*. Notice that since the first chip is replaced before selecting the second chip, the bag will have the same color and types of chips for both selections. Thus, neither of the simple events will have any bearing on the outcome of the other event. These represent independent events. You can use the following formula to calculate the probability that two independent events, A and B, will occur.

$$P(A \text{ and } B) = P(A) \cdot P(B)$$

Use the probability formula for two independent events to solve the problem.

Step 1 Calculate the probability of Tonya's selecting a purple chip from the bag. There are 21 total chips in the bag, and 7 of those represent the favorable outcome of selecting a purple chip.

$$P(\text{purple}) = \frac{7}{21} = \frac{1}{3}$$

Step 2 Find the probability that Tonya will select a white chip after replacing the chip selected in Step 1. There are still 21 total chips in the bag, 6 of which are white chips.

$$P(\text{white}) = \frac{6}{21} = \frac{2}{7}$$

Step 3 Find the probability.

$$P(\text{purple and white}) = \frac{1}{3} \cdot \frac{2}{7} = \frac{2}{21}$$

Solution

The probability that Tonya will select a purple chip and a white chip after replacing the first chip is $\frac{2}{21}$.

More Problems

Guided Instruction

Problem 2

A cookie jar contains 8 chocolate chip cookies, 12 peanut butter cookies, and 6 oatmeal cookies. What is the probability that Julie will randomly select an oatmeal cookie, and then that Mark will randomly select a chocolate chip cookie?

In this example, the outcome of the first simple event will affect the outcome of the second event. If A and B are dependent events, the probability of both A and B occurring is given by the following formula.

$$P(A \text{ and } B) = P(A) \cdot P(B, \text{given that } A \text{ has occurred})$$

Step 1 Find the probability that Julie will randomly select an oatmeal cookie. There are 26 total cookies, and 6 of them are oatmeal.

$$P(\text{oatmeal}) = \frac{6}{26} = \frac{3}{13}$$

Step 2 Next, find the probability that Mark will select a chocolate chip cookie after Julie has selected an oatmeal cookie. Now there are 25 cookies left, and 8 are chocolate chip.

$$P(\text{chocolate chip}) = \frac{8}{25}$$

Step 3 Use the probability formula for two dependent events.

$$P(\text{oatmeal and chocolate chip}) = \frac{3}{13} \cdot \frac{8}{25} = \frac{24}{325}$$

Solution The probability that Julie will select an oatmeal cookie and then Mark will select a chocolate chip cookie is $\frac{24}{325}$.

Problem 3

If Tina rolls a number cube, labeled 1 through 6, and then flips a coin, what is the probability that she will roll an odd number and that the coin will be heads?

Step 1 These are independent events since they will have no bearing on each other. First, find the probability of rolling an odd number.

$$P(\text{odd number}) = \frac{3}{6} = \frac{1}{2}$$

Step 2 Find the probability of flipping heads with the coin.

$$P(\text{heads}) = \frac{1}{2}$$

Step 3 The probability that both independent events will occur is the product of the probabilities that the two simple events will occur.

$$P(\text{odd and heads}) = \frac{1}{2} \cdot \frac{1}{2} = \frac{1}{4}$$

Solution The probability that Tina will roll an odd number and that the coin will be heads is $\frac{1}{4}$.

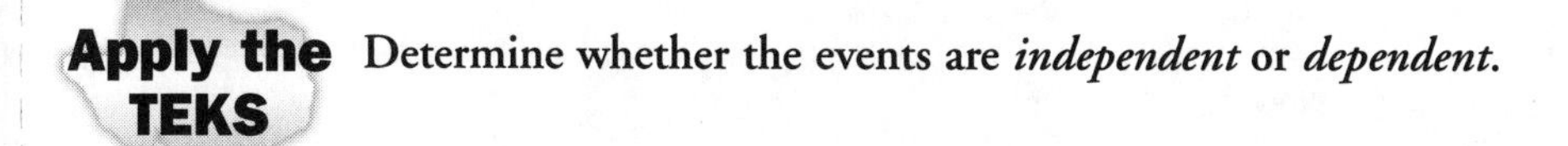

Apply the TEKS **Determine whether the events are *independent* or *dependent*.**

1. Monica rolls a number cube, notes the number, then rolls it again.

   ____

2. James picks a number from a hat and keeps it. Then Lawrence picks a number from the hat.

   ____

3. Mary draws a card from a deck of cards. Without replacing it, she then draws another card.

   ____

4. Juanita draws a name from a hat but does not replace it, and then flips a coin.

   ____

Maxwell spins each of the spinners one time and records the result. Find each probability.

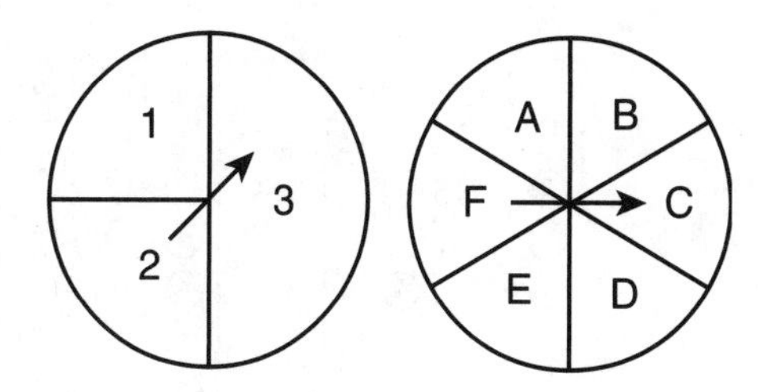

5. P(2 and B)

   ____

6. P(***not*** 1 and a vowel)

   ____

7. P(odd number and D)

   ____

8. P(real number and a vowel)

   ____

A jar contains 11 quarters, 7 dimes, and 12 nickels. A coin is selected at random and not replaced. Then another coin is randomly selected. Find each probability.

9. P(quarter and nickel)

   ____

10. P(nickel and dime)

   ____

11. P(2 nickels)

   ____

Answer each question.

12. What does it mean for two events to be dependent events? Give an example.

   ____

13. What does it mean for two events to be independent events? Give an example.

   ____

TAKS Objective 9 The student will demonstrate an understanding of percents, proportional relationships, probability, and statistics in application problems.

TEKS 8.11A

DIRECTIONS Read each question. Then circle the letter for the correct answer. If a correct answer is not here, circle the letter for "Not Here."

1 Events A and B are dependent events. The probability of event A is 0.25 and the probability of event B, given that event A has occurred, is 0.44. What is the probability of A and B?

Record your answer and fill in the bubbles on the grid below. Be sure to use the correct place value.

				.			
0	0	0	0		0	0	0
1	1	1	1		1	1	1
2	2	2	2		2	2	2
3	3	3	3		3	3	3
4	4	4	4		4	4	4
5	5	5	5		5	5	5
6	6	6	6		6	6	6
7	7	7	7		7	7	7
8	8	8	8		8	8	8
9	9	9	9		9	9	9

2 A number cube with sides labeled 1 through 6 is rolled, and then a second number cube also labeled 1 through 6 is rolled. What is the probability that both number cubes will show the same number?

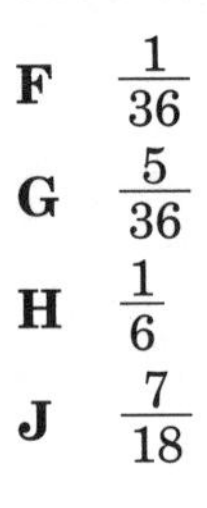

F $\frac{1}{36}$

G $\frac{5}{36}$

H $\frac{1}{6}$

J $\frac{7}{18}$

3 A 3-person committee is selected by placing the names of 12 employees in a hat and then randomly choosing 3 of the names. If there are 7 female employees and 5 male employees, what is the probability that the committee will be made up of all females?

A $\frac{35}{288}$

B $\frac{7}{44}$

C $\frac{7}{12}$

D Not Here

4 Nora rolls a number cube labeled 1 through 6, flips a coin, and then rolls the number cube again. What is the probability that she will roll two even numbers and that the coin will show tails?

F $\frac{3}{16}$

G $\frac{1}{8}$

H $\frac{1}{12}$

J $\frac{1}{16}$

5 Ten cards are numbered from 1 to 10 and placed in a bag. One card is selected and not replaced, and then a second card is selected. What is the probability of selecting an odd number and the next consecutive integer?

A $\frac{1}{2}$

B $\frac{3}{16}$

C $\frac{1}{9}$

D $\frac{1}{18}$

Focus on TEKS

Lesson 57 Measures of Central Tendency

TEKS 8.12A Select the appropriate measure of central tendency to describe a set of data for a particular purpose.

You can interpret and draw conclusions from a set of data by using measures of central tendency. These include the mean, median, and mode.

The **mean** of a set of numbers is found by adding all of the numbers and dividing by the total numbers in the set. It is also called the *average*.

The **median** is the middle number when the numbers in the data set are arranged from least to greatest.

The **mode** is the number or numbers that occur most frequently in the data set.

Problem 1

The table at the right shows the midterm exam grades in Mr. Franklin's algebra class. Which measure of central tendency best describes the average grade on the test?

Student	Grade
01	75
02	65
03	75
04	0
05	67
06	69
07	75
08	72
09	75
10	72

Each of the measures of central tendency is a type of average. The most appropriate measure to describe the data depends on the distribution of the data.

Step 1 Find the mean of the data by adding all of the grades and dividing by 10.

$$\text{Mean} = \frac{75 + 65 + 75 + 0 + 67 + 69 + 75 + 72 + 75 + 72}{10} = \frac{645}{10} = 64.5$$

Step 2 To find the median and mode, it may be helpful to sketch a line plot of the data. Place a dot over each score along the line to see how the data are distributed.

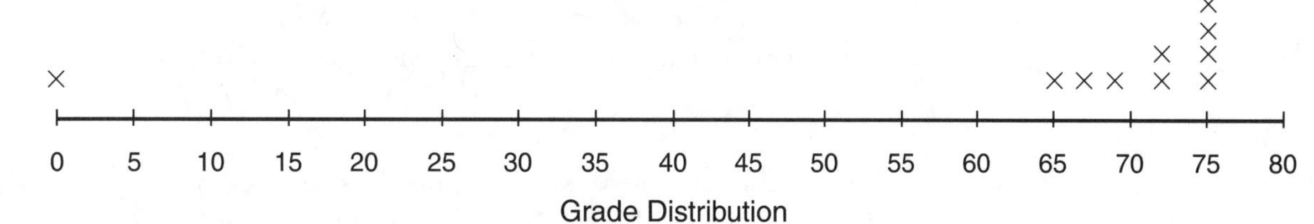

Step 3 The median is the middle number of the data. Since there is an even number of data points, the median is the mean of the middle two numbers.

0 65 67 69 72 72 75 75 75 75

$$\text{Median} = \frac{72 + 72}{2} = 72$$

Step 4 The mode is the grade that occurs most frequently. This is easily seen in the line plot as 75.

Solution

The mean is dragged down by the score of 0, so it is probably too low to be a good description of the average grade. The mode happens to be the highest grade scored on the test, so it is not a very good measure of central tendency. Most of the test scores are clustered very near the median score of 72. So, the median is the best measure of central tendency.

Another Problem

Guided Instruction

Problem 2

Fifteen students recorded their heart rates (in beats per minute) after running laps around the gym. The data points are shown in the table. Create a stem-and-leaf plot of the data, and find the mean, median, and mode.

Student	01	02	03	04	05	06	07	08	09	10	11	12	13	14	15
Heart Rate	98	116	122	105	129	110	122	110	131	99	126	130	107	110	125

In a *stem-and-leaf plot*, the stems represent the greatest common place values of the data, and the leaves are the next greatest place value. For example, 9|4 represents 94 and 13|5 represents 135. When creating a stem-and-leaf plot, list the leaves in ascending order.

Step 1 Choose the appropriate stems for the plot. Since the heart rates range from the 90s to the 130s, let the stems be 9, 10, 11, 12, and 13. Then, fill in the appropriate leaves in ascending order as shown.

Stem	Leaf
9	8 9
10	5 7
11	0 0 0 6
12	2 2 5 6 9
13	0 1

Step 2 Calculate the mean of the heart rates. The sum of all 15 of the heart rates is 1,740.

$$\text{Mean} = \frac{1{,}740}{15} = 116$$

Step 3 Since there are 15 data points, the median will be the eighth point. Locate the data point in the plot that has 7 points above it and 7 points below it. This is point 116.

Median = 116

Step 4 The mode also can be located easily using the stem-and-leaf plot. Simply look for the leaf that occurs most frequently. In this case, the mode is 110.

Mode = 110

Solution

Both the mean and the median of the data are 116 beats per minute. For this set of data, the range is 33(131-98). The mode of the students' heart rates is 110 beats per minute.

Although range is not a measure of central tendency, it is often included with mean, median, and mode. Range is the difference between the greatest and least values in a set.

Apply the TEKS Determine which measure of central tendency was used to characterize each set of data and reach the following conclusions. Write *mean, median,* or *mode.*

1. Half of the bowlers in Mike's league had a score of 148 or lower.

____

2. The most common number of pets per household was 2.

____

3. The average final grade in Ms. Landon's class was 87.4.

____

4. Players ranking in the top half of the scores will qualify to play in the next round of the tournament.

____

Find the mean, median, and mode for each set of data.

5. 9, 12, 4, 10, 17, 11, 4, 5

mean: ________

median: ________

mode: ________

6. 165, 175, 165, 140, 150, 175

mean: ________

median: ________

mode: ________

7. 0.1, 0.5, 0.3, 0, 0.9, 1.2, 0.4, 0.6

mean: ________

median: ________

mode: ________

Answer each question.

8. Write a set of data with at least 7 values that has a median of 54 and a mean of 57.

____

9. Write a set of data with at least 7 values that has a mean of 6, a median of 6, and a mode of 7.

____

10. Last week, the sales commissions earned by employees at a retail store were $785, $640, $830, $625, $1,750, $715, $660, $850, $705, and $690. Create a stem-and-leaf plot in the space below, and find the mean, median, and mode.

mean: ____________

median: ____________

mode: ____________

11. In Exercise 10, which measure of central tendency best describes the average sales commission? Explain.

____

TAKS Objective 9 The student will demonstrate an understanding of percents, proportional relationships, probability, and statistics in application problems.
TEKS 8.12A

DIRECTIONS Read each question. Then circle the letter for the correct answer. If a correct answer is not here, circle the letter for "Not Here."

1 Which of the following best describes the median of a set of data?

A The median is also known as the average of a set of data.

B The median is the middle number of the set of data when arranged in ascending order.

C The median is the number that occurs most frequently in a set of data.

D Not Here

2 What is the mode of the line plot shown below?

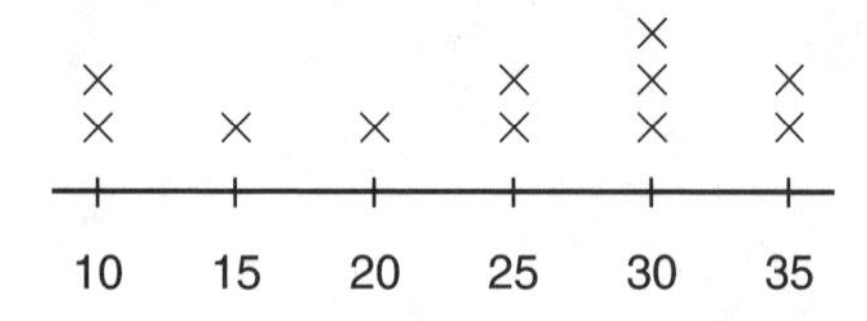

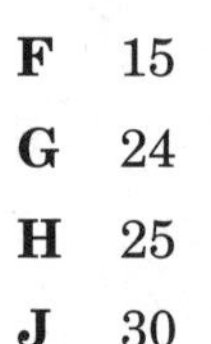

F 15

G 24

H 25

J 30

3 Lewis has scores of 87, 90, 98, and 95 on his first four tests. What must he score on the final test to have an average of at least 93?

A 98

B 95

C 92

D 89

4 Consider the following statement: The average American household owns 2.37 cars. Which measure of central tendency was most likely used to reach this conclusion?

F Mean

G Median

H Mode

J Not Here

5 What is the median of the data depicted in the stem-and-leaf plot below?

Stem	Leaf
4	1 3 9 9
5	0 4 6
6	1 1 2
7	3 5 5 8 9
8	2 4

A 56

B 61

C 67

D 73

Focus on TEKS

Lesson 58 Graphs and Histograms

TEKS 8.12C Construct circle graphs, bar graphs, and histograms.

It is often useful to display statistical data in the form of a graph, such as a bar graph, a circle graph, or a histogram.

A **circle graph** compares percents of a whole. The full circle represents 100%, and each sector represents a part of the whole.

Guided Instruction

Problem 1

Sherri charted her expenses last month to study her budget. She had the following expenses: rent, \$600; transportation, \$375; food, \$225; entertainment, \$180; clothing, \$120. Create a circle graph depicting Sherri's expense budget.

Step 1 Find the sum of all the items. This amount will be represented by the whole of the circle.

$600 + 375 + 225 + 180 + 120 = 1{,}500$

Step 2 Divide each budget item by \$1,500 to find what percent of the whole it represents.

These percents will translate to proportionally sized sectors in the circle graph.

Rent: $\frac{600}{1{,}500} = 0.4 = 40\%$

Transportation: $\frac{375}{1{,}500} = 0.25 = 25\%$

Food: $\frac{225}{1{,}500} = 0.15 = 15\%$

Entertainment: $\frac{180}{1{,}500} = 0.12 = 12\%$

Clothing: $\frac{120}{1{,}500} = 0.08 = 8\%$

Step 3 There are 360° in a circle. To find the size of the central angle for each sector of the graph, multiply the percents by 360°.

Rent: $0.4 \cdot 360° = 144°$

Transportation: $0.25 \cdot 360° = 90°$

Food: $0.15 \cdot 360° = 54°$

Entertainment: $0.12 \cdot 360° = 43.2°$

Clothing: $0.08 \cdot 360° = 28.8°$

Step 4 Use a compass, a protractor, and a straightedge to sketch a circle with the appropriately sized sectors. In doing so, you can approximate 43.2° as 43° and 28.8° as 29°. Label each sector with the proper title as well as the percent of the total budget.

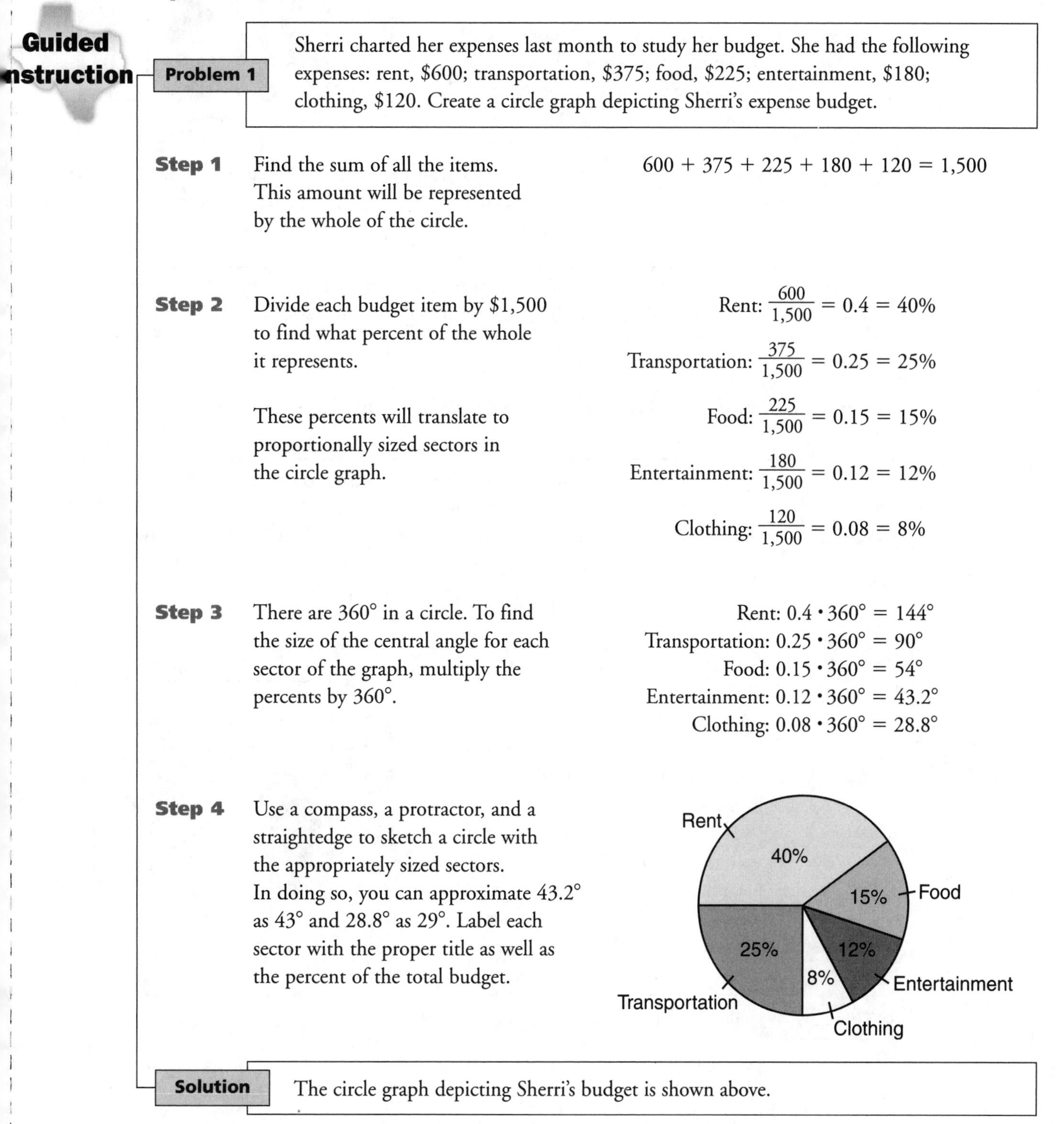

Solution The circle graph depicting Sherri's budget is shown above.

Guided Instruction

A **bar graph** compares amounts and quantities using vertical or horizontal bars.

More Problems

Problem 2

The bar graph shows the final scores of a 3-game volleyball match. What was the result of each game, and what was the result of the match?

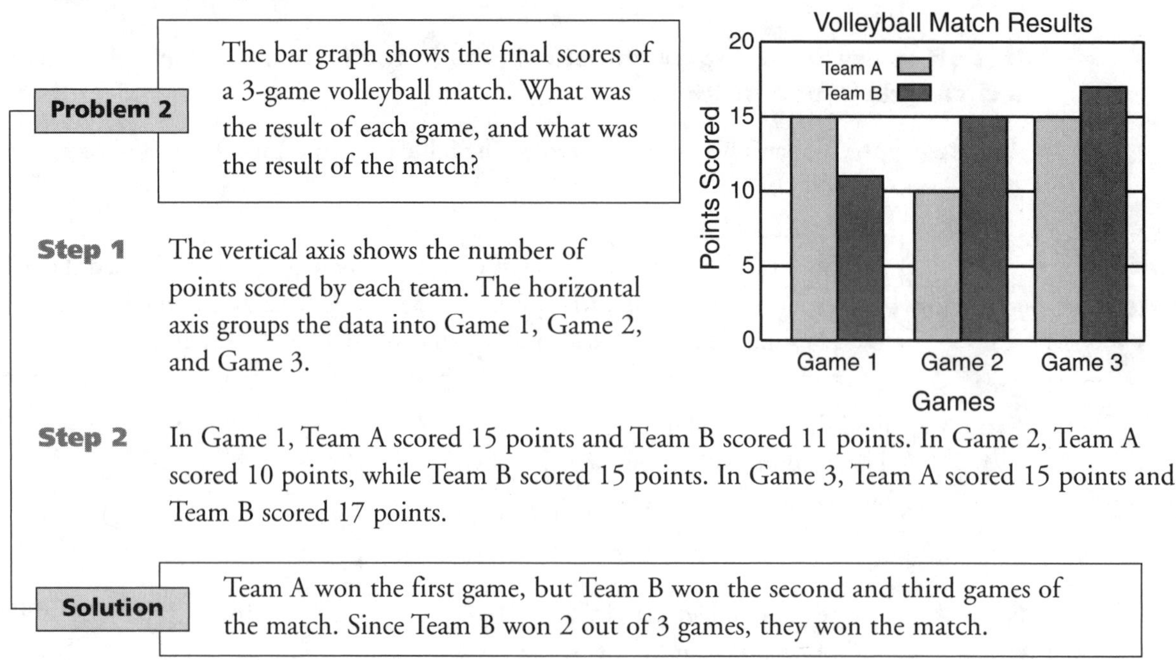

Step 1 The vertical axis shows the number of points scored by each team. The horizontal axis groups the data into Game 1, Game 2, and Game 3.

Step 2 In Game 1, Team A scored 15 points and Team B scored 11 points. In Game 2, Team A scored 10 points, while Team B scored 15 points. In Game 3, Team A scored 15 points and Team B scored 17 points.

Solution Team A won the first game, but Team B won the second and third games of the match. Since Team B won 2 out of 3 games, they won the match.

A **histogram** is a bar graph that shows the frequency of data within equal intervals.

Problem 3

During a sales promotion, the manager of a sporting goods store charted the number of pairs of running shoes sold during the day. The store sold 29 pairs between 9 A.M. and noon, 35 pairs between noon and 3 P.M., 41 pairs between 3 P.M. and 6 P.M., and 32 pairs between 6 P.M. and 9 P.M. Create a histogram depicting the number of shoes sold in each time period.

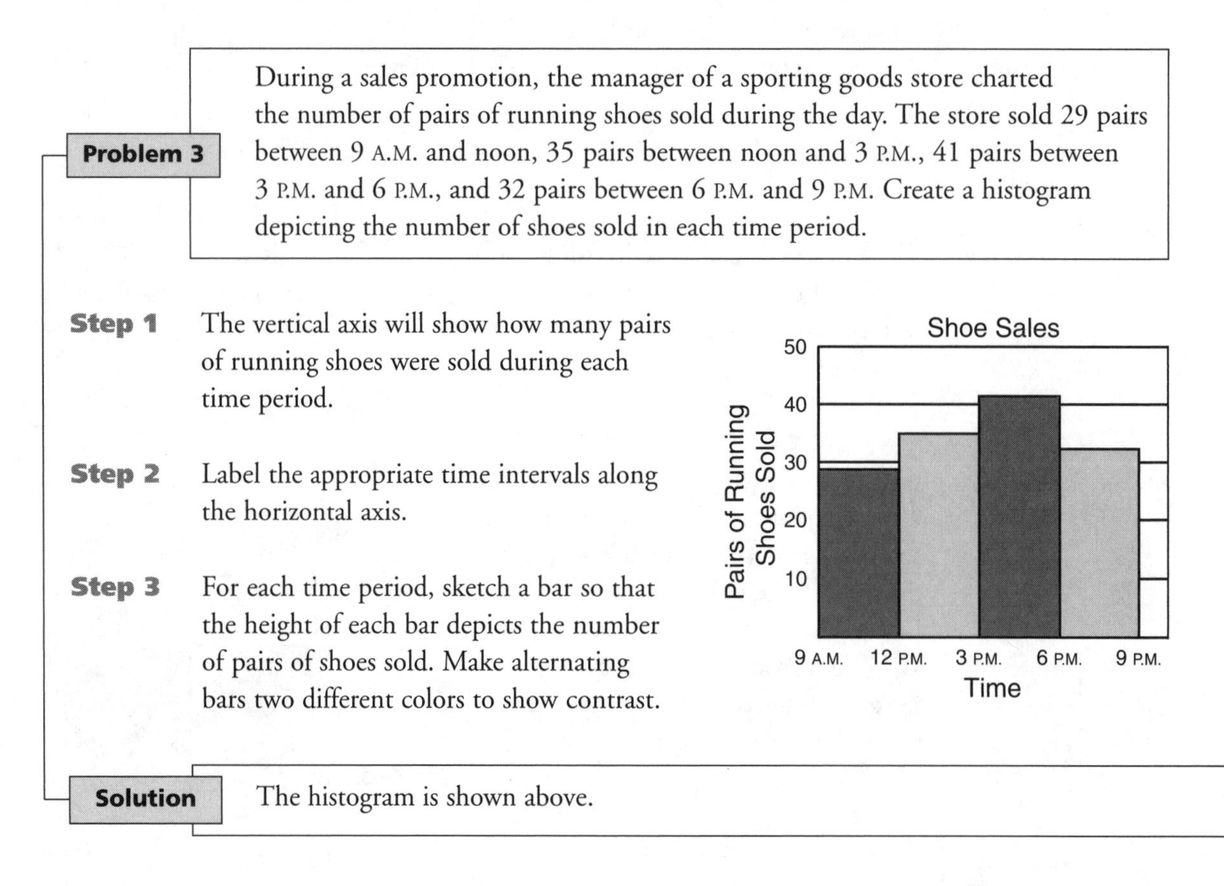

Step 1 The vertical axis will show how many pairs of running shoes were sold during each time period.

Step 2 Label the appropriate time intervals along the horizontal axis.

Step 3 For each time period, sketch a bar so that the height of each bar depicts the number of pairs of shoes sold. Make alternating bars two different colors to show contrast.

Solution The histogram is shown above.

Apply the TEKS For each circle graph, tell how many degrees would comprise the central angle of each sector.

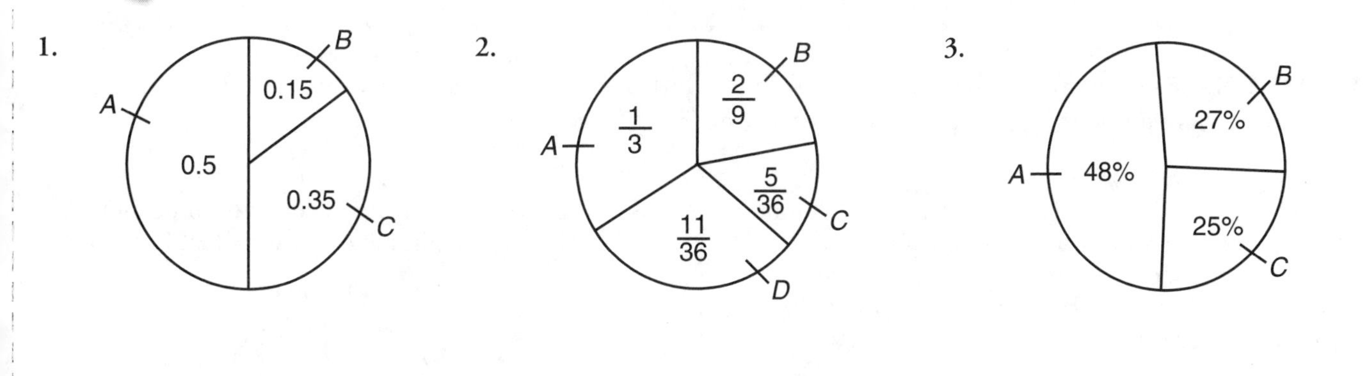

______________________ ______________________ ______________________

Which kind of graph would be most appropriate to depict each set of data? Choose the letter for the correct type of graph for each situation.

A. Circle graph

B. Bar graph

C. Histogram

4. Carl and Roger want to compare their sales figures during each of the last 6 months. ________

5. The state of Texas publishes a report depicting how tax dollars are spent. ________

6. The Miller family calculates their anticipated expense budget while on vacation. ________

7. For his statistics class, Gabe polled his classmates to find out how many hours of television they watched each day. ________

Refer to the bar graph to answer the following questions.

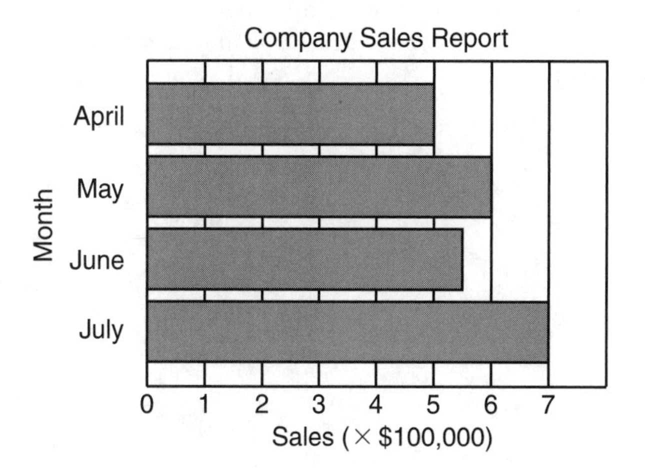

8. What were the total sales during the month of April?

____

9. During which month was there a loss in sales from the previous month?

____

10. Which month showed the greatest increase in sales over the previous month's sales?

____

TAKS Objective 9 The student will demonstrate an understanding of percents, proportional relationships, probability, and statistics in application problems.

TEKS 8.12C

DIRECTIONS Read each question. Then circle the letter for the correct answer. If a correct answer is not here, circle the letter for "Not Here."

1 In Maria's monthly budget, her utilities account for 7.5% of her total expenses. She wants to create a circle graph depicting where her money is spent each month. How many degrees should be in the central angle of the utilities sector?

A 54°

B 30°

C 27°

D 15°

2 The histogram shows the grade distribution for the quarter in Mr. Andrew's history class.

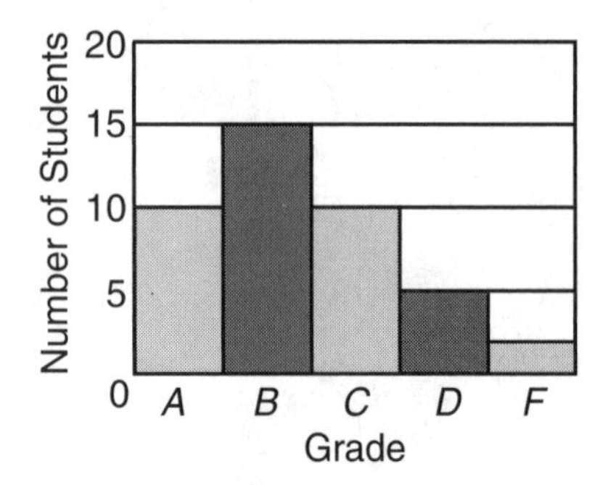

How many more students earned a B for the quarter than earned a D for the quarter?

F 5

G 10

H 12

J 15

3 The circle graph shows the ages of people who visited a certain movie theater last Saturday.

Ages of Movie Theater Visitors

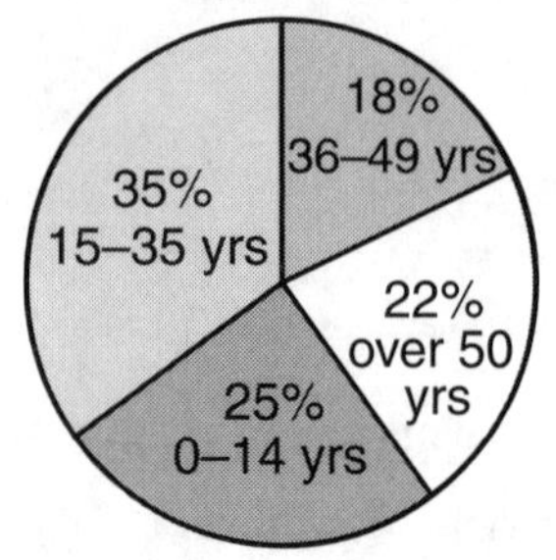

If 850 people visited the theater during the day, how many of them were between the ages of 36 and 49?

A 214

B 201

C 153

D 144

4 A real estate agent works in 3 different counties. He has collected data on how many houses he has sold in each county over the last 9 months. Which type of graph would best depict the data for comparison?

F A circle graph

G A bar graph

H A histogram

J Not Here

Focus on TEKS

Lesson 59 Predictions and Conclusions Based on Collected Data

TEKS 8.13A Evaluate methods of sampling to determine validity of an inference made from a set of data.
TEKS 8.13B Recognize misuses of graphical or numerical information and evaluate predictions and conclusions based on data analysis.

When conclusions are drawn from a set of data, the validity of those conclusions depends on how the data were collected.

Surveys are conducted to gather information about a particular group.
The entire group that is of interest is called the **population**.
Typically, only a **sample** of the population is surveyed, since it is not convenient to survey the whole group.
A **random sample** is an unbiased sample that is representative of the entire population.

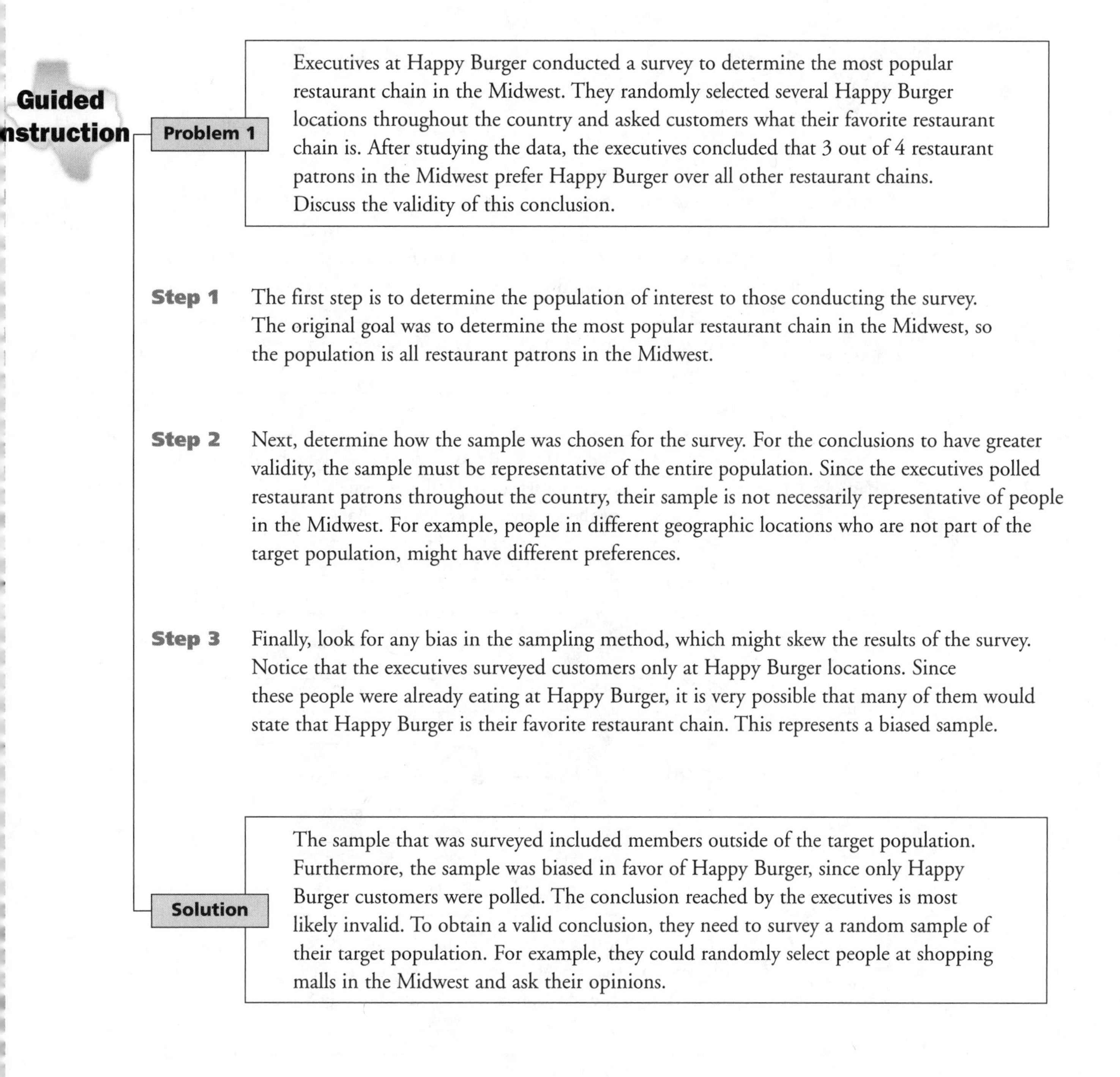

Guided Instruction

Problem 1

Executives at Happy Burger conducted a survey to determine the most popular restaurant chain in the Midwest. They randomly selected several Happy Burger locations throughout the country and asked customers what their favorite restaurant chain is. After studying the data, the executives concluded that 3 out of 4 restaurant patrons in the Midwest prefer Happy Burger over all other restaurant chains. Discuss the validity of this conclusion.

Step 1 The first step is to determine the population of interest to those conducting the survey. The original goal was to determine the most popular restaurant chain in the Midwest, so the population is all restaurant patrons in the Midwest.

Step 2 Next, determine how the sample was chosen for the survey. For the conclusions to have greater validity, the sample must be representative of the entire population. Since the executives polled restaurant patrons throughout the country, their sample is not necessarily representative of people in the Midwest. For example, people in different geographic locations who are not part of the target population, might have different preferences.

Step 3 Finally, look for any bias in the sampling method, which might skew the results of the survey. Notice that the executives surveyed customers only at Happy Burger locations. Since these people were already eating at Happy Burger, it is very possible that many of them would state that Happy Burger is their favorite restaurant chain. This represents a biased sample.

Solution

The sample that was surveyed included members outside of the target population. Furthermore, the sample was biased in favor of Happy Burger, since only Happy Burger customers were polled. The conclusion reached by the executives is most likely invalid. To obtain a valid conclusion, they need to survey a random sample of their target population. For example, they could randomly select people at shopping malls in the Midwest and ask their opinions.

More Problems

Guided Instruction

Problem 2

An employment recruiter is trying to convince Amanda to take a sales position with an insurance company. The recruiter tells Amanda that the average sales commission earned by other salespeople at the company last month was nearly $10,000. The data used to make this claim are shown in the table. Explain why this is a misleading use of statistics.

Employee	01	02	03	04	05
Commission	$5,000	$4,550	$6,000	$5,450	$27,250

Step 1 Notice that what the recruiter told Amanda is true. The average commission earned last month was nearly $10,000.

Average Commission Earned: $\frac{5{,}000 + 4{,}550 + 6{,}000 + 5{,}450 + 27{,}250}{5} = \$9{,}650$

Step 2 However, the average commission was skewed by the commission earned by Employee 05. This employee appears to have had an exceptional month of sales, but this does not seem to be typical, since no other employee was even close to that amount. If you disregard this figure, the average commission earned last month was closer to $5,000.

Solution The employment recruiter used a statistic creatively to try to make a job appear more appealing.

Problem 3

The soccer team polled 100 students to determine the school's most popular sport. Their results are shown in the following graph. Explain what is misleading about the results of the survey as presented in the graph.

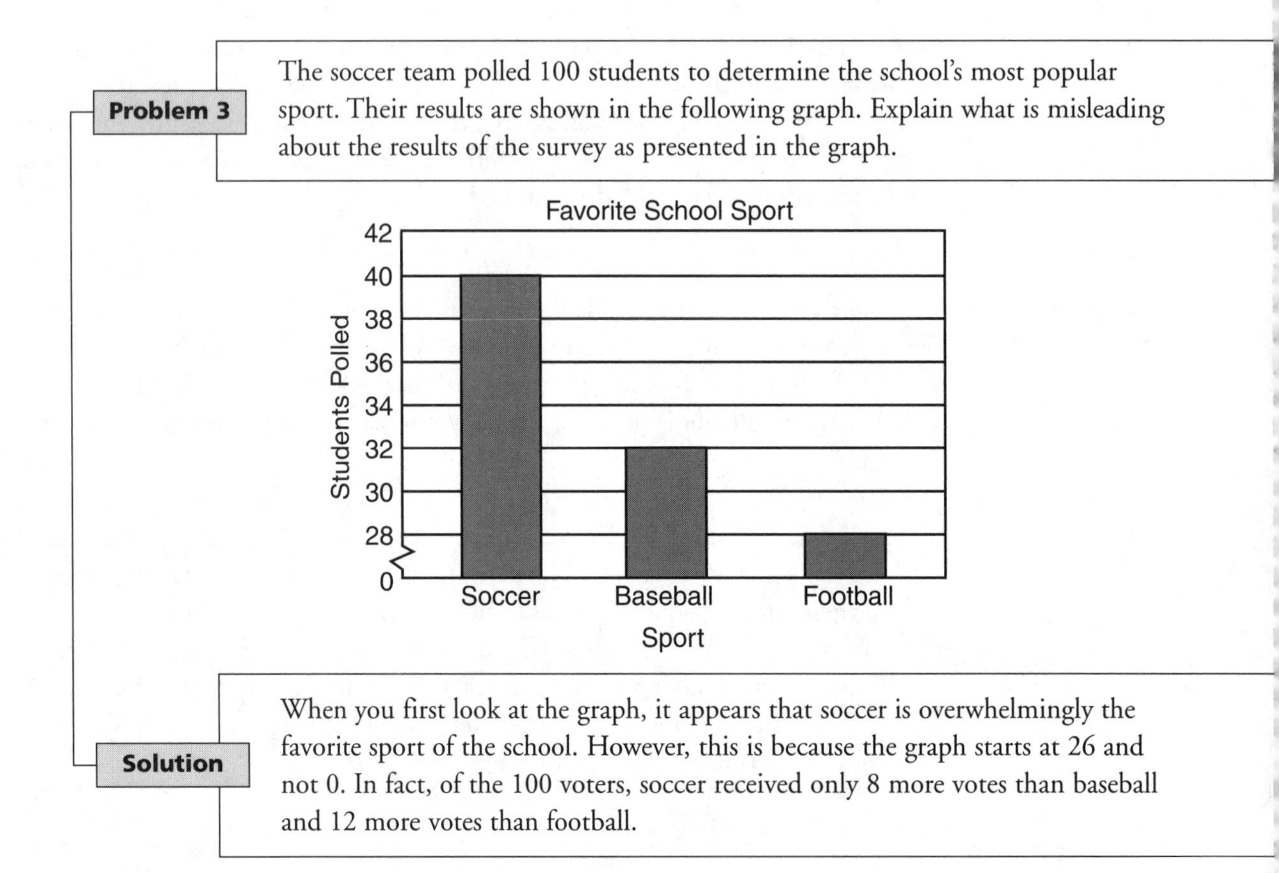

Solution When you first look at the graph, it appears that soccer is overwhelmingly the favorite sport of the school. However, this is because the graph starts at 26 and not 0. In fact, of the 100 voters, soccer received only 8 more votes than baseball and 12 more votes than football.

Apply the TEKS **Determine whether each sampling method is a good way to obtain an unbiased sample for the specified survey. If it is biased, explain why.**

1. A marketing group wants to know what kind of soft drink teenagers like most. They randomly poll 1,000 teenage students in schools across the country.

____

2. A college study wants to know about career choices made by young adults. They poll students enrolled in a computer science program at a local college.

____

3. A survey is interested in knowing the favorite country performer in a particular city. The surveyors randomly poll people at a Garth Brooks concert.

____

Solve the problem.

4. There are 65,000 registered voters living in a town. If an unbiased survey found that 180 out of 250 randomly selected voters approve of the mayor's performance, what can you conclude about the total population of registered voters? Round to the nearest thousand voters in your conclusion.

____

Explain how each situation misuses statistics to make a point.

5.

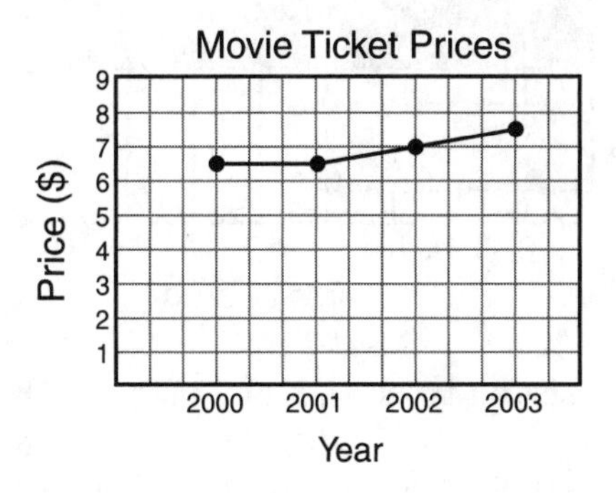

Claim: Ticket prices remained steady over the past 3 years.

____

____

6.

Test Scores

Participant	01	02	03	04
Score	850	740	1,560	855

Claim: Our math team had an average score of more than 1,000 points on the test.

____

____

TAKS Objective 9 The student will demonstrate an understanding of percents, proportional relationships, probability, and statistics in application problems.
TEKS 8.13A, **8.13B**

DIRECTIONS Read each question. Then circle the letter for the correct answer. If a correct answer is not here, circle the letter for "Not Here."

1 There are 1,450 students in a school. In a survey of an unbiased sample of 200 students, 110 said that they were planning on attending the football team's final home game. About how many students can be expected to attend the game?

A 950

B 800

C 700

D 650

2 A researcher wants to find out what type of transportation is used by people who work downtown full time. Which of the following sample groups would lead to the most valid conclusion?

F He randomly interviews 100 people at a shopping mall on a Monday afternoon.

G He randomly interviews people entering a large office building downtown during work hours.

H He chooses people living in the neighboring suburbs from a list of residents and interviews them over the phone.

J He interviews customers at a downtown diner during lunch hour.

3 The Playground Day Care advertised that its child accident rate was cut in half from last year to this year. Last year, the Playground Day Care had 6 child accidents. Which of the following best describes why this is a misleading statistic?

A Cutting the child accident rate in half is not a significant improvement.

B The day-care center should not be satisfied until they have no child accidents.

C The accident rate only showed a 50% drop.

D The number of child accidents dropped from 6 to 3 during the past year. This is not a significant decrease.

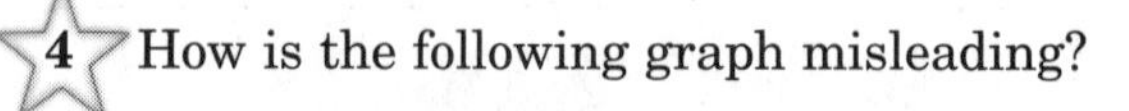

4 How is the following graph misleading?

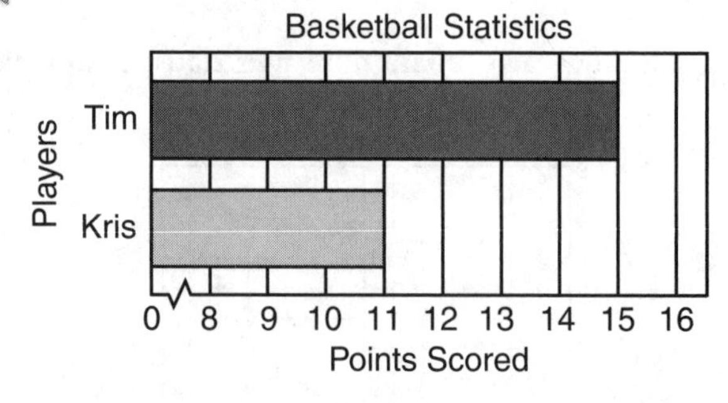

F Tim scored twice as many points as Kris.

G The graph is cut off since the points scored axis only starts at 7.

H The bars are shown horizontally instead of vertically.

J Not Here

Building Stamina™

DIRECTIONS Read each question. Then circle the letter for the correct answer. If a correct answer is not here, circle the letter for "Not Here."

1 A computer was originally priced at $950. During a weekend sale, the price of the computer was reduced by 15%. What was the price of the computer during the weekend sale?

A $758

B $807.50

C $835.75

D $860

2 A 3-member student council is to be randomly chosen from among 12 students. Four of the students are juniors, and 8 of them are seniors. What is the probability that the student council will be made up of 2 seniors and 1 junior?

F $\frac{28}{55}$

G $\frac{14}{55}$

H $\frac{36}{135}$

J Not Here

3 In a survey designed to study American working habits, most respondents said that they fall into the category "about 40 hours a week." Which measure of central tendency is represented by this situation?

A Mean

B Median

C Mode

D Not Here

4 What is the value of x in the following proportional equation?

$$\frac{2(x-2)}{3} = \frac{x+3}{2}$$

Record your answer and fill in the bubbles on the grid below. Be sure to use the correct place value.

				.			
0	0	0	0		0	0	0
1	1	1	1		1	1	1
2	2	2	2		2	2	2
3	3	3	3		3	3	3
4	4	4	4		4	4	4
5	5	5	5		5	5	5
6	6	6	6		6	6	6
7	7	7	7		7	7	7
8	8	8	8		8	8	8
9	9	9	9		9	9	9

5 There are 840 students in Allison's school. She conducted a survey of an unbiased sample of 90 students and found that 54 of them ride the bus to school. About how many students in Allison's school would you say ride the bus to school?

A 625

B 504

C 479

D Not Here

6 What is the probability of flipping 3 heads in 3 tosses with a nickel?

F $\frac{1}{4}$

G $\frac{3}{8}$

H $\frac{2}{5}$

J Not Here

7 Carlos figures he will spend on average $780 per month in rent and utilities. His total monthly expenses will total $1,950. He wants to create a circle graph depicting his monthly budget. How many degrees should be in the central angle of the home expense sector?

A 108°

B 125°

C 144°

D 170°

8 A 12-foot-high gazebo casts a 9-foot-long shadow at the same time that an oak tree casts a 45-foot-long shadow. What is the height of the oak tree?

F 85 ft

G 70 ft

H 60 ft

J 50 ft

9 What is the median of the data depicted in the stem-and-leaf plot below?

Stem	Leaf
6	7 8 8 8
7	3 7 9
8	0 0 1 4
9	6 7
10	4 5 5 6
11	0 1 9

A 68

B 74

C 82.5

D 90.25

10 Events A and B are independent events. The probability that event A will occur is 0.34, and the probability that event B will occur is 0.125. What is the probability of A and B both occurring?

F 0.465

G 0.218

H 0.084

J 0.0425

11 A set of golf clubs that regularly sells for $290 is reduced 10% during a clearance sale. The sales tax rate in the state is 6%. What is the total cost of the golf clubs during the sale, including tax?

A $261

B $264.52

C $276.66

D $307.40

12 For which of the following probabilities is an event most likely to occur?

F 0.061

G $\frac{1}{5}$

H $\frac{1}{3}$

J 0.345

13 Which of the following ratios is proportional to $\frac{11}{16}$?

A $\frac{44}{64}$

B $\frac{22}{34}$

C $\frac{42}{72}$

D $\frac{21}{46}$

14 What is the mean of the data shown in the line plot?

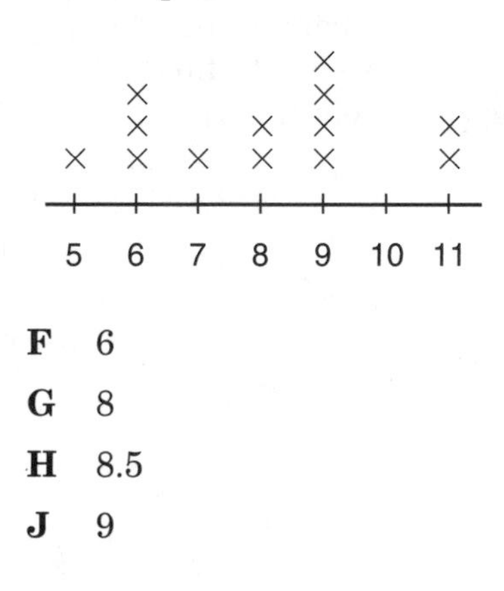

F 6

G 8

H 8.5

J 9

15 A researcher is trying to determine the most popular kind of chewing gum among teenagers. Which of the following sample groups would lead to the most valid conclusion?

A The researcher interviews the parents of teenagers at a basketball game.

B The researcher randomly interviews teenagers at several shopping malls throughout the country.

C The researcher mails out surveys to every fifth resident in a phone book.

D Not Here

16 Carla saved $36.75 by purchasing a desk during a sale. If the original price of the desk was $245, what was the percent of the discount during the sale?

F 5%

G 10%

H 15%

J 20%

17 A quality control team examined 350 aquarium air pumps and found that 7 of the pumps were defective. In a production run of 8,000 air pumps, how many would you expect to be defective?

Record your answer and fill in the bubbles on the grid below. Be sure to use the correct place value.

				.			
0	0	0	0		0	0	0
1	1	1	1		1	1	1
2	2	2	2		2	2	2
3	3	3	3		3	3	3
4	4	4	4		4	4	4
5	5	5	5		5	5	5
6	6	6	6		6	6	6
7	7	7	7		7	7	7
8	8	8	8		8	8	8
9	9	9	9		9	9	9

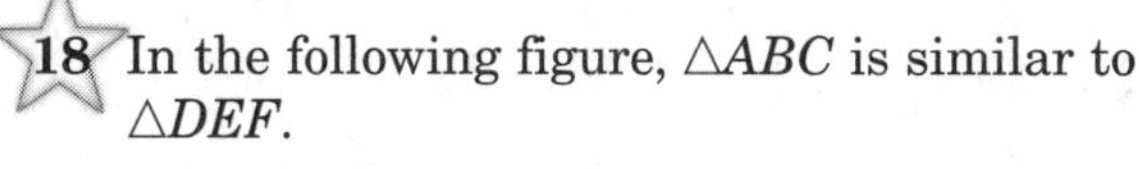

18 In the following figure, $\triangle ABC$ is similar to $\triangle DEF$.

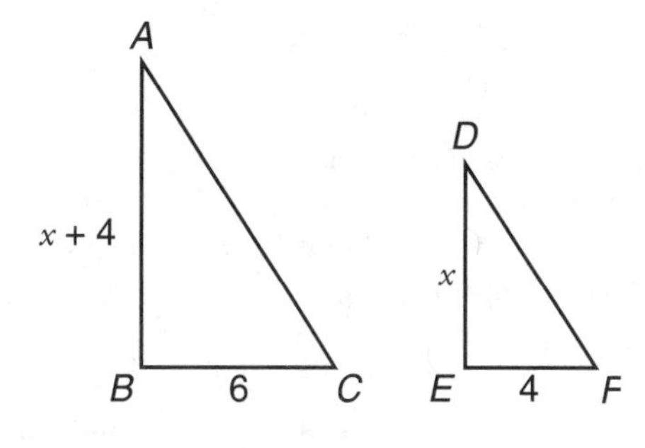

What is the value of x?

F 6

G 8

H 10

J 12

19 In a blind taste test, people were asked to choose which soda they liked the most. The sodas were labeled *A*, *B*, *C*, and *D*. The results of the taste test are shown in the histogram.

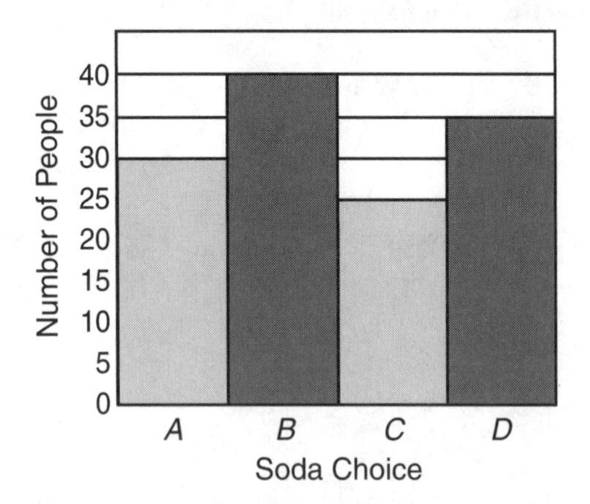

What percent of all the participants preferred soda B? Round to the nearest percent.

A 21%

B 28%

C 31%

D 44%

20 When Jamaar first began lifting weights, he was able to bench-press 130 pounds. After six weeks his bench-press weight had increased 25%. How much was Jamaar able to bench-press?

Record your answer and fill in the bubbles on the grid below. Be sure to use the correct place value.

21 Edwin rolls a number cube, labeled 1 through 6, flips 2 coins, and then rolls the number cube again. What is the probability that he will roll a 3 then a 5, and that he will flip the first coin heads and the other coin tails?

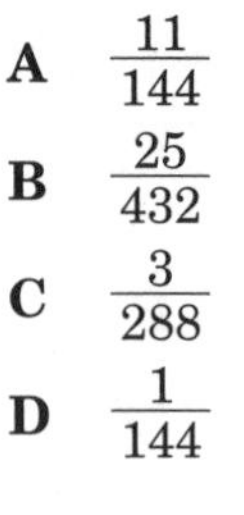

A $\frac{11}{144}$

B $\frac{25}{432}$

C $\frac{3}{288}$

D $\frac{1}{144}$

22 The following line graph shows the increasing cost of a milk shake at Cool Treats ice cream shops.

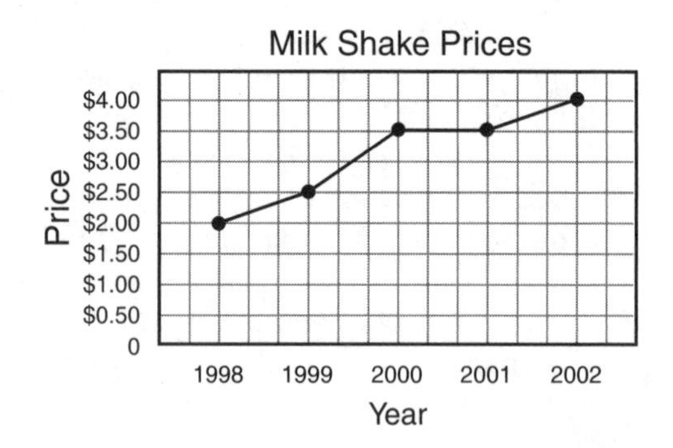

The executives at Cool Treats want to create a line graph that makes the price increases appear smaller. What increment should they use along the vertical axis instead of $0.50 to have the greatest effect?

F $0.15

G $0.25

H $0.75

J $1.00

PART 2 Building Stamina™

DIRECTIONS Read each question. Then circle the letter for the correct answer. If a correct answer is not here, circle the letter for "Not Here."

1 Which of the following is NOT a true statement?

A Two points denote a straight line.

B Space is the set of all points.

C A plane is a curved surface that extends in all directions.

D A point is a location.

2 If the radius of Earth is approximately 3,960 miles, what is the approximate surface area?

F 24,881.41 mi^2

G 49,265,199.36 mi^2

H 93,000,000 mi^2

J 197,060,797.4 mi^2

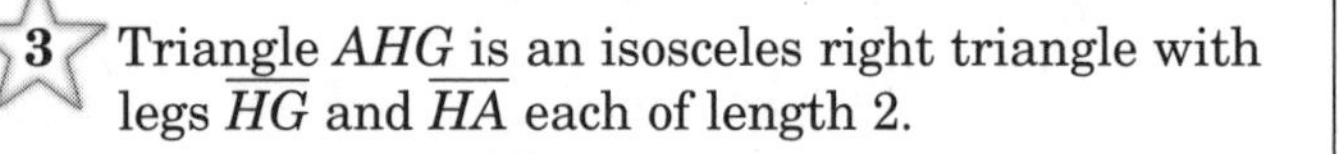

3 Triangle *AHG* is an isosceles right triangle with legs $\overline{HG}$ and $\overline{HA}$ each of length 2.

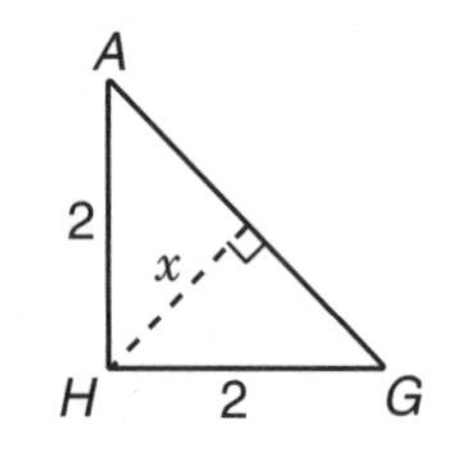

Find the value of *x*.

A 1

B $\sqrt{2}$

C $\sqrt{6}$

D Not Here

4 Which of the following is NOT the net of a cube?

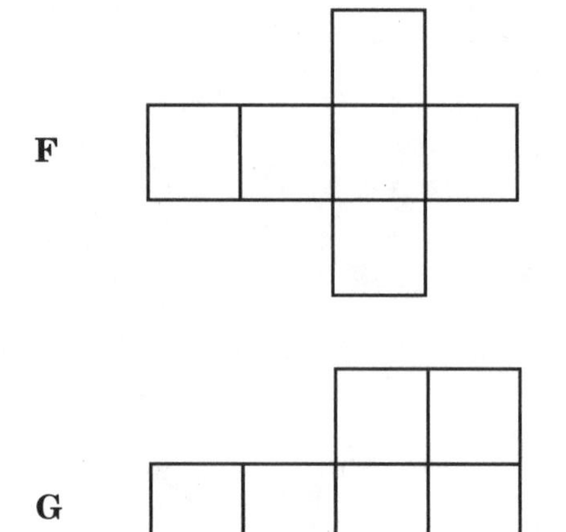

F

G

H

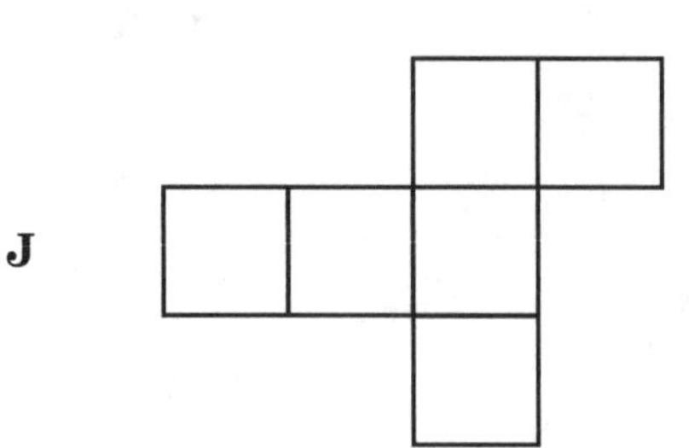

J

5 The circumference of a basketball is 75 centimeters. What is the surface area rounded to the nearest thousandth in square centimeters? Use $\pi = 3.14$.

Record your answer and fill in the bubbles on the grid below. Be sure to use the correct place value.

				.			
0	0	0	0		0	0	0
1	1	1	1		1	1	1
2	2	2	2		2	2	2
3	3	3	3		3	3	3
4	4	4	4		4	4	4
5	5	5	5		5	5	5
6	6	6	6		6	6	6
7	7	7	7		7	7	7
8	8	8	8		8	8	8
9	9	9	9		9	9	9

6 A globe is a kind of coordinate plane that uses lines of latitude and longitude to designate locations instead of x- and y-coordinates. Which of the following circles on the face of a globe is NOT a great circle?

F The lines of longitude

G The Prime Meridian

H The equator

J The lines of latitude other than the equator

7 Senior photos come in 5 sizes, 2×3, 4×5, 5×7, 8×10, and 10×13. Which sizes are similar?

A 5×7 and 10×13

B 4×5 and 8×10

C 2×3 and 5×7

D 2×3 and 4×5

8 Look at the congruent triangles below.

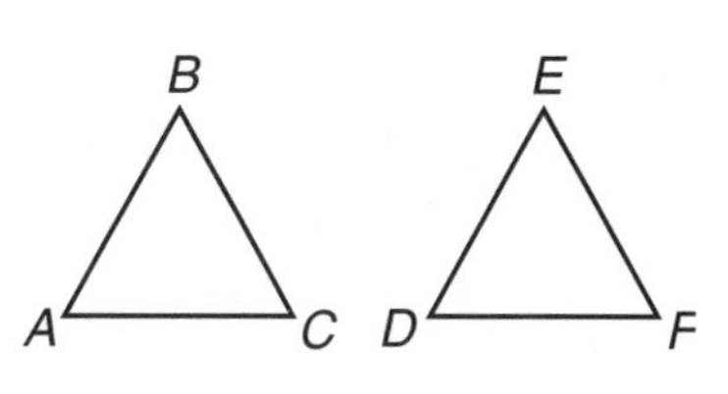

$$\angle A \cong \angle D$$
$$m\angle A = (2x)^\circ$$
$$m\angle D = (x + 30)^\circ$$
$$AB = 2x - 10$$
$$DE = x + 20$$
$$AC = x + 10$$
$$DF = 3x - 50$$

What is the length of $\overline{DE}$?

F 50

G 80

H 110

J Not Here

9 If the figure below is used as a target in a balloon toss, what is the probability that a balloon landing somewhere on target would hit $\triangle AIB$?

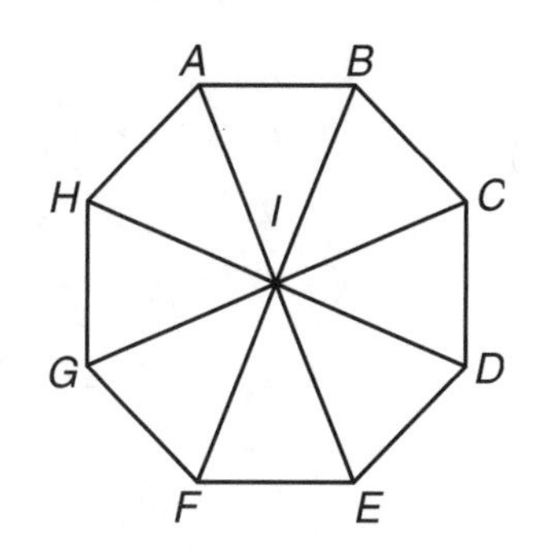

Round your answer to the nearest hundredth.

A 0.07

B 0.08

C 0.13

D 0.14

10 What is the next term in the sequence below?

$$\frac{1}{25}, \frac{1}{16}, \frac{1}{9}, \frac{1}{4}, \ldots$$

F 0

G $\frac{1}{3}$

H $\frac{1}{2}$

J $\frac{1}{1}$

11 Laura worked this summer baby-sitting to earn money for her college expenses. She earned $1,575, which was 350% of what she needed for books. How much did she need for books?

A $450

B $630

C $1,225

D Not Here

12 A triangle has sides that are 5, 9, and x, where x is an integer. What are the possible values for x?

F $x < 14$

G $4 < x < 14$

H $x > 14$

J Not Here

13 What is the degree measure of the angle formed by the hands of the clock?

Record your answer and fill in the bubbles on the grid below. Be sure to use the correct place value.

				.			
0	0	0	0		0	0	0
1	1	1	1		1	1	1
2	2	2	2		2	2	2
3	3	3	3		3	3	3
4	4	4	4		4	4	4
5	5	5	5		5	5	5
6	6	6	6		6	6	6
7	7	7	7		7	7	7
8	8	8	8		8	8	8
9	9	9	9		9	9	9

14 Look at the graph below.

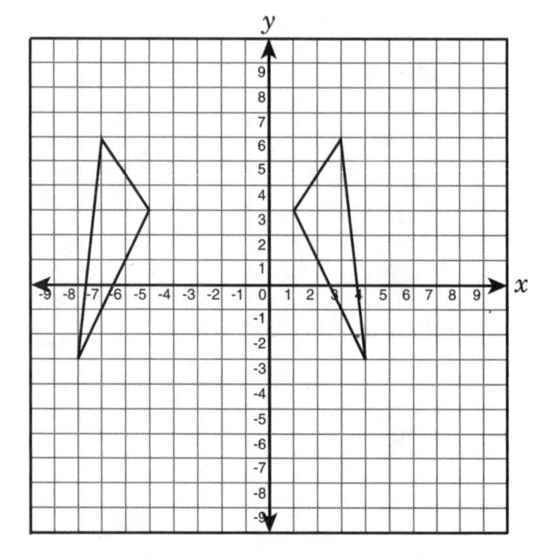

The graph shows an example of what type of transformation?

F A dilation

G A rotation

H A reflection

J A tessellation

15 The following is an example of what type of reasoning?
All 4-sided figures are quadrilaterals. ABCD has 4 sides, therefore, ABCD is a quadrilateral.

A Inductive reasoning

B Deductive reasoning

C Both inductive and deductive reasoning

D Neither inductive nor deductive reasoning

16 The standard tip rate is 15%. Angelle and Jeremy always tip more because they both started out working in restaurants. If their bill at the steakhouse is $96.44 and they tip 25%, what is the difference in dollars and cents between what they gave and the standard tip?

Record your answer and fill in the bubbles on the grid below. Be sure to use the correct place value.

				•			
0	0	0	0		0	0	0
1	1	1	1		1	1	1
2	2	2	2		2	2	2
3	3	3	3		3	3	3
4	4	4	4		4	4	4
5	5	5	5		5	5	5
6	6	6	6		6	6	6
7	7	7	7		7	7	7
8	8	8	8		8	8	8
9	9	9	9		9	9	9

17 Look at the wallpaper pattern below.

What type(s) of transformation is NOT shown in the wallpaper pattern?

A Rotation

B Reflection

C Translation

D Not Here

18 Portia has four shapes: a rectangle, a parallelogram, a rhombus, and a trapezoid. What is the greatest number of Portia's shapes that could be squares?

F 1 shape

G 2 shapes

H 3 shapes

J 4 shapes

19 Teresa is helping her Aunt Elena to make a quilt. She begins by cutting 6-inch squares from different colored fabric. She then cuts the squares in half along a diagonal.

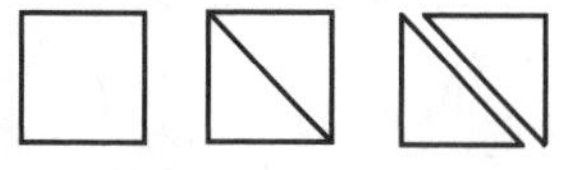

Which postulate does NOT assure that all of the triangles are congruent?

A SSS

B SAS

C SAA

D Not Here

20 Which of the following statements is not necessarily true for parallelograms?

F The opposite sides are parallel.

G The opposite sides are congruent.

H The opposite angles are congruent.

J The opposite angles are complementary.

21 Look at the grid below.

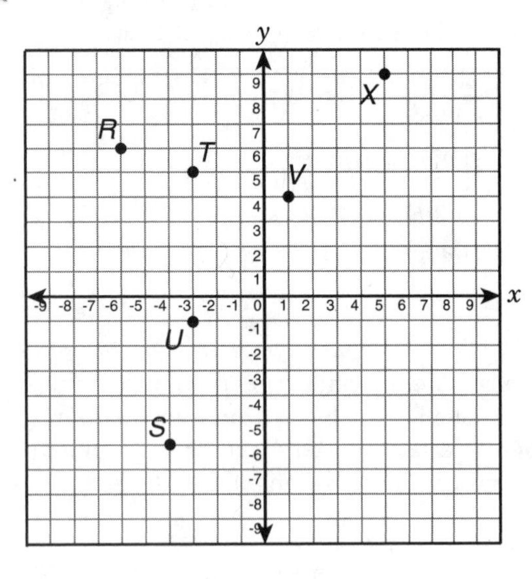

Which set of points is collinear?

A *R*, *T*, and *V*

B *S*, *U*, and *T*

C *S*, *V*, and *X*

D *U*, *V*, and *X*

22 Samantha's new living room has 4 recessed panels of equal size. Each panel has a semicircular top.

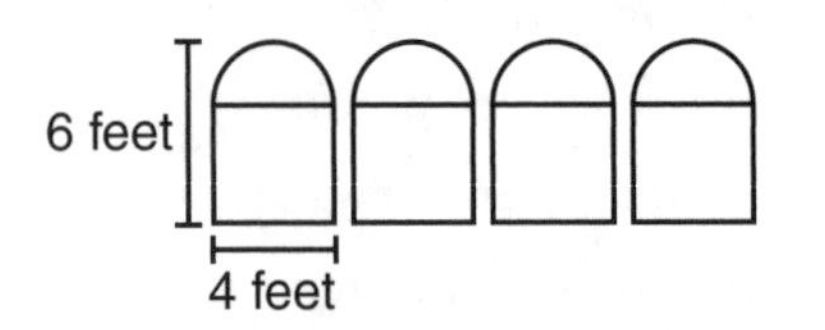

Samantha wants to cover the panels with antique wallpaper. How many square feet of wallpaper will she need? Round your answer to the nearest hundredth.

F 89.12 square feet

G 114.24 square feet

H 121.12 square feet

J 146.24 square feet

23 Thuy likes to do her homework as soon as she gets home from school everyday. The following table shows the time she spent on homework on 4 afternoons last week.

Day	Time
Monday	60 minutes
Tuesday	62 minutes
Wednesday	61 minutes
Thursday	59 minutes

Thuy's aunt wants to take her shopping Friday for a birthday gift for her mother. If Thuy gets home from school at 3:30, what is the earliest time she should tell her aunt to pick her up?

A 3:30

B 4:30

C 5:30

D 6:30

24 Last week, Lisa worked 48 hours. This week, she worked 51 hours. What is the percent increase in her work time?

Record your answer and fill in the bubbles on the grid below. Be sure to use the correct place value.

25 Which of the following could be a top view of the blocks below?

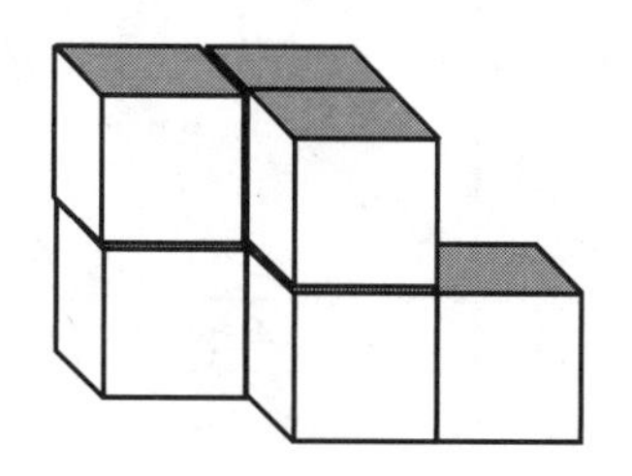

A

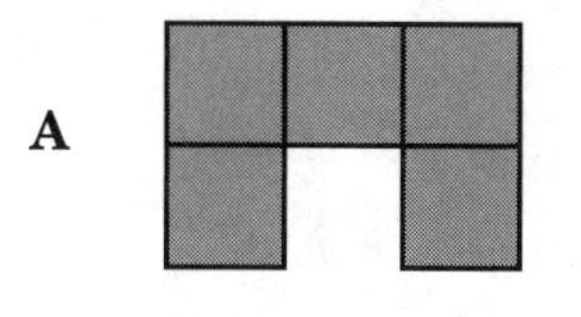

B

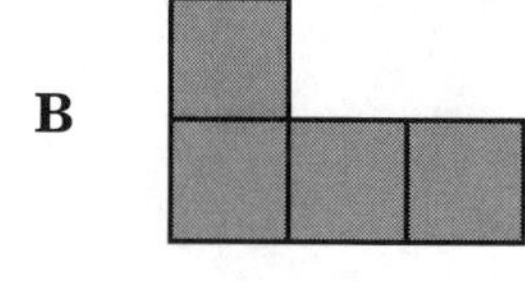

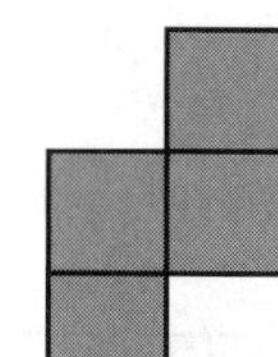

D

26 Ranata set the cruise control on her car for a constant speed of 60 miles per hour once she entered the interstate highway. Which graph shows the distance Ranata drove on the highway?

F

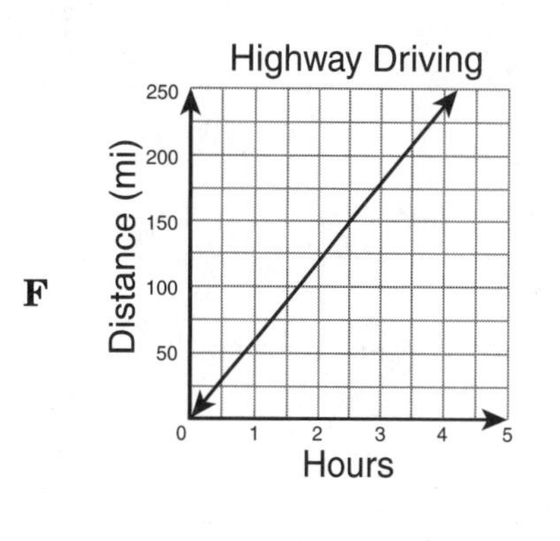

G

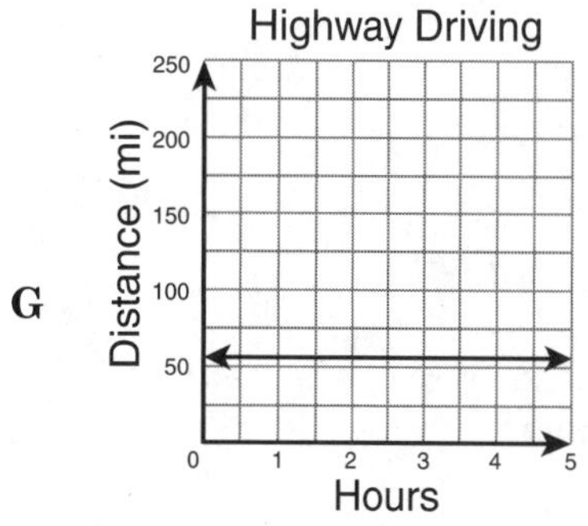

H

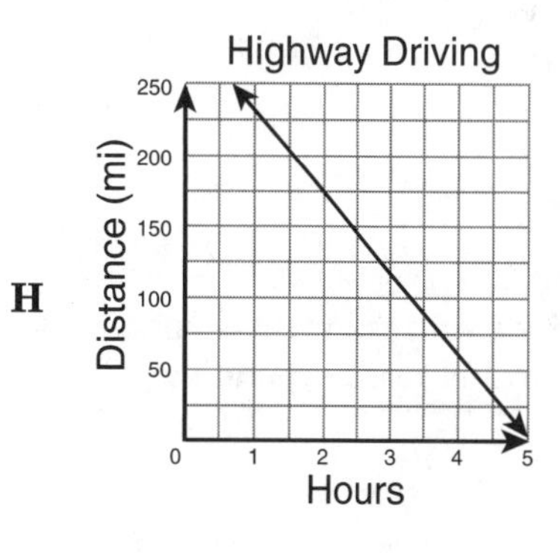

J

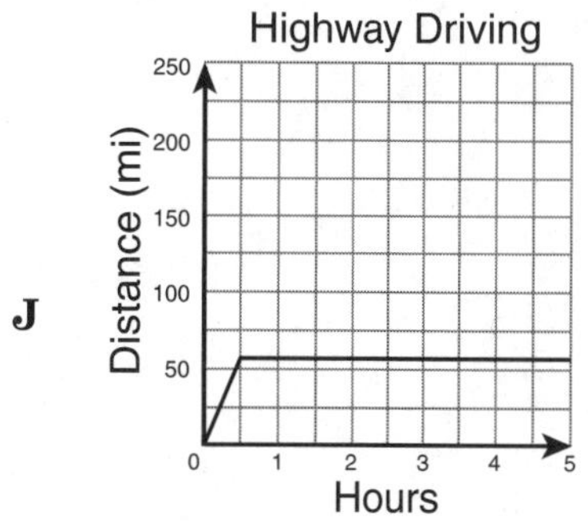

Use the equations below to answer Questions 27–29.

I $5x - 2y = 2$

II $y = 5x + 3$

III $y = \frac{5}{2}x$

IV $y = -\frac{2}{5}x + 2$

V $y = -\frac{1}{5}x$

27 Which equations represent lines that are parallel?

A I and II

B I and III

C I and IV

D III and IV

28 Which equations represent lines that are perpendicular?

F I and III

G I and V

H II and III

J II and V

29 Which equations represent lines that are neither parallel nor perpendicular?

A I and II

B II and V

C III and IV

D Not Here

30 Look at the drawing of a cube below.

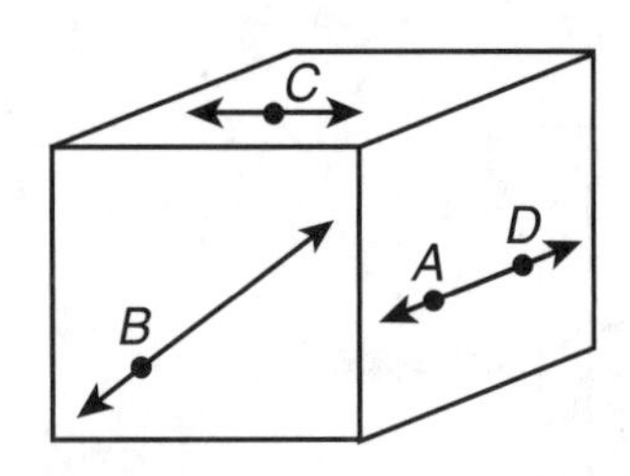

Which of the following is true according to the planes and lines drawn?

F *A* and *B* are coplanar.

G *C* and *D* are coplanar.

H *A* and *D* are coplanar and collinear.

J *B* and *C* are coplanar and collinear.

31 What are the 3 regular polygons that tessellate?

A Hexagon, pentagon, octagon

B Rectangle, triangle, pentagon

C Octagon, rectangle, triangle

D Triangle, square, hexagon

32 Mama Marie's sells four different sizes of pizza.

Pizza	Diameter	Price
Small	10"	$5.99
Medium	12"	$6.99
Large	14"	$8.99
Extra Large	16"	$9.99

The math club wants to order pizza for its next monthly meeting. Which size pizza is the best deal?

F Small

G Medium

H Large

J Extra large

33 The cheerleading squad has decided to begin the pep rally in a grand manner. They've found a large rectangular box that is 7 ft × 4 ft × 4 ft. They plan to cover it in crepe paper stamped with the team's logo and have the captain of the football team burst out of the box at the appropriate moment in the rally. If the paper they are using comes in sheets that are 24 in. × 30 in., how many sheets will they need if they allow for a 1 in. overlap at each end of the sheets?

Record your answer and fill in the bubbles on the grid below. Be sure to use the correct place value.

				.			
0	0	0	0		0	0	0
1	1	1	1		1	1	1
2	2	2	2		2	2	2
3	3	3	3		3	3	3
4	4	4	4		4	4	4
5	5	5	5		5	5	5
6	6	6	6		6	6	6
7	7	7	7		7	7	7
8	8	8	8		8	8	8
9	9	9	9		9	9	9

34 Mr. Green made a table of his stock earnings (in dollars) over the last six months.

Jan.	Feb.	Mar.	Apr.	May	Jun.
+500	−1000	+500	−1000	+500	+500

According to the table, what was Mr. Green's net profit for the six months?

F −$2,000

G $0

H $2,000

J Not Here

35 Which of the following is the net for a cylinder?

A

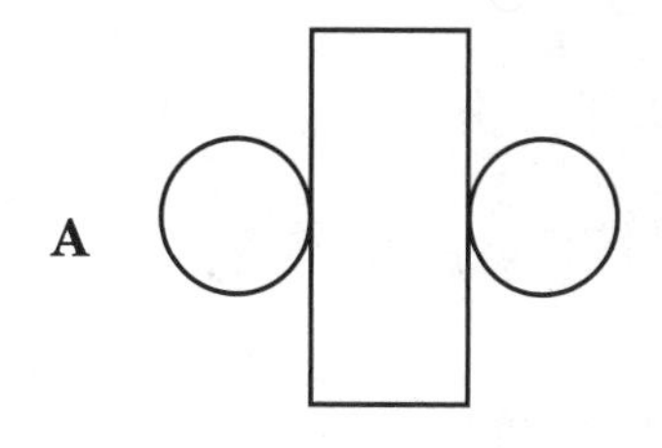

B

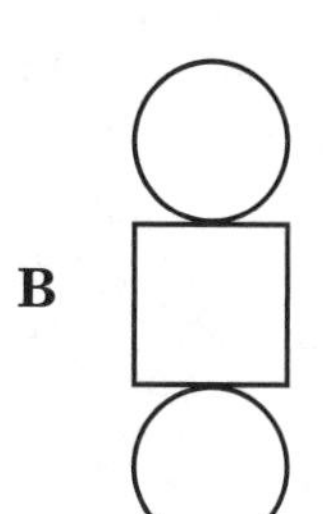

C

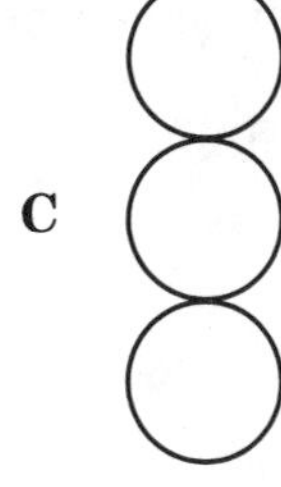

D

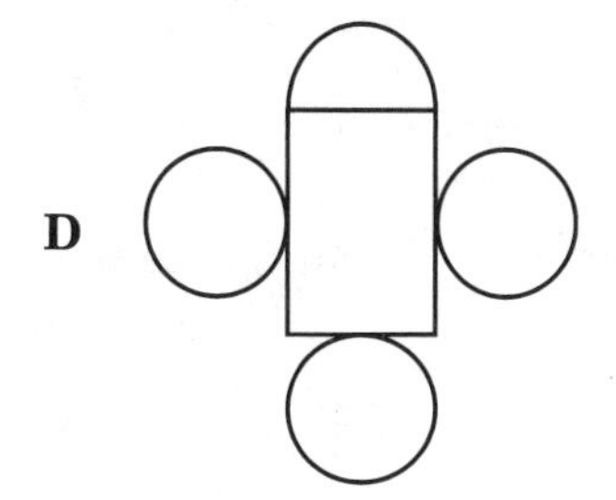

36 Look at the compass below.

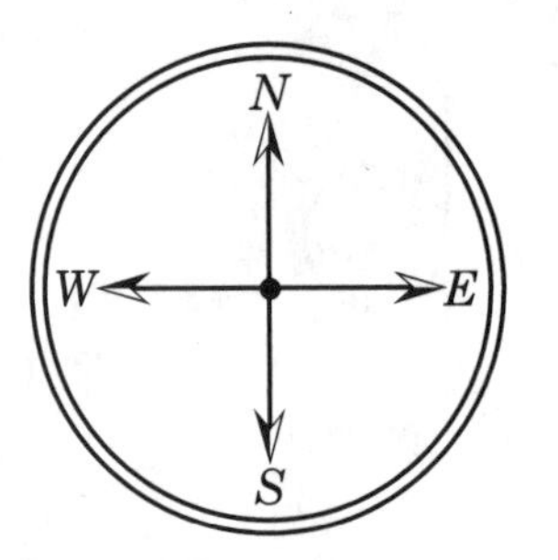

Which pair of compass directions are on opposite rays?

F East and south

G East and west

H South and west

J North and west

37 Joey is drawing a scale model of his garden. He has made two dots to show where he would like to place his rosebushes. Joey would like to build a round fountain with a center halfway between the rose bushes.

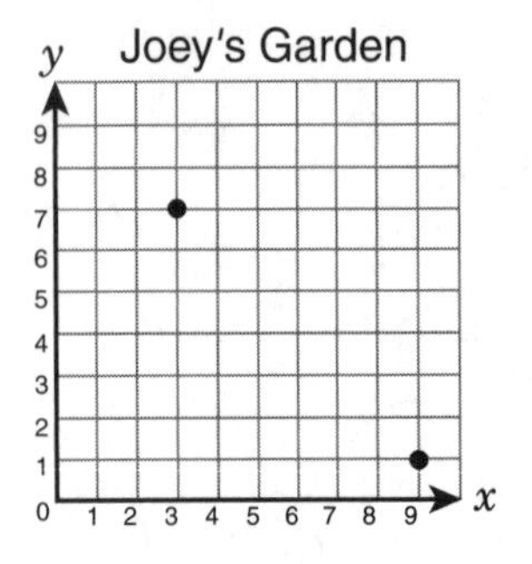

At which coordinates should Joey place the center of the fountain?

A (8, 2)

B (6, 4)

C (4, 6)

D (2, 8)

38 The length of a cube's side is increased by 2 inches.

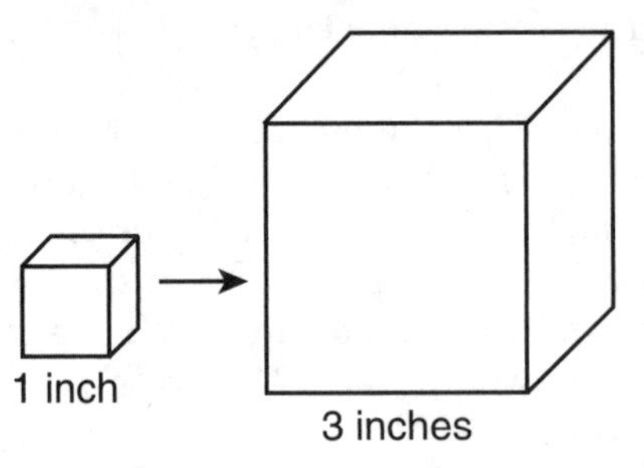

What is the volume of the larger cube?

F 3 in.^{3}

G 9 in.^{3}

H 27 in.^{3}

J 81 in.^{3}

39 Ronika is planting a garden in a semicircle. She wants to place a running fence along both the inside and outside arcs and also along each of the 11 3-foot borders shown in the diagram below.

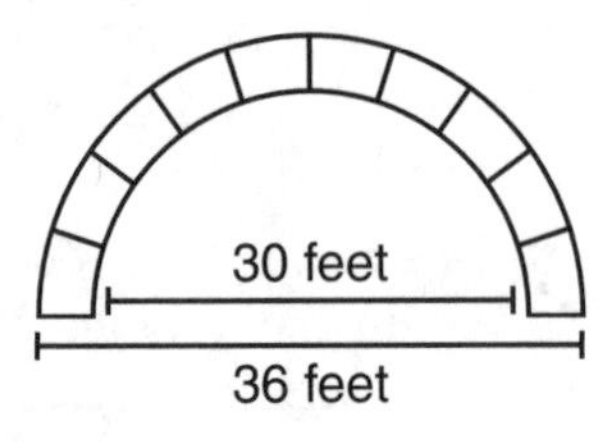

At least how many yards of running fence must she buy? Round your answer to the nearest yard.

Record your answer and fill in the bubbles on the grid below. Be sure to use the correct place value.

				.			
0	0	0	0		0	0	0
1	1	1	1		1	1	1
2	2	2	2		2	2	2
3	3	3	3		3	3	3
4	4	4	4		4	4	4
5	5	5	5		5	5	5
6	6	6	6		6	6	6
7	7	7	7		7	7	7
8	8	8	8		8	8	8
9	9	9	9		9	9	9

40 Fay needed to find the distance across a river. She tied a rope to an empty jug and tried to throw it across the river. When the jug washed ashore, it was 30 feet downstream. The distance between Fay and the jug was 40 feet.

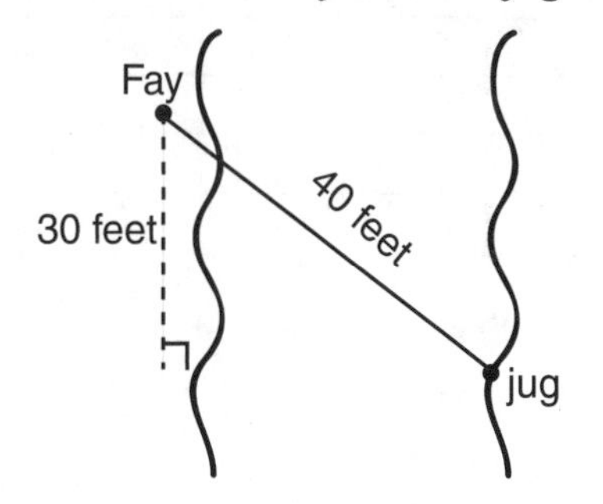

To the nearest hundredth of a foot, what was the distance across the river?

Record your answer and fill in the bubbles on the grid below. Be sure to use the correct place value.

				.			
0	0	0	0		0	0	0
1	1	1	1		1	1	1
2	2	2	2		2	2	2
3	3	3	3		3	3	3
4	4	4	4		4	4	4
5	5	5	5		5	5	5
6	6	6	6		6	6	6
7	7	7	7		7	7	7
8	8	8	8		8	8	8
9	9	9	9		9	9	9

41 When it is noon in New York, it is 9 A.M. in Los Angeles. A one-hour time zone is equal to 15 degrees of longitude. How many degrees of longitude separate New York and Los Angeles?

A 0°

B 15°

C 30°

D 45°

42 A circle, shown below, has center *C*.

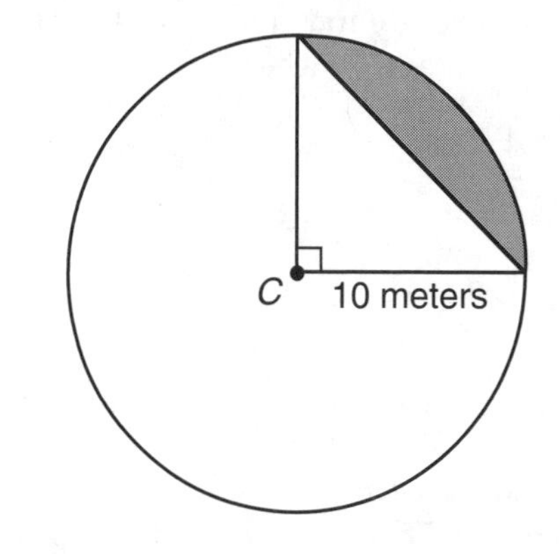

Approximately what is the area of the shaded part of the circle?

F 28.5 m^2

G 78.5 m^2

H 214 m^2

J 264 m^2

43 There are 5 red marbles, 1 blue marble, 2 green marbles, and 4 yellow marbles in a bag.

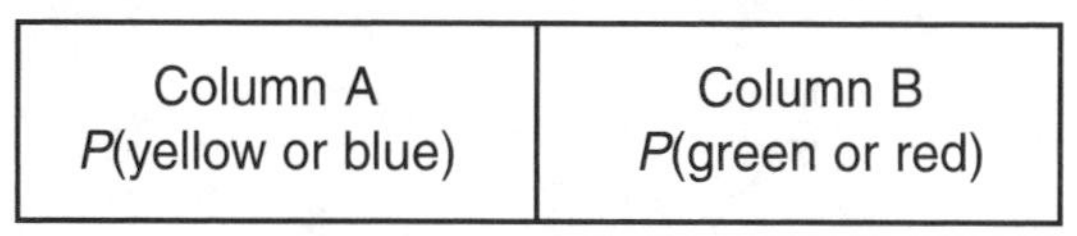

Column A	Column B
P(yellow or blue)	*P*(green or red)

What is the difference of the probabilities in Column A and Column B? Choose the answer in decimal form rounded to the nearest hundredth.

A 0.17

B 0.42

C 0.50

D 0.58

44 The circumference of a ball is 35 inches. What is its surface area rounded to the nearest thousandth in square inches? Use $\pi = 3.14$.

F 97.532 in.^{2}

G 390.127 in.^{2}

H 1,560.510 in.^{2}

J 2,174.277 in.^{2}

45 Brad worked part-time and earned $855, enough to cover 75% of the cost of a trip to Mexico. About what is the cost of Brad's trip?

A $640

B $880

C $1,140

D $1,490

46 What is the next term in the sequence below?

$$0, \frac{1}{3}, \frac{1}{2}, \frac{3}{5}, \frac{2}{3}, \ldots$$

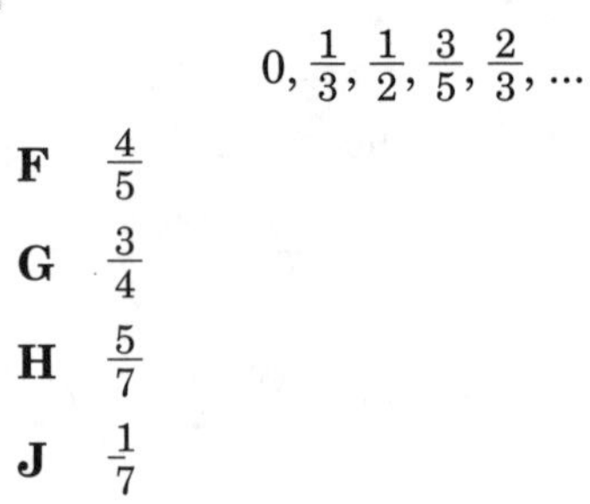

F $\frac{4}{5}$

G $\frac{3}{4}$

H $\frac{5}{7}$

J $\frac{1}{7}$

47 Ken was 66 inches tall on his last birthday. This year he is 70 inches tall. What is the percent increase rounded to the nearest tenth of a percent?

A 5.7%

B 5.9%

C 6.1%

D Not Here

48 Kurt's company sells crates in the sizes listed in the table below.

#	Dimensions	Price
1	1' × 1.5' × 1'	$0.75
2	2' × 2.5' × 2'	$1.15
3	3' × 2' × 3'	$1.85
4	4' × 6' × 4'	$3.20
5	5' × 5.5' × 5'	$4.20

Which pair of crates in the table are similar?

F Crates 1 and 4

G Crates 1 and 5

H Crates 2 and 5

J Crates 3 and 4

49 Through how many degrees will the minute hand of a clock spin in the time between 6 P.M. and 9 P.M.?

Record your answer and fill in the bubbles on the grid below. Be sure to use the correct place value.

				.			
0	0	0	0		0	0	0
1	1	1	1		1	1	1
2	2	2	2		2	2	2
3	3	3	3		3	3	3
4	4	4	4		4	4	4
5	5	5	5		5	5	5
6	6	6	6		6	6	6
7	7	7	7		7	7	7
8	8	8	8		8	8	8
9	9	9	9		9	9	9

50 Gary drew the net below.

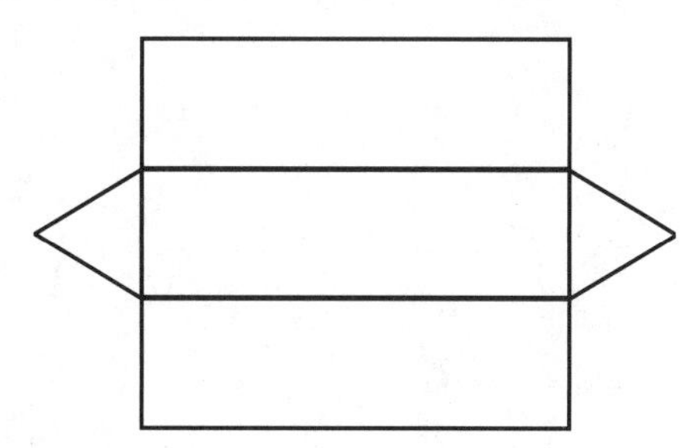

What type of figure can be formed by folding this net?

F Cone

G Prism

H Triangle

J Pyramid

51 Look at the grid below.

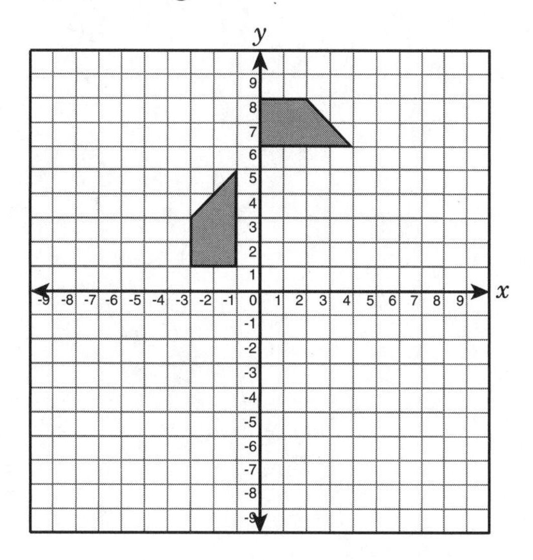

Which of the following transformations is shown on the graph?

A Dilation

B Rotation

C Reflection

D Translation

52 A ball has a surface area of 803.84 square inches. What is the volume of the smallest rectangular box into which this ball can fit? Use $\pi = 3.14$.

F 256 in.^{3}

G 512 in.^{3}

H 4096 in.^{3}

J 32,768 in.^{3}

53 At Kelly's new job, she earns $400 per week. Every week, she deposits 30% of her paycheck into a savings account. If Kelly makes a weekly deposit and makes no withdrawals, which of the following graphs could show the balance of Kelly's saving account over time?

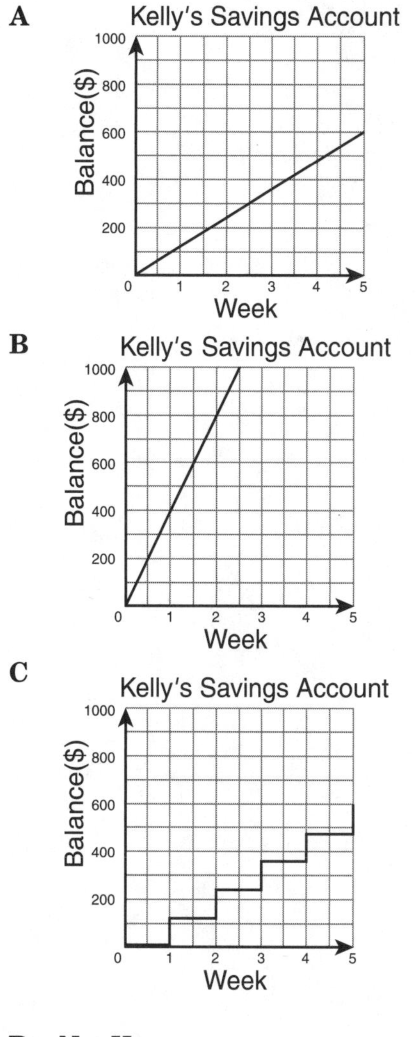

D Not Here

Notes

End-of-Book

Building Stamina™

The end-of-book **Building Stamina**™ is a comprehensive review of all the TEKS covered in the lessons.

By practicing with these challenging, broad-based, higher-level thinking questions, you will be building up your stamina to succeed on the TAKS and in other academic endeavors that require higher-level thinking.

DIRECTIONS Read each question. Then circle the letter for the correct answer. If a correct answer is <u>not here</u>, circle the letter for "Not Here."

1 Tony's geometry teacher asked the class to identify a "mystery quadrilateral" from the following information.

It has two pairs of congruent sides. All 4 angles are congruent.

What is the "mystery quadrilateral"?

A Trapezoid

B Rhombus

C Triangle

D Rectangle

2 In the inheritance tables below, B denotes the gene for brown eyes, and b denotes the gene for blue eyes. Every person must be either BB, Bb, or bb. If a person has at least one B, they will have brown eyes. Which table shows a 50% probability of offspring inheriting blue eyes?

F

Mother is BB

		B	B
Father	B	BB	BB
is BB	B	BB	BB

G

Mother is BB

		B	B
Father	B	BB	BB
is Bb	b	Bb	Bb

H

Mother is Bb

		B	b
Father	B	BB	Bb
is Bb	b	Bb	bb

J

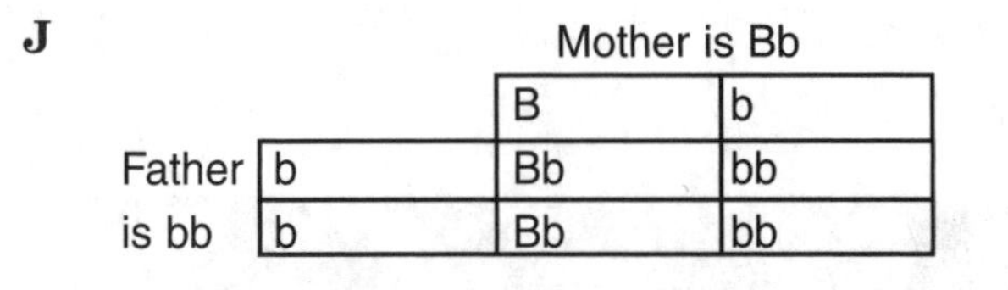

Mother is Bb

		B	b
Father	b	Bb	bb
is bb	b	Bb	bb

3 Find the roots of $4x^2 - 16 = 0$.

A $x = 2, x = -2$

B $x = 2, x = -8$

C $x = 4, x = -4$

D $x = 8, x = -2$

4 Two school buses approach the school from different directions. Bus A is 16 miles north of the school, and bus B is 12 miles west. How far apart are the buses in miles?

Record your answer and fill in the bubbles on the grid below. Be sure to use the correct place value.

				.			
0	0	0	0		0	0	0
1	1	1	1		1	1	1
2	2	2	2		2	2	2
3	3	3	3		3	3	3
4	4	4	4		4	4	4
5	5	5	5		5	5	5
6	6	6	6		6	6	6
7	7	7	7		7	7	7
8	8	8	8		8	8	8
9	9	9	9		9	9	9

5 On a 28-question test, 12 multiple-choice questions are worth 3 points each, and 16 free response questions are worth 4 points each. Which equation shows the total score s of a student who answers m multiple-choice questions incorrectly and also answers f free response questions incorrectly?

A $3m + 4f = s$

B $3(12 - m) + 4(16 - f) = s$

C $4(12 - m) + 3(16 - f) = s$

D Not Here

6 What is the slope of the line below?

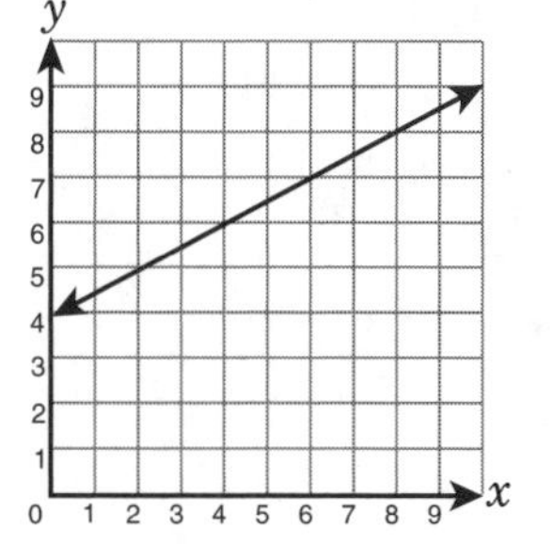

F 2

G $\frac{1}{2}$

H $-\frac{1}{2}$

J −2

7 The measure of a television screen is given according to the measure of its diagonal. If a store advertises a 32-inch television for sale and the actual height of the screen is 20 inches, what is its actual width? Round your answer to the nearest thousandth.

Record your answer and fill in the bubbles on the grid below. Be sure to use the correct place value.

				.			
0	0	0	0		0	0	0
1	1	1	1		1	1	1
2	2	2	2		2	2	2
3	3	3	3		3	3	3
4	4	4	4		4	4	4
5	5	5	5		5	5	5
6	6	6	6		6	6	6
7	7	7	7		7	7	7
8	8	8	8		8	8	8
9	9	9	9		9	9	9

8 If the equation of the parabola $y = 2x^2$ is changed to $y = \frac{1}{2}x^2$, the curve will —

F widen

G narrow

H be reflected over the x-axis

J be reflected over the y-axis

9 The distance one can see is a function of the viewer's height above Earth's surface. This relationship can be shown by the formula

$$d = \sqrt{\frac{3h}{2}}$$

where d is the distance in miles and h is the height above Earth. From a height of 5,000 feet, how far can you see in miles? Round your answer to the nearest thousandth.

Record your answer and fill in the bubbles on the grid below. Be sure to use the correct place value.

				.			
0	0	0	0		0	0	0
1	1	1	1		1	1	1
2	2	2	2		2	2	2
3	3	3	3		3	3	3
4	4	4	4		4	4	4
5	5	5	5		5	5	5
6	6	6	6		6	6	6
7	7	7	7		7	7	7
8	8	8	8		8	8	8
9	9	9	9		9	9	9

10 The Junior ROTC uses tents with fronts that form equilateral triangles with sides of 84 inches. Will the members of the basketball team, all of whom are between 6 feet, 4 inches and 7 feet tall, be able to stand up in the tents?

F Yes, all can stand.

G No, none can stand.

H Some can stand but not all.

J Not Here

11 In the quadratic equation $ax^2 + bx + c = 0$, which of the following is determined by the sign of the coefficient a?

A The y-intercept

B The x-intercept

C The origin

D Whether the parabola opens up or down

12 In the word below, what fraction of the letters have rotational symmetry?

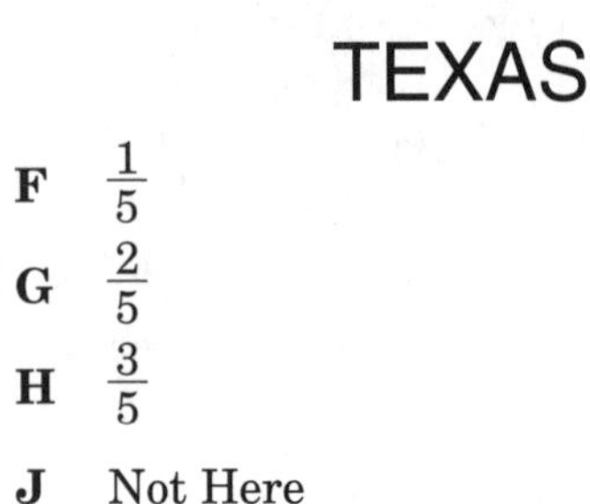

F $\frac{1}{5}$

G $\frac{2}{5}$

H $\frac{3}{5}$

J Not Here

13 Jonathan's job at the golf course consists of making sure that the sprinklers are properly adjusted. The sprinklers must turn through an angle of 320 degrees and be able to spray water from 0 to 70 feet from the sprinkler. What is the total area each sprinkler must be able to water, to the nearest square foot? Use 3.14 for π.

A 17,309 ft^2

B 15,386 ft^2

C 14,104 ft^2

D 13,676 ft^2

14 Which of the following relations is NOT a function?

F (−8, 0), (0, 8), (0, −8)

G (−8, 0), (0, 8), (8, 0)

H (4, 5), (3, 4), (2, 3)

J (7, 6), (4, 1), (5.5, 3.5)

15 If the letters in the word TEXARKANA were placed in a hat, what would be the probability of drawing an A?

A $\frac{3}{6}$

B $\frac{3}{9}$

C $\frac{1}{8}$

D $\frac{1}{9}$

16 In the figure below, what is x?

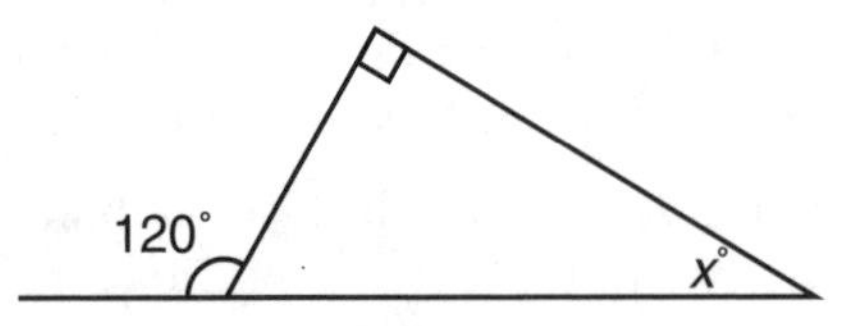

Record your answer and fill in the bubbles on the grid below. Be sure to use the correct place value.

				.			
0	0	0	0		0	0	0
1	1	1	1		1	1	1
2	2	2	2		2	2	2
3	3	3	3		3	3	3
4	4	4	4		4	4	4
5	5	5	5		5	5	5
6	6	6	6		6	6	6
7	7	7	7		7	7	7
8	8	8	8		8	8	8
9	9	9	9		9	9	9

17 The scatterplot shows the height and shoe size of a group of boys in the junior class. About how tall would you expect a junior boy with shoe size 7 to be?

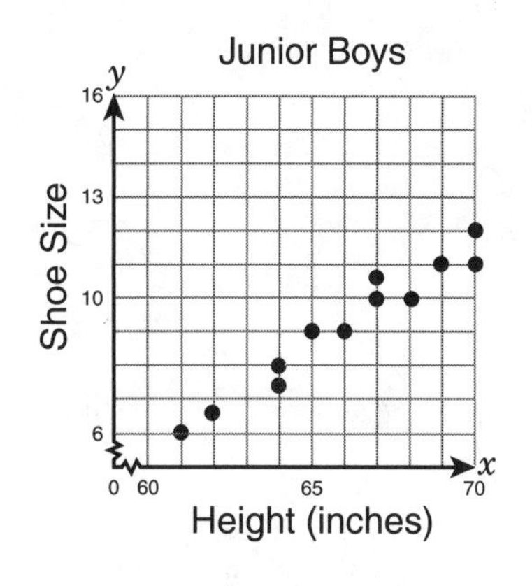

A 5 ft

B 5 ft 2 in.

C 5 ft 6 in.

D Not Here

18 Mr. Brady's car will be in the shop for repairs for 13 days. In the meantime, he will have to get a rental car. One company offers a daily rate d of \$34.95 and a weekly rate w of \$240.95. Which inequality shows which rate will cost him less?

F $34.95 - d > 240.95 - w$

G $34.95d > 240.95w$

H $240.95w < 34.95d$

J $w + 34.95 > d + 240.95$

19 For each revolution of its tires, a car travels a distance equal to the circumference of those tires. If a car has tires with a 7-inch radius, about how far, in feet, will a car travel during 1 revolution of those tires? Use $\pi = 3.14$.

A 87.92 ft

B 43.96 ft

C 3.66 ft

D Not Here

20 Rudy is designing a square deck with a side length of 12 feet. In the middle of the deck will be a round pool 9 feet in diameter, as shown below.

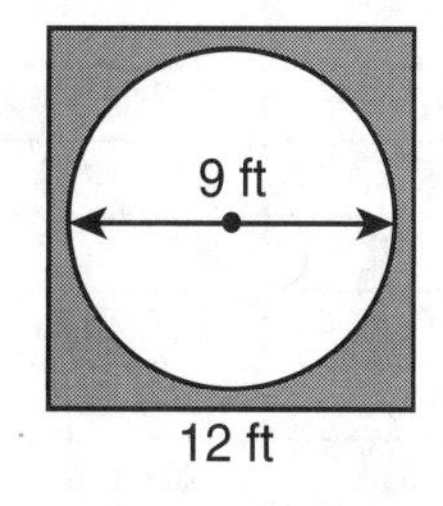

To the nearest square foot, what is the area of the deck?

F 64 ft^2

G 80 ft^2

H 144 ft^2

J Not Here

21 The circle below has been divided into 8 equal sections.

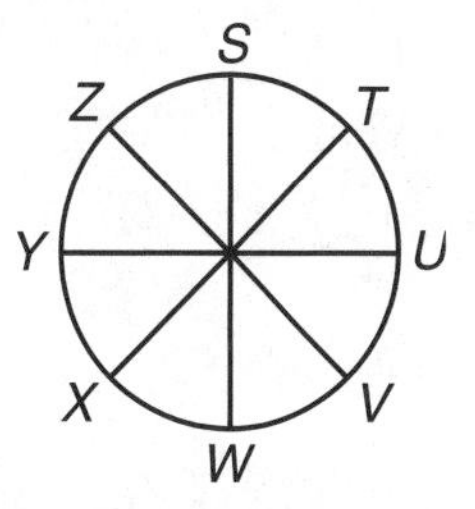

What is the arc length from Y to X if the length of $\overline{ZV}$ is equal to 12? Use 3.14 for π.

Record your answer and fill in the bubbles on the grid below. Be sure to use the correct place value.

				.			
0	0	0	0		0	0	0
1	1	1	1		1	1	1
2	2	2	2		2	2	2
3	3	3	3		3	3	3
4	4	4	4		4	4	4
5	5	5	5		5	5	5
6	6	6	6		6	6	6
7	7	7	7		7	7	7
8	8	8	8		8	8	8
9	9	9	9		9	9	9

For Questions 22–24, use the information below.

This table shows the value of a car from 1997 through 2002.

Year	Price
1997	$12,500
1998	$10,500
1999	$10,000
2000	$9,500
2001	$9,000
2002	$8,300

In 2002, Luis was considering buying a 5-year old vehicle. The asking price was $11,500. He checked on the Web to find the selling prices for recent-year models of the same vehicle and made a table.

22 At what average rate has the value of the car decreased?

F $500 per year

G $840 per year

H $2,150 per year

J $4,200 per year

23 Based on the data in his table, Luis thinks he is being charged too much. What is the difference between the price in the table and the seller's asking price?

A $1,000

B $2,500

C $3,200

D Not Here

24 Which graph correctly displays the data in the table?

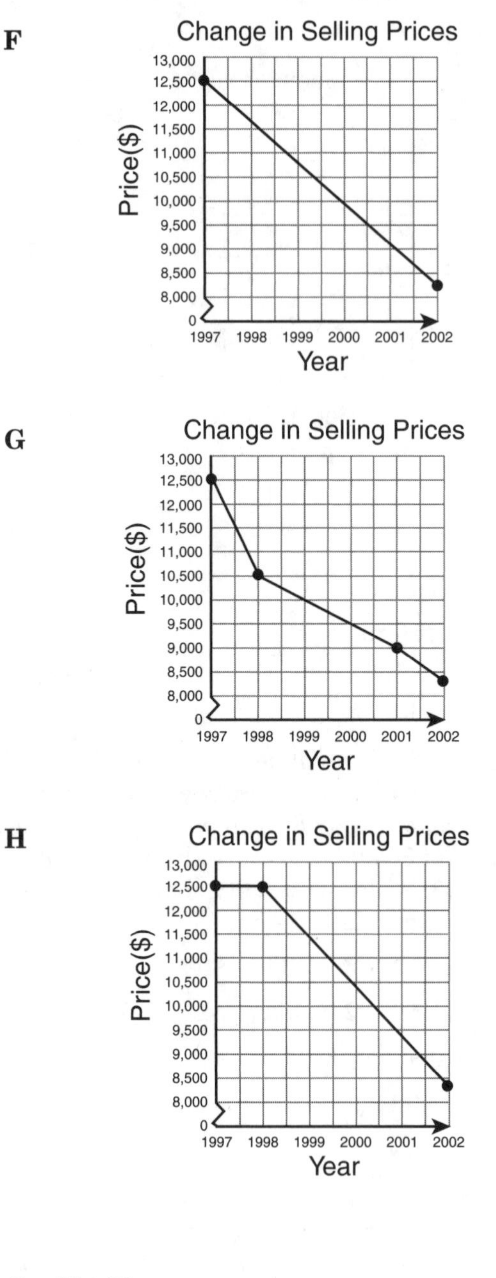

J Not Here

25 What is the difference in inches between the circumference of a tire with a 13-inch radius and a tire with a 14-inch radius? Use 3.14 for π.

Record your answer and fill in the bubbles on the grid below. Be sure to use the correct place value.

				.			
0	0	0	0		0	0	0
1	1	1	1		1	1	1
2	2	2	2		2	2	2
3	3	3	3		3	3	3
4	4	4	4		4	4	4
5	5	5	5		5	5	5
6	6	6	6		6	6	6
7	7	7	7		7	7	7
8	8	8	8		8	8	8
9	9	9	9		9	9	9

26 The oak tree outside of Brian's house casts a 12-foot shadow at a certain time of day. At the same time Brian, who is 6 feet tall, casts a 2-foot shadow. How tall is the tree?

F 15 ft

G 18 ft

H 24 ft

J 36 ft

27 Which of the following is true?

A If two lines are not coplanar, they must intersect.

B Parallel lines are also skew.

C Skew lines that are coplanar never intersect.

D Parallel lines are coplanar.

28 What would be the coordinates of J and K for $J'K'L'M'N'$ to be a reduction?

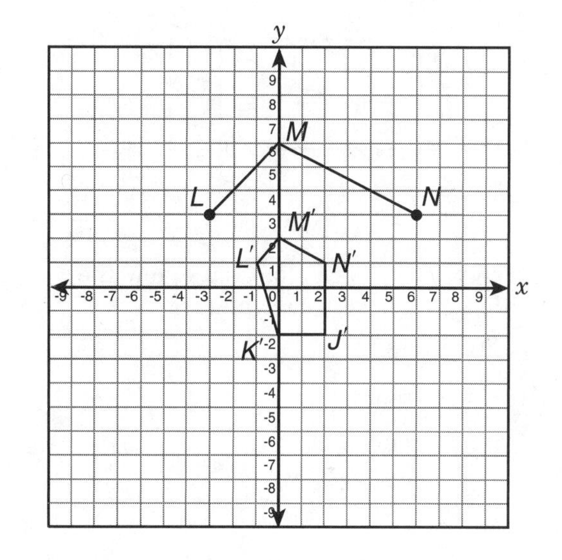

F $J(6, -6)$ and $K(0, -6)$

G $J(3, -3)$ and $K(-3, 0)$

H $J(4, -4)$ and $K(-6, 0)$

J Not Here

29 Lacy made a block building for her baby brother by stacking blocks.

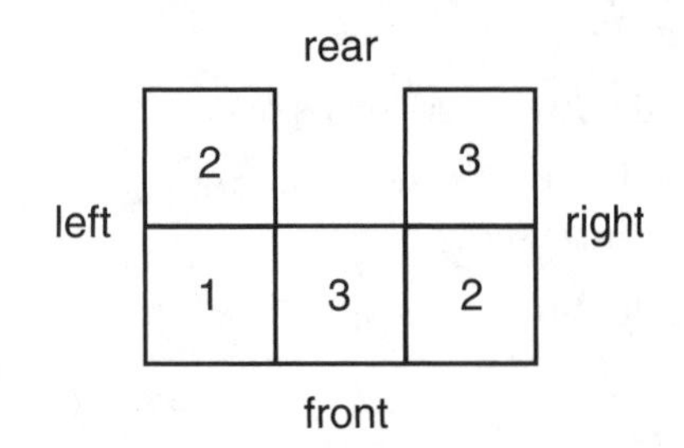

Then Lacy made the sketch below of the building.

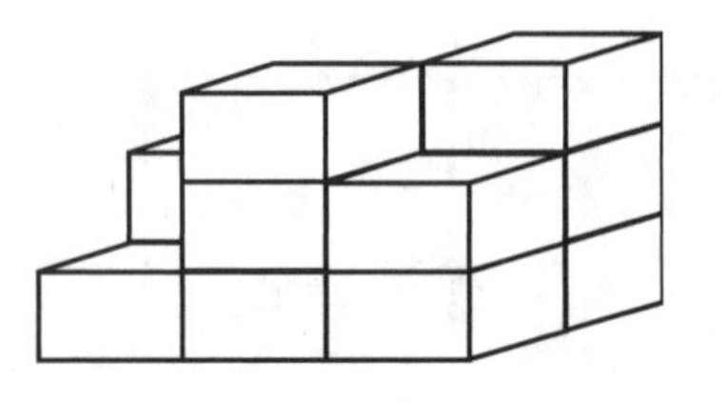

From which position did Lacy view the building while she sketched it?

A Left rear

B Right rear

C Left front

D Right front

30 If a day on Earth is 24 hours long, what is the degree measure of the arc of the Earth's rotation in 2 hours?

Record your answer and fill in the bubbles on the grid below. Be sure to use the correct place value.

				.			
0	0	0	0		0	0	0
1	1	1	1		1	1	1
2	2	2	2		2	2	2
3	3	3	3		3	3	3
4	4	4	4		4	4	4
5	5	5	5		5	5	5
6	6	6	6		6	6	6
7	7	7	7		7	7	7
8	8	8	8		8	8	8
9	9	9	9		9	9	9

31 Which of the following shows the result of moving each point on the graph of $y = -x^2 - 1$ up two units?

A

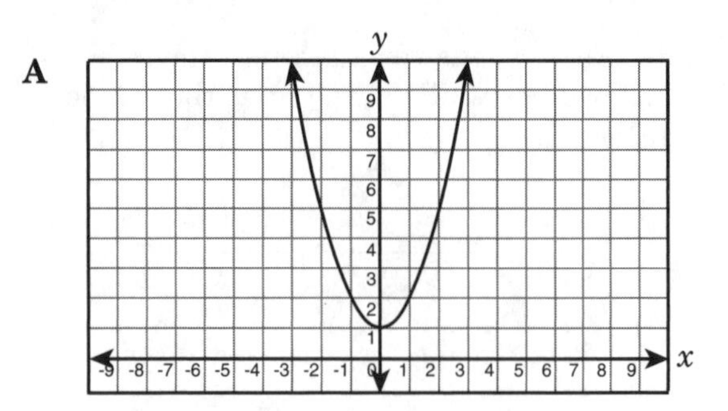

B

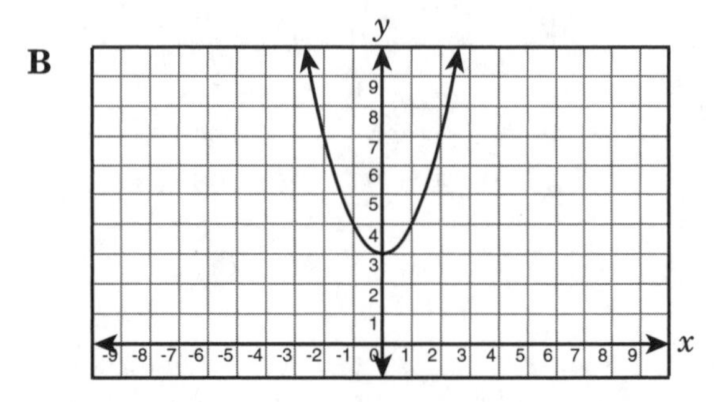

C

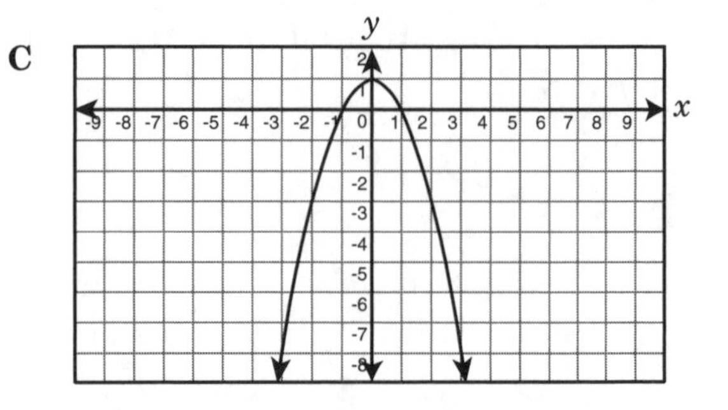

D

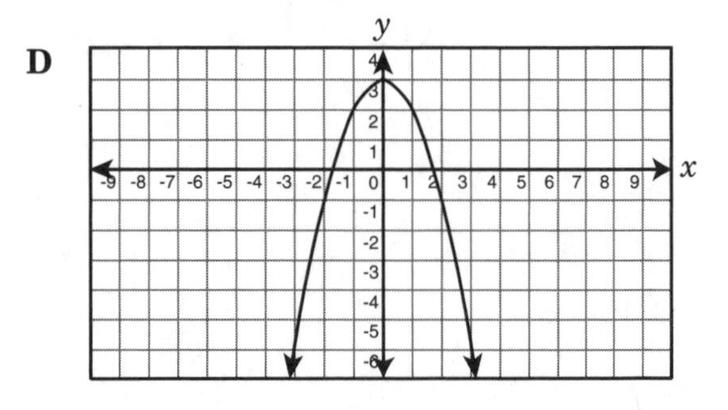

32 For a function, the variable y varies directly with the square of x. If x is 4 when y is 24, find y when x is 2.

F 4

G 6

H 12

J 48

33 Ramon works with his uncle during the summer cleaning swimming pools. If an inlet pipe takes 20 hours to fill a pool, and an outlet pipe takes 15 hours to empty the pool, how long will it take to empty the full pool if both pipes are left open?

A 5 h

B 30 h

C 35 h

D 60 h

34 For their upcoming production, the drama club built the old-fashioned schoolhouse shown below.

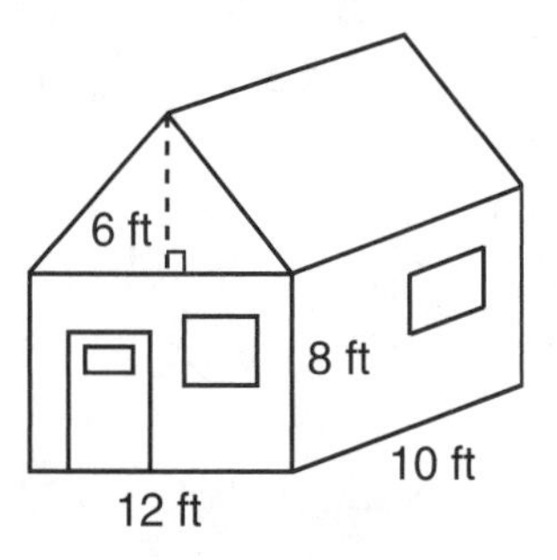

The club members want to paint the entire structure red, except the roof, door, and windows. If one gallon of paint covers 300 square feet, and the door and windows total 60 square feet, which is the minimum number of gallons of paint they must buy?

F 1 gal

G 2 gal

H 3 gal

J Not Here

35 $ABCD$ and $EFGH$ are squares. The length of side $\overline{AB}$ is x and the length of side $\overline{EF}$ is $2x$. How many squares the size of $ABCD$ are needed to completely cover square $EFGH$?

A 2

B 4

C 6

D 8

36 In the quadratic equation $ax^2 + bx + c = 0$, which of the following on the graph is determined by the parameter c?

F The y-intercept

G The x-intercept

H The origin

J Not Here

37 Ron is filling a 55-gallon drum from a faucet that flows at a rate of 3.3 gallons per minute. The drum leaks at a rate of 0.8 gallon per minute. How many minutes will it take Ron to fill the drum?

Record your answer and fill in the bubbles on the grid below. Be sure to use the correct place value.

38 Four friends held a car wash to earn money for their trip to Astroworld. They agreed that each would receive a percentage of the amount raised based on the number of hours worked. Austin worked 8 hours. David worked from 12 to 4. Robert worked from 10 to 4. Andy worked from 2 to 4. How much should each receive of the $600 they earned?

F Austin - $240, David - $120, Robert - $180 Andy - $60

G Austin - $300, David $100, Robert - $15, Andy - $25

H Austin - $500, David - $45, Robert - $30, Andy - $25

J Austin - $600, David - $0, Robert - $0, Andy - $0

39 To the nearest hundredth, what is the probability that if a number cube, labeled 1 through 6 is tossed, the result will be a number greater than 4?

A 0.17

B 0.33

C 0.50

D 0.67

40 If the distance on the map from Houston to New York, measured with a centimeter ruler, is 4.7, and the map scale is 1 centimeter = 500 kilometers, what is the actual distance in kilometers?

Record your answer and fill in the bubbles on the grid below. Be sure to use the correct place value.

				.			
0	0	0	0		0	0	0
1	1	1	1		1	1	1
2	2	2	2		2	2	2
3	3	3	3		3	3	3
4	4	4	4		4	4	4
5	5	5	5		5	5	5
6	6	6	6		6	6	6
7	7	7	7		7	7	7
8	8	8	8		8	8	8
9	9	9	9		9	9	9

41 Anna's plant has outgrown its pot. At the hardware store, Anna saw four larger pots, two cubes, and two cylinders. She made a sketch of each so she could compare them later. Anna did not make her sketches to scale.

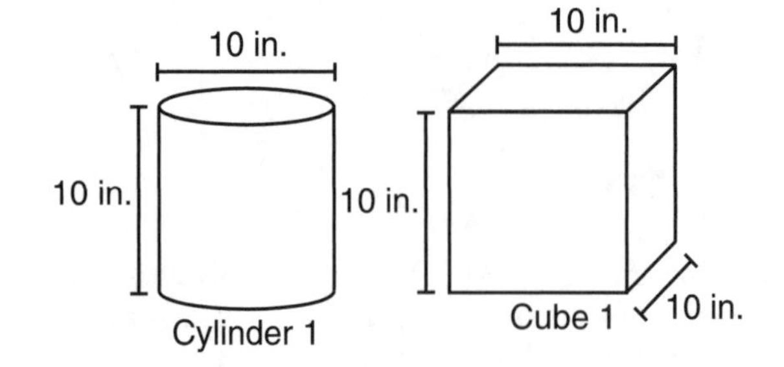

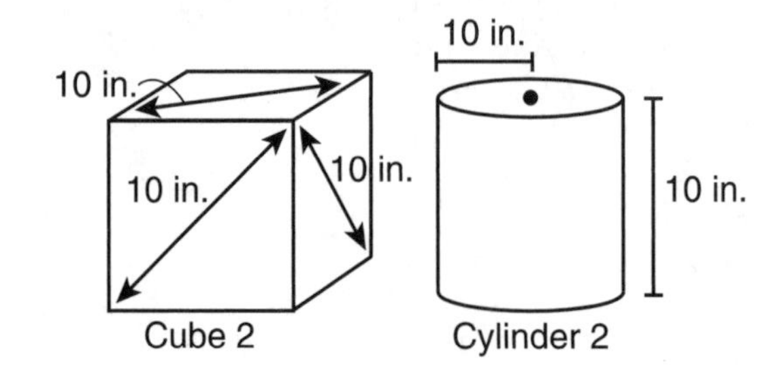

Which of the four pots will give Anna's plant the most room?

A Cube 1

B Cube 2

C Cylinder 1

D Cylinder 2

42 Which of the following relations is NOT a function?

F (1, 0), (2, 3), (4, 5)

G (3, 0), (0, −2), (3, −4)

H (4, 2), (−3, 1), (2, 0)

J (−1, 2), (5, −6), (4, 2)

43 In May of 2002, Dr. Arnando and Dr. Nadi worked rotating shifts at the hospital.

May 2002						
S	M	T	W	T	F	S
			1	2	3	4
5	6	7	8	9	10	11
12	13	14	15	16	17	18
19	20	21	22	23	24	25
26	27	28	29	30	31	

Dr. Armando worked the late shift every 3rd weekday, and Dr. Nadi worked the late shift every 5th weekday. If they both worked the late shift on the May 3, what is the next date they will both work the late shift?

A May 8

B May 10

C May 21

D May 24

44 $\triangle ABC$ has vertices at $(-4, -2)$, $(-5, -4)$, and $(-2, -4)$. If $\triangle ABC$ is reflected across both the x- and y-axes, in what quadrant would it lie?

F IV

G III

H II

J I

Use the information below to answer Questions 45–47.

The annual salaries of the 12 employees at a car dealership are as follows.

301,000	40,000	58,000	52,000
60,000	40,000	66,000	40,000
44,000	40,000	60,000	39,000

45 Find the mean, the median, and the mode of the salaries. Which of the following shows the mean, median, and mode in order from greatest to least?

A Mean, median, mode

B Median, mean, mode

C Mode, mean, median

D Mode, median, mean

46 If you were representing management during contract negotiations, which measure would you use to show that most of the employees are not underpaid?

F Median

G Mode

H Mean

J Range

47 Which measure of central tendency is affected most by the removal of the highest salary?

A Median

B Mean

C Mode

D Not Here

48 Julio put 20 gallons of gas into his car's gas tank at the start of a 360-mile trip. At his destination, there are only 5 gallons left in the gas tank. Which of the following describes how a graph would look if it showed how the amount of gas in Julio's car changed over the course of his trip if he drove at a constant speed and did not stop?

F Linear with a positive slope

G Linear with a negative slope

H Linear with no slope

J Linear with an undefined slope

49 Leona wrote the set of ordered pairs: (8, 5), (6, 8), (x, 11), (0, 12). If the set of ordered pairs belongs to a function, which of the following could NOT be the value of x?

A 12

B 11

C 8

D 5

50 Brian and Brandon each have newspaper routes. Brian has 18 customers. Brandon has 30 customers. If Brian gets 3 new customers per week, and Brandon gets 2, how many weeks will pass before they each have the same number of customers?

F 4 weeks

G 6 weeks

H 10 weeks

J Not Here

51 Celeste is redecorating her home. She made the rough sketch of the different areas shown below.

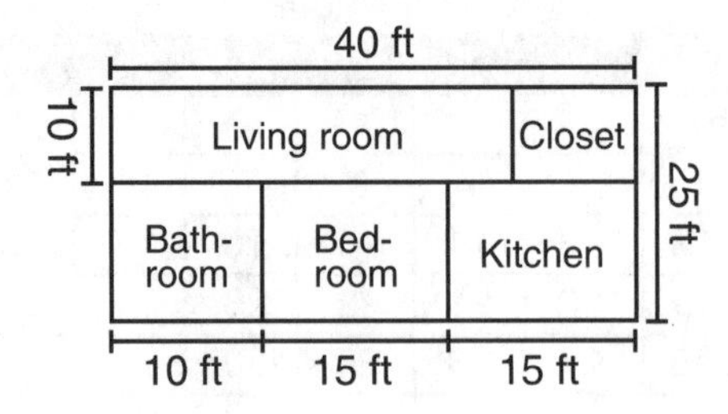

Celeste plans to carpet her entire home, except for her bathroom and kitchen. She plans to calculate the area of carpet she will need and then add 5% to her order in case she needs extra. How many square feet of carpet will Celeste order? Round your answer to the nearest hundredth.

Record your answer and fill in the bubbles on the grid below. Be sure to use the correct place value.

				.			
0	0	0	0		0	0	0
1	1	1	1		1	1	1
2	2	2	2		2	2	2
3	3	3	3		3	3	3
4	4	4	4		4	4	4
5	5	5	5		5	5	5
6	6	6	6		6	6	6
7	7	7	7		7	7	7
8	8	8	8		8	8	8
9	9	9	9		9	9	9

52 A hexagonal prism has a base of 8 square meters, a height of 30 meters, and a volume of v cubic meters. If the area of the base is doubled but the height is not changed, which is the new volume?

F $2v$

G $4v$

H $8v$

J $16v$

53 The arching roof of a tunnel is modeled by the quadratic function $y = -0.1x^2 + 20$. At a distance of x feet from the center of the tunnel, the roof is y feet high. A two-lane road divides the tunnel evenly.

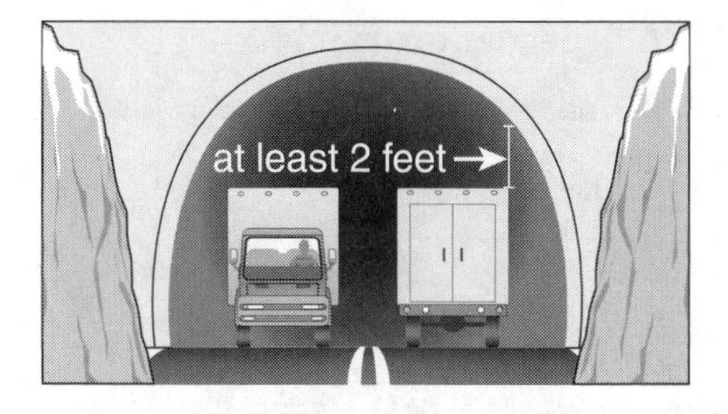

Jake's trailer trucks are 8-feet wide. What is the height of the tallest truck Jake can send through the tunnel, if the truck must stay in its own lane and be no closer than 2 feet to the roof of the tunnel?

A 18.0 ft

B 16.4 ft

C 13.6 ft

D 11.6 ft

54 What is the y-intercept of the line containing points $(-7, -1)$ and $(5, 2)$?

F -1

G 0

H $\frac{3}{4}$

J 1

55 Mrs. DeJean's art students plan to cover the sides of ten 12-foot tall columns with a reflective fabric. If each column has a 3-foot radius, how many square yards of the fabric will they need? Use 3.14 for π.

A 125.6 yd^2

B 251.2 yd^2

C 376.8 yd^2

D 753.6 yd^2

56 Sally made a map to show the location of several nearby towns.

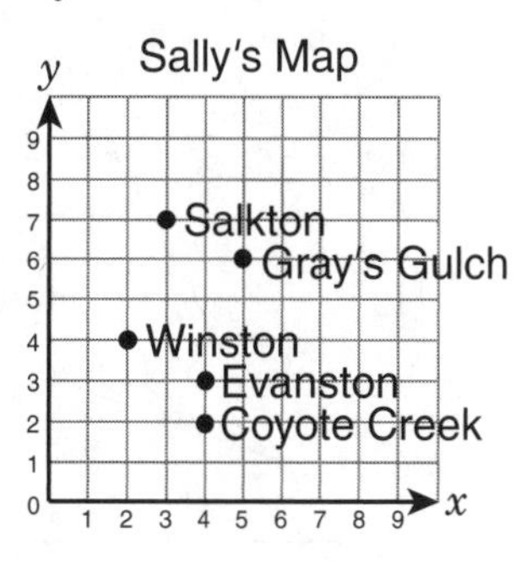

On Sally's map, what are the coordinates of Evanston?

F (2, 4)

G (3, 4)

H (4, 2)

J (4, 3)

57 The scores on the math exam are shown in the frequency table. What is the probability that a student picked at random scored 80% or above?

Score	Frequency
60	3
70	3
80	10
90	12
100	2

A 24%

B 47%

C 88%

D Not Here

58 Find the distance between the midpoints of $\overline{XY}$ and $\overline{XZ}$. Round your answer to the nearest thousandth.

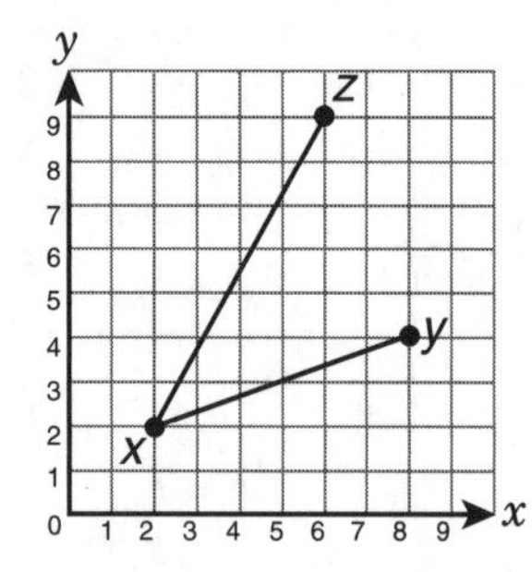

Record your answer and fill in the bubbles on the grid below. Be sure to use the correct place value.

				.			
0	0	0	0		0	0	0
1	1	1	1		1	1	1
2	2	2	2		2	2	2
3	3	3	3		3	3	3
4	4	4	4		4	4	4
5	5	5	5		5	5	5
6	6	6	6		6	6	6
7	7	7	7		7	7	7
8	8	8	8		8	8	8
9	9	9	9		9	9	9

59 The city is building a memorial garden with a circular lake in the center. The lake will have a depth of 8 feet and a volume of 40,000 cubic feet. A bridge will cross the lake, passing over its center. To the nearest foot, what will be the length of the bridge?

A 20 ft

B 40 ft

C 80 ft

D Not Here

60 Solve the equation $x^2 - x - 6 = 0$ for x.

F {1, −6}

G {2, −3}

H {3, −2}

J {6, −1}

61 Which is represented by x in the table below?

x	−1	0	3	5
$f(x)$	−3	−1	5	9

A An independent variable

B A dependent variable

C A linear function

D A quadratic function

62 Joey drew a floor plan of a house that uses the scale 1 inch = 3 feet. What dimensions should Joey use in his floor plan to show a living room with the dimensions 16 × 14 feet?

F $5\frac{1}{3} \times 3\frac{2}{3}$ in.

G $5\frac{1}{3} \times 4\frac{2}{3}$ in.

H 45 × 39 in.

J 48 × 42 in.

63 Nelle buys athletic shoes from the factory for $35 per pair. She sells them for $120 per pair. By what percent does Nelle mark up the price of the sneakers she sells? Round to the nearest whole percent.

A 29%

B 71%

C 243%

D 343%

64 For a function, the variable g varies inversely with h. If h is 20 when g is 5, find h when g is 4.

F 16

G 19

H 21

J 25

65 What is the equation of the line determined by the function table?

x	$f(x)$
−1	−3
0	−1
1	1
2	3

A $f(x) = x - 1$

B $f(x) = x - 2y$

C $f(x) = 2x - 1$

D $f(x) = 3x + 2$

66 Which equation describes a line that passes through the points of the scatterplot below?

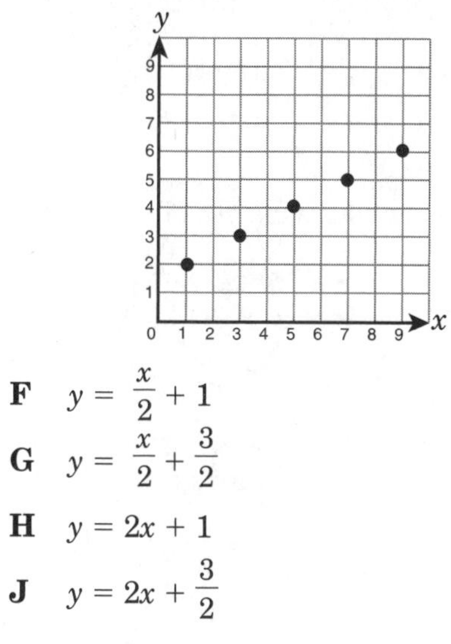

F $y = \frac{x}{2} + 1$

G $y = \frac{x}{2} + \frac{3}{2}$

H $y = 2x + 1$

J $y = 2x + \frac{3}{2}$

67 What is the domain of $y = \frac{4}{x} - 2$?

A All real numbers except 0

B All real numbers except 2

C All real numbers such that $x > 4$

D All real numbers such that $x < 4$

68 What are the roots of the function $x^2 + 5x + 6 = 0$?

F (0, 6)

G (2, 0), (3, 0)

H (−2, 0), (−3, 0)

J Not Here

69 Dave spends 25% of his salary on rent, 10% on food, 10% on his car, 5% on entertainment, and saves 50%. Which graph could best be used to display how Dave divides his salary?

A

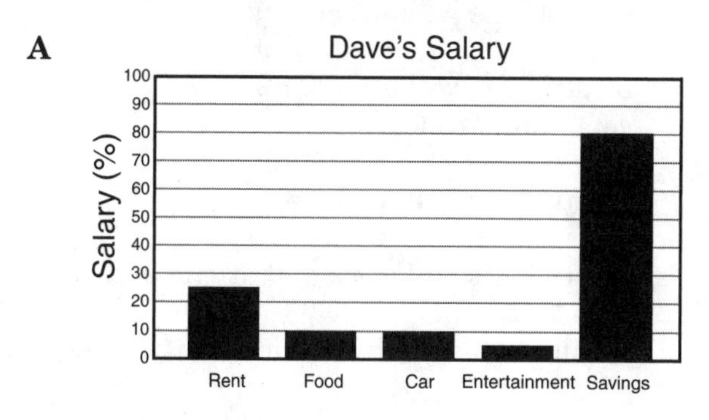

B

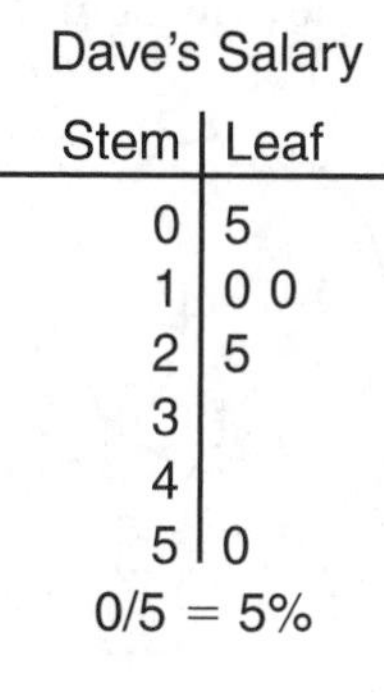
Dave's Salary

Stem	Leaf
0	5
1	0 0
2	5
3	
4	
5	0

0/5 = 5%

C

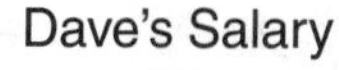

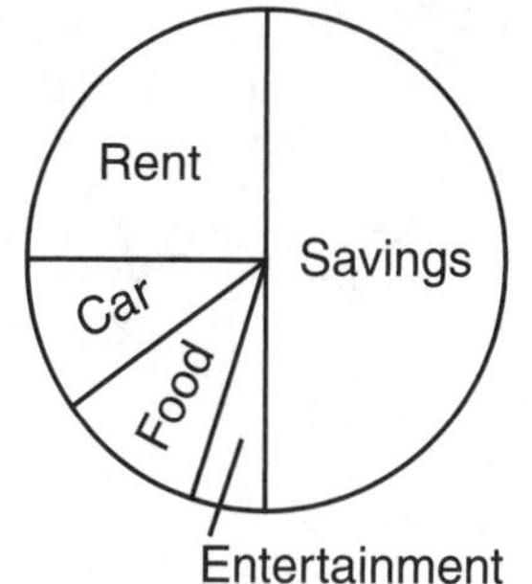

D

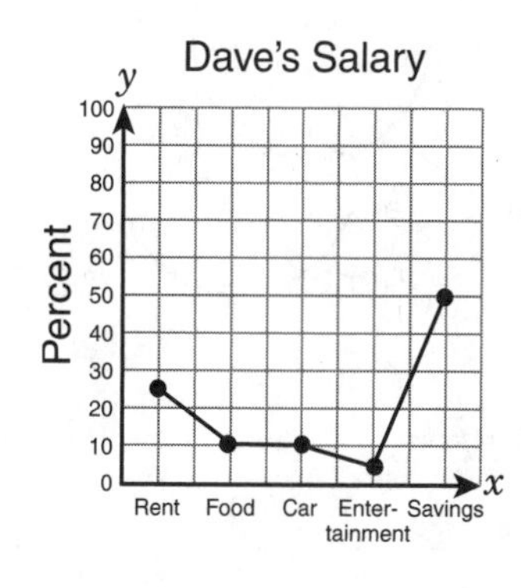

70 Brenda quizzed her graduating classmates about their plans for the next year. Her results are listed below.

50 students will attend a university.

30 students will attend a 2-year community college.

60 students will work.

15 students will work and attend a university.

7 will work and attend community college.

Which Venn diagram correctly displays this information about the senior class?

F

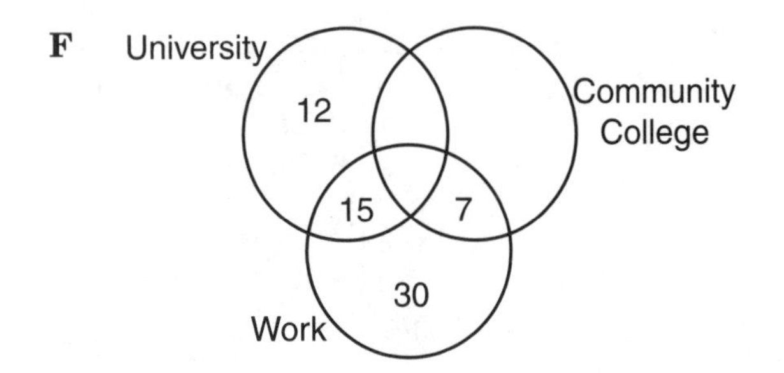

G

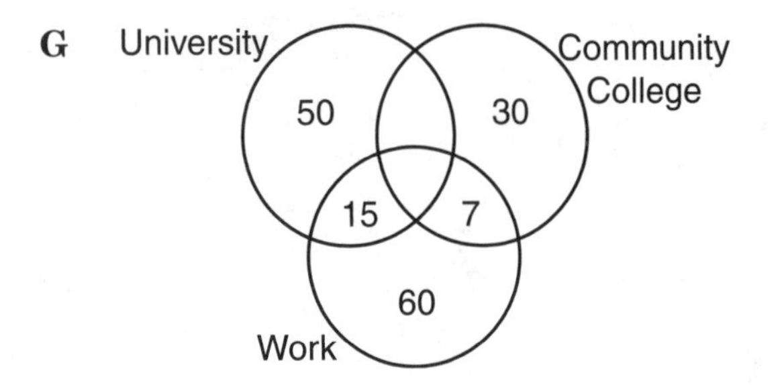

H

University
Community College
Work
65
37
15
7
90

J Not Here

71 The carat is a unit of measure used to determine the mass of gemstones. The mass of 1 carat is equal to 200 milligrams. For her engagement, Rosa received a $2\frac{1}{4}$ carat diamond ring. What is the mass of the diamond in milligrams?

Record your answer and fill in the bubbles on the grid below. Be sure to use the correct place value.

				.			
0	0	0	0		0	0	0
1	1	1	1		1	1	1
2	2	2	2		2	2	2
3	3	3	3		3	3	3
4	4	4	4		4	4	4
5	5	5	5		5	5	5
6	6	6	6		6	6	6
7	7	7	7		7	7	7
8	8	8	8		8	8	8
9	9	9	9		9	9	9

72 Carrie wrote the following set of equations.

$$y = \frac{x}{5} + 4$$
$$3x + 2y = 8$$
$$y = x$$
$$y = \frac{2}{x}$$

What percent of the equations are linear?

F 100%

G 75%

H 50%

J 25%

73 Many ancients believed the most pleasing rectangles to look at had a length to width ratio of 1.62:1. This was called the golden ratio. Rectangles with that characteristic are sill called golden rectangles. Which of the following photo sizes is closest to a golden rectangle?

A 5×8

B 8×10

C 8×11

D 10×13

74 Amy has two containers. Both containers have the same diameter, but container A is 3 times as tall as container B.

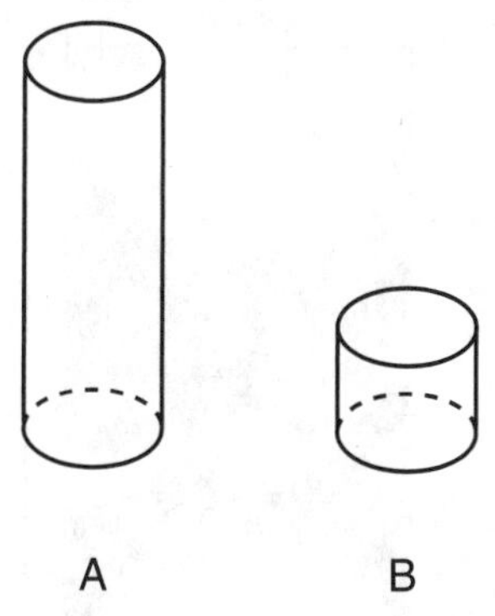

Which equation correctly describes the relationship of the volume of A as a function of the volume of B?

F $f(B) = B + 3$

G $f(B) = B + 6$

H $f(B) = 3B$

J $f(B) = 6B$

75 Mindy drew the first three steps in the pattern shown below.

Which expression can be used to determine the number of stars in the nth step?

A n^2

B $2n$

C $2(n - 1)$

D $n(n + 1)$

76 Which graph shows a domain and range of {0, 1, 2,}?

F

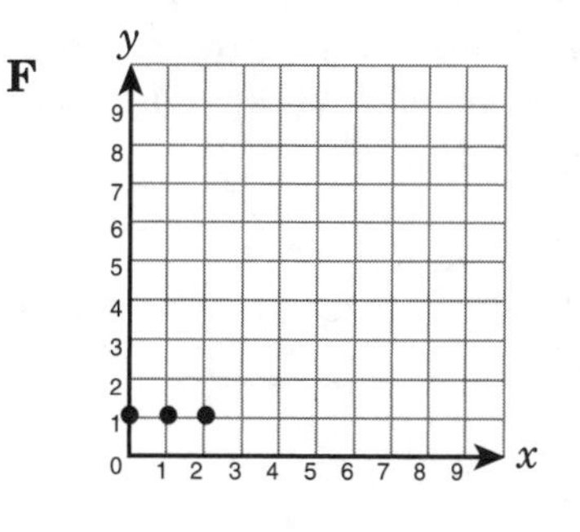

G

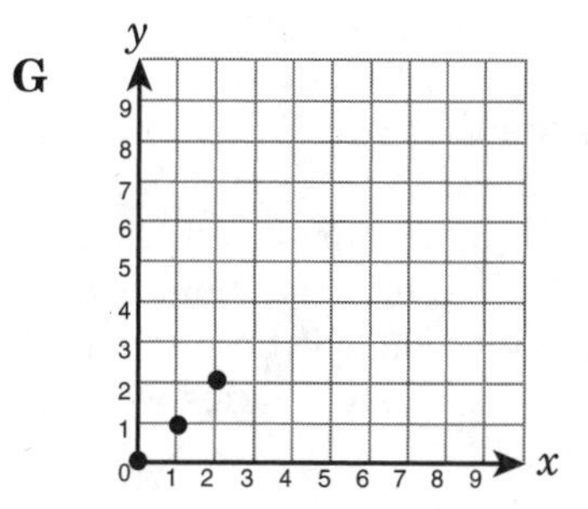

H

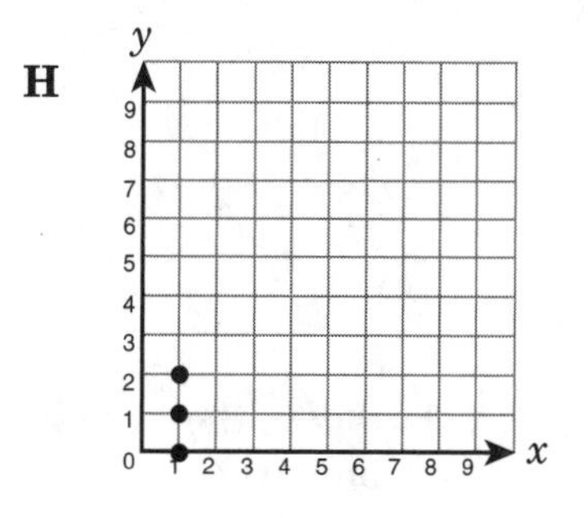

J

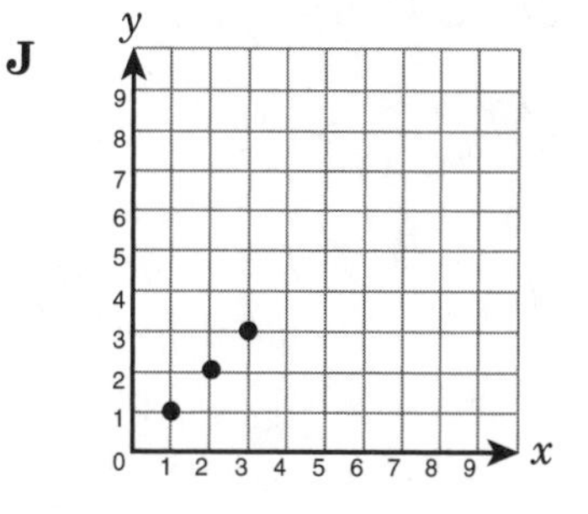

77 Lola earns $8 for every hour she works during the week. She earns $12 for every hour she works on Saturday and Sunday. Which equation shows Lola's total salary s if she works x hours during the week, and y hours during the weekend?

A $20(x + y) = s$

B $4(2x + 3y) = s$

C $4(8x + 12y) = s$

D Not Here

78 Jason had 1 cookie that was 6 inches in diameter. Pete offered to trade him 2 cookies each with a 3-inch diameter. Jason wasn't sure if this was a good deal or a bad deal. How many 3-inch cookies would it take to equal 1 6-inch cookie, if both size cookies were of equal thickness?

F 2 cookies

G 3 cookies

H 4 cookies

J 5 cookies

79 Which fraction of the letters in the word below have a vertical line of symmetry?

HOUSTON

A $\frac{1}{7}$

B $\frac{3}{7}$

C $\frac{5}{7}$

D $\frac{6}{7}$

80 Paul cut a rectangular piece of paper. Then he cut off a semi-circular piece from each end, as shown below.

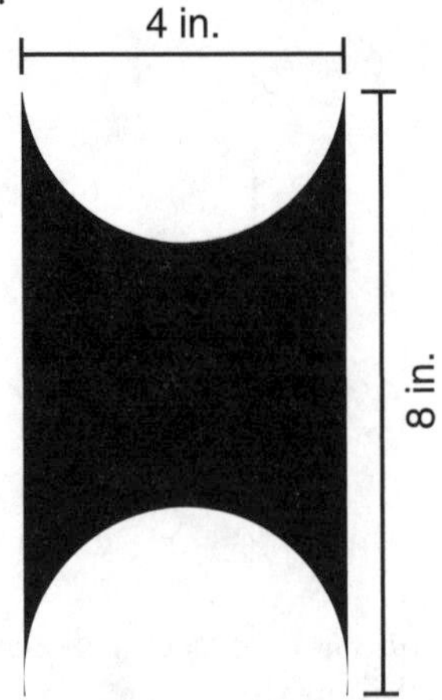

What is the area of the remaining paper? Use 3.14 for π.

F 19.44 in.^{2}

G 25.72 in.^{2}

H 28.86 in.^{2}

J 32.00 in.^{2}

81 Ben's store sold melons for $0.80 per pound yesterday. Today, the price is $0.65. What is the percent discount to the nearest whole percent?

A 19%

B 23%

C 31%

D 38%

82 A triangular prism has a base of 5 square meters, a length of 8 meters, and a volume of v cubic meters. If the perimeter of the base is doubled, which is the new volume?

F $2v$

G $4v$

H $8v$

J Not Here

83 What is the x-coordinate of the midpoint of the line segment with endpoints $(-6, 1)$ and $(4, 3)$?

A -2

B 2

C 5

D Not Here

84 For $\triangle ABC$ below, which relationship must be true?

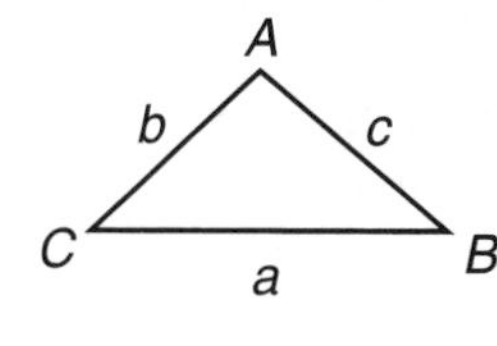

F $b = a - c$

G $a < c + b$

H $c^2 = a^2 + b^2$

J $c < a - b$

85 A turkey should be roasted in a 350°F oven for 15 to 20 minutes per pound. If a 22-pound turkey is placed in the oven at 6:00 A.M., what is the earliest it will be ready to eat?

A 9:00 A.M.

B 11:30 A.M.

C 1:30 P.M.

D 5:00 P.M.

86 Which is the positive root of $4x^2 - 4x - 8 = 0$?

F 1

G 2

H 4

J 8

87 Solve the equation $x^2 - 4x - 12 = 0$ for x.

A $\{2, -6\}$

B $\{3, -4\}$

C $\{4, -3\}$

D $\{6, -2\}$

88 Which is the slope of the line connecting the midpoints of $\overline{XY}$ and $\overline{XZ}$?

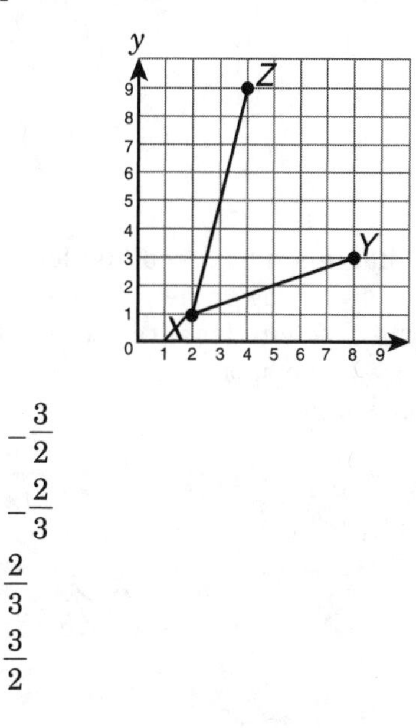

F $-\frac{3}{2}$

G $-\frac{2}{3}$

H $\frac{2}{3}$

J $\frac{3}{2}$

89 In the quadratic equation $ax^2 + bx + c = 0$, multiplying a by a number greater than 1 will have which effect?

A Make the parabola narrower

B Make the parabola wider

C Move the parabola up

D Move the parabola down

90 Pam wrote a set of four functions.

I $f(x) = 2x + 1$

II $f(x) = x^2 - 3x - 18$

III $f(x) = x^2$

IV $f(x) = -3x - 17$

Evaluate the functions for $x = -3$ and arrange them in order from greatest to least.

F I, III, II, IV

G IV, II, I, III

H III, I, II, IV

J III, II, I, IV

91 Jeff found that when he stood 500 feet from the base of a radio tower, he was the same height as the guy wire from the tower. Jeff was also 5 feet from the spot where the wire reached the ground.

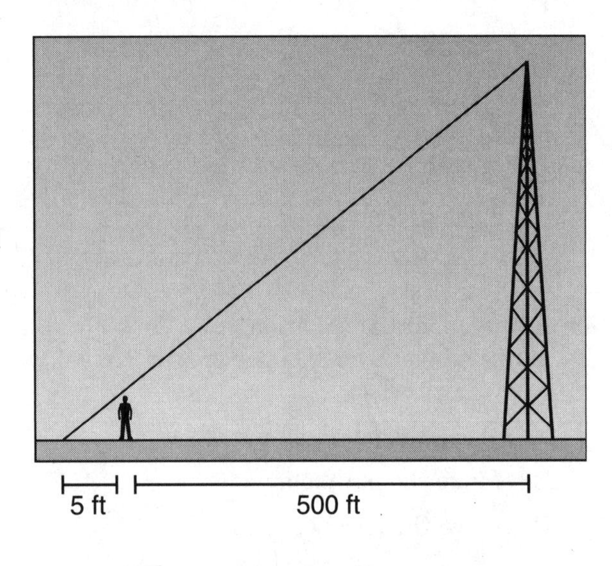

If Jeff is 60 inches tall, how tall is the radio tower to the nearest foot?

A 500 ft

B 2,500 ft

C 3,000 ft

D Not Here

92 A circular rug with a radius of 12 feet is placed in a square living room so that the rug covers the floor as shown below.

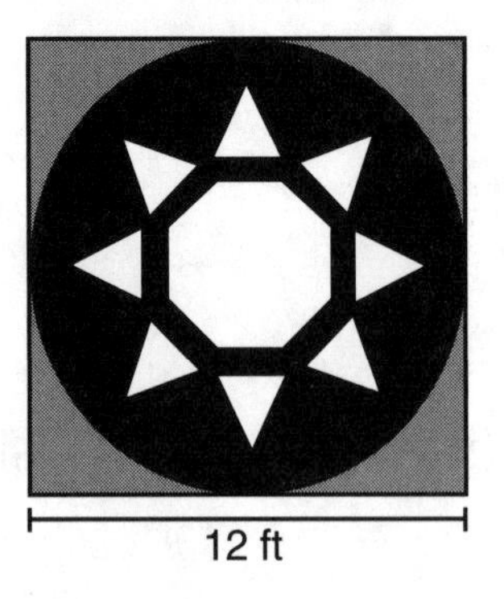

How much of the floor is not covered by the rug? Use 3.14 for π.

F 30.96 m^2

G 68.64 m^2

H 75.36 m^2

J 113.04 m^2

93 Five friends earned $1,400 mowing lawns together. They agreed that each person would receive an amount that was proportional to the number of hours he or she had worked. According to the table, which amount should Scott receive?

Name	Hours Worked
Scott	20
Lou	15
Gina	10
Dave	25
Amanda	30

Record your answer and fill in the bubbles on the grid below. Be sure to use the correct place value.

				.			
0	0	0	0		0	0	0
1	1	1	1		1	1	1
2	2	2	2		2	2	2
3	3	3	3		3	3	3
4	4	4	4		4	4	4
5	5	5	5		5	5	5
6	6	6	6		6	6	6
7	7	7	7		7	7	7
8	8	8	8		8	8	8
9	9	9	9		9	9	9

94 The square of the length of the hypotenuse of an isosceles right triangle is 32. What is the length of one of the legs of the triangle?

Record your answer and fill in the bubbles on the grid below. Be sure to use the correct place value.

				.			
0	0	0	0		0	0	0
1	1	1	1		1	1	1
2	2	2	2		2	2	2
3	3	3	3		3	3	3
4	4	4	4		4	4	4
5	5	5	5		5	5	5
6	6	6	6		6	6	6
7	7	7	7		7	7	7
8	8	8	8		8	8	8
9	9	9	9		9	9	9

95 What is the y-coordinate of the midpoint of the line segment with endpoints (9, 2) and (5, 7)?

A 3.5

B 4.5

C 7

D 8

96 Rob has two boxes. Both boxes are cubes, but box A has a side length that is 3 times the side length of box B.

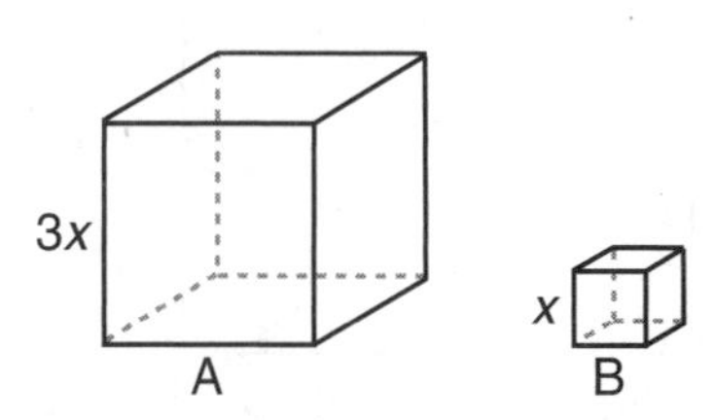

Rob spent 20 minutes painting box B. About how long should it take him to paint box A?

F 60 min

G 1 h 40 min

H 2 h 20 min

J 3 h

97 A gondola travels on a cable that can be described by the function $y = \frac{x}{3}$.

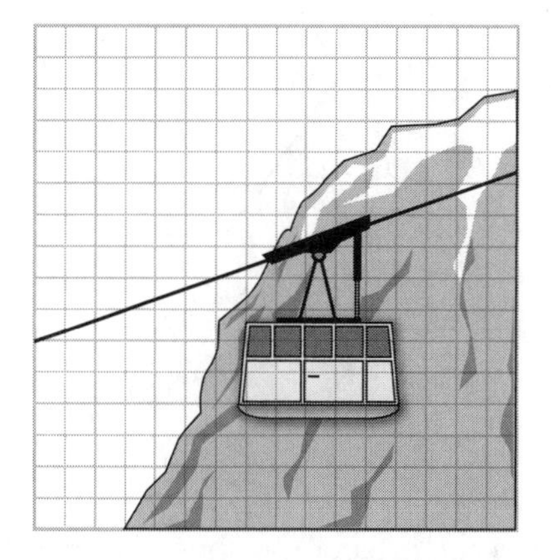

To the nearest foot, how far must the gondola travel to get to the top of a 400-foot mountain?

A 1,200 ft

B 1,265 ft

C 1,333 ft

D 1,600 ft

98 Rob and Sam were going door to door selling magazine subscriptions. Both Rob and Sam stopped at the 1st house on Green Street. Afterward, Rob stopped at every 3rd house and Sam stopped at every 4th house. If there are 30 houses on Green Street, how many will both Rob and Sam stop at, including the 1st house?

F 3 houses

G 5 houses

H 7 houses

J 10 houses

99 Triangles ABC and $A'B'C'$ are similar triangles.

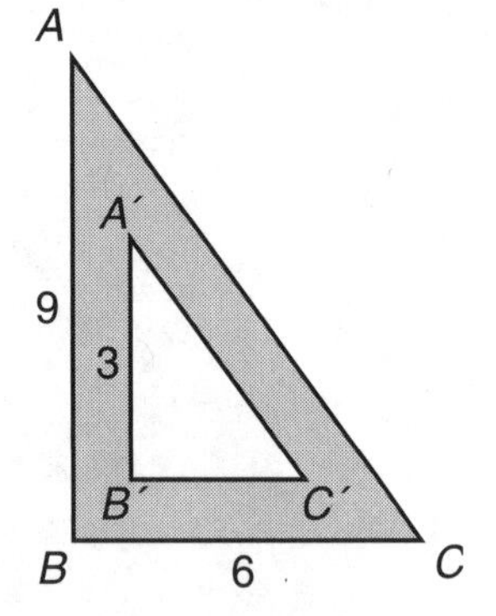

What is the area of the shaded region?

A 21 square units

B 24 square units

C 27 square units

D Not Here

100 Gary made the function table below.

x	1	2	3	4
$f(x)$	3	5	7	9

Which function describes the numbers in this pattern?

F $f(x) = x + 2$

G $f(x) = 2x$

H $f(x) = 4x - 1$

J $f(x) = 2x + 1$

101 Sharon made the function table below.

x	1	2	3	4
$f(x)$	5	8	11	14

$s = f(1) + f(2) + f(3) + f(4) + f(5) + f(6)$

What is the value of s?

A 20

B 38

C 55

D 75

102 If $ABCD$ is an isosceles trapezoid, what is its area to the nearest whole number?

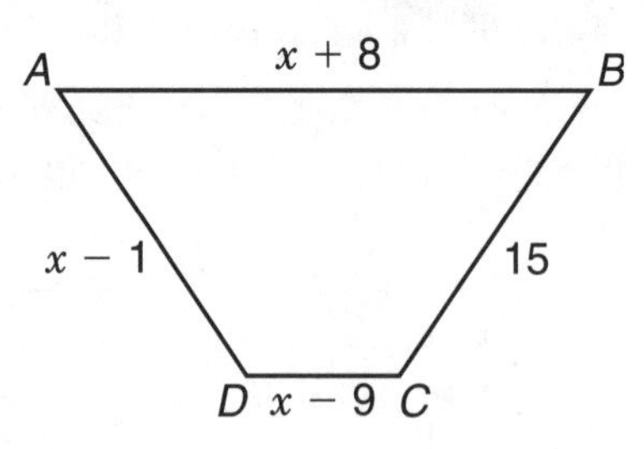

Record your answer and fill in the bubbles on the grid below. Be sure to use the correct place value.

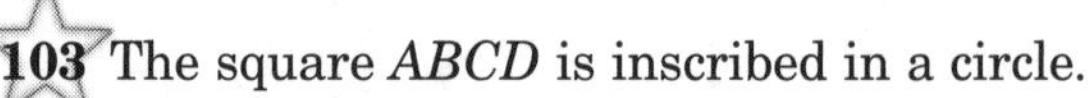

103 The square $ABCD$ is inscribed in a circle.

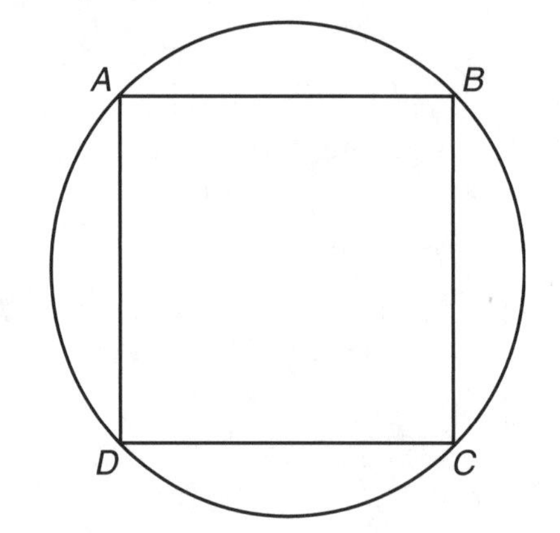

If the sides of the square are 10 meters, what is the radius of the circle to the nearest hundredth?

A 3.16 m

B 4.47 m

C 7.07 m

D 14.14 m

104 The salespeople at a car dealership made a graph to show the sales for the month of November.

Which table shows the data that was used to make the graph?

F

Name	# of cars sold
Nelson	20
Carol	22
Ruth	24
Maria	26
Roger	26

G

Name	# of cars sold
Nelson	5
Carol	8
Ruth	6
Maria	8
Roger	7

H

Name	# of cars sold
Nelson	24
Carol	28
Ruth	25
Maria	28
Roger	26

J

Name	# of cars sold
Nelson	20
Carol	26
Ruth	22
Maria	26
Roger	24

105 Matt bought an amount of stock worth $550. After 4 years, this stock had a value of $800. To the nearest dollar, what was the average annual value of the stock?

A $63

B $88

C $250

D $675

106 What is the difference between the y-intercepts of the lines below?

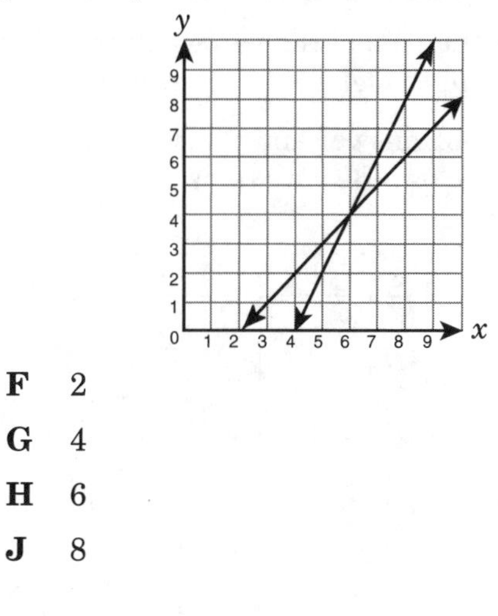

F 2

G 4

H 6

J 8

107 What is the equation of the line determined by the function table?

x	$f(x)$
−2	−5
1	4
3	10

A $f(x) = \frac{1}{3}x + 1$

B $f(x) = 2x + 1$

C $f(x) = 3x + 1$

D Not Here

Use Myrtle's table of values to answer Questions 108–112.

Myrtle decided to assign a value to each letter of the alphabet. Then she began to make a table of her values.

Letter	Value
A	\$0.01
B	\$0.02
C	\$0.04
D	\$0.08
E	\$0.16
F	\$0.32

108 What is the sum of the values Myrtle assigned to the letters in the word CAGE?

Record your answer and fill in the bubbles on the grid below. Be sure to use the correct place value.

				.			
0	0	0	0		0	0	0
1	1	1	1		1	1	1
2	2	2	2		2	2	2
3	3	3	3		3	3	3
4	4	4	4		4	4	4
5	5	5	5		5	5	5
6	6	6	6		6	6	6
7	7	7	7		7	7	7
8	8	8	8		8	8	8
9	9	9	9		9	9	9

109 If Myrtle chooses a letter at random, what is her probability of choosing a letter that has a value of more than \$1.00?

A $\frac{1}{26}$

B $\frac{1}{19}$

C $\frac{19}{26}$

D Not Here

110 Which expression is equal to the value of the nth term in the sequence?

F $0.01 + 0.01n$

G $0.02n + 1$

H $0.01(2n^2)$

J $0.01(2^{n-1})$

111 What is the difference between the sum of the values of the letters in the words HEDGE and BADGE?

A \$1.28

B \$1.41

C \$2.32

D Not Here

112 What is the percent increase in value of a letter over the letter immediately before it?

F 25%

G 50%

H 100%

J 200%

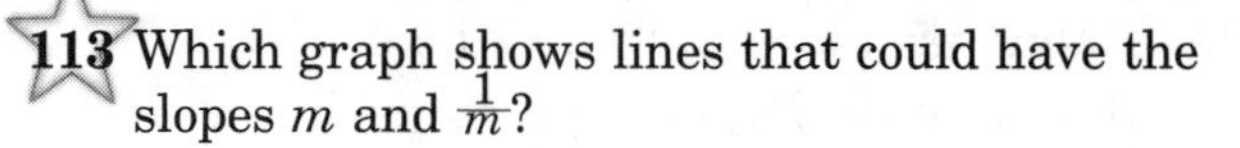

113 Which graph shows lines that could have the slopes m and $\frac{1}{m}$?

A

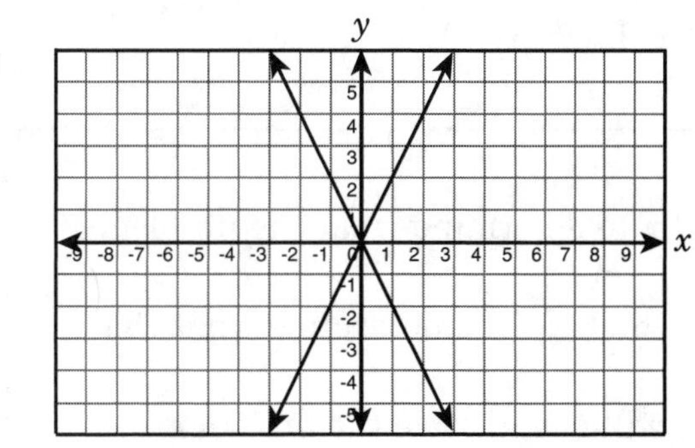

B

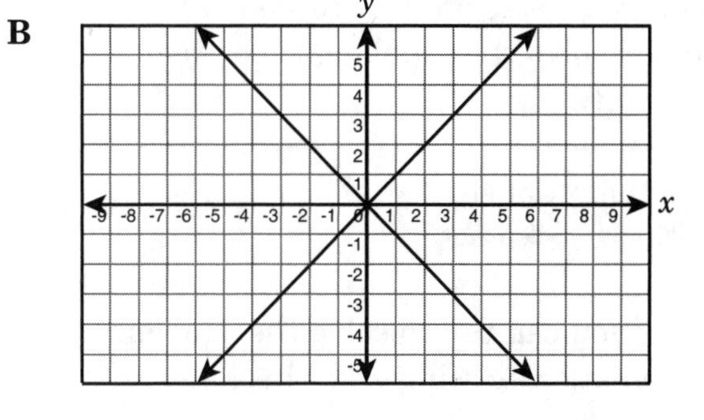

C

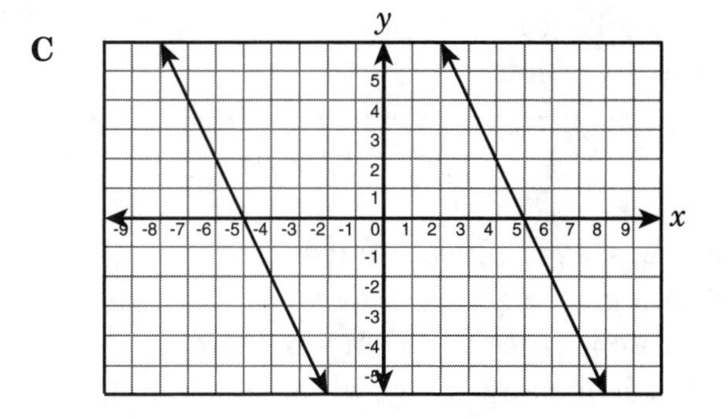

D

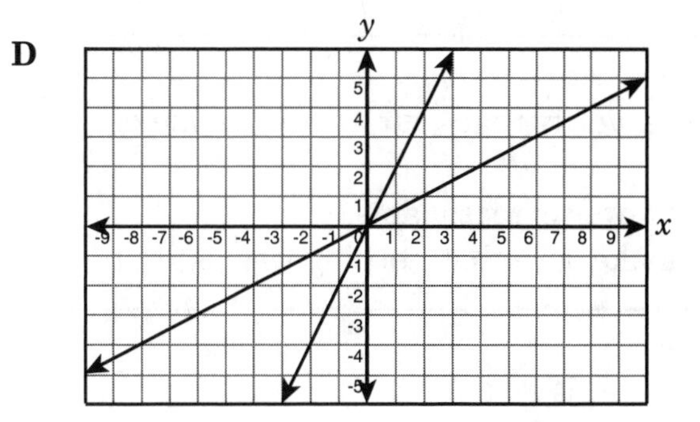

114 The equations of two lines are $y = 2x + 2$ and $4y - 8x = 12$.

At which point do these lines intersect?

F $(-2, -2)$

G $(1, 4)$

H $(8, 3)$

J Not Here

115 The points $M(-3, 8)$ and $N(9, 3)$ are the endpoints of the diameter of a circle. To the nearest tenth, what is the length of the radius of the circle?

Record your answer and fill in the bubbles on the grid below. Be sure to use the correct place value.

				.			
0	0	0	0		0	0	0
1	1	1	1		1	1	1
2	2	2	2		2	2	2
3	3	3	3		3	3	3
4	4	4	4		4	4	4
5	5	5	5		5	5	5
6	6	6	6		6	6	6
7	7	7	7		7	7	7
8	8	8	8		8	8	8
9	9	9	9		9	9	9

116 Sarah ordered a meal and drink priced at \$12.50. Including the tip, the cost of Sarah's meal was \$14.63. To the nearest percent, how much of the bill did Sarah tip?

F 15%

G 17%

H 21%

J Not Here

Problem-Solving Guide

There are many different kinds of mathematical problems. Some are simple and routine, where you plug a number into a formula; others are more complex and require problem-solving skills to answer. The following four-step model can be used to solve any problem. Just be sure to take it one step at a time.

Step 1	UNDERSTAND the problem. • Read the entire problem carefully to determine what the problem is asking you to find. • Underline the information that will help you determine what the problem is asking you to find. • Circle any information that you will use to solve the problem. • Cross out any irrelevant information. • If there is a graphic, make important notes on it. If there is no graphic and a picture will help you solve the problem, then create one of your own and label it carefully.
Step 2	PLAN the steps needed to answer the problem. • Write out the relevant information you know. • Write out what you need to know. • Think about a range of strategies you can use to solve the problem such as Look for a Pattern, Systematic Guessing and Checking, or Making a Table. • List any formulas you may use to solve the problem. • Use the formulas on the Mathematics Chart provided.
Step 3	SOLVE the problem. • Follow your plan. • Take the time to write out the steps, even if you are using a calculator to complete any operations. • If you use a calculator, enter the steps twice and compare your answers to make sure you did not make any errors while keying in numbers and operations.
Step 4	CHECK your answer. • If the question is multiple choice, verify that your answer is one of the choices. • Estimate to determine if your answer is reasonable. • Review the steps you wrote to make sure that nothing was left out.

Using the Graphing Calculator

Use this information as a quick reference for the graphing calculator. Some keys are defined and explained on the next page.

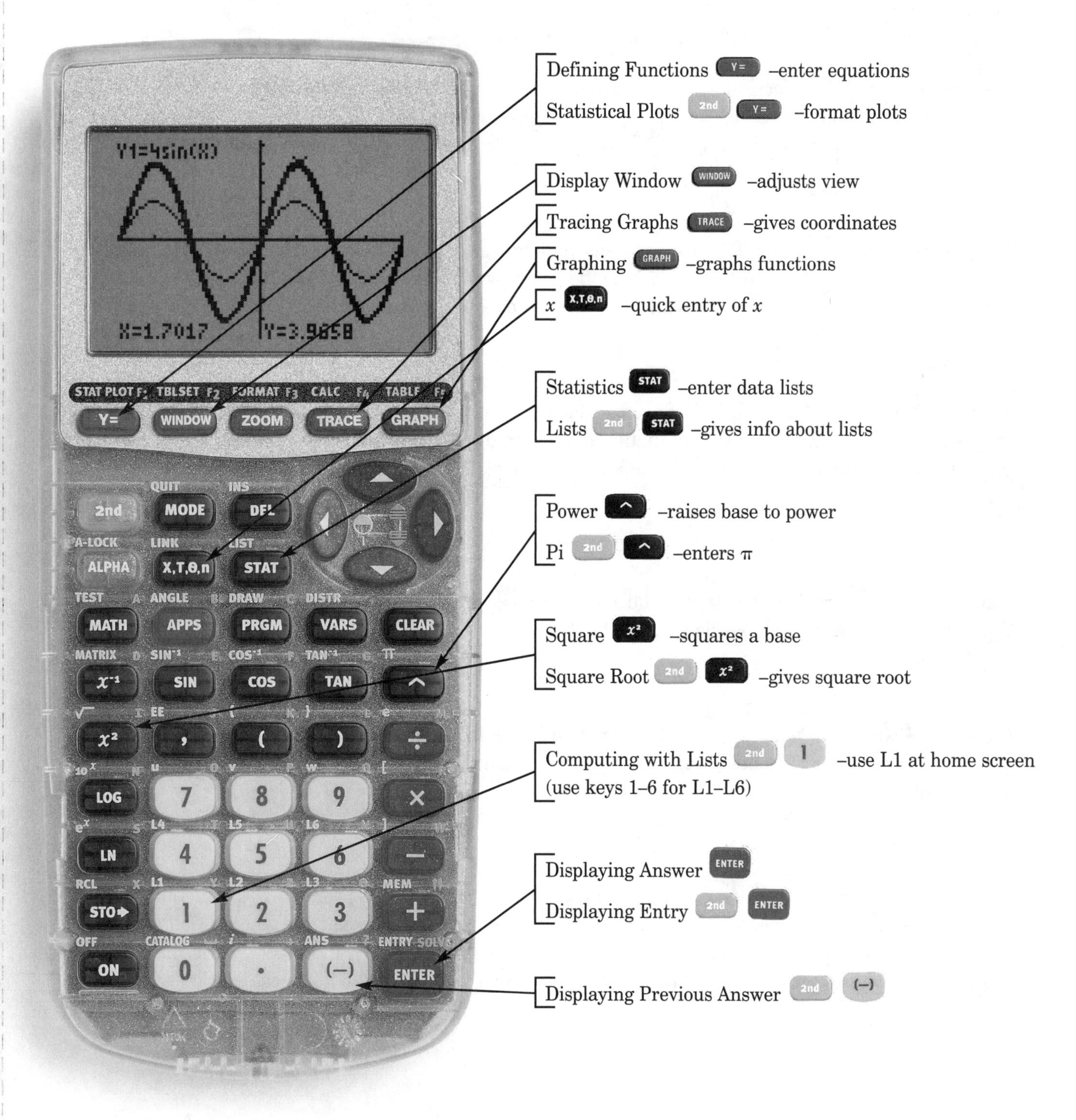

Artwork provided courtesy of Texas Instruments

Defining Functions – [Y=] The function editor allows you to store up to 10 equations. If you want the graph to be displayed, you must be sure that the equation is defined and selected. You can display the graph of one equation or multiple equations.

To define a function, move the cursor to the y_n line that you want assigned to the equation. Be sure that the function you are entering is already in the form of y =.

To select or deselect a function, move the cursor over the = symbol on a line and press [ENTER]. If the = symbol has a black rectangle over the symbol, the equation is selected and will be displayed when you view the graph screen. Pressing [ENTER] acts as a toggle to select and deselect equations.

Statistical Plots – [2nd] [Y=] This is the second feature of the [Y=] key also called STAT PLOT. By accessing this screen you can turn on one of the three plots to be displayed when you view the graph screen. When you select a plot, you can then turn it on or off and select the type of plot to display.

Display Window – [WINDOW] You will have to adjust your viewing window as needed when you view the graph screen. You can control the minimum and maximum scale of the x-axis and y-axis. You can also choose the interval for each scale. The default window has maximum and minimum scale values of -10 and 10 with intervals of 1.

Statistics – [STAT] To enter data into a list, use the [STAT] key. Select edit and then enter the data into L_n. You can also sort and clear lists using this key.

Power – [^] To calculate any power other than 2, use this key. Enter the base, [^], and the power to which the base is being raised. If you have a fractional base or exponent, you need to use parentheses.

Displaying Entry – [2nd] [ENTER] When you need to enter the previous problem with only minor changes, you can use the display entry feature, and then use the arrow keys to go back and overwrite any character or number that needs to change. When you press enter, the problem will be calculated using the new information. This feature works only when you are at the home calculation screen.

Mathematics Chart

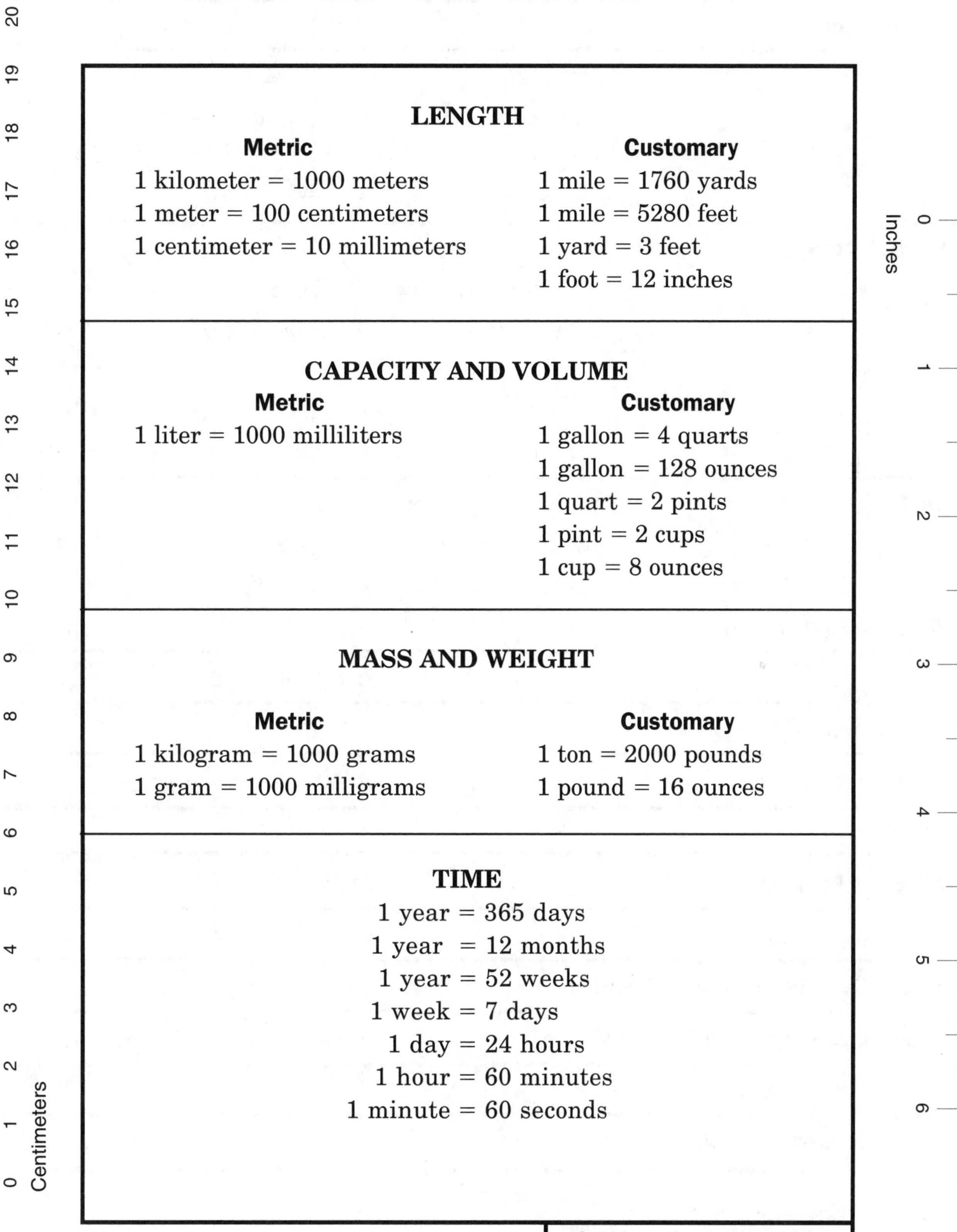

LENGTH

Metric	Customary
1 kilometer = 1000 meters	1 mile = 1760 yards
1 meter = 100 centimeters	1 mile = 5280 feet
1 centimeter = 10 millimeters	1 yard = 3 feet
	1 foot = 12 inches

CAPACITY AND VOLUME

Metric	Customary
1 liter = 1000 milliliters	1 gallon = 4 quarts
	1 gallon = 128 ounces
	1 quart = 2 pints
	1 pint = 2 cups
	1 cup = 8 ounces

MASS AND WEIGHT

Metric	Customary
1 kilogram = 1000 grams	1 ton = 2000 pounds
1 gram = 1000 milligrams	1 pound = 16 ounces

TIME

1 year = 365 days
1 year = 12 months
1 year = 52 weeks
1 week = 7 days
1 day = 24 hours
1 hour = 60 minutes
1 minute = 60 seconds

Continued on other side

Mathematics Chart (continued)

Perimeter	rectangle	$P = 2l + 2w$ or $P = 2(l + w)$
Circumference	circle	$C = 2\pi r$ or $C = \pi d$
Area	rectangle	$A = lw$ or $A = bh$
	triangle	$A = \frac{1}{2}bh$ *or* $A = \frac{bh}{2}$
	trapezoid	$A = \frac{1}{2}(b_1 + b_2)h$ *or* $A = \frac{(b_1 + b_2)h}{2}$
	circle	$A = \pi r^2$
Surface Area	cube	$S = 6s^2$
	cylinder (lateral)	$S = 2\pi rh$
	cylinder (total)	$S = 2\pi rh + 2\pi r^2$ or $S = 2\pi r(h + r)$
	cone (lateral)	$S = \pi rl$
	cone (total)	$S = \pi rl + \pi r^2$ or $S = \pi r(l + r)$
	sphere	$S = 4\pi r^2$
Volume	prism or cylinder	$V = Bh$*
	pyramid or cone	$V = \frac{1}{3}Bh$*
	sphere	$V = \pi r^3$
**B represents the area of the Base of a solid figure.*		
Pi	π	$\pi \approx 3.14$ or $\pi \approx \frac{22}{7}$
Pythagorean Theorem		$a^2 + b^2 = c^2$
Distance Formula		$d = \sqrt{(x_2 - x_1)^2 + (y_2 - y_1)^2}$
Slope of a Line		$m = \frac{y_2 - y_1}{x_2 - x_1}$
Midpoint Formula		$M = \left(\frac{x_1 + x_2}{2}, \frac{y_1 + y_2}{2}\right)$
Quadratic Formula		$x = \frac{-b \pm \sqrt{b^2 - 4ac}}{2a}$
Slope-Intercept Form of an Equation		$y = mx + b$
Point-Slope Form of an Equation		$y - y_1 = m(x - x_1)$
Standard Form of an Equation		$Ax + By = C$
Simple Interest Formula		$I = prt$

A

altitude (altura) a perpendicular segment from a vertex of a triangle to the side opposite that vertex (Lesson 42)

Angle-Angle-Side (AAS) Congruence Postulate (Postulado de congruencia ángulo-ángulo-lado [AAL]) two triangles are congruent if two angles and a nonincluded side of one triangle are congruent to two angles and the corresponding nonincluded side of another triangle (Lesson 50)

Angle-Angle (AA) Similarity Postulate (Postulado de semejanza ángulo-ángulo [AA]) two triangles are similar if two angles of one triangle are congruent to two angles of another triangle (Lesson 52)

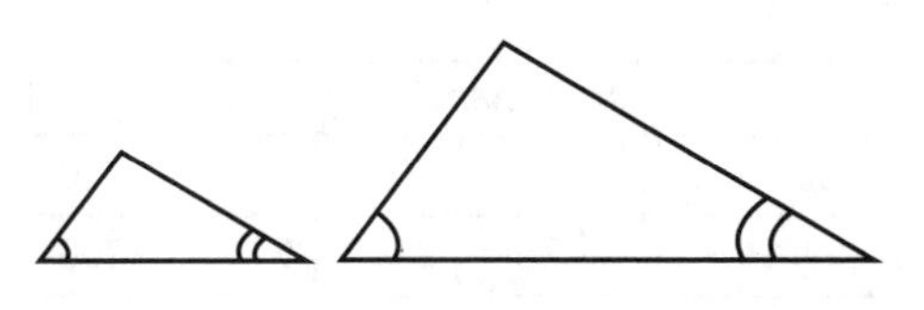

Angle-Side-Angle (ASA) Congruence Postulate (Postulado de congruencia ángulo-lado-ángulo [ALA]) two triangles are congruent if two angles and the included side of one triangle are congruent to two angles and the included side of another triangle (Lesson 50)

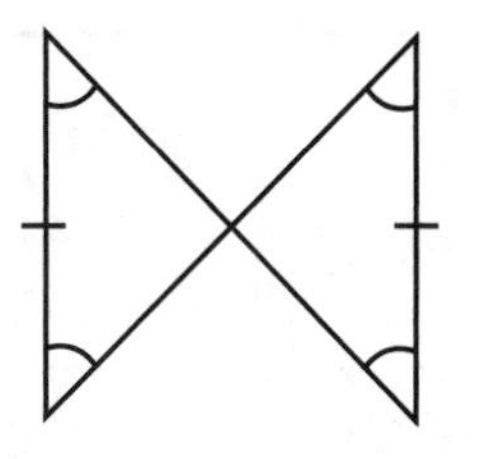

arc (arco) a section of the circumference of a circle between two distinct points on the circle (Lesson 45)

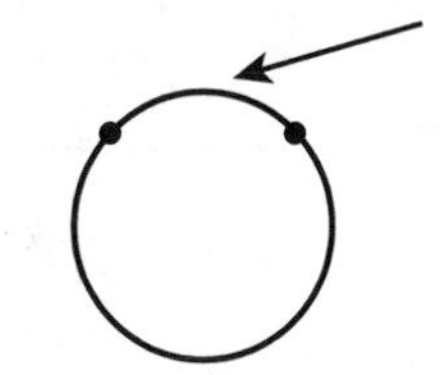

arc length (longitud del arco) the measure of a fraction of the circumference of a circle (Lesson 45)

area (área) the number of square units in the interior of a polygon (Lesson 44)

Associative Property (Propiedad asociativa) mathematical property that states that for any real numbers a, b, and c, $(a + b) + c = a + (b + c)$ and $(ab)c = a(bc)$ (Lesson 10)
Example: $(4 + 8) + 7 = 4 + (8 + 7)$ and $(4 \cdot 8) \cdot 7 = 4(8 \cdot 7)$

B

bar graph (gráfica de barras) graph that compares amounts and quantities using vertical or horizontal bars (Lesson 58)

C

chord (cuerda) a segment with endpoints on a circle (Lesson 46)

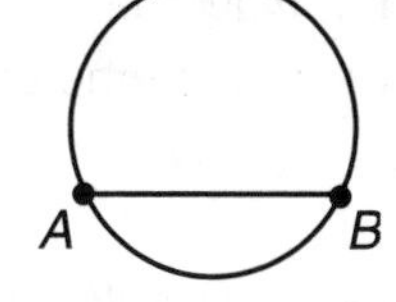

circle graph (gráfica circular) graph that compares percents of a whole. The full circle represents 100%, and each sector represents a part of the whole. (Lesson 58)

coefficient (coeficiente) a number multiplied by a variable (Lesson 3)
Example: In $5x$, 5 is the coefficient.

Commutative Property (Propiedad conmutativa) mathematical property that states that for any real numbers a and b, $a + b = b + a$ and $a \cdot b = b \cdot a$ (Lesson 10) *Example*: $14 + 22 = 22 + 14 = 36$ and $14 \cdot 22 = 22 \cdot 14 = 308$

compound event (suceso compuesto) event comprised of two or more simple events (Lesson 56)

concave (cóncavo) a figure is concave if a line segment can be drawn connecting two points so that some of the points on the line segment are not points of the figure. Opposite of *convex* (Lesson 38)

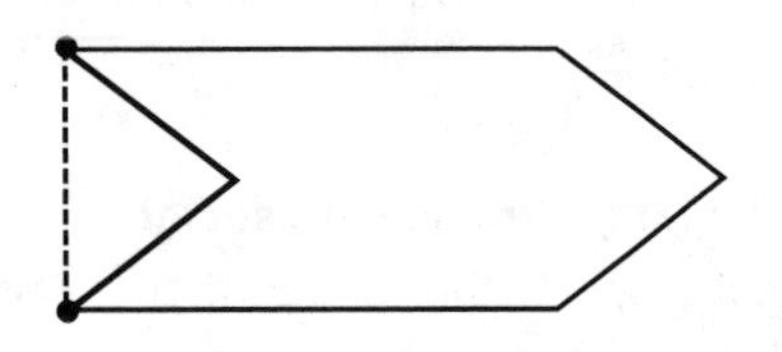

conditional statement (oración condicional) an *if-then* statement. The part that follows *if* is the *hypothesis*, and the part that follows *then* is the *conclusion*. (Lesson 35)

cone (cono) a solid with a curved surface; one circular base, and one vertex (Lesson 38)

congruent figures (figuras congruentes) two figures that have the exact same size and shape (Lesson 30)

conjecture (conjetura) in inductive reasoning, an educated guess based on patterns among data and figures (Lesson 36)

constant of variation (constante de variación) in the direct variation equation, $y = kx$, the constant of variation is the nonzero constant k (Lessons 16, 26)

continuous function (función continua) a function that when graphed has connected points (Lesson 4)

convex (convexo) if a line segment can be drawn connecting two points of a figure, and all points that lie along that line are points of the figure, then the figure is convex. Opposite of *concave* (Lesson 38)

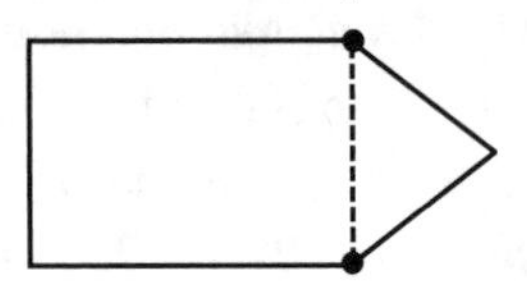

counterexample (contraejemplo) an example that shows that a conditional statement is false, such as an example for which the hypothesis is true, but the conclusion is false (Lesson 35)

cross section (sección transversal) the intersection of a solid and a plane. When a plane intersects a three-dimensional object, the cross section is either a point, line, polygon, or curved plane figure. (Lesson 39)

cylinder (cilindro) a solid that has a curved surface and two circular bases (Lesson 38)

D

deductive reasoning (razonamiento deductivo) technique in which you assume that the hypothesis of a statement is true, and then write a series of statements and reasons that lead to the conclusion (Lesson 36)

dependent events (sucesos dependientes) probability situation in which the outcome of one event affects the outcome of another event (Lesson 56)

dependent quantity (cantidad dependiente) the number that relies on, and is determined by, the other number in a dependent relationship (Lesson 1)

dependent relationship (relación dependiente) a relationship in which one number depends directly on another number (Lesson 1)

direct variation (variación directa) a linear function described by the equation $y = kx$, where k is the nonzero constant, called the *constant of variation*. This can be described as *y varies directly as x*. (Lesson 16)

Junior Class Raffle				
Tickets Sold t	10	20	30	40
Money Raised m	\$50	\$100	\$150	\$200

discontinuous function (función discontinua) a function whose plotted points, when graphed, are not connected because the points represented by the line would not make sense in relation to the function (Lesson 4)

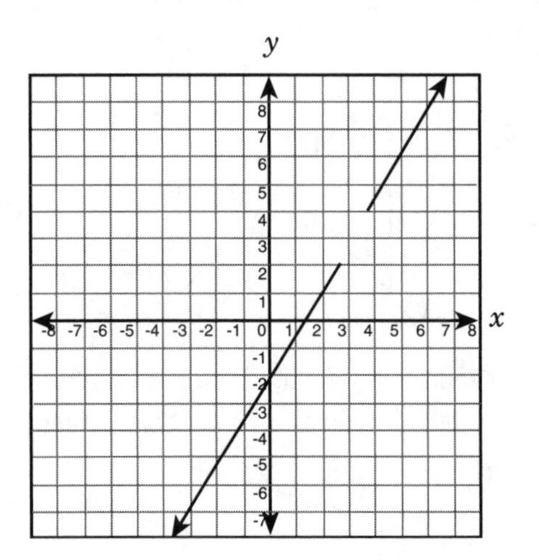

distance (distancia) length of the line segment connecting two points (Lesson 43)

Distributive Property (Propiedad distributiva) mathematical property that states that for any real numbers a, b, and c, $a(b + c) = ab + ac$, $a(b - c) = ab - ac$, and $(b - c)a = ba - ca$ (Lesson 10)

domain (dominio) set of input values for which the function is defined, the x-coordinates (Lesson 6)
Example: In the set of values for the function $y = 3x$, {(3,9), (4,12), (5,15), (6,18)}, the domain is {3, 4, 5, 6}

E

edge (arista) line where two faces of a solid figure intersect (Lesson 38)

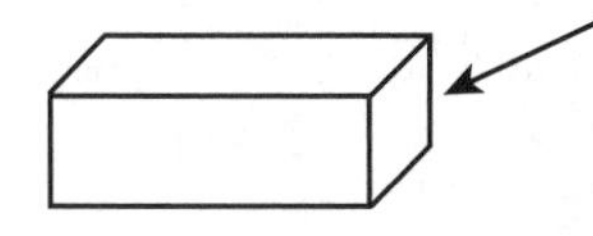

Euclidean geometry (geometría euclídea) system of geometry based on the postulates or assumptions of the Greek mathematician Euclid who lived around 300 B.C.E. (Lesson 28)

Euler's formula (fórmula de Euler) in a polyhedron, the sum of the number of faces and the number of vertices is 2 more than the number of edges. This relationship is represented by the formula $F + V - E = 2$ (Lesson 38)

exponential growth function (función de crecimiento exponencial) a function in the form $y = C(1 + r)^t$, where C is the starting amount, r is the percent increase, and t is the time. Compound interest is an example of exponential growth. (Lesson 27)

F

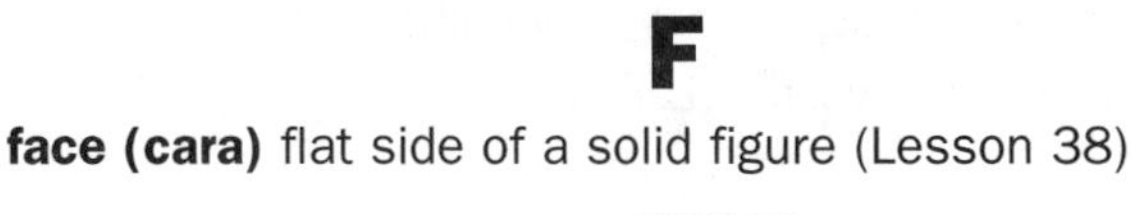

face (cara) flat side of a solid figure (Lesson 38)

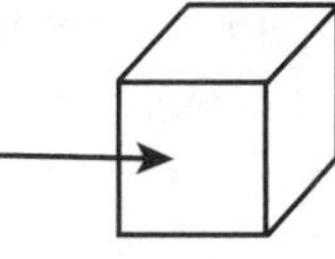

fractal (fractal) geometric object with repeating patterns containing shapes that are like the whole object, but of varying sizes (Lesson 32)

function (función) a set of ordered pairs, where each first value is paired with exactly one second value, the first value being the independent quantity, and the second value being the dependent quantity (Lesson 2)

H

histogram (histograma) a bar graph that shows the frequency of data within equal intervals (Lesson 58)

hypotenuse (hipotenusa) side of a right triangle opposite the right angle (Lesson 33)

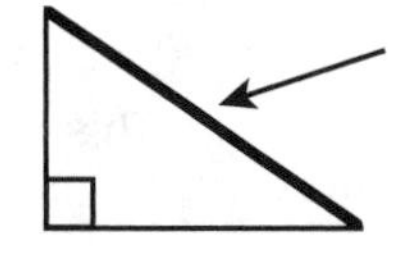

Hypotenuse-leg (HL) Postulate (Postulado de congruencia hipotenusa-cateto [HC]) two triangles are congruent if the hypotenuse and leg of one right triangle are congruent to the hypotenuse and leg of another right triangle (Lesson 50)

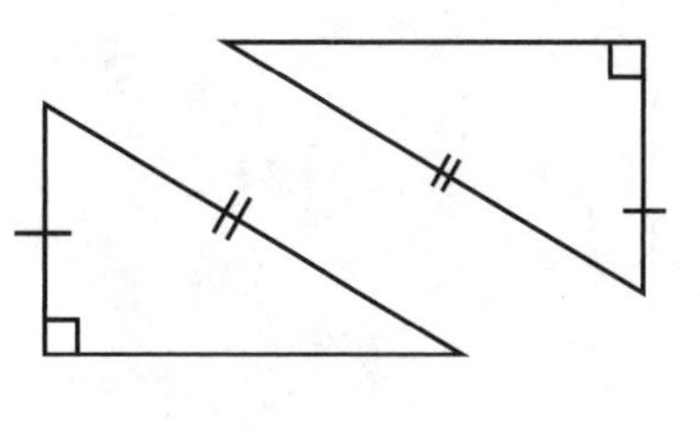

I

image (imagen) figure created by a transformation (Lesson 31)

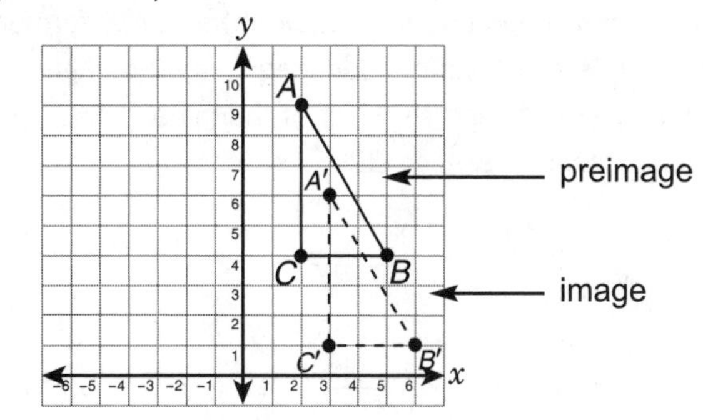

independent events (sucesos independientes) probability situation in which the outcome of one event has no effect on the outcome of another event (Lesson 56)

independent quantity (cantidad independiente) the number that determines the dependent quantity (Lesson 1)

inductive reasoning (razonamiento inductivo) process by which a pattern is sought among data and figures, and the pattern is used to make a generalized educated guess about the data or figures (Lesson 37)

intercept (intersección) the point where a line intersects an axis on a graph (Lesson 13)

inverse variation (variación inversa) a function described by the equation $y = \frac{k}{x}$, where k is a nonzero constant, called the *constant of variation*. This variation can be described by saying that y *varies inversely as* x. (Lesson 26)

isometric drawing (dibujo isométrico) a corner view of a three-dimensional object in which the shape of the object has been preserved (Lesson 41)

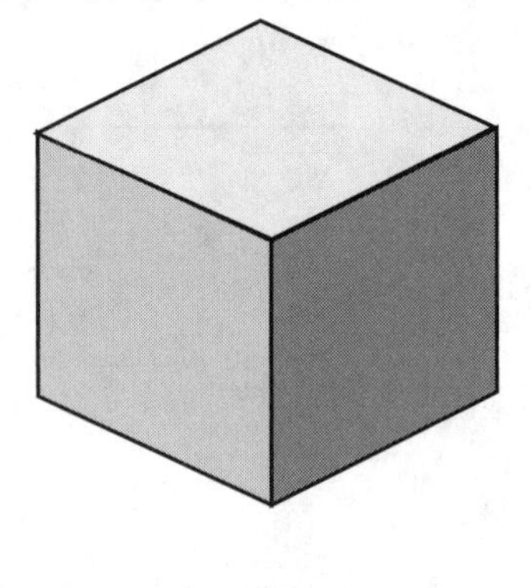

K

Koch snowflake (copo de nieve de Koch) a fractal formed using multiple iterations of adding equilateral triangles to the center third of each segment of the initial equilateral triangle (Lesson 32)

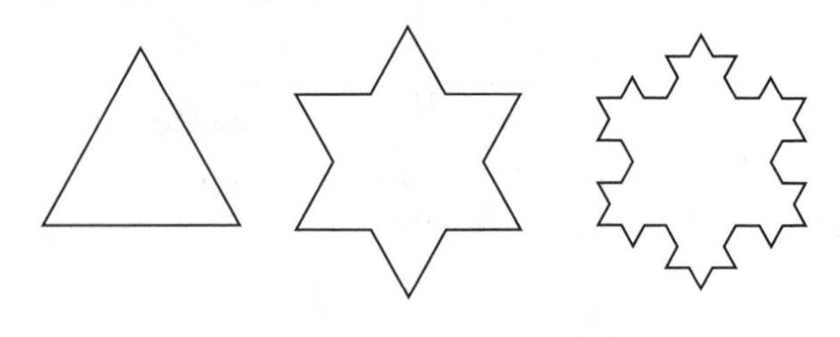

L

lateral area (área lateral) the surface area of a cone, cylinder, prism, or pyramid excluding the bases (Lesson 48)

legs (catetos) sides of a right triangle that form the right angle (Lesson 33)

linear equation (ecuación lineal) an equation for which the graph is a straight line (Lesson 12)

linear function (función lineal) a function whose graph can be defined by a linear equation (Lessons 5, 12)

linear inequality (desigualdad lineal) when the equal sign of a linear equation is replaced with a greater than (>), less than (<), or not equal to (≠) symbol (Lesson 18)
Examples: $45 + 62 > 100$ or $27 - 16 \neq 10$

M

maximum value (valor máximo) the vertex of a parabola that opens downward, identified by the *y*-coordinate of the vertex (Lesson 23)

mean (media) in a set of numbers, the *average* found by adding all of the numbers and dividing by how many numbers are in the set (Lesson 57)
Example: In the set of numbers, {24, 28, 33, 18, 21}, the *mean* is 24.8.

median (mediana) the middle number when the numbers in a data set are arranged from least to greatest (Lesson 57)
Example: In the set of numbers, {24, 28, 33, 18, 21}, the *median* is 24.

midpoint (punto medio) a point on a line segment that is halfway between the endpoints of that segment (Lesson 43)

minimum value (valor mínimo) the vertex of a parabola that opens upwards, identified by the *y*-coordinate of the vertex (Lesson 23)

mode (modo) the number or numbers that occur most frequently in a data set (Lesson 57)
Example: In the set of numbers, {33, 28, 33, 24, 18, 21, 24, 33}, the *mode* is 33.

N

net (patrón) a diagram of two-dimensional shapes that can be folded to form a three-dimensional figure (Lesson 40)

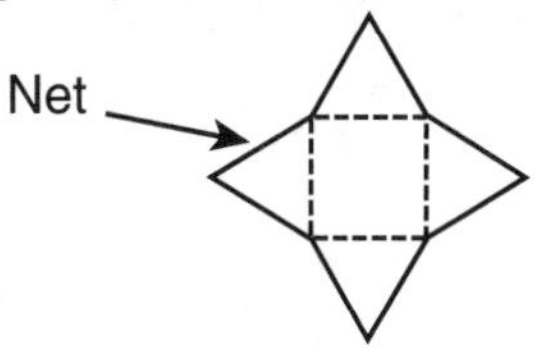

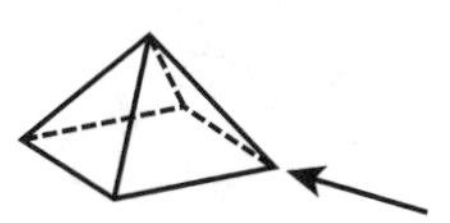

non-Euclidean geometry (geometría no euclídea) the systems of geometry that are not based on some of or all Euclid's postulates (Lesson 28)

O

ordered pair (par ordenado) two numbers related to each other in some way (Lesson 1)

orthographic drawing (dibujo ortográfico) a straight-on view of a solid object that appears two-dimensional because only one face of the object is seen (Lesson 41)

P

parabola (parábola) the U-shaped curve of a quadratic function. The highest or lowest point on the parabola is the vertex. (Lesson 22)

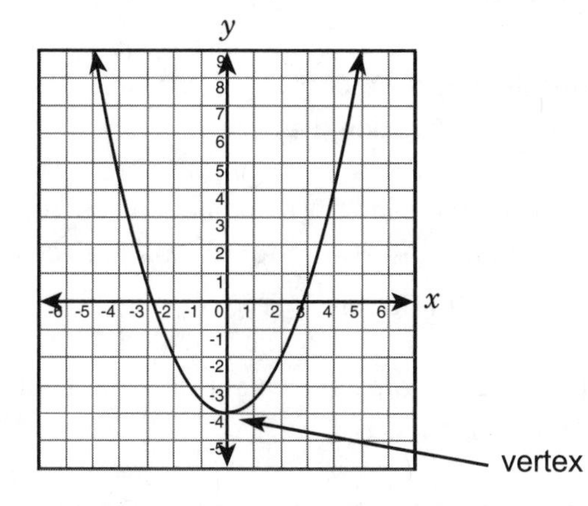

parallel lines (rectas paralelas) lines that lie on the same plane in space and do not intersect (Lesson 29)

parallelogram (paralelogramo) a quadrilateral with two pairs of parallel sides (Lesson 42)

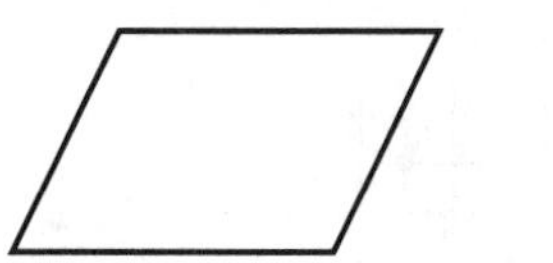

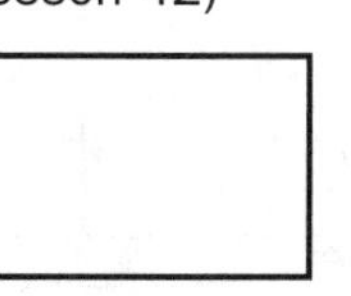

parent function (función principal) the most basic function upon which a family of functions is based (Lesson 5)

percent (porcentaje) a ratio that compares a number to 100 (Lesson 54)

perimeter (perímetro) the distance around a polygon, found by adding the lengths of all the sides (Lesson 44)

perpendicular lines (rectas perpendiculares) lines that intersect to form right angles (Lesson 29)

perpendicular bisector (mediatriz del segemento) a segment that is perpendicular to another segment at its midpoint (Lesson 43)

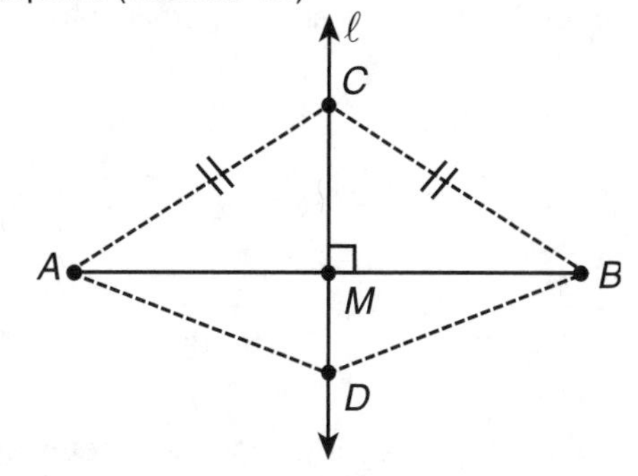

point of tangency (punto de tangencia) the point at which a tangent intersects a circle. The radius that contains the point of tangency is perpendicular to the tangent line. (Lesson 46)

polygon (polígono) a closed plane figure formed by three or more line segments. One way to classify polygons is by the number of sides. (Lesson 44)

Examples: These figures are common polygons.

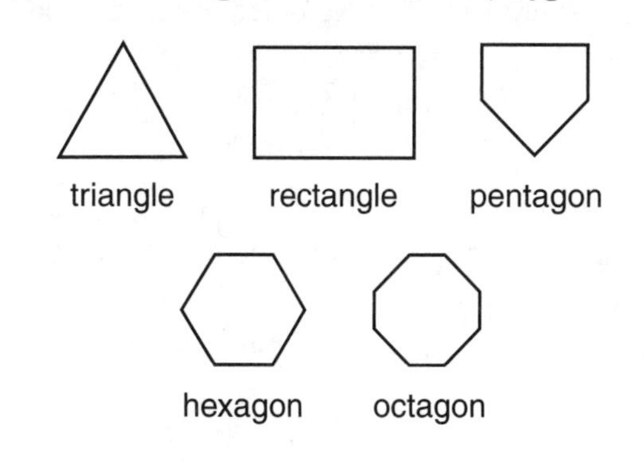

polyhedron (poliedro) a solid figure formed by polygons (Lesson 38)
Examples: These figures are common polyhedra.

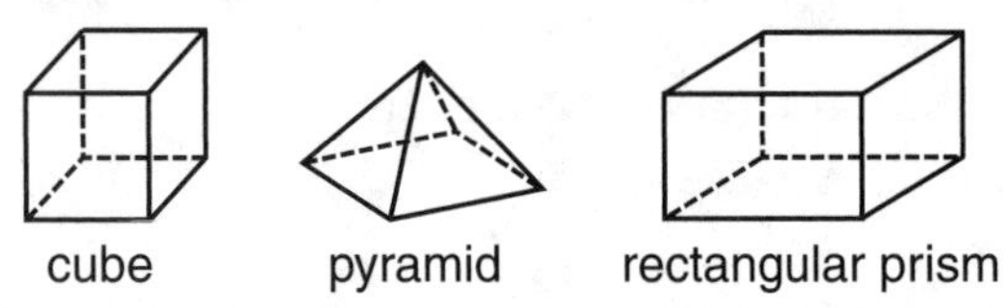

population (población) in a survey, the entire group of interest (Lesson 59)

preimage (preimagen) figure before a transformation (Lesson 31)

prism (prisma) a polyhedron with two parallel, congruent bases and lateral faces that are all parallelograms (Lesson 38)
Examples: These figures are common prisms.

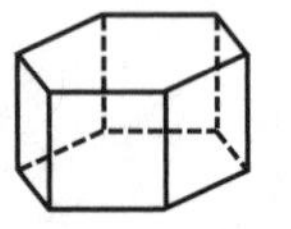
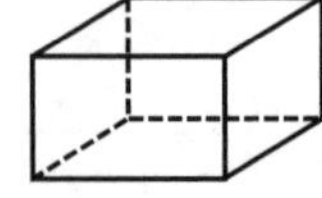

probability (probabilidad) a numerical value between 0 and 1 measuring the likelihood that an event will occur. The closer the probability is to 1, the more likely the event will occur. (Lesson 55)

proof (demostración) in deductive reasoning, the set of statements and reasons that lead to the conclusion (Lesson 36)

proportion (proporción) an equation which states that two ratios are equivalent. The two ratios are said to be *proportional* or *in proportion*. (Lesson 53)
Example: In the proportion $\frac{7}{3} = \frac{21}{x}$, $x = 9$.

pyramid (pirámide) a polyhedron with a single base and faces that are all triangles intersecting at a vertex (Lesson 38)
Examples: These figures are common pyramids.

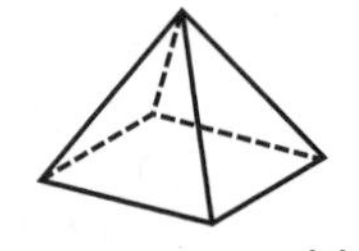

Pythagorean theorem (teorema de Pitágoras) the sum of the squares of the lengths of the legs of a right triangle equals the square of the length of the hypotenuse; $a^2 + b^2 = c^2$ (Lesson 33)
Example: Using the Pythagorean theorem with the triangle below, $6^2 + 8^2 = c^2$, and $c = 10$.

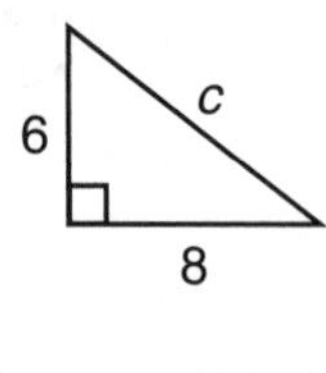

Q

quadratic function (función cuadrática) a function in the form $y = ax^2 + bx + c$, where a, b, and c are real numbers and $a \neq 0$. The graph of a quadratic equation is U-shaped. (Lessons 5, 22)

quadrilateral (cuadrilátero) a four-sided polygon (Lesson 42)
Examples: These figures are all common quadrilaterals.

R

random sample (muestra aleatoria) an unbiased sample that is representative of the entire population (Lesson 59)

range (rango) the set of output values, the y-coordinates, of a function (Lesson 6)

ratio (razón) a comparison of two numbers (Lesson 53)
Examples: Here are three ways to express the same ratio: 60 to 55, 60 : 55, or $\frac{60}{55}$.

rectangle (rectángulo) a parallelogram with four right (90°) angles (Lesson 42)

reflection (reflejo) a transformation where all points are flipped across a line to form a new image (Lesson 31)

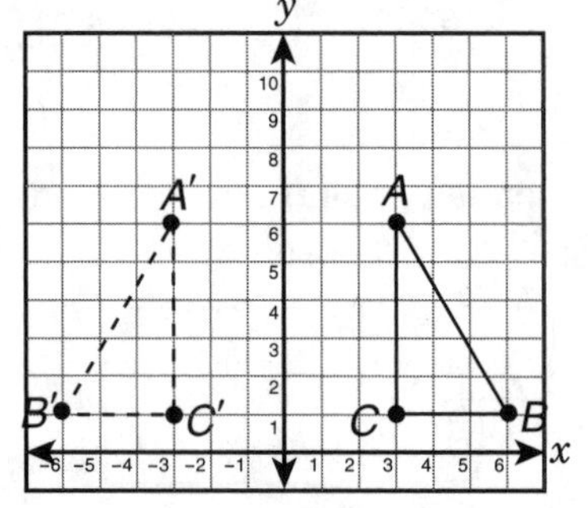

relationship (relación) a set of ordered pairs (Lesson 1)

rhombus (rombo) a quadrilateral with two pairs of parallel congruent sides (Lesson 42)

right triangle (triángulo rectángulo) a triangle with one right angle (Lesson 33)

roots (raíces) the values of the x-intercepts of the graph of the solution of a quadratic equation (Lesson 24)

rotation (rotación) a transformation where a figure is rotated about a given point in the plane to create a new image (Lesson 31)

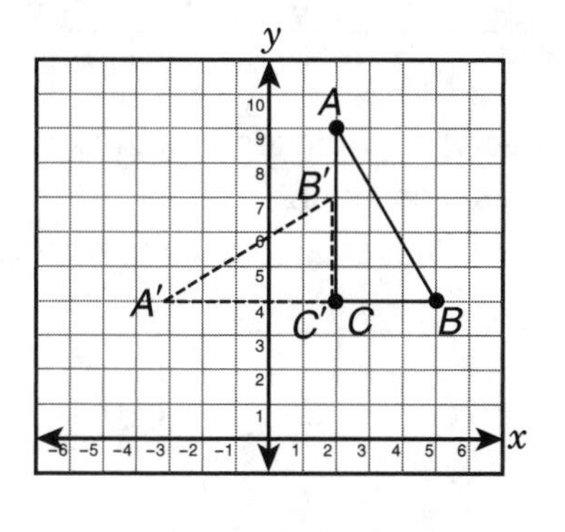

S

sample (muestrea) a small portion of a population that is surveyed since it is not convenient to survey the whole group (Lesson 59)

sample space (espacio muestral) the set of all possible outcomes of an event (Lesson 55)
Example: The sample space for tossing three coins is (H,H,H), (H,H,T), (H,T,H) (H,T,T), (T,H,H), (T,T,H), (T,T,T), (T,H,T).

scale factor (factor de escala) the ratio of corresponding sides (Lesson 51)

scatterplot (gráfica de dispersión) a graph in which two sets of data are plotted as ordered pairs on a coordinate grid (Lesson 8)

secant (secante) a continuous line that intersects a circle at two points (Lesson 46)

sector (sector) a region bounded by two radii of a circle and their intercepted arc. The area of a sector is the product of the fraction of the circumference the arc represents and the area of the circle. (Lesson 45)

Side-Angle-Side (SAS) Congruence Postulate (Postulado de congruencia lado-ángulo-lado [LAL]) two triangles are congruent if two sides and the included angle of one triangle are congruent to two sides and the included angle of another triangle (Lesson 50)

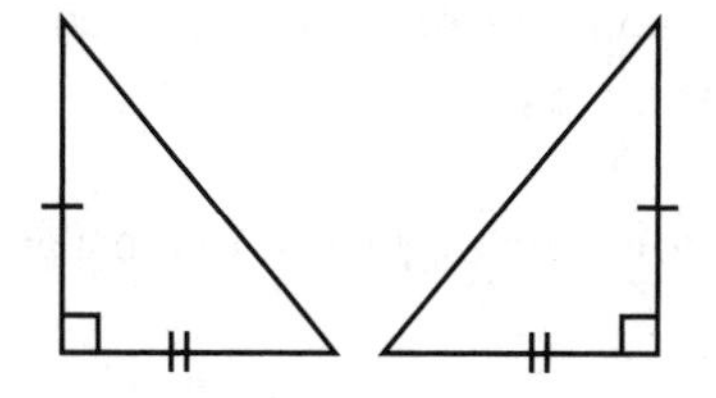

Side-Angle-Side (SAS) Similarity Theorem (teorema de semejanza lado-ángulo-lado [LAL]) two triangles are similar if an angle of one triangle is congruent to an angle of another triangle and the sides including those angles are proportional (Lesson 52)

Side-Side-Side (SSS) Similarity Theorem (Teorema de semejanza lado-lado-lado [LLL]) two triangles are similar if the corresponding sides of the triangles are proportional (Lesson 52)

similar figures (figuras semejantes) two figures that have the same shape and are of different sizes based on a ratio (Lesson 30)

similar polygons (polígonos semejantes) polygons that have congruent corresponding angles and proportional corresponding sides (Lesson 51)

similar solids (sólidos semejantes) solid figures that have the same shape and in which all the corresponding measures are proportional (Lesson 51)

slope (pendiente) the rate of change. The slope of a line or line segment is the ratio of the change in the y-coordinates compared to the change in x-coordinates. (Lesson 13)

slope-intercept (pendiente-intersección) the form of a line for the equation $y = mx + b$, where m is the slope and b is the y-intercept (Lesson 15)

solution of a quadratic equation (solución de una ecuación cuadrática) the values where the graph of the equation crosses the x-axis, or the x-intercepts of the graph. These solutions are called the *roots* of the equation. (Lesson 24)

sphere (esfera) a solid that has no bases or vertices, and is a set of all points in space at a constant radius from a central point (Lesson 38)
Example: Common *spheres* include globes, basketballs, and marbles.

square (cuadrado) a rectangle with four congruent sides (Lesson 42)

standard form (forma usual) the form of the quadratic equation $d = ax^2 + bx + c$ when $d = 0$ (Lesson 24)

surface area (área de la superficie) the sum of the areas of all the faces and bases of a three-dimensional object (Lesson 47)

survey (encuesta) study conducted to gather information about a particular group (Lesson 59)

system of linear equations (sistema de ecuaciones lineales) a set of two or more linear equations (Lesson 19)
Example: $x + 2y = 16$
$4x - y = 28$

T

tangent (tangente) a line that intersects a circle at exactly one point (Lesson 46)

tessellation (teselado) repeating pattern of figures that completely covers a plane with no gaps or overlaps (Lesson 32)

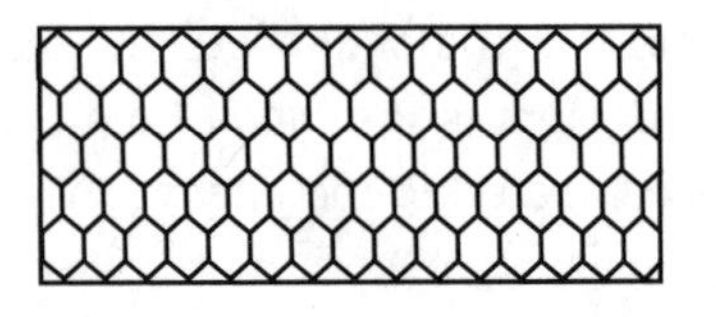

transformation (transformación) change in the position, size, or shape of a geometric figure (Lesson 31)

translation (translación) a transformation in which all points of the figure move, or slide an equal distance to create a new image (Lesson 31)

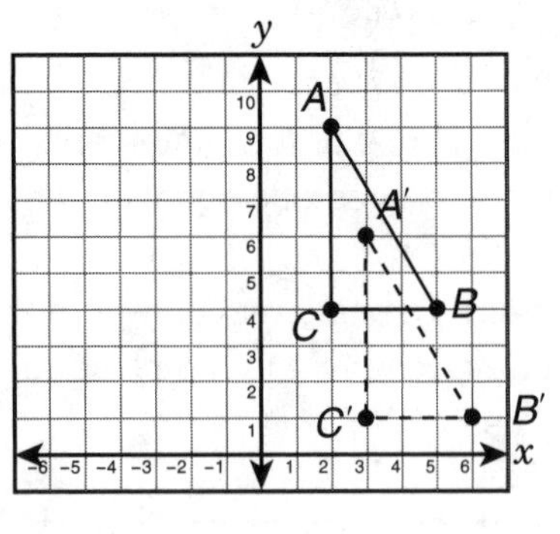

trapezoid (trapecio) a quadrilateral with exactly one pair of parallel sides (Lesson 42)
Examples: These figures are common trapezoids:

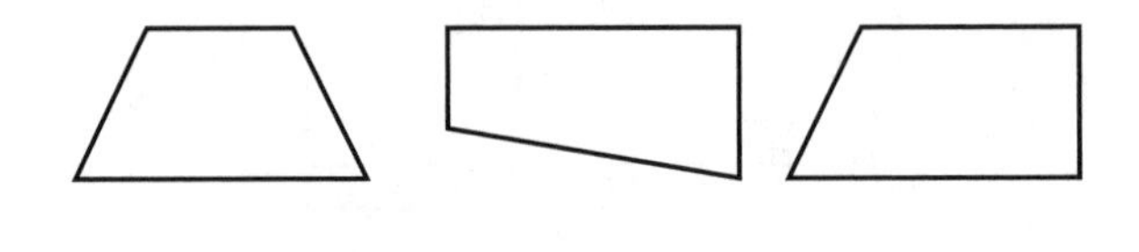

V

variable (variable) symbol used to represent a quantity
Example: $x = 5$, $x + 3 = 8$ (Lesson 3)

vertex (vértice) the highest or lowest point of the parabola graph of a quadratic function (Lesson 23); the point where three or more edges of a solid figure intersect (Lesson 38)

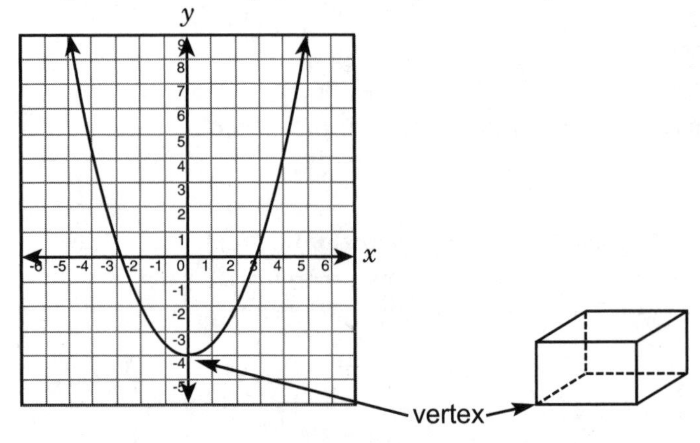

volume (volumen) the number of cubic units needed to fill a three-dimensional object (Lesson 47)